ZAGAT®

New York City Restaurants

2008

Plus Special Bonus Section
Excerpt from the new
2008 NYC Gourmet Shopping
& Entertaining Guide

EDITORS
Curt Gathje and Carol Diuguid
COORDINATOR
Larry Cohn

Published and distributed by
Zagat Survey, LLC
4 Columbus Circle
New York, NY 10019
T: 212.977.6000
E: newyork@zagat.com
www.zagat.com

ACKNOWLEDGMENTS

We thank Caren Weiner Campbell, Leigh Crandall, Mikola De Roo, Lynn Hazlewood, Bernard Onken, Mary Phillips-Sandy, Blake Royer, Laura Siciliano-Rosen, Miranda Van Gelder, as well as the following members of our staff: Josh Rogers (assistant editor), Rachel McConlogue (assistant editor), Sean Beachell, Maryanne Bertollo, Amy Cao, Sandy Cheng, Reni Chin, Bill Corsello, Deirdre Donovan, Caitlin Eichelberger, Alison Flick, Jeff Freier, Shelley Gallagher, Michelle Golden, Randi Gollin, Caroline Hatchett, Karen Hudes, Roy Jacob, Natalie Lebert, Mike Liao, Christina Livadiotis, Allison Lynn, Dave Makulec, Chris Miragliotta, Andre Pilette, Becky Ruthenburg, Troy Segal, Robert Seixas, Carla Spartos, Kelly Stewart, Kilolo Strobert, Donna Marino Wilkins, Liz Borod Wright, Yoji Yamaguchi, Sharon Yates and Kyle Zolner.

The reviews published in this guide are based on public opinion surveys, with numerical ratings reflecting the average scores given by all survey participants who voted on each establishment and text based on direct quotes from, or fair paraphrasings of, participants' comments. Phone numbers, addresses and other factual information were correct to the best of our knowledge when published in this guide; any subsequent changes may not be reflected.

Contents

Ratings & Symbols

Zagat Top Spot	Name	Symbols		Cuisine	Zagat Ratings			
					FOOD	DECOR	SERVICE	COST

Area, Address & Contact
Ⓩ **Tim & Nina's** ◖ *Deli*   ▽ 23 | 9 | 13 | $15
W 50s | 4 Columbus Circle (8th Ave.) | 212-977-6000 | www.zagat.com

Review, surveyor comments in quotes
"What a dump!" – open 7 days a week, 24 hours a day, this successful "deep dive" started the "deli-tapas craze" (i.e. tidbits of pastrami, corned beef, etc. on cracker-size pieces of stale rye); though the place looks like a "none-too-clean garage" and T&N "never heard of reservations", "dirt-cheap" prices for "great eats" draw demented crowds.

Ratings

Food, Decor and **Service** are rated on a scale of 0 to 30.

0 – 9	poor to fair
10 – 15	fair to good
16 – 19	good to very good
20 – 25	very good to excellent
26 – 30	extraordinary to perfection
▽	low response | less reliable

Cost reflects our surveyors' average estimate of the price of a dinner with one drink and tip and is a benchmark only. Lunch is usually 25% less.

For **newcomers** or survey **write-ins** listed without ratings, the price range is indicated as follows:

I	$25 and below
M	$26 to $40
E	$41 to $65
VE	$66 or more

Symbols

Ⓩ	Zagat Top Spot (highest ratings, popularity and importance)
◖	serves after 11 PM
Ⓢ	closed on Sunday
Ⓜ	closed on Monday
⊄	no credit cards accepted

Maps

Index maps show restaurants with the highest Food ratings in those areas.

About This Survey

Here are the results of our **2008 New York City Restaurants Survey,** which covers 2,069 establishments throughout the five boroughs. Like all of our guides, it's based on the collective opinions of thousands of savvy local consumers who have been there before you.

WHO PARTICIPATED: Input from 34,678 frequent diners forms the basis for the ratings and reviews in this guide (their comments are shown in quotation marks within the reviews). Of these surveyors, 52% are women, 48% men; the breakdown by age is 11% in their 20s; 25%, 30s; 19%, 40s; 22%, 50s; and 23%, 60s or above. Collectively they bring roughly six million annual meals' worth of experience to this Survey. We sincerely thank each of these participants – this book is really "theirs."

HELPFUL LISTS: Whether you're looking for a celebratory meal, a hot scene or a bargain bite, our lists can help you find exactly the right place. See Key Newcomers (page 9), Most Popular (page 10), Top Ratings (pages 11–22) and Best Buys (pages 23–26). We've also provided 47 handy indexes; especially check our Sleepers and Critic-Proof indexes.

OUR TEAM: We especially thank our editors, Curt Gathje and Carol Diuguid, for their hard work over the years; this is the seventh edition of this guide that they have collaborated on. Thanks also to Larry Cohn, who coordinated the data collection for this book and has been ensuring our accuracy since 1994.

ABOUT ZAGAT: This marks our 29th year reporting on the shared experiences of consumers like you. What started in 1979 as a hobby involving 200 of our friends has come a long way. Today we have over 300,000 surveyors and now cover dining, entertaining, golf, hotels, movies, music, nightlife, resorts, shopping, spas, theater and tourist attractions worldwide.

SHARE YOUR OPINION: We invite you to join any of our upcoming surveys – just register at **zagat.com,** where you can rate and review establishments year-round. Each participant will receive a free copy of the resulting guide when published.

AVAILABILITY: Zagat guides are available in all major bookstores, by subscription at **zagat.com** and for use on a wide range of Web-enabled mobile devices via **Zagat To Go** or **zagat.mobi.** Either of the latter two products will allow you to contact any restaurant by phone with one click.

FEEDBACK: There is always room for improvement, thus we invite your comments and suggestions about any aspect of our performance. Just contact us at newyork@zagat.com.

New York, NY
October 10, 2007

Nina and Tim

Nina and Tim Zagat

What's New

The NYC restaurant scene showed remarkable strength over the past year, continuing to grow and diversify with 234 new openings vs. 88 closings. This year's crop of newcomers (see page 9), fueled by a young, upwardly mobile clientele, represents a vast range of cuisines and styles, with increasing informality and very little change in overall pricing.

DRESSING DOWN: The move toward more casual dining sans tablecloths and dress codes persisted with the arrival of a wide variety of inexpensive newcomers. Intimacy was the word at hot boîtes like Maze, Morandi, Wakiya and Waverly Inn. In contrast, 2006 was highlighted by a mega-restaurant invasion, e.g. Buddakan, Buddha Bar, Craftsteak, Del Posto and Morimoto.

 DOLLARS AND SENSE: Although NYC restaurant prices remain the most expensive of any American city at $39.46 per dinner, they are virtually unchanged from last year's $39.43. This represents a multiyear pattern, with an average annual inflation of 0.97% since 2001; credit for this goes to a slew of inexpensive newcomers for keeping the cost average steady. Indeed, NYC continues to be a place where good cheap meals are abundant – this Survey includes 697 restaurants offering dinners for less than $30.

HIGH-PRICED DINING: Inflation among the 20 most expensive eateries has been far higher. Since 2001, the average price at these places has jumped an average of 11.6% a year, i.e. from $84.45 to $143.06. The arrival of restaurants such as L'Atelier de Joël Robuchon, Masa and Per Se contributed to this sea change.

SMALL PLATES ARE BIG: One of the phenomena noted this year is the growing number of restaurants offering small-plate menus. Though the cost per plate is lower, the catch is it takes twice as many of them to fill you up. Consumers remain wary, however, with 75% reporting that traditional menus offer better value.

 HIGH TIMES FOR LOW FOOD: In keeping with this year's casual mood, some less-than-sophisticated food groups got haute spins. The lowly hamburger was reinterpreted at BLT Burger, brgr, Five Guys, 67 Burger and Stand (with rumors of California's In-N-Out Burger on the way). And BBQ caught its second wind with the arrivals of Fette Sau, Georgia's Eastside BBQ, Hill Country, Johnny Utah's, Smoke Joint and Southern Hospitality.

AVERAGE EATING: NYers report eating out an average of 3.3 times per week – which, they might be surprised to learn, puts them squarely in the average ranks, behind leaders such as Houston and Dallas/Ft. Worth (4.2 and 4.0 times per week, respectively) and ahead of the likes of Boston and Philly (both 2.7 times per week).

WEB DINING: The Internet's influence on dining out made itself felt: 66% of surveyors report consulting online menus before selecting a restaurant – we have over 10,000 menus on zagat.com – while 17% make their reservations online or via e-mail (up from just 7% in 2005).

THE GREENING OF NY: Diners continue to express concern about the healthfulness of what they eat: 52% of surveyors report they're willing to pay more for sustainably raised food. The NYC Health Department's banning of trans fat-heavy frying oils similarly won the support of over two-thirds of our voters. And a notorious video of a rat-infested Taco Bell caused an uproar, triggering stepped-up inspections and a record number of (temporary) shutterings; 65% of respondents called the closings warranted.

NEW RESTAURANT ROWS: The South Street Seaport's Front Street was the city's latest Restaurant Row, where an international mix of newcomers arrived: Il Brigante (Italian), Nelson Blue (New Zealand), Stella Maris (European) and Suteishi (Japanese). On the horizon, the Meatpacking District's Gansevoort Street looks hot thanks to Sue Torres' new Mexican cantina, Los Dados, soon to be followed by Merkato 55 from Marcus Samuelsson.

THE SCENE IN A NUTSHELL: Rating NYC's overall dining scene, surveyors gave it a 27 (out of a possible 30 points) for choice/diversity and a 24 for creativity, but a mere 13 for table availability and a 15 for hospitality. This huge discrepancy is confirmed by the fact that service remains the industry's weak link, with 50% calling it the most irritating part of the dining experience, followed by noise/crowds (34%) and prices (11%).

CASE CLOSED: Gone but not forgotten were such notables as Alain Ducasse, Brasserie LCB, Cité, Devi, En Plo, 50 Carmine, Honmura An, Inside, Jerry's, Jezebel, Kitchen 22, Lenox Room, March and 66. Happily, some of the restaurateurs behind these establishments (among them Alain Ducasse, Tony Fortuna and Alan Stillman) are working on projects for the coming year.

RANDOM NOTES: Survey winners this year included Daniel for Food, Asiate for Decor, Per Se for Service and Union Square Cafe for Most Popular; Gordon Ramsay was voted Top Newcomer... Haute Chinese cooking, still struggling to assert itself, got a big boost with the arrival of Wakiya in the Gramercy Park Hotel, headed up by the renowned toque Yuji Wakiya... Reclaimed wood was the design feature du jour, turning up at BLT Market, Borough Food & Drink, The E.U., Johnny Utah's and Spitzer's Corner... Tipping continues to edge up, with this year's average rising to 19% (compared to 18.1% in 2001)... Italian (at 30%) held its lead as diners' favorite cuisine, followed by French, Japanese, American and Thai... Finally, after years of critiquing the looks of others, we thought it time for a face-lift of our own. In this redesigned edition you'll find new fonts, easier-to-use indexes and, by popular demand, our first dining map of Brooklyn.

New York, NY
October 10, 2007

Nina and Tim

Nina and Tim Zagat

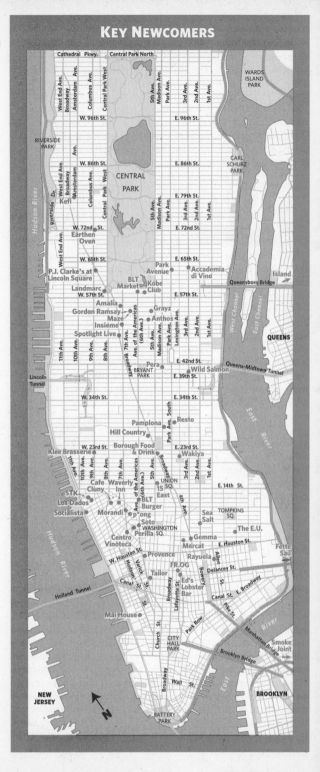

KEY NEWCOMERS

Cathedral Pkwy.

Central Park North

WARDS ISLAND PARK

West End Ave.
Broadway
Amsterdam Ave.
Columbus Ave.
Central Park West

5th Ave.
Madison Ave.
Park Ave.
3rd Ave.
2nd Ave.
1st Ave.

W. 96th St.

E. 96th St.

RIVERSIDE PARK

Riverside Dr.

West End Ave.
Amsterdam Ave.
Columbus Ave.
Central Park West

W. 86th St.

E. 86th St.

CARL SCHURZ PARK

CENTRAL PARK

Hudson River

Kefi

5th Ave.
Madison Ave.
Park Ave.
3rd Ave.
2nd Ave.
1st Ave.

E. 79th St.

W. 72nd St.

Earthen Oven

West End Ave.

E. 72nd St.

W. 65th St.

E. 65th St.

Park Avenue

Accademia di Vino

P.J. Clarke's at Lincoln Square

Island

Landmarc

BLT Market

Kobe Club

Queensboro Bridge

W. 57th St.

E. 57th St.

Amalia

Grayz

Gordon Ramsay
Maze

Anthos

QUEENS

Insième

11th Ave.
10th Ave.
9th Ave.
8th Ave.
7th Ave.
Broadway
Ave. of the Americas (6th Ave.)
5th Ave.
Madison Ave.
Park Ave.
Lexington Ave.
3rd Ave.
2nd Ave.
1st Ave.

Spotlight Live

E. 42nd St.

Queens-Midtown Tunnel

Pera

Wild Salmon

BRYANT PARK

E. 39th St.

Lincoln Tunnel

W. 34th St.

E. 34th St.

East River

Pamplona

Resto

Park Ave. South

Hill Country

Klee Brasserie

W. 23rd St.

Borough Food & Drink

E. 23rd St.

Wakiya

10th Ave.
9th Ave.
8th Ave.
7th Ave.
Ave. of the Americas (6th Ave.)

3rd Ave.
2nd Ave.
1st Ave.

Cafe
Cluny

Waverly Inn

15 East

UNION SQ.

E. 14th St.

STK

BLT Burger

TOMPKINS SQ.

Los Dados

p*ong

Sea Salt

The E.U.

Socialista

Morandi

Soto

Hudson River

Centro Vinoteca

Perilla

WASHINGTON SQ.

Gemma

Fette Sau

Mercat

E. Houston St.

Provence

Rayuela

W. Houston St.

Allen St.

Tailor

FR.OG

Delancey St.

Canal St.

Ed's Lobster Bar

Canal St.

E. Broadway

Pike St.

Holland Tunnel

Broadway
Lafayette St.

Park Row

Mai House

Church St.

Manhattan Bridge

Smoke Joint

CITY HALL PARK

East River

NEW JERSEY

Brooklyn Bridge

N

Broadway

Wall St.

BROOKLYN

BATTERY PARK

subscribe to zagat.com

Key Newcomers

Our take on the most notable new arrivals of the past year. For a full list, see the Noteworthy Newcomers index on page 334.

Accademia di Vino | *Italian*

Amalia | *Mediterranean*

Anthos | *Greek*

BLT Burger | *Hamburgers*

BLT Market | *American*

Borough Food/Drink | *American*

Cafe Cluny | *American/French*

Centro Vinoteca | *Italian*

Earthen Oven | *Indian*

Ed's Lobster Bar | *Seafood*

E.U., The | *European*

Fette Sau | *BBQ*

15 East | *Japanese*

FR.OG | *Eclectic/French*

Gemma | *Italian*

Gordon Ramsay | *French*

Grayz | *Eclectic*

Hill Country | *BBQ*

Insieme | *Italian*

Island | *Mediterranean*

Kefi | *Greek*

Klee Brasserie | *Amer./Euro.*

Kobe Club | *Steak*

Landmarc (TWC) | *French*

Los Dados | *Mexican*

Mai House | *Vietnamese*

Maze | *French*

Mercat | *Spanish*

Morandi | *Italian*

Pamplona | *Spanish*

Park Avenue . . . | *American*

Pera | *Med./Turkish*

Perilla | *American*

P.J. Clarke's/Lincoln Sq. | *Pub*

p*ong | *Dessert*

Provence | *French*

Rayuela | *Pan-Latin*

Resto | *Belgian*

Sea Salt | *Med./Seafood*

Smoke Joint | *BBQ*

Socialista | *Cuban*

Soto | *Japanese*

Spotlight Live | *American*

STK | *Steak*

Tailor | *Dessert*

Wakiya | *Chinese*

Waverly Inn | *American*

Wild Salmon | *Seafood*

The year to come shows plenty of potential with a number of big-name projects on tap: Daniel Boulud is cooking up **Bar Boulud** near Lincoln Center as well as **DBGB** on the Bowery; Alain Ducasse plans to open **Adour** in the former Lespinasse space, plus a spin-off of his Parisian brasserie **Benoît** in La Côte Basque's previous digs; Marcus Samuelsson will bring African cuisine to the Meatpacking District via **Merkato 55;** the Bromberg brothers' empire continues to expand with a new **Blue Ribbon Sushi** off Columbus Circle; and the legendary **2nd Avenue Deli** will be reborn – the name notwithstanding – at 33rd and 3rd.

Most Popular

Each surveyor has been asked to name his or her five favorite places. This list reflects their choices (also see the gatefold map in the back of the book).

1. Union Square Cafe
2. Gramercy Tavern
3. Le Bernardin
4. Babbo
5. Jean Georges
6. Daniel
7. Gotham Bar & Grill
8. Peter Luger
9. Bouley
10. Balthazar
11. Blue Water Grill
12. Eleven Madison Park
13. Nobu
14. Per Se*
15. Rosa Mexicano
16. Modern, The
17. Aureole
18. Del Posto
19. Four Seasons
20. Café Boulud
21. Atlantic Grill
22. Spice Market
23. Buddakan
24. Picholine
25. Artisanal
26. Il Mulino
27. Telepan
28. Chanterelle
29. Tabla
30. Aquavit
31. Palm
32. Carmine's
33. Becco
34. Café des Artistes
35. davidburke/donatella
36. Del Frisco's
37. Aquagrill
38. Lupa
39. Bar Americain
40. Pastis
41. Felidia
42. Mesa Grill
43. Craft
44. One if by Land
45. Blue Hill
46. L'Impero
47. Sparks
48. Nobu 57
49. db Bistro Moderne
50. Ouest*

It's obvious that many of the above restaurants are among NYC's most expensive, but if popularity were calibrated to price, we suspect that a number of other places would join their ranks. Given the fact that both our surveyors and readers love to discover dining bargains, we have added several lists of Best Buys on pages 23-26. These are restaurants that give real quality at extremely reasonable prices.

* Indicates a tie with restaurant above

Top Food Ratings

Ratings are to the left of names. Lists exclude places with low votes.

28 | Daniel
Sushi Yasuda
Le Bernardin
Per Se
Peter Luger (Brooklyn)
Jean Georges
Bouley

27 | Chanterelle
Sushi Seki
L'Atelier de Joël Robuchon
Nobu
Gotham Bar & Grill
Café Boulud
Gramercy Tavern
Di Fara (Brooklyn)
La Grenouille
Babbo
Saul (Brooklyn)
Annisa
Il Mulino
Aureole
Masa
Picholine
Roberto (Bronx)

26 | Union Square Cafe

Blue Hill
Gari/Sushi
Pearl Oyster Bar
Aquagrill
Veritas
Eleven Madison Park
Cru
Al Di La (Brooklyn)
Sripraphai (Queens)
Nobu 57
Scalini Fedeli
Danube
Poke
Il Tinello
Milos
Grocery, The (Brooklyn)
Modern, The
Trattoria L'incontro (Queens)
River Café (Brooklyn)
Yakitori Totto
L'Impero
Bouley, Upstairs
Tomoe Sushi
Il Giglio
Tocqueville

BY CUISINE

AMERICAN

28 | Per Se
27 | Gotham Bar & Grill
Gramercy Tavern
Saul
Annisa
Aureole

AMERICAN (REGIONAL)

26 | Pearl Oyster Bar/NE
25 | Roy's NY/Hawaiian
22 | Carl's Steaks/Philly
21 | Michael's/CA
19 | Great Jones Cafe/Cajun
Delta Grill/Cajun

BARBECUE

24 | Daisy May's
23 | Smoke Joint
22 | Dinosaur BBQ
Blue Smoke
20 | RUB BBQ
Virgil's Real BBQ

CARIBBEAN

23 | Don Pedro's/Carib.
22 | Café Habana/Cuban
Sofrito/Puerto Rican
21 | Cuba/Cuban
El Malecon/Dominican
Victor's Cafe/Cuban

CHINESE

25 | Tse Yang
24 | Oriental Garden
Phoenix Garden
Shun Lee Palace
23 | Mr. K's
Tang Pavilion

COFFEEHOUSES

22 | Ferrara
Once Upon a Tart
19 | Le Pain Quotidien
Cafe Lalo
Omonia Cafe
18 | Edgar's Cafe

DELIS

23 Barney Greengrass
   Katz's Deli
21 Carnegie Deli
   Mill Basin Deli
20 Stage Deli
19 Pastrami Queen

DESSERT

25 Chocolate Room
24 ChikaLicious
   La Bergamote
   Payard Bistro
23 Veniero's
22 L & B Spumoni

DIM SUM

24 Oriental Garden
22 Ping's Seafood
21 Shun Lee Cafe
   Excellent Dumpling
   Chinatown Brasserie
20 Mandarin Court

FRENCH

28 Daniel
   Le Bernardin
   Jean Georges
   Bouley
27 Chanterelle
   L'Atelier de Joël Robuchon
   Café Boulud
   La Grenouille
26 Eleven Madison Park
   Modern, The
   Tocqueville
25 Fleur de Sel

FRENCH (BISTRO)

25 db Bistro Moderne
24 Raoul's
   Tournesol
   JoJo
   Le Gigot
   Le Tableau

GREEK

26 Milos
25 Taverna Kyclades
   Pylos
24 Avra
   Agnanti
23 Periyali

HAMBURGERS

24 burger joint/Parker M.
23 DuMont Burger

   Shake Shack
22 Corner Bistro
   Island Burgers
21 Rare B&G

HOTEL DINING

28 Jean Georges
      (Trump Intl. Hotel)
27 L'Atelier de Joël Robuchon
      (Four Seasons Hotel)
   Café Boulud
      (Surrey Hotel)
25 Gordon Ramsay
      (London NYC)
   Norma's
      (Le Parker Meridien)
   db Bistro Moderne
      (City Club Hotel)

INDIAN

25 Tamarind
24 Amma
23 Chola
   Dawat
   Adä
   Banjara

ITALIAN

27 Babbo
   Il Mulino
   Roberto
26 Al Di La
   Scalini Fedeli
   Il Tinello
   Trattoria L'incontro
   L'Impero
   Il Giglio
   Alto
   Aurora
25 Spigolo

JAPANESE/SUSHI

28 Sushi Yasuda
27 Sushi Seki
   Nobu
   Sugiyama
   Kanoyama
   Masa
26 Gari/Sushi
   Nobu 57
   Poke
   Yakitori Totto
   Tomoe Sushi
25 Blue Ribbon Sushi

KOREAN

- 23 Hangawi
- Woo Lae Oak
- 21 Do Hwa
- Kum Gang San
- 20 Mandoo Bar
- 19 Mill Korean

KOSHER

- 22 Prime Grill
- 21 Chennai Garden
- Mill Basin Deli
- Pongal
- 20 Le Marais
- 19 Abigael's

MEDITERRANEAN

- 27 Picholine
- 25 Convivium Osteria
- Tempo
- Il Buco
- 24 Savoy
- Red Cat

MEXICAN

- 25 Pampano
- 23 Mexicana Mama
- Hell's Kitchen
- Itzocan
- Maya
- Sueños

MIDDLE EASTERN

- 27 Tanoreen
- 24 Taboon
- 23 Hummus Place
- 22 Zaytoons
- 21 Miriam
- Moustache

NEWCOMERS

- 25 Gordon Ramsay
- 23 Kefi
- Maze
- Smoke Joint
- 22 Pera
- 21 Earthen Oven
- Mai House
- Klee Brasserie

NOODLE SHOPS

- 24 Momofuku Noodle Bar
- Soba-ya
- 22 Great NY Noodle
- 21 Pho Bang
- 20 Bao Noodles
- Menchanko-tei

PIZZA

- 27 Di Fara
- 25 Denino's
- Grimaldi's
- 24 Lombardi's
- Nick's
- 23 Adrienne's Pizza

RAW BARS

- 26 Aquagrill
- 25 Blue Ribbon
- 23 Blue Water Grill
- Lure Fishbar
- Balthazar
- BLT Fish

SEAFOOD

- 28 Le Bernardin
- 26 Pearl Oyster Bar
- Aquagrill
- Milos
- Oceana
- 25 Esca

SMALL PLATES

- 27 L'Atelier de Joël Robuchon
- 26 Degustation
- 24 Perbacco
- Frankies Spuntino
- 23 Alta
- 'inoteca

SOUTH AMERICAN

- 26 Caracas
- 23 Churrascaria
- Pio Pio
- 22 Tierras Colombianas
- 21 Porcão Churrascaria
- Hacienda de Argentina

SOUTHERN/SOUL

- 22 Amy Ruth's
- Maroons
- 20 Pink Tea Cup
- Rack & Soul
- 19 Kitchenette
- B. Smith's

SOUTHWESTERN

- 24 Mesa Grill
- 21 Los Dos Molinos
- 19 Canyon Road
- 18 Miracle Grill
- Agave
- 17 Cilantro

SPANISH/TAPAS

25 Casa Mono
24 Tía Pol
   Bolo
23 Sevilla
   Boqueria
   El Faro

STEAKHOUSES

28 Peter Luger
25 Sparks
   Del Frisco's
   Strip House
   Wolfgang's
24 Jake's
   Dylan Prime
   BLT Steak
   BLT Prime
   Quality Meats
   Palm
   Keens

THAI

26 Sripraphai
24 Song
23 Land
   Kittichai

Joya
22 Erawan

TURKISH

23 Ali Baba
22 Turkish Kitchen
   Pera
21 Beyoglu
   Pasha
20 Turkish Cuisine

VEGETARIAN

23 Candle
   Hangawi
   Vatan
   Hummus Place
22 Pure Food & Wine
   Counter

VIETNAMESE

23 Omai
22 Nam
   Sapa
   Saigon Grill
21 Pho Bang
   Nha Trang

BY SPECIAL FEATURE

BREAKFAST

Balthazar
Barney Greengrass
Bubby's
Café Sabarsky
Clinton St. Baking
Good Enough to Eat
Jean Georges
Norma's
Payard Bistro
Popover Cafe
Regency
Sarabeth's

BRUNCH MIDTOWN

Artisanal
Blue Water Grill
Cafeteria
Cafe Un Deux Trois
Eatery
elmo
Friend of a Farmer
L'Express
Norma's
Penelope
Rainbow Room
Water Club

BRUNCH DOWNTOWN

Aquagrill
Balthazar
Bubby's
Clinton St. Baking
Essex
Félix
Five Points
Jane
Odeon
Pastis
Prune
Schiller's

BRUNCH UPTOWN

Annie's
Arté Café
Atlantic Grill
Carlyle
Good Enough to Eat
Isabella's
JoJo
Miss Mamie's/Maude's
Ocean Grill
Ouest
Popover Cafe
Sarabeth's

BUSINESS LUNCH/ DOWNTOWN

- Bouley
- City Hall
- Delmonico's
- Dylan Prime
- fresh
- Gotham Bar & Grill
- Harry's
- Les Halles
- MarkJoseph
- Nobu
- Provence
- Wolfgang's

BUSINESS LUNCH/ MIDTOWN

- Alto
- Amma
- Anthos
- Aquavit
- Bar Americain
- BLT Steak
- Felidia
- Four Seasons
- Le Bernardin
- Lever House
- Modern, The
- Sparks

CELEBRATIONS

- Aureole
- Bouley
- Cru
- Daniel
- FireBird
- Four Seasons
- Le Bernardin
- Le Cirque
- Rainbow Room
- River Café
- Tavern on the Green
- Water's Edge

CELEBRITY SCENES

- Balthazar
- Cipriani Downtown
- Da Silvano
- Elaine's
- Fresco
- Joe Allen
- Nobu
- Per Se
- Rao's
- Spotted Pig
- Wakiya
- Waverly Inn

CHILD-FRIENDLY

- American Girl Place
- Bubby's
- Cowgirl
- EJ's Luncheonette
- ESPN Zone
- Hard Rock Cafe
- Ninja
- Peanut Butter & Co.
- Serendipity 3
- Soda Shop
- Spotlight Live
- Two Boots

DINING AT THE BAR

- Aquagrill
- Babbo
- Centro Vinoteca
- Four Seasons (lunchtime)
- Gotham Bar & Grill
- Gramercy Tavern
- Hearth
- Perry Street
- Picholine
- Red Cat
- Tabla (Bread Bar)
- Union Square Cafe

GROUP DINING

- Asia de Cuba
- Buddakan
- Carmine's
- China Grill
- Churrascaria Plataforma
- Hill Country
- Rosa Mexicano
- Ruby Foo's
- Sambuca
- Stanton Social
- Tao
- Tony's Di Napoli

HIPSTER HANGOUTS

- Cafe Gitane
- Employees Only
- Five Points
- Freemans
- La Esquina
- Orchard, The
- Public
- Schiller's
- Spitzer's Corner
- Stanton Social
- wd-50
- Zum Schneider

HOTTEST SERVERS

- Asia de Cuba
- Brother Jimmy's
- Cafeteria
- Coffee Shop
- Del Frisco's
- Food Bar
- 44 & X Hell's Kit.
- Hawaiian Tropic Zone
- Indochine
- Pastis
- Spice Market
- Tao

LATE DINING

- Balthazar
- Baraonda
- Blue Ribbon
- Blue Ribbon Sushi
- Frank
- 'ino
- Mas
- Pastis
- Raoul's
- Spotted Pig
- West Bank Cafe
- Wollensky's

MEET FOR A DRINK/ DOWNTOWN

- Balthazar
- Bond Street
- Buddha Bar
- City Hall
- Employees Only
- Gotham Bar & Grill
- Harry's
- Morimoto
- Odeon
- Rayuela
- Spice Market
- Stanton Social

MEET FOR A DRINK/ MIDTOWN

- Barbounia
- Blue Fin
- Country, Café at
- Django
- Grayz
- Houston's
- Koi
- Maze
- Michael Jordan's
- Modern, The
- Nobu 57
- Town

MEET FOR A DRINK/ UPTOWN

- Aix Brasserie
- Atlantic Grill
- Café Gray
- Cafe Luxembourg
- Compass
- Daniel
- Demarchelier
- Geisha
- Jean Georges
- Landmarc
- Ouest
- 212

MILESTONES

100th	Barney Greengrass
75th	Patsy's Pizzeria (Harlem)
25th	Cafe Luxembourg
	Jackson Diner
	Orso
	Paola's
	Tomoe Sushi
20th	Aureole
	Isabella's
	Rocking Horse Cafe
	San Domenico
	Trattoria Dell'Arte

POWER SCENES

- Coco Pazzo
- Daniel
- Elio's
- Four Seasons
- Jean Georges
- Le Bernardin
- Lever House
- Michael's
- Regency
- Sant Ambroeus
- Smith & Wollensky
- 21 Club

SINGLES SCENES

- Baraonda
- Buddakan
- Buddha Bar
- Butter
- Coffee Shop
- Employees Only
- 'inoteca
- La Esquina
- STK
- SushiSamba
- Tao
- Thor

EAST VILLAGE

27	Kanoyama
26	Degustation
	Caracas
25	Jewel Bako
	Hearth
	Pylos

FINANCIAL DISTRICT

25	Roy's NY
24	MarkJoseph
23	Adrienne's Pizza
22	Bridge Cafe
	Harry's
	Bobby Van's

FLATIRON/ UNION SQUARE

27	Gramercy Tavern
26	Union Square Cafe
	Veritas
	Tocqueville
25	Tamarind
	Craft

GARMENT DISTRICT

24	Keens
	Osteria Gelsi
23	Uncle Jack's
22	Nick & Stef's
21	Frankie & Johnnie's
	Kum Gang San

GRAMERCY/ MADISON PARK

26	Eleven Madison Park
25	Tabla
	Casa Mono
	A Voce
24	Yama
	BLT Prime

GREENWICH VILLAGE

27	Gotham Bar & Grill
	Babbo
	Annisa
	Il Mulino
26	Blue Hill
	Pearl Oyster Bar

HARLEM

22	Dinosaur BBQ
	Amy Ruth's
	Rao's
21	Mo-Bay
20	Papaya King
	Patsy's Pizzeria

LITTLE ITALY

23	Angelo's of Mulberry St.
	Il Cortile
22	Pellegrino's
	Ferrara
	Nyonya
21	Da Nico

LOWER EAST SIDE

25	Falai
24	Clinton St. Baking
	Orchard, The
	ápizz
	Frankies Spuntino
23	Stanton Social

MEATPACKING DISTRICT

24	Valbella
23	Old Homestead
22	Spice Market
21	Ono
	Son Cubano
	Macelleria

MURRAY HILL

25	Sushi Sen-nin
	Wolfgang's
23	Mishima
	Rossini's
	Artisanal
	Asia de Cuba

NOHO

25	Bond Street
	Il Buco
22	Five Points
	Sala
21	Chinatown Brasserie
19	Great Jones Cafe

NOLITA

24	Lombardi's
	Peasant
23	Public
22	Tasting Room
	Café Habana
20	Cafe Gitane

SOHO

26	Aquagrill
25	Blue Ribbon Sushi
	Blue Ribbon
	Fiamma Osteria
24	Raoul's
	Savoy

TRIBECA

28	Bouley
27	Chanterelle
	Nobu
26	Scalini Fedeli
	Danube
	Bouley, Upstairs

WEST 40s

26	Gari/Sushi
25	Sushiden
	Esca
	Del Frisco's
	db Bistro Moderne
	Sushi Zen

WEST 50s

28	Le Bernardin
27	Sugiyama
26	Nobu 57
	Il Tinello
	Milos
	Modern, The

WEST 60s

28	Per Se
	Jean Georges
27	Masa
	Picholine
25	Telepan
	Café Gray

WEST 70s

26	Gari/Sushi
23	Tenzan
	Ocean Grill
	Hummus Place
	Kefi
	'Cesca

WEST 80s

25	Ouest
24	Celeste
23	Barney Greengrass
	Land
22	Neptune Room
	Nёo Sushi

WEST 90s & UP

25	Gennaro
23	Max SoHa
	Pisticci
	Indus Valley
	Pio Pio
22	Awash

WEST VILLAGE

26	Wallsé
25	Piccolo Angolo
	Mary's Fish Camp
24	Da Andrea
	Little Owl
	Perry Street

OUTER BOROUGHS

BRONX

27	Roberto
24	Jake's
	Riverdale Garden
23	Enzo's
	Pasquale's Rigoletto
	Pio Pio

BROOKLYN: BAY RIDGE

27	Tanoreen
25	Areo
24	Tuscany Grill
	Agnanti
23	Pearl Room
22	Chadwick's

BROOKLYN: HTS/DUMBO

26	River Café
25	Grimaldi's
	Henry's End
24	Noodle Pudding
	Queen
21	Five Front

BROOKLYN: CARROLL GARDENS/BOERUM HILL/COBBLE HILL

27	Saul
26	Grocery, The
24	Frankies Spuntino
23	Chestnut
	Fragole
	Joya

BROOKLYN: PARK SLOPE

26	Al Di La
25	Blue Ribbon Sushi
	Chocolate Room
	Convivium Osteria
	Blue Ribbon
	Tempo

BROOKLYN: WILLIAMSBURG

28	Peter Luger
26	Aurora
24	Dressler

23	DuMont
	Bamonte's
22	Fornino

BROOKLYN: OTHER

27	Di Fara (Midwood)
	Garden Cafe (Prospect Hts.)
26	Good Fork (Red Hook)
23	Franny's (Prospect Hts.)
	Tenzan (Bensonhurst)
	Farm on Adderley (Ditmas Pk.)

QUEENS: ASTORIA/L.I.C.

26	Trattoria L'incontro
25	Piccola Venezia
	Taverna Kyclades
24	Tournesol (LIC)
	Agnanti
23	Water's Edge (LIC)

QUEENS: OTHER

26	Sripraphai (Woodside)
25	Sapori D'Ischia (Woodside)
	Don Peppe (Ozone Park)
24	Park Side (Corona)
	Nick's (Forest Hills)
23	Uncle Jack's (Bayside)

STATEN ISLAND

25	Denino's
24	Da Noi
	Trattoria Romana
20	South Fin Grill
	American Grill
19	China Chalet

Top Decor Ratings

Ratings are to the left of names.

28 Asiate
Daniel
Per Se
River Café
La Grenouille

27 Four Seasons
Buddakan
Danube
Rainbow Room
Kittichai
Tao*
Le Bernardin

26 Spice Market
Megu
Buddha Bar
Chanterelle
Eleven Madison Park
Del Posto
Cávo
Matsuri*
Modern, The
One if by Land
Water's Edge
Bouley
Café des Artistes

Carlyle
Public
Morimoto
Suba
Kings' Carriage House
Jean Georges

25 Aureole
EN Japanese
FireBird
Piano Due
Gramercy Tavern
Sapa
Russian Tea Room
Tabla
Dressler
Thalassa
Porter House NY
Terrace in the Sky*
Boathouse
Alto
Scalini Fedeli
Gotham Bar & Grill
Le Cirque

24 Sea Grill
Tavern on the Green

GARDENS

Barbetta
Battery Gardens
Bottino
Cávo
Da Nico
Farm on Adderley
Five Front
Gascogne
Gnocco Caffe
Grocery, The
I Coppi
I Trulli

Jolie
L & B Spumoni
Le Jardin Bistro
Paradou
Park, The
Patois
Pure Food & Wine
Revel
Riverdale Garden
Sripraphai
Surya
Tavern on the Green

PRIVATE PARTIES

(max. capacity)

Barbetta (120)
Buddakan (800)
Café Gray (300)
City Hall (180)
Country (60)
Del Frisco's (85)
Del Posto (200)
Fiamma Osteria (50)
Four Seasons (350)

Le Cirque (80)
Oceana (60)
Patroon (60)
Per Se (60)
Picholine (22)
River Café (100)
Spice Market (30)
Tavern on the Green (1,000)
21 Club (150)

ROMANCE

Aureole
Bouley
Café des Artistes
Chanterelle
Convivium Osteria
Daniel
Danube
Erminia
Gascogne
Il Buco
Kings' Carriage House
Le Refuge
L'Impero
Mas
One if by Land
Petrossian
Piccola Venezia
Rainbow Room
Raoul's
River Café
Scalini Fedeli
Suba
Wallsé
Water's Edge

VIEWS

Alma
Asiate
Battery Gardens
Boathouse
Café Gray
Gigino (Wagner Park)
Modern, The
Per Se
Porter House NY
River Café
River Room
Sea Grill
Terrace in the Sky
View, The
Water Club
Water's Edge

Top Service Ratings

Ratings are to the left of names.

28 Per Se
Daniel
Le Bernardin

27 Chanterelle
La Grenouille
Jean Georges
Bouley
Gramercy Tavern

26 Masa
Il Tinello
Café Boulud
Aureole
Union Square Cafe
Danube
Four Seasons
L'Atelier de Joël Robuchon
Eleven Madison Park
Gotham Bar & Grill
River Café
Cru
Annisa

25 Veritas
Picholine
Blue Hill
Asiate

Scalini Fedeli
Erminia
Degustation
Tocqueville
Mas
Tabla
Alto
Babbo
Gordon Ramsay

24 Grocery, The
One if by Land
Piano Due
Del Posto
Le Perigord
Trattoria L'incontro
Aquavit
Modern, The
21 Club
Capsouto Frères
Sushi Yasuda
Hearth
Carlyle
Oceana
Saul
Craft

Best Buys

Everyone loves a bargain, and NYC offers plenty of places that fill the bill. Three things to bear in mind: lunches typically cost 25 to 30% less than dinners, outer-borough restaurants are less costly than those in Manhattan and biannual Restaurant Weeks (usually in January and July) offer the chance to sample some of the city's finest at greatly reduced prices.

ALL YOU CAN EAT

23 Chola
   Churrascaria
   Vatan
22 Becco
   Turkish Kitchen
21 Chennai Garden
   Porcão Churrascaria
   Yuka
   Utsav
20 Mangia
   East Buffet
19 Green Field

BYO/MANHATTAN

26 Poke
24 Kuma Inn∇
   Phoenix Garden
23 Hummus Place
22 Peking Duck
   Nook
   Tartine
   Amy Ruth's
   Wondee Siam
21 Cube 63
   Pho Bang
   Angelica Kit.
20 Meskerem
19 Zen Palate
18 La Taza de Oro
   X.O.
   Bereket

BYO/OUTER BOROUGHS

27 Di Fara
   Tanoreen
   Lucali∇
22 Zaytoons
21 Pho Bang
   Sweet Melissa
20 Babouche∇

FAMILY-STYLE

27 Roberto
25 Don Peppe
   Piccolo Angolo
24 Supper
   Oriental Garden
   Phoenix Garden
   Frank
   Nick's
23 Posto
   Pisticci
22 Dominick's
   China Grill

PRIX FIXE LUNCH

28 Jean Georges ($24)
   Bouley ($38)
27 Gotham Bar & Grill ($31)
   Aureole ($38)
26 Milos ($24)
   Tocqueville ($24)
25 Tabla ($32)
   Fleur de Sel ($29)
   Pampano ($25)
24 Perry Street ($24)
   Petrossian ($28)
   Duane Park Cafe ($24)

PRIX FIXE DINNER

28 Sushi Yasuda ($21)
27 Garden Cafe ($32)
26 Poke ($20)
25 Henry's End ($23)
   Aki ($28)
   Ouest ($33)
24 Duane Park Cafe ($35)
   Caviar Russe ($30)
23 L'Ecole ($40)
   Artisanal ($35)
   ViceVersa ($35)
   Hangawi ($38)

BEST BUYS: FULL MENU

Alice's Tea Cup | *tearoom*
Bereket | *Turkish*
Big Wong | *Chinese*
Brennan & Carr | *sandwiches*
Chickpea | *Middle Eastern*
Chipotle | *Mexican*
Congee | *Chinese*
Cubana Café | *Cuban*
Doyers | *Vietnamese*
El Malecon | *Dominican*
Energy Kitchen | *health food*
Excellent Dumpling | *Chinese*
Goodies | *Chinese*
Great NY Noodle | *noodles*
Hope & Anchor | *American*
Hummus Place | *Israeli*
Joya | *Thai*
Land | *Thai*
L & B Spumoni | *Italian*
La Taqueria | *Mexican*
La Taza de Oro | *Puerto Rican*
Mama's Food | *American*
Mandoo Bar | *Korean*
Mill Basin Deli | *deli*
Mill Korean | *Korean*
Momofuku Noodle | *noodles*
Nha Trang | *Vietnamese*
Nyonya | *Malaysian*
Pepe . . . To Go | *Italian*
Pho Bang | *Vietnamese*
Pho Pasteur | *Vietnamese*
Pho Viet Huong | *Vietnamese*
Pio Pio | *Peruvian*
Pump | *health food*
Rice | *Eclectic*
Saigon Grill | *Vietnamese*
SEA | *Thai*
Smoke Joint | *BBQ*
Song | *Thai*
Sripraphai | *Thai*
Sweet-n-Tart | *Chinese*
teany | *vegetarian*
Thai Pavilion | *Thai*
Tierras | *Colombian*
Whole Foods | *Eclectic*
Wo Hop | *Chinese*
X.O. | *Chinese*
Zaytoons | *Middle Eastern*

BEST BUYS: SPECIALTY SHOPS

Amy's Bread | *baked goods*
Better Burger | *burgers*
Blue 9 Burger | *burgers*
brgr | *burgers*
burger joint/P.M. | *burgers*
Burritoville | *Mexican*
Caracas | *arepas*
Carl's | *cheese steaks*
ChikaLicious | *desserts*
Chipotle | *Mexican*
Chocolate Room | *desserts*
Chop't Creative | *salads*
Coals | *pizza*
Corner Bistro | *burgers*
Cozy Soup | *burgers*
Denino's | *pizza*
Di Fara | *pizza*
Dishes | *sandwiches*
Dumpling Man | *dumplings*
Empanada Mama | *empanadas*
Ess-a-Bagel | *deli*
F & B | *European hot dogs*
Ferrara | *Italian pastry*
goodburger | *burgers*
Gray's Papaya | *hot dogs*
Grimaldi's | *pizza*
Hale & Hearty | *soup*
Hampton Chutney | *Indian*
Joe's Pizza | *pizza*
Kati Roll Co. | *Indian*
La Bergamote | *bakery*
Lenny's | *sandwiches*
New York Burger Co. | *burgers*
Nicky's | *Vietnamese sandwiches*
99 Miles to Philly | *cheese steaks*
Once Upon a Tart | *baked goods*
Papaya King | *hot dogs*
Peanut Butter | *sandwiches*
Pizza 33 | *pizza*
Press 195 | *sandwiches*
Rickshaw | *dumplings*
Roll-n-Roaster | *sandwiches*
Shake Shack | *burgers*
S'mac | *mac 'n' cheese*
Sweet Melissa | *pastry*
Veniero's | *Italian pastry*
Waldy's | *pizza*
Zip Burger | *burgers*

LUNCH

Abboccato	$28	La Petite Auberge	20
Adä	17	L'Ecole	27
Al Bustan	25	Le Perigord	32
Alto	30	Le Veau d'Or	20
Angelo & Maxie's	21	Le Zie 2000	15
Anthos	28	L'Impero	35
Aquavit	39	Mercer Kitchen	24
Artisanal	25	Michael Jordan's	24
Asiate	24	Milos	24
Atlantic Grill	24	Molyvos	25
Avra	28	Morimoto	24
Baldoria	28	Mr. K's	28
Beacon	32	Oceana	33
Becco	17	Ocean Grill	24
Bistro du Nord	18	Olives	24
Bouley	38	Orsay	26
Brasserie 8½	25	Osteria del Circo	25
Café Boulud	32	Pampano	25
Cafe Luxembourg	30	Patroon	27
Capsouto Frères	24	Patsy's	34
Carlyle	24	Periyali	26
Chin Chin	24	Perry Street	24
Churrascaria	33	Petrossian	28
Cibo	28	Post House	25
davidburke/donatella	24	Remi	24
Dawat	16	René Pujol	24
Del Frisco's	30	Roc	25
Demarchelier	25	Roy's NY	30
Django	24	San Domenico	38
Duane Park Cafe	24	Shun Lee Palace	20
etcetera etcetera	24	Solera	26
Felidia	30	Spice Market	17
FireBird	30	Sushi Yasuda	21
Fleur de Sel	29	Tabla	32
Gallagher's	20	Tamarind	24
Gascogne	20	Tao	24
Gavroche	20	Tavern on the Green	38
Giorgio's/Gramercy	20	Thalassa	24
Gotham Bar & Grill	31	Thalia	17
Gusto	20	Tía Pol	15
Hangawi	20	Tocqueville	24
I Trulli	28	Trata Estiatorio	22
Inagiku	35	Tribeca Grill	24
Jean Georges	24	Tse Yang	28
JoJo	24	Turkish Kitchen	17
Josephina	25	21 Club	35
Kellari Taverna	25	Utsav	16
Kings' Carriage House	19	ViceVersa	24
Korea Palace	18	Vong	20
La Boîte en Bois	25	Water's Edge	35
La Mangeoire	17	Zarela	17

PT = pre-theater only; where two prices are listed, the first is pre-theater and the second for normal dinner hours.

Abboccato/PT	$38	Le Boeuf/Mode	39
Akdeniz	20	L'Ecole	40
Aki/PT	28	Le Madeleine	32
Alcala	40	Le Rivage	35
Alouette/PT	24	Le Singe Vert/PT	27
Anthos/PT	38	Levana	30
A.O.C. Bedford/PT	32	Luca	23
Artisanal	35	Madison Bistro	31
Atlantic Grill/PT	28	Mamlouk	40
Avra/PT	37	Maria Pia	22
Baldoria/PT	38	Marseille	29
Bay Leaf/PT	21	McCormick/Schmick's/PT	30
Becco	22	Métisse/PT	20
Bistro du Nord/PT	20	Metrazur	35
Bistro 61/PT	21	Mi Cocina/PT	30
Bombay Palace	24/30	Molyvos/PT	35
Brasserie Julien/PT	25	Montparnasse	23
Bryant Park Grill/PT	30	Ocean Grill/PT	28
B. Smith's	30	Odeon/PT	32
Cafe Centro	35	Osteria del Circo	35
Cafe Un Deux	29	Ouest/PT	33
Capsouto Frères	35	Pascalou/PT	19
Cascina/PT	25	Pasha/PT	24
Caviar Russe	30	Payard Bistro	35
Cebu/PT	21	Pigalle/PT	25
Chez Napoléon	30	p*ong	25
Chin Chin	35	Quercy	25
Cibo	30	Remi/PT	35
Compass	35	Russian Samovar	28
Del Frisco's/PT	40	San Domenico/PT	38
Demarchelier	25	Sharz Cafe/PT	20
Dervish Turkish/PT	24	Shula's Steak/PT	35
Duane Park Cafe	35	Sorrel	25
etcetera etcetera	35	Sugiyama/PT	32
Garden Cafe	32	Sushi Yasuda	21
Gascogne/PT	28	Table d'Hôte	23/27
Gavroche/PT	20	Tempo	25
Gigino	28	Thalia/PT	35
Hangawi	38	Todai	26
Henry's End/PT	23	Trata Estiatorio/PT	25
HQ/PT	25	Trattoria Dopo Teatro/PT	23
Indochine/PT	28	Turkish Cuisine	27
Jarnac	36	21 Club/PT	40
Jewel of India/PT	28	Utsav/PT	28
Kellari Taverna/PT	30	Vatan	24
Klee Brasserie/PT	30	ViceVersa	35
Koi/PT	39	Villa Berulia	35
La Baraka	25/37	Village	29
La Boîte en Bois/PT	36	Vincent's	30
La Mangeoire	25/32	Vivolo/PT	26
La Mediterranée/PT	25	Vong/PT	35
La Petite Auberge	27	Water Club/PT	40

RESTAURANT
DIRECTORY

	FOOD	DECOR	SERVICE	COST

Abboccato *Italian*

22 | 19 | 21 | $62

W 50s | Blakely Hotel | 136 W. 55th St. (bet. 6th & 7th Aves.) | 212-265-4000 | www.abboccato.com

"Interesting", "refined" Italian fare and an "unbeatable location" across from City Center ensure this "sophisticated" Midtowner is a "hit" with the "pre-theater" crowd; "high-end" from the "dim", "retro-feeling" room and "attentive" service to the "costly" tab, it pleases all but a frugal few.

Abigael's *Pan-Asian*

19 | 14 | 17 | $47

Garment District | 1407 Broadway (bet. 38th & 39th Sts.) | 212-575-1407 | www.abigaels.com

Kosher "pioneer"/"celebrity chef" Jeffrey Nathan is in the kitchen at this "solid" bi-level Garment Districter that pleases the observant with its Pan-Asian fare and sushi served at street level and steaks downstairs; now if only the "outdated" decor and "mediocre" service could get an "uplift."

Aburiya Kinnosuke *Japanese*

24 | 18 | 21 | $45

E 40s | 213 E. 45th St. (bet. 2nd & 3rd Aves.) | 212-867-5454

You can travel "to Tokyo" without leaving East Midtown via this perpetually "packed", "upscale" Japanese grill that's prized for its "extremely flavorful" robata specialties and "charming" crew; check out the "chalkboard" specials, then "sit in the back to watch your food cook."

Acappella *Ⓩ Italian*

23 | 20 | 23 | $70

TriBeCa | 1 Hudson St. (Chambers St.) | 212-240-0163 | www.acappella-restaurant.com

"Dark" and "romantic", this "white-tablecloth" TriBeCa Northern Italian piles on the antipasti and other "delicious" "old-world" delights served "with flair" by "over-the-top" waiters; just "hold your breath when the bill comes" – and "decide the tip" before downing the gratis "housemade grappa."

NEW Accademia di Vino *Italian*

- | - | - | M

E 60s | 1081 Third Ave. (bet. 63rd & 64th Sts.) | 212-888-6333

The former Mainland space has been reworked into this new UES enoteca/trattoria, a grottolike affair with two wine bars and a long, meandering dining room; Italian small plates and mains can be paired with vino from its 500 bottle–strong cellar or rotating by-the-glass list.

Acqua *Italian*

18 | 17 | 18 | $38

W 90s | 718 Amsterdam Ave. (bet. 94th & 95th Sts.) | 212-222-2752 | www.acquanyc.com

Every neighborhood could use a "solid", "casual" Italian like this "steady" Upper Westsider; although service can be "slow", at least its "cozy" space is "easier to navigate" than the always-packed "Gennaro's down the street."

Adä *Indian*

23 | 21 | 21 | $53

E 50s | 208 E. 58th St. (bet. 2nd & 3rd Aves.) | 212-371-6060 | www.adanyc.com

"Towering above the usual", this "quiet" East Midtown "upmarket Indian" is where "incredible flavors and presentations" arrive via an "amiable, professional" staff; if dinner is slightly "pricey" for the genre, there's always the $14.95 prix fixe lunch.

Adrienne's Pizzabar ❶ *Pizza*   23 | 16 | 15 | $23

Financial District | 87 Pearl St. (bet. Broad St. & Hanover Sq.) | 212-248-3838

"Always packed", this Financial District Italian purveys "heavenly" thin-crust pizzas and other eats for little dough; the scene approaches "bedlam" (especially at lunch) and service "needs work", but to most it's "worth it" – especially if you nab a table out on "charming" Stone Street.

Aesop's Tables 🅂 🅼 *American/Mediterranean*   ▽ 21 | 18 | 20 | $42

Staten Island | 1233 Bay St. (Maryland Ave.) | 718-720-2005

Delivering "enjoyable meals and evenings" for years, this "cozy" Staten Island Med–New American remains a "friendly" refuge from Manhattan prices; even those who find it just "decent" "always return with the warm weather" when the "beautiful garden" is open.

Afghan Kebab House *Afghan*   19 | 10 | 17 | $23

E 70s | 1345 Second Ave. (bet. 70th & 71st Sts.) | 212-517-2776
W 50s | 764 Ninth Ave. (bet. 51st & 52nd Sts.) | 212-307-1612
Jackson Heights | 74-16 37th Ave. (bet. 74th & 75th Sts.) | Queens | 718-565-0471

"Smoky, juicy" kebabs "bursting with flavor" are the "highlight" at these "friendly" Afghan eateries that are "cheap, cheap" – especially when you factor in the BYO policy; ignore the "hole-in-the-wall" atmosphere and just focus on the "feast."

Agata & Valentina Ristorante *Italian*   18 | 18 | 17 | $44

E 70s | 1513 First Ave. (79th St.) | 212-452-0691 | www.agatavalentina.com

"*Delizioso*" Sicilian fare made with the "freshest ingredients" have this "low-key" UES Italian gaining status as a "strong neighborhood" entry; it gets the nod for its "soaring", recently "reconfigured" space, but service still "needs polishing."

Agave ❶ *Southwestern*   18 | 18 | 17 | $36

W Village | 140 Seventh Ave. S. (bet. Charles & W. 10th Sts.) | 212-989-2100 | www.agaveny.com

It feels like "Santa Fe" at this "noisy" Villager whose "clean, white" setting provides a "comfortable" backdrop for its "zippy margs" and "solid" Southwestern eats; "reasonable" prices and "sidewalk seating" perfect for "people-watching" make the "slooow" service easy to overlook.

Agnanti ❶ *Greek*   24 | 15 | 19 | $33

Bay Ridge | 7802 Fifth Ave. (78th St.) | Brooklyn | 718-833-7033
Astoria | 19-06 Ditmars Blvd. (19th St.) | Queens | 718-545-4554
www.agnantimeze.com

Meze-loving masses laud this Astoria–Bay Ridge taverna twosome for its "irresistible" Greek fare at "easy" rates; factor in "warm" service and "pleasant" sidewalk seats, and it's no wonder there are "killer waits on weekends."

Aix Brasserie *French*   20 | 21 | 19 | $59

W 80s | 2398 Broadway (88th St.) | 212-874-7400 | www.aixnyc.com

The menu, revamped last year, is "still creative" at this multilevel UWS French "neighborhood brasserie"; while the bar – which does a "delicious burger" – remains "buzzing", critics citing "mediocre" output say the overall experience "isn't worth" the tab.

Aja ● *Pan-Asian*

| 20 | 22 | 19 | $44 |

E 50s | 1068 First Ave. (58th St.) | 212-888-8008

A "swanky", "cool place" for midpriced Pan-Asian fare, this "dimly lit" "surprise" near the Queensboro Bridge lures a "young", "energetic" crowd with its "exotic" setup "complete with giant Buddha" and "see-through floor"/koi pond; N.B. a Village offshoot is expected soon.

AJ Maxwell's Steakhouse ⊠ *Steak*

| 22 | 19 | 22 | $67 |

W 40s | 57 W. 48th St. (bet. 5th & 6th Aves.) | 212-262-6200 | www.ajmaxwells.com

"Not bad for a new steakhouse", this "expense account"–oriented Rock Center arrival's setting is somewhat "sparse", save for a "beautiful mural" behind the bar; though the rib-eyes are "huge" and the service "personal", up till now the vibe has been on the "sedate" side.

Akdeniz ⊠ *Turkish*

| 20 | 12 | 19 | $29 |

W 40s | 19 W. 46th St. (bet. 5th & 6th Aves.) | 212-575-2307 | www.akdenizturkishusa.com

"You can make a wonderful meal of the meze" alone at this "tiny", "reliable" Midtown Turk considered a "true find"; the "breads, spreads and grilled fish" come to the table "fast and fresh", transporting you to "Istanbul" at "bargain" rates – especially via the $19.95 dinner prix fixe.

Aki Ⓜ *Japanese*

| 25 | 14 | 21 | $43 |

G Village | 181 W. Fourth St. (bet. Barrow & Jones Sts.) | 212-989-5440

Maybe it's not such a "secret anymore", but this "friendly" Village Japanese sliver is "still one of the best bargains" around given its "innovative", "exceptional" Caribbean-influenced sushi; groupies gush it's "Nobu at half the price" – and way less than half the space.

Aki Sushi *Japanese*

| 19 | 12 | 18 | $31 |

E 70s | 1425 York Ave. (bet. 75th & 76th Sts.) | 212-628-8885
Garment District | 128 W. 36th St. (bet. B'way & 7th Ave.) | 212-868-8091
Gramercy | 121 E. 27th St. (bet. Lexington Ave. & Park Ave. S.) | 212-213-9888
W 50s | 366 W. 52nd St. (bet. 8th & 9th Aves.) | 212-262-2888

It's "nothing fancy" – just "good, cheap sushi" – which suits fine the many fans of this "reliable" Japanese mini-chain; still, some who note that there's "no decor at all" opt for "fast delivery."

NEW A La Turka ● *Turkish*

| 18 | 12 | 16 | $35 |

E 70s | 1417 Second Ave. (74th St.) | 212-744-2424 | www.alaturkarestaurant.com

Generally considered a "good UES addition", this "casual", "inexpensive" Turk (from the team that ran Sultan) dishes up "reliable" meze and other classics; still, the less enthused say it has almost "no atmosphere" and a staff that tends toward "disorganized."

Al Bustan *Lebanese*

| 19 | 13 | 18 | $42 |

E 50s | 827 Third Ave. (bet. 50th & 51st Sts.) | 212-759-5933 | www.albustanny.com

"Dependable" as ever, this longtime Lebanese remains a good bet for a "tasty" Midtown meal; however, given the "dog-eared" "'80s decor" and merely "acceptable" service, a few feel the experience "isn't worth the price tag."

Alcala *Spanish*   ▽ 20 | 16 | 21 | $48

E 40s | 342 E. 46th St. (bet. 1st & 2nd Aves.) | 212-370-1866 | www.alcalarestaurant.com

"Tucked away near the U.N.", this "intimate" Spanish-Basque bastion and its "charming" staff caters to a "traditional" crowd with "delicious" "real-deal" dishes; for best results, sit in the "lovely garden" and "forget you're in" Midtown.

NEW Alchemy M *American*   ▽ 18 | 21 | 17 | $36

Park Slope | 56 Fifth Ave. (bet. Bergen St. & St. Marks Pl.) | Brooklyn | 718-636-4385 | www.alchemybrooklyn.com

While this New American has practiced alchemy by turning an old Park Slope hardware shop into a Brit-style gastropub, it's "still working out some kinks"; most agree it's a "nice addition" to Fifth Avenue, but be prepared for "crowds" and "squished" seating at communal tables.

Z Al Di La *Italian*   26 | 18 | 22 | $45

Park Slope | 248 Fifth Ave. (Carroll St.) | Brooklyn | 718-783-4565 | www.aldilatrattoria.com

"Al-di-lightful", this "really special" Park Slope Venetian showcases Anna Klinger's "superlative" cuisine, served by a "caring" crew in a "cozy" "communal" dining room; the "no-reservations policy" leads to "painful waits", though, so "get your gondola there early" – or try their "wonderful" "around-the-corner" wine bar.

Alfama *Portuguese*   22 | 21 | 21 | $49

W Village | 551 Hudson St. (Perry St.) | 212-645-2500 | www.alfamarestaurant.com

Everything from the "Lisboa"-worthy fare to the "attentive" service and "lovely blue-and-white-tiled" decor makes it feel like "an evening in Portugal" at this slightly "pricey" Village "charmer"; for the ultimate "transporting" experience, come for Wednesday's live *fado* fest.

Al Forno Pizzeria *Pizza*   19 | 13 | 17 | $25

E 70s | 1484 Second Ave. (bet. 77th & 78th Sts.) | 212-249-5103

"Easygoing" and "affordable", this UES pie parlor is a hit with "families and groups" who come for the "delicious thin-crust" pizzas from a "real brick oven" and "mammoth salads"; better still, you avoid the waits at nearby rivals.

Alfredo of Rome *Italian*   19 | 18 | 18 | $46

W 40s | 4 W. 49th St. (bet. 5th & 6th Aves.) | 212-397-0100 | www.alfredos.com

"Reliably good" but "no surprises" is the word on this slightly "pricey" Rock Center Italian with branches in Rome and Las Vegas; maybe it's a bit "touristy" with staffers too focused on "turning over tables", but as for that namesake dish, it's "the best ever."

Algonquin Hotel Round Table *American*   16 | 23 | 19 | $52

W 40s | Algonquin Hotel | 59 W. 44th St. (bet. 5th & 6th Aves.) | 212-840-6800 | www.algonquinhotel.com

"History, location and atmosphere" highlight this Theater District former "literary hangout", but not the "overpriced", just "average"

Traditional American eats; ergo, most agree it's "best for drinks" in the "elegant" "wood-paneled" lobby or cabaret in the next-door Oak Room.

Alias *American* `23` `15` `20` `$36`

LES | 76 Clinton St. (Rivington St.) | 212-505-5011 | www.aliasrestaurant.com

Where "hipsters" head to "go off the diet", this "friendly" LES American spins "upscale twists on comfort food" using "fresh, seasonal ingredients"; "reasonable" prices and "spruced-up diner" digs make a "refreshing change" from the ordinary; P.S. the $25 Sunday dinner prix fixe is a "steal."

Ali Baba *Turkish* `23` `14` `17` `$29`

Murray Hill | 212 E. 34th St. (bet. 2nd & 3rd Aves.) | 212-683-9206 | www.alibabaturkishcuisine.com

"The Bosporus" meets Murray Hill at this Turkish house of "delicious" kebabs, "Middle Eastern–style" pizzas and "various dips" offered at "bargain" rates; devotees could "eat here for 1,001 nights", "slow" service and "cramped" quarters notwithstanding; P.S. "dine in the garden when it's open."

Alice's Tea Cup *Tearoom* `19` `21` `18` `$25`

E 60s | 156 E. 64th St. (Lexington Ave.) | 212-486-9200
NEW **E 80s** | 220 E. 81st St. (bet. 2nd & 3rd Aves.) | 212-734-4832
W 70s | 102 W. 73rd St. (bet. Amsterdam & Columbus Aves.) | 212-799-3006
www.alicesteacup.com

"It's always tea time" at these "pastel" "wonderlands" of "decadent scones", finger sandwiches and other "dainty" treats that are a hit with "girls aged 8 to 80" (it's the culinary "equivalent of a chick flick"); just "beware the jabberwocky" – "long waits" and "spacey service."

Aliseo Osteria del Borgo Ⓜ *Italian* ▽ `23` `20` `23` `$43`

Prospect Heights | 665 Vanderbilt Ave. (bet. Park & Prospect Pls.) | Brooklyn | 718-783-3400

"Delicious", "inventive" dishes inspired by the Marche region and built on "artisanal" ingredients make this "tiny" Prospect Heights Italian a local standout; "personal service" and decor with "grandma charm" add to the overall "relaxed" vibe.

Alma *Mexican* `20` `21` `18` `$32`

Carroll Gardens | 187 Columbia St., 2nd fl. (Degraw St.) | Brooklyn | 718-643-5400 | www.almarestaurant.com

Score a "coveted rooftop table" to best enjoy this "offbeat" Carroll Gardens Mexican and its "spectacular" view of the harbor and "Manhattan skyline"; the "killer margaritas" and "fresh", affordable fare are also agreeable, as is the "downstairs bar" where you can while away the inevitable "wait."

NEW Almond Flower Bistro *American* ▽ `23` `22` `24` `$32`

Little Italy | 96 Bowery (bet. Grand & Hester Sts.) | 212-966-7162 | www.almondflowerbistro.com

No, it's not another Chinese eatery along the Bowery – this new bistro is a "welcome surprise" with its "sensational" New American fare at "bargain prices"; "attentive" service and a downtown-stylish, yet "romantic", space are two other reasons early-goers call it a "hit."

	FOOD	DECOR	SERVICE	COST

NEW Aloe ⓜ *Eclectic* — | — | — | M

E Village | 406 E. Ninth St. (bet. Ave. A & 1st Ave.) | 212-358-8400
Its name is short for 'a little of everything', so it's no surprise that this tiny East Villager specializes in Eclectic eats, happily offered at affordable rates; its rustic space holds just three tables on the ground level, but there's more seating in a log cabin-like subterranean room.

Alouette ⓪ *French*   20 | 17 | 18 | $44

W 90s | 2588 Broadway (bet. 97th & 98th Sts.) | 212-222-6808 | www.alouettenyc.com
Upper Westsiders say "*oui*" to this "warm" neighborhood bistro where the "traditional" French fare is "consistently" good and the overall mood "inviting"; relatively "reasonable checks" plus a $24 early-bird dinner prix fixe compensate for digs that are "a little tight."

Alta *Mediterranean*   23 | 21 | 19 | $45

G Village | 64 W. 10th St. (bet. 5th & 6th Aves.) | 212-505-7777 | www.altarestaurant.com
"Behind a hidden doorway" dwells this "cozy" "tavernlike" Villager serving up "inventive" Med small plates paired with a "terrific" wine list; its "warm fireplace" abets an atmosphere that's so "romantic", you don't notice how those bitty dishes "can add up" to an alta tab.

Ⓩ Alto Ⓢ *Italian*   26 | 25 | 25 | $81

E 50s | 11 E. 53rd St. (bet. 5th & Madison Aves.) | 212-308-1099 | www.altorestaurant.com
As chef Michael White picks up where Scott Conant left off, "power" patrons are watching to see how this "formal" East Side Italian evolves; known for its "fantastic", "intriguing" cuisine, "outstanding" wine list and "ultrachic", glass wine cellar-lined decor, all hope that everything stays the same, except maybe the "sky-high prices."

Ama *Italian*   22 | 19 | 19 | $52

SoHo | 48 MacDougal St. (bet. King & Prince Sts.) | 212-358-1707 | www.amanyc.com
"Creative approaches to pasta" and other Puglia-inspired foods "delight" fashionable followers of this "white-walled" SoHo Southern Italian; the "friendly owner" justifiably "takes pride" in the place, making for "pleasant" overall experiences despite service that can be "slow."

NEW Amalia *Mediterranean*   ▽ 21 | 22 | 19 | $60

W 50s | 204 W. 55th St. (bet. B'way & 7th Ave.) | 212-245-1234 | www.amalia-nyc.com
Carved out of a "renovated carriage house", this bi-level newcomer adjacent to Midtown's Dream Hotel exudes downtown "cool" with its brick walls, black chandeliers and industrial-chic basement; surveyors are "pleasantly surprised" by the "pricey" coastal Med fare – if only it would work out the service "kinks."

Amaranth ⓪ *Mediterranean*   20 | 17 | 19 | $57

E 60s | 21 E. 62nd St. (bet. 5th & Madison Aves.) | 212-980-6700 | www.amaranthrestaurant.com
It's "kiss, kiss, hug, hug" at this "noisy", pricey East Side Mediterranean bistro favored by a "very attractive" "Euro" crowd; despite "solid" fare, it's really more about the "scene" ("many women seem to be with

their uncles"), and, as for the service, it's either "lovely" or "arrogant" depending on who you know.

Amarone ● *Italian* | 19 | 13 | 19 | $37 |

W 40s | 686 Ninth Ave. (bet. 47th & 48th Sts.) | 212-245-6060 | www.amaronenyc.com

"Dependable" Italian classics worthy of your "nonna", "solid service" and "accessible" prices make it easy to overlook the "cramped quarters" at this Hell's Kitchen trattoria; still, its main virtue may be its "pre-theater" "convenience."

NEW Amazing 66 *Chinese* | ▽ 23 | 14 | 17 | $23 |

Chinatown | 66 Mott St. (bet. Bayard & Canal Sts.) | 212-334-0099

"Truly amazing" is the early word on this "fresh, delicious" C-town Cantonese newcomer that's "drawing crowds" with its extensive menu and astounding $4.95 lunch special; its menu features the usual suspects plus specialties like frog and conch for the more daring.

Amber ● *Pan-Asian* | 22 | 22 | 19 | $37 |

E 80s | 1406 Third Ave. (80th St.) | 212-249-5020

Upper Eastsiders pack this "jazzed-up" Pan-Asian, where the "hot staff" and "hip" decor lend a "downtown-comes-uptown" vibe; while the "noisy" bar scene may overshadow the "quality" sushi and other "fusion" fare, there's always the more "serene" back room.

American Girl Place Café *American* | 13 | 22 | 19 | $34 |

E 40s | 609 Fifth Ave. (49th St.) | 212-644-1145 | www.americangirlplace.com

A "mother-daughter" must-do, this "little girls' paradise" can "provide a laugh-a-minute experience, if you have doll guests at your table"; as ratings show, the American food is decent enough – with the afternoon tea party as the highlight.

American Grill *American* | 20 | 18 | 19 | $45 |

Staten Island | 1180 Victory Blvd. (Clove Rd.) | 718-442-4742 | www.americangrillnyc.com

Following its move and ownership change a few years back, surveyors split over this still "solid" Staten Island American: depending on who you ask, the food "quality has gone up" or it's "not as good", while it's either "overpriced" or "worth every penny"; your call.

Amma *Indian* | 24 | 17 | 22 | $43 |

E 50s | 246 E. 51st St. (bet. 2nd & 3rd Aves.) | 212-644-8330 | www.ammanyc.com

With food so "amazing" it's almost "unfair" to the rest of the city's tandoori houses, this Midtown Northern Indian provides a "gourmet experience" in "calm", if "cramped", quarters; "gracious" service rounds out the "refined" experience; P.S. the $85 tasting menu with wine pairings is "a must!"

Ammos *Greek* | 22 | 22 | 21 | $51 |

E 40s | 52 Vanderbilt Ave. (bet. 44th & 45th Sts.) | 212-922-9999

Astoria | 20-30 Steinway St. (bet. 20th Ave. & 20th Rd.) | Queens | 718-726-7900 ● Ⓜ

www.ammosnewyork.com

The "haute-classic" Greek fare is a "cut above" the norm at these "up-market" Midtown-Astoria siblings known for their "impeccably fresh" seafood; "transporting" "island" decor and "friendly" service complete the "pricey", but always "enjoyable", picture.

Amorina ⓂⓂ Pizza   ▽ 23 | 14 | 18 | $22

Prospect Heights | 624 Vanderbilt Ave. (Prospect Pl.) | Brooklyn | 718-230-3030 | www.amorinapizza.com

It's not "your conventional slice" at this "reasonable" Prospect Heights pizzeria/trattoria where many of the "fantabulous" Roman-style pies are topped with "quirky" ingredients (think "figs and Gorgonzola"); fortunately for more traditional types, there are also pastas and other Italian "comfort" favorites.

Amy Ruth's Soul Food   22 | 11 | 17 | $24

Harlem | 113 W. 116th St. (bet. Lenox & 7th Aves.) | 212-280-8779 | www.amyruthsharlem.com

"For a few fabulous greasy minutes", you're "back in Dixie" as you tuck into an "artery-clogging feast" at this Harlem "soul-food classic"; regulars attest "you won't be disappointed" with the fried chicken, waffles and such – or the "cheap" prices; if you've been partying late, keep in mind that it's "open all night" on weekends; N.B. the departure of founder Carl Redding puts the above ratings in question.

Amy's Bread Sandwiches   23 | 11 | 16 | $13

Chelsea | Chelsea Mkt. | 75 Ninth Ave. (bet. 15th & 16th Sts.) | 212-462-4338
G Village | 250 Bleecker St. (bet. Carmine & Leroy Sts.) | 212-675-7802
W 40s | 672 Ninth Ave. (bet. 46th & 47th Sts.) | 212-977-2670
www.amysbread.com

"Magical ovens" must produce the "stellar" breads and other "addictive" treats at this "wholesome" bakery/sandwich shop trio; but "rushed" counter service and "always-crowded", "no-atmosphere" digs mean many feel they're best for "popping in" and out.

Angelica Kitchen ⌇ Vegan/Vegetarian   21 | 15 | 18 | $24

E Village | 300 E. 12th St. (bet. 1st & 2nd Aves.) | 212-228-2909 | www.angelicakitchen.com

A "vegan heaven" since 1976, this "bohemian" East Villager still has fans "lining up" for its "tasty" bargain organic eats, "communal tables" and "crunchy" staffers; you'll leave its "spartan" quarters in a "Zen state of mind" – just remember to "bring cash" (no credit cards).

Angelina's Italian   ▽ 23 | 19 | 20 | $57

Staten Island | 26 Jefferson Blvd. (Annadale Rd.) | 718-227-7100 | www.angelinasristorante.com

Italian fare "excellent" enough to "rival Manhattan's best" makes this a "Staten Island staple", which also boasts "music, dancing" and a hostess who "makes meals memorable" with "jokes and magic tricks"; given all that, most don't mind much if prices are "a bit high."

Angelo & Maxie's ● Steak   21 | 18 | 19 | $55

Flatiron | 233 Park Ave. S. (19th St.) | 212-220-9200 | www.angelo-maxies.com

"Young corporate types" gravitate to this "high-energy" Flatiron meetery for its "big, juicy" steaks and bustling (à la "Joey from Long Island/hot divorcée") "bar scene"; sure, it's "crowded" and "loud", but relatively "reasonable prices" compensate; P.S. check out the "bargain" $21 lunch prix fixe.

	FOOD	DECOR	SERVICE	COST

Angelo's of Mulberry Street ⦿ Ⓜ *Italian*
23 | 16 | 20 | $44

Little Italy | 146 Mulberry St. (bet. Grand & Hester Sts.) | 212-966-1277 | www.angelomulberry.com

More than a century old and "still going strong", this "festive" Little Italy "landmark" gratifies "pasta and garlic lovers" with "quintessential" red-sauce dishes to make you "think you died and went to Naples"; it's one of the "best bets" on the strip, but remember "you go for the food, not the decor."

Angelo's Pizzeria *Pizza*
20 | 12 | 15 | $24

E 50s | 1043 Second Ave. (55th St.) | 212-521-3600
W 50s | 117 W. 57th St. (bet. 6th & 7th Aves.) | 212-333-4333
W 50s | 1697 Broadway (bet. 53rd & 54th Sts.) | 212-245-8811
www.angelospizzany.com

Thin-crust pizzas with "just-right" sauce and "quality" toppings "are the thing" at these "casual" Midtown Italians; a boon to "lunching coworkers" and "families with kids", they offer "decent prices" that override "spotty" service and "uninspiring" settings.

Angus McIndoe ⦿ *American*
16 | 14 | 18 | $40

W 40s | 258 W. 44th St. (bet. B'way & 8th Ave.) | 212-221-9222 | www.angusmcindoe.com

"Basic" American fare with a heaping side of "B'way buzz" is the deal at this "raucous hangout" for "performers and their public" in the Theater District; just don't be surprised if the servers are more interested in being "your star" than "your waiter."

Annie's *American*
18 | 14 | 16 | $29

E 70s | 1381 Third Ave. (bet. 78th & 79th Sts.) | 212-327-4853

"Get your brunch fix on" at this UES American whose "generously portioned" "comfort" food may be "a little too popular" (expect "hourlong waits"); "oblivious service" and a "no-stroller policy" "don't deter" the morning masses, but "dinners are good too" and "not crowded."

Ⓩ Annisa *American*
27 | 22 | 26 | $73

G Village | 13 Barrow St. (bet. 7th Ave. S. & W. 4th St.) | 212-741-6699 | www.annisarestaurant.com

"Top-tier chef" Anita Lo's Village oasis woos patrons with "refined, beautiful" New American cuisine, "impeccable service" and "stylish" "white-curtained" decor that add up to "magical" meals; such "superior" experiences don't come cheap, but for a relative bargain "go for the tasting menu" at $88.

Anthony's *Italian*
▽ 21 | 15 | 20 | $23

Park Slope | 426A Seventh Ave. (bet. 14th & 15th Sts.) | Brooklyn | 718-369-8315

"Hearty", "fresh" pastas and such plus "feather"-light "crispy-crust" pizzas are what keep Park Slopers coming back to this "homey", "friendly" "neighborhood" Southern Italian and its "garden in back"; fans sigh if only "it were bigger" and easier to "get into."

NEW Anthos Ⓢ *Greek*
▽ 25 | 21 | 24 | $66

W 50s | 36 W. 52nd St. (bet. 5th & 6th Aves.) | 212-582-6900

The "amazing" "haute Greek cuisine" based on the "finest fresh ingredients" and "fabulous service" provide the wow factor at this Midtown newcomer from Donatella Arpaia (davidburke & donatella) and rising toque Michael Psilakis (Kefi); the space is "pleasant" but on the plain side for such "top-of-the-line prices."

Antica Venezia *Italian*

FOOD	DECOR	SERVICE	COST
▽ 23	23	25	$52

W Village | 396 West St. (W. 10th St.) | 212-229-0606 | www.avnyc.com
West Villagers are "transported to Italy" via this "off-the-beaten-track" "charmer" that romances diners with "mouthwatering" food, "phenomenal sunset" views "over the Hudson" and "warm", "class-act" service; in short, "grab a table while you can."

Antonucci *Italian*

FOOD	DECOR	SERVICE	COST
20	16	18	$51

E 80s | 170 E. 81st St. (bet. Lexington & 3rd Aves.) | 212-570-5100
"Spirited and enjoyable", this "welcoming" UES "storefront" Italian is fast becoming a local standby for "solid" fare enjoyed in "friendly" (if "noisy") environs; though not cheap, it's possible to have "a good night out" here for less than at bigger-ticket destinations.

A.O.C. ◗ *French*

FOOD	DECOR	SERVICE	COST
20	17	18	$36

W Village | 314 Bleecker St. (Grove St.) | 212-675-9463 | www.aocnyc.com
Enjoying a "local" following for its "dependable" French classics, this "solid" West Village bistro also offers a "comfortable" atmosphere at competitive prices – not to mention a "pleasant" "garden out back"; the only complaint is service that "could be better."

A.O.C. Bedford *European*

FOOD	DECOR	SERVICE	COST
23	20	21	$49

G Village | 14 Bedford St. (bet. Downing & Houston Sts.) | 212-414-4764
"Teeny" and "inviting", this Greenwich Village Southern European has established itself as a "neighborhood favorite", where "tight seating" is easy to take given the "terrific" food and "classy" service; generally "reasonable", it becomes a downright "bargain" when you factor in the prix fixe deals and BYO nights.

ápizz ⓢ *Italian*

FOOD	DECOR	SERVICE	COST
24	21	20	$45

LES | 217 Eldridge St. (bet. Rivington & Stanton Sts.) | 212-253-9199 | www.apizz.com
A "nondescript facade" belies the "bright" "fresh, seasonal" menu at this "relaxed, hip" LES Italian; specializing in pizzas and other rustic "wood-oven" dishes, it has relatively "reasonable" prices that help compensate for its "not-ideal" location.

applewood Ⓜ *American*

FOOD	DECOR	SERVICE	COST
25	20	22	$48

Park Slope | 501 11th St. (bet. 7th & 8th Aves.) | Brooklyn | 718-768-2044 | www.applewoodny.com
"Tapping into the zeitgeist" perfectly, this "unpretentious" Park Slope New American bases its "excellent" menu on organic ingredients "culled from local farms"; its dining room is "cozy and warm", its staff "couldn't be nicer" and it's an area "top choice for brunch."

AQ Cafe Ⓢ *Scandinavian*

FOOD	DECOR	SERVICE	COST
▽ 20	16	12	$19

Murray Hill | Scandinavia House | 58 Park Ave. (bet. 37th & 38th Sts.) | 212-847-9745 | www.aquavit.org
"How Swede it is" say those who get their "meatball and lingonberry fixes" via Marcus Samuelsson's lunch-only Murray Hill Scandinavian cafeteria that's like "Aquavit on a budget"; "spartan" digs, "surly" service and frequent "long lines" are made up for by those "great-deal" prices.

	FOOD	DECOR	SERVICE	COST

☑ Aquagrill *Seafood*   26 | 19 | 23 | $58

SoHo | 210 Spring St. (6th Ave.) | 212-274-0505 | www.aquagrill.com
Still a "winner" for "ocean-fresh" fare (don't miss the "fantastic raw bar"), this ever-"popular" SoHo seafooder sparkles with "friendly, polished service" and an overall "comfortable" vibe; if seating is a bit "cramped", the "comparably reasonable prices" make up for a lot.

Aquamarine ● *Pan-Asian*   21 | 23 | 20 | $37

Murray Hill | 713 Second Ave. (bet. 38th & 39th Sts.) | 212-297-1880
Decor touches like a "waterfall" and "tranquil birch forest" have locals calling this "trendy" Pan-Asian a "much-needed" addition to Murray Hill; "better-than-average" cuisine (including sushi) and "caring service" round out the locals' endorsement.

☑ Aquavit *Scandinavian*   25 | 24 | 24 | $96

E 50s | 65 E. 55th St. (bet. Madison & Park Aves.) | 212-307-7311 | www.aquavit.org
Chef Marcus Samuelsson's Midtown prix fixe–only Scandinavian is "a classic, and deservedly so" thanks to its near-"flawless" offerings (e.g. "life-changing" herring and aquavit), "serene", "modern" decor and "first-rate" service; however, if you can't "find someone else to pick up" the tab, consider trying the "more casual front cafe."

Arabelle *American/French*   21 | 26 | 22 | $78

E 60s | Plaza Athénée Hotel | 37 E. 64th St. (Madison Ave.) | 212-606-4647 | www.arabellerestaurant.com
An "enchanting" "throwback" in the Plaza Athénée, this "formal", prix fixe–only French-American boasts a "European-feeling" dining room and "old-world" pro service that unfortunately outshine the "pricey" cuisine; it's ideal for a "romantic dinner" (or "to take your mother"), but detractors detect a "snooty" attitude.

Areo ●Ⅿ *Italian*   25 | 19 | 20 | $50

Bay Ridge | 8424 Third Ave. (bet. 84th & 85th Sts.) | Brooklyn | 718-238-0079
"Always delicious" and "always packed", this "boisterous" Bay Ridge Italian is a perennial "hot spot"; given its "generous portions" of "traditional" favorites, "friendly, flirtatious service" and "pleasant" (if "noisy") air, it's no wonder that "getting a table" is a "challenge."

Arezzo ☒ *Italian*   ▽ 22 | 17 | 20 | $53

Flatiron | 46 W. 22nd St. (bet. 5th & 6th Aves.) | 212-206-0555 | www.arezzo-nyc.com
This "wonderful" Flatiron Italian is relatively "undiscovered" despite the fact that it produces "fantastic" Tuscan dishes from a "wood-burning oven", whose "warmth" extends to the "attentive" service and "cozy", "rustic" digs; with a "pretty back garden" and prices that are "reasonable" given the "upscale experience", more people should check it out.

Arno ☒ *Italian*   ▽ 20 | 17 | 21 | $46

Garment District | 141 W. 38th St. (bet. B'way & 7th Ave.) | 212-944-7420 | www.arnoristorante.com
A "busy, noisy" Italian with "old-school" "charm" to spare, this Garmento Italiano turns out "consistently good" Tuscan standards at a "fair" price; the decor may be "getting tired", but still there Arno major complaints – especially in this restaurant-challenged zone.

	FOOD	DECOR	SERVICE	COST

Aroma *Italian* — ▽ 24 | 17 | 21 | $40

NoHo | 36 E. Fourth St. (bet. Bowery & Lafayette St.) | 212-375-0100 |
www.aromanyc.com
"Scrumptious, always fresh" seasonal Italian fare is the forte of this
"tiny", "homey" NoHo nook that also offers wine pairings from a list
boasting a few "rarities"; "warm" service and "affordable" checks cement its standing as a "true gem."

Arqua *Italian* — 22 | 21 | 21 | $55

TriBeCa | 281 Church St. (White St.) | 212-334-1888 |
www.arquaristorante.com
Remaining a "solid standby" for over 20 years, this "sophisticated"
TriBeCa Northern Italian is a "trustworthy" source for "excellent"
cooking delivered by a "caring" staff; its "serene", "spacious" digs actually allow diners to "talk and hear" – i.e. here's an eatery "for adults."

Arté *Italian* — 19 | 18 | 20 | $42

G Village | 21 E. Ninth St. (bet. 5th Ave. & University Pl.) | 212-473-0077
A "steady performer in the old-school model", this midpriced Village
Italian attracts a "mature crowd" with "tasty", "traditional" dishes and
"accommodating" service; its quarters are "a bit faded", but it's hard to
argue with "garden" seating in summer and "great fireplaces" in winter.

Arté Café *Italian* — 18 | 17 | 17 | $34

W 70s | 106 W. 73rd St. (bet. Amsterdam & Columbus Aves.) |
212-501-7014 | www.artecafenyc.com
Ensconced in "newly renovated" digs with an "amazing back garden",
this Lincoln Center–area "standby" remains a "good bet" for "basic"
Italian eats pre-curtain; "dirt-cheap" prices mean that most diners
happily endure the "rushed" service.

Artie's *Seafood* — 22 | 17 | 20 | $35

Bronx | 394 City Island Ave. (Ditmars St.) | 718-885-9885 |
www.artiesofcityisland.com
"Fresh" seafood and steaks at "prices that won't soak you" is the lure
at this "friendly" City Island vet; its "loyal", largely "local", clientele
doesn't mind the "lack of a water view" – or internal view for that matter since the "price is right."

Artie's Deli *Deli* — 18 | 10 | 14 | $22

W 80s | 2290 Broadway (bet. 82nd & 83rd Sts.) | 212-579-5959 |
www.arties.com
At this "reincarnation" of the "old UWS Jewish deli" complete with
the "noise" and theatrically "crotchety waiters", you can skip the
"schlep" elsewhere for "overstuffed" sandwiches and "cure-all" matzo
ball soup; ignore the nothing-special Formica decor and "just keep
the dills coming."

ⓩ Artisanal *French* — 23 | 20 | 20 | $52

Murray Hill | 2 Park Ave. (enter on 32nd St., bet. Madison & Park Aves.) |
212-725-8585 | www.artisanalbistro.com
It's a "cheese-lover's paradise" and French brasserie rolled into one at
Terrance Brennan's "consistently delicious", always "bustling" Murray
Hill place; you may have to "bring a megaphone" to be heard, then ask
your "friendly waiter" what's ripe "in the cave" today.

	FOOD	DECOR	SERVICE	COST

Arturo's Pizzeria ● *Italian* | 21 | 12 | 15 | $24

G Village | 106 W. Houston St. (Thompson St.) | 212-677-3820
Still "solid" after more than a half-century of peddling pizza, this
Village Italian supplies "consistently satisfying" crisp, coal-oven pies
to penny-wise patrons who relish the "old NY" atmosphere and "live
jazz piano", if not the "long" waits.

Z Asia de Cuba *Asian/Cuban* | 23 | 24 | 20 | $58

Murray Hill | Morgans Hotel | 237 Madison Ave. (bet. 37th & 38th Sts.) |
212-726-7755 | www.chinagrillmgt.com
The "formula still works" at this eternally "glam" Murray Hill Cuban-
Asian known for its "fabulous fusion" flavors, "happening" vibe and
"stunning white-on-white" Philippe Starck–designed space; it all
comes accessorized with "NYC's finest hotties", blaring "noise levels", sometimes-"snobby" service and "pricey" tabs that allow you to
"pretend" you're in "South Beach."

NEW Asiakan *Japanese/Pan-Asian* ▽ | 19 | 18 | 20 | $32

W 90s | 710 Amsterdam Ave. (bet. 94th & 95th Sts.) | 212-280-8878
"A little more upscale" than the "plethora" of Pan-Asian sushi joints
that grace the UWS, this yearling is hailed by locals as a "welcome addition"; depending on whom you poll, the food is either "great" or "average", but all agree the service and prices are "quite nice."

Z Asiate *French/Japanese* | 24 | 28 | 25 | $84

W 60s | Mandarin Oriental Hotel | 80 Columbus Circle, 35th fl. (60th St.
at B'way) | 212-805-8881 | www.mandarinoriental.com
Plan to be blown away by the "breathtaking views" "high above Central
Park" – as well as "beautiful" decor rated No. 1 in NYC – as you savor
"exciting" Japanese-French "fusion at its best" and enjoy "impeccable" service at chef Noriyuki Sugie's "posh" dining room at the Mandarin
Oriental Hotel; if the "sky-high" setting doesn't induce vertigo, the
towering tab may – though the $24 lunch prix fixe is a "bargain."

Aspen ●Z *American* | 20 | 24 | 17 | $49

Flatiron | 30 W. 22nd St. (bet. 5th & 6th Aves.) | 212-645-5040 |
www.aspen-nyc.com
If you "snag a seat by the fire", the "ski lodge" decor at this "cool" Flatiron
New American can transport you to "the slopes of Colorado"; the newfangled tapas may be "tasty", but you come for the "vibe" (this is where
"beautiful women flock" and "beer flows like wine"), not the food.

Z Atlantic Grill ● *Seafood* | 22 | 19 | 20 | $51

E 70s | 1341 Third Ave. (bet. 76th & 77th Sts.) | 212-988-9200 |
www.brguestrestaurants.com
It's "smooth sailing" at Steve Hanson's "delicious fish haunt", which
UES locals "pack" "every night of the week" to dive into the "freshest"
seafood at "totally doable" prices; "after all these years", angling for a
reservation is still a challenge – "that says it all!"

August *European* | 23 | 21 | 20 | $45

W Village | 359 Bleecker St. (bet. Charles & W. 10th Sts.) | 212-929-4774 |
www.augustny.com
Pleased patrons "happily return" to this "rustic", "romantic"
Villager for its "robust" regional European cuisine ("anything out

| | FOOD | DECOR | SERVICE | COST |

of the wood-burning oven is awesome"); the "glassed-in patio" makes it all the more "great for a date", as does the fact that they now take reservations.

Au Mandarin *Chinese* | 20 | 15 | 18 | $32 |

Financial District | World Financial Ctr. | 200-250 Vesey St. (West St.) | 212-385-0313 | www.aumandarin.com

Expect to find "much better than average" Chinese dishes "served with style" and "priced to match" at this restaurant inside the World Financial Center; just note that the "atrium" acoustics make you feel like "you're eating inside of a mall."

☑ Aureole ☒ *American* | 27 | 25 | 26 | $105 |

E 60s | 34 E. 61st St. (bet. Madison & Park Aves.) | 212-319-1660 | www.charliepalmer.com

Excelling "in all categories", Charlie Palmer's "flower-filled" East Side "celebratory dining spot" continues to delight with "outstanding" prix fixe-only New American fare and "phenomenal service" that add up to a "royal experience" surely "worth the cost"; N.B. à la carte ordering is an option at lunch, when there's also a "bargain" $38 set menu.

Aurora *Italian* | 26 | 22 | 20 | $43 |

NEW SoHo | 510 Broome St. (bet. Thompson St. & W. B'way) | 212-334-9020 | www.auroraristorante.com

Williamsburg | 70 Grand St. (Wythe Ave.) | Brooklyn | 718-388-5100 | www.aurorabk.com ⊅

"Wonderful" and "constantly getting better" is the word on this "top-notch" Piedmontese duo where you'll swear the ingredients "were harvested yesterday"; the "rustic" decor of the Williamsburg original is echoed at the newer SoHo offshoot, while service is "warm" and prices simpatico at both; P.S. in Brooklyn, go for the "magical" garden in warmer months.

Austin's Steakhouse *Steak* | ▽ 21 | 18 | 20 | $56 |

Bay Ridge | 8915 Fifth Ave. (90th St.) | Brooklyn | 718-439-5000 | www.austinssteakhouseny.com

"Steaks and sides" "done right" come with a helping of "chatty", "friendly" service at this "small" Bay Ridge chophouse; all in all, it's a pleasant place, but perhaps a "tad expensive" "for the area."

A Voce *Italian* | 25 | 20 | 22 | $67 |

Gramercy | 41 Madison Ave. (26th St.) | 212-545-8555 | www.avocerestaurant.com

Chef Andrew Carmellini is a "true innovator" who's "giving a new voice" to Italian cuisine at this Madison Square Park "standout"; "efficient" pro service helps offset "pricey" tabs and a room that some find hard to warm up to given its "metallic" look and "deafening" acoustics – there's now outdoor seating as an alternative.

Avra ● *Greek* | 24 | 21 | 21 | $55 |

E 40s | 141 E. 48th St. (bet. Lexington & 3rd Aves.) | 212-759-8550 | www.avrany.com

"Always bustling", this Greek bistro in East Midtown features some of the "freshest fish around", "prepared beautifully"; add "pleasant" surroundings and "attentive" service, and you have happy diners who forgive the "high decibels" and steep "by-the-pound" prices.

	FOOD	DECOR	SERVICE	COST

Awash *Ethiopian* — 22 | 12 | 16 | $22

E Village | 338 E. Sixth St. (bet. 1st & 2nd Aves.) | 212-982-9589 ●
W 100s | 947 Amsterdam Ave. (bet. 106th & 107th Sts.) | 212-961-1416
www.awashnyc.com

"Great platters" of "flavorful" Ethiopian fare and a steady supply of "spongy bread" make this East Village–UWS pair "popular with students" and others who find it "fun" to eat with their hands; maybe the "slow" service and "drab" decor are "hard to digest", but "smashing-good-deal" prices go down easy.

Azafran 🅂🅜 *Spanish* — 21 | 19 | 20 | $48

TriBeCa | 77 Warren St. (bet. Greenwich St. & W. B'way) | 212-284-0578 |
www.azafrannyc.com

Made for "group grazing", this "trendy" TriBeCa *taperia* tenders "delicious" Spanish tidbits from an "open kitchen"; those small plates "add up fast" and the "deafening din makes the place "azafrantic at times."

Azul Bistro ● *Argentinean/Steak* — ▽ 22 | 18 | 17 | $41

LES | 152 Stanton St. (Suffolk St.) | 646-602-2004 | www.azulnyc.com

"Red meat lovers" "devour" "tender, tasty" Argentine steaks and "wash everything down" with "affordable" wines at this "funky" Lower Eastsider with a "youthful" vibe and clientele; the only real complaint is about service that could "be better."

Azuri Cafe 🄵 *Israeli* — ▽ 25 | 3 | 8 | $14

W 50s | 465 W. 51st St. (bet. 9th & 10th Aves.) | 212-262-2920

Fans of "fantastic falafel and shimmering schwarma" brace themselves to "just eat and deal" at this West Side Israeli kosher "hole-in-the-wall"; "dingy" decor and a perpetually "grouchy" proprietor are part of the package, but "at these prices, who can kvetch?"

🆉 Babbo ● *Italian* — 27 | 23 | 25 | $76

G Village | 110 Waverly Pl. (bet. MacDougal St. & 6th Ave.) | 212-777-0303 |
www.babbonyc.com

"When it's this good" "it's not hype" is still the consensus as Mario Batali and Joe Bastianich celebrate the 10th anniversary of their "fabulously popular" Village flagship that's voted NYC's No. 1 Italian; given its "mind-blowing" cuisine, "epic wine list", "superlative" service and "cozy" carriage house setting, you'd better "keep their reservation number on redial"; sure, it's "expensive", but it's "worth every *centesimo*."

NEW Babouche *French/Moroccan* — ▽ 20 | 23 | 19 | $42

SoHo | 92 Prince St. (bet. B'way & Mercer St.) | 212-219-8155
Park Slope | 2 Lincoln Pl. (5th Ave.) | Brooklyn | 718-636-2100 ●
www.babouchenyc.com

With "sumptuous interiors" straight out of Marrakech, this SoHo French-Moroccan (with a newer outpost in Park Slope) attracts a "hip crowd" that grooves on "great flavors" both "strong and subtle"; so go "lounge on pillows", eat and imagine you're in the casbah.

Baci & Abbracci ● *Italian* — ▽ 20 | 18 | 20 | $33

Williamsburg | 204 Grand St. (bet. Bedford & Driggs Aves.) | Brooklyn |
718-599-6599 | www.baciabbracciny.com

Along with the "fantastic" brick-oven pizza, there are other "fresh", "homey" dishes made "with love" at this "laid-back" Williamsburg

Italian; its "beautiful garden" beats the "mod" dining room, but anywhere you dine, you'll be treated "wonderfully."

Baldoria *Italian*

| 22 | 17 | 20 | $54 |

W 40s | 249 W. 49th St. (bet. B'way & 8th Ave.) | 212-582-0460 | www.baldoriamo.com

A spin-off of Rao's "but easier to get into", Frank Pellegrino Jr.'s "consistently good" Theater District Italian serves "red-sauce" favorites in "stepped-back-in-time" digs; it may be "noisy" and "a bit pricey", but hey, "you can't beat those meatballs" – or the "great jukebox."

☑ Balthazar ◑ *French*

| 23 | 23 | 20 | $53 |

SoHo | 80 Spring St. (bet. B'way & Crosby St.) | 212-965-1414 | www.balthazarny.com

Still *"très bon"* "after all these years", Keith McNally's exuberantly "chaotic" SoHo brasserie delivers "wonderful" French food in an "amazingly authentic" "Parisian" setting; it successfully caters to everyone from sunglasses-sporting "celebs" and "socialites" to "tourists" and "B&T" types, all of whom pack in "elbow-to-elbow" for a taste of "big, brassy, fun."

Baluchi's *Indian*

| 18 | 14 | 15 | $26 |

E 50s | 224 E. 53rd St. (bet. 2nd & 3rd Aves.) | 212-750-5515
E 80s | 1724 Second Ave. (bet. 89th & 90th Sts.) | 212-996-2600
E Village | 104 Second Ave. (6th St.) | 212-780-6000 ◑
Gramercy | 329 Third Ave. (bet. 24th & 25th Sts.) | 212-679-3434
G Village | 361 Sixth Ave. (Washington Pl.) | 212-929-2441
G Village | 90 W. Third St. (bet. Sullivan & Thompson Sts.) | 212-529-5353
SoHo | 193 Spring St. (bet. Sullivan & Thompson Sts.) | 212-226-2828
TriBeCa | 275 Greenwich St. (Warren St.) | 212-571-5343
W 50s | 240 W. 56th St. (bet. B'way & 8th Ave.) | 212-397-0707
Forest Hills | 113-30 Queens Blvd. (bet. 76th Ave. & 76th Rd.) | Queens | 718-520-8600
www.baluchis.com
Additional locations throughout the NY area

"Dependably tasty" if "not exciting" Indian eats make this "cheap" chain a "reliable" choice when "you want your chicken tikka"; the "50-percent-off lunch" is one of the "best deals in town", but at other times the "worn-out decor" and poky service make "delivery" the way to go.

Bamonte's *Italian*

| 23 | 15 | 21 | $43 |

Williamsburg | 32 Withers St. (bet. Lorimer St. & Union Ave.) | Brooklyn | 718-384-8831

Dating to 1900, this Williamsburg "classic" serves "plentiful portions" of "quintessential" Italian fare to local "families" and "fauxhemians"; the "fabulous food" "makes up for" the "dated" decor, and you can expect good service from the "tuxedoed" waiters – some of whom look like they've been there "since day one."

Bandol Bistro *French*

| 19 | 16 | 18 | $46 |

E 70s | 181 E. 78th St. (bet. Lexington & 3rd Aves.) | 212-744-1800 | www.bandolbistro.com

This "neighborhood refuge" on the UES serves a "limited" but "flavorful French" lineup and "great wines by the glass" in a "romantic, cozy" space; however, the fact that it recently came under "new management" puts the above ratings in question.

	FOOD	DECOR	SERVICE	COST

Banjara ◐ *Indian* — 23 | 16 | 17 | $31

E Village | 97 First Ave. (6th St.) | 212-477-5956 |
www.banjarany.com

"Finer fare" distinguishes this "value"-oriented East Village Indian
considered a "step above" the Curry Row competition; it "may not be
the fanciest" place and service is "hit-or-miss", but all the same it's
voted "worth a detour."

Bann *Korean* — ▽ 24 | 24 | 21 | $46

W 50s | Worldwide Plaza | 350 W. 50th St. (bet. 8th & 9th Aves.) |
212-582-4446 | www.bannrestaurant.com

At this "sceney", "innovative Korean", the drill is cook-it-yourself barbecue and "wonderful" "fresh" fusion fare in a "somewhat hidden"
Worldwide Plaza location; the "serene setting" and "unrushed service" make it all the more "worth" it to those in-the-know.

Bann Thai *Thai* — 21 | 18 | 19 | $29

Forest Hills | 69-12 Austin St. (Yellowstone Blvd.) | Queens | 718-544-9999 |
www.bannthairestaurant.com

"Typical Thai" but "still delicious" is the feeling about this "steady"
Forest Hills standby, where the "small quarters are "comfortable"
and the service "gracious"; still, a handful of sophisticates says "why
eat here" when there's real-deal Thai "minutes away"?

Bao Noodles *Vietnamese* — 20 | 15 | 16 | $25

Gramercy | 391 Second Ave. (bet. 22nd & 23rd Sts.) | 212-725-7770

"Tiny", "funky" and "no-frills", this Gramercy joint specializes in
"pho-licious" Vietnamese soups and sandwiches that are "way better
than average"; sure, "service lacks", but given the "just-right prices",
it may offer the "best bang for the buck" in the area.

Bao 111 ◐ *Vietnamese* — 21 | 19 | 17 | $38

E Village | 111 Ave. C (bet. 7th & 8th Sts.) | 212-254-7773 |
www.bao111.com

"Full of kick and life", this "hip", "more upscale" East Village
Vietnamese has a winning formula of "flavorful" food, "lethal drinks"
and "late-night" hours; with all the "noise", you almost forget any service flaws – and the extra cost "for the trendy setting."

Ⓩ Bar Americain *American* — 23 | 23 | 22 | $61

W 50s | 152 W. 52nd St. (bet. 6th & 7th Aves.) | 212-265-9700 |
www.baramericain.com

"Big flavors", "big space" and electric "energy" sums up Bobby Flay's
"spirited romp" that updates American comfort classics in one of those
Midtown "places to be seen" filled with "media execs on expense accounts"; factor in service that's "charming and efficient", and everyone "comes away happy."

Baraonda ◐ *Italian* — 18 | 17 | 15 | $47

E 70s | 1439 Second Ave. (75th St.) | 212-288-8555 |
www.baraondany.com

At this UES "Euro-centric" Italian, the "upbeat" vibe "never goes out of
style" and the "hot crowd" outweighs "subpar service"; most rate the
kitchen's output "decent", but given the "colorful" scenery and wee-
hours "tabletop dancing", "who cares about food?"

	FOOD	DECOR	SERVICE	COST

Barbès ● *French/Moroccan*   22 | 18 | 19 | $43

Murray Hill | 21 E. 36th St. (bet. 5th & Madison Aves.) | 212-684-0215
Murray Hill's own "Arabian dream", this "adorable" French-Moroccan is an "unexpected find" for a "succulent" "taste of Fez" and "warm service" at "budget-minded" prices; the "intimate" space "gets very tight", but still it's the area's bès bet for "a change from the usual."

Barbetta ●🅂🅼 *Italian*   20 | 23 | 21 | $59

W 40s | 321 W. 46th St. (bet. 8th & 9th Aves.) | 212-246-9171 | www.barbettarestaurant.com
A Restaurant Row "monument" dating back "over 100 years", this "brownstone" Northern Italian is a redoubt of "rococo" "elegance" where "gracious" staffers serve "reliably fine food"; a few deem it "dated", but it "continues to impress" and the "lovely" garden remains "a real treat"; N.B. check out the private party rooms.

Barbounia *Mediterranean*   20 | 22 | 18 | $52

Flatiron | 250 Park Ave. S. (20th St.) | 212-995-0242 | www.barbounia.com
This "refined" Flatiron Mediterranean attracts a "noisy", "trendy" crowd with its "eye-catching" but "comfy" space and "terrific" food; despite scattered criticism for "absent-minded" service, overall most agree it's "worthy" of the relatively "big" tab.

Barbuto *Italian*   22 | 18 | 18 | $50

W Village | 775 Washington St. (bet. Jane & W. 12th Sts.) | 212-924-9700 | www.barbutonyc.com
"Freshness is key" to Jonathan Waxman's "innovative", "market-driven" menu at this West Village Italian in a "converted garage" with a "hip" "industrial vibe"; the "lackadaisical" staff and "painful" acoustics detract, but you'll still "feel cool" even if it's hot.

Bardolino ● *Italian*   18 | 15 | 18 | $34

E 70s | 1496 Second Ave. (78th St.) | 212-734-9050 | www.bardolinorestaurantnyc.com
Freshly expanded, this UES "neighborhood Italian" now offers more room to enjoy its "decent" "homestyle cooking" and "solid service"; the experience may be "ordinary", but considering the "relaxed" feel and "reasonable prices" that's "all to the good."

NEW BarFry ● *Eclectic/Japanese*   - | - | - | M

G Village | 50 Carmine St. (bet. Bedford & Bleecker Sts.) | 212-929-5050 | www.barfrynyc.com
From chef Josh DeChellis (ex Sumile Sushi) comes this new Village tempura bar where the mostly Japanese menu is tricked up with po' boys, beef beignets and a smartly parsed wine list; the casual, white-tiled room dominated by a long bar seems designed with a young crowd in mind, ditto the low price point.

Barking Dog *American*   15 | 13 | 14 | $24

E 70s | 1453 York Ave. (77th St.) | 212-861-3600
E 90s | 1678 Third Ave. (94th St.) | 212-831-1800 ⊄
Murray Hill | Affinia Dumont | 150 E. 34th St. (bet. Lexington & 3rd Aves.) | 212-871-3900
"Chowhounds" can park with "Fido outside" this East Side trio, whose "cutesy" "canine theme" and "low-cost" American "basics" get a

"paws up" from the "stroller set"; then again, the menu needs "some new tricks" and you'll have to "sit up and beg" for service.

barmarché ● American
| | 19 | 19 | 16 | $38 |

NoLita | 14 Spring St. (Elizabeth St.) | 212-219-2399 | www.barmarche.com

"Casual" and "cozy", this "cool" NoLita bistro gives its "hip" habitués an economical "place to unwind" over "fresh" "New American variations" and "above-average cocktails"; it's a favored break from the "more trendy spots" in spite of service so "unhurried" it's "aloof."

NEW Bar Martignetti ● American
| | 18 | 16 | 14 | $40 |

Little Italy | 406 Broome St. (bet. Centre & Lafayette Sts.) | 212-680-5600 | www.barmartignetti.com

Done up in "faux brasserie" fashion, this "loud", boisterous Little Italy newcomer is already overflowing with stylish types looking to fill up on "decent" New American fare before (or after) "partying" at nearby bars; tipplers who don't want to travel too far head for the "downstairs club."

Barney Greengrass ⓂⲀ Deli
| 23 | 8 | 14 | $26 |

W 80s | 541 Amsterdam Ave. (bet. 86th & 87th Sts.) | 212-724-4707 | www.barneygreengrass.com

"You haven't had Nova on a bagel" till you visit this Upper West Side "institution", which is once again voted NYC's No. 1 deli thanks to its "blissfully authentic" "Jewish breakfasts"; if the "tumult", "shabby" surroundings and servers' "shtick" elicit an "oy vey", "consider takeout."

Barolo Italian
| 18 | 21 | 17 | $52 |

SoHo | 398 W. Broadway (bet. Broome & Spring Sts.) | 212-226-1102 | www.nybarolo.com

It's "all about" the "enchanting" alfresco "escape" at this sprawling SoHo Italian whose "transporting" garden is "legendary"; the menu is "consistently good" too ("albeit not cheap"), but most look for "romance" "in the atmosphere, not the food."

Bar Pitti ●Ⲁ Italian
| 22 | 14 | 17 | $39 |

G Village | 268 Sixth Ave. (bet. Bleecker & Houston Sts.) | 212-982-3300

"Prime sidewalk" tables (not the bland interior) make this "hopping" Village Italian a "perennial place to be" for "robust pastas with "a celeb or two" on the side; it's a "solid" "alternative to Da Silvano" with "decent prices", but "pitti the fool" at the rear of the line to get in.

NEW Bar Stuzzichini Italian
| - | - | - | M |

Flatiron | 928 Broadway (bet. 21st & 22nd Sts.) | 212-780-5100 | www.barstuzzichini.com

Stuzzichini (small plates) are the focus at this new Flatiron Southern Italian where customers pick from three seating areas: a front wine bar, a marble antipasto bar or the dining room; perfect for the tapaslike lineup, its list of vinos includes lots of choices by the glass.

Bar Toto ● Italian
| 19 | 18 | 18 | $27 |

Park Slope | 411 11th St. (6th Ave.) | Brooklyn | 718-768-4698 | www.bartoto.com

"Lots of locals" turn up at this "friendly" Park Slope Italian to "kick back" and scarf "tasty" pastas, pizzas and panini "for cheap"; it's a toto-ly "low-key" "joint" with "outdoor seating" and "few surprises" – and there's "nothing wrong with that."

Basilica ●Ⓜ *Italian* | 19 | 14 | 18 | $31

W 40s | 676 Ninth Ave. (bet. 46th & 47th Sts.) | 212-489-0051

Devotees "squeeze" in to this "dark", "postage stamp-size" Hell's Kitchen "secret" for "fresh" Italian classics and "quick" service "pre-show"; as for prices, the $24 prix fixe including "a bottle of decent wine" ranks with "the best bargains in town."

NEW Basso56 ● *Italian* | ▽ 23 | 18 | 22 | $44

W 50s | 234 W. 56th St. (bet. B'way & 8th Ave.) | 212-265-2610 | www.basso56.com

Westsiders already feel "at home" at this "consummate" midpriced Italian following a "welcome move from Downtown" that left its "delicious" "homespun preparations" intact; the "sleek" space and "engaging" service has its new neighborhood calling it a "winner."

Basta Pasta *Italian* | 21 | 16 | 19 | $42

Flatiron | 37 W. 17th St. (bet. 5th & 6th Aves.) | 212-366-0888 | www.bastapastanyc.com

"The usual pastas" take some "curveballs" at this "informal" Flatiron Italian thanks to the "inventive" "merging" of "flavorful" "Japanese touches" from a "team of professionals" manning the "open kitchen"; it's "confusing at first", but "curious" converts concede "somehow it works."

Battery Gardens *American/Continental* | 18 | 24 | 18 | $51

Financial District | SW corner of Battery Park (State St.) | 212-809-5508 | www.batterygardens.com

For a "scenic" recharge in Battery Park, this American-Continental commands a "peerless" "harbor view" that's best admired from the "wonderful" patio; the menu is also "commendable", but the panorama is what makes going "out of the way" to get here "worthwhile."

Bay Leaf *Indian* | 19 | 15 | 16 | $37

W 50s | 49 W. 56th St. (bet. 5th & 6th Aves.) | 212-957-1818

"Very decent quality" with "no pretensions" sums up this white-tablecloth Indian near Carnegie Hall that's possibly most "noteworthy" for its $14.95 lunch buffet; dinner is also "satisfying" – though "at a price" – but critics say the service "needs to try harder."

Bayou *Cajun* | ▽ 22 | 20 | 21 | $33

Staten Island | 1072 Bay St. (bet. Chestnut & St. Mary's Aves.) | 718-273-4383 | www.bayoustatenisland.com

"Staten Island's version of the Big Easy", this ultra-"cozy" Cajun-Creole kitchen's "addictive" cooking and down-home decor conjure up a "genuine" "N'Awlins feel"; with a "friendly" crew that keeps the mood "relaxed", it's a "no-lose situation" for a Dixie fix.

Beacon *American* | 22 | 21 | 21 | $60

W 50s | 25 W. 56th St. (bet. 5th & 6th Aves.) | 212-332-0500 | www.beaconnyc.com

Waldy Malouf will "light your fire" at this Midtown New American, which produces "memorable" "wood-grilled" fare in an "impressive" "multilevel" space; it's a "mecca for corporate" types willing to drop "a lot of dollars", though the "prix fixe deals" are a beacon for all.

Beast *Mediterranean*   ▽ 20 | 16 | 17 | $30

Prospect Heights | 638 Bergen St. (Vanderbilt Ave.) | Brooklyn | 718-399-6855

"Dependable" and "different", this "funky" "local" "hangout" in Prospect Heights features a "reasonable" "eclectic" Med menu whose "savory" small plates are a step up from "the typical" pub grub; the "dark", "totally cozy" setting is "relaxing", and service is likewise "leisurely."

Z Becco ● *Italian*   22 | 18 | 21 | $43

W 40s | 355 W. 46th St. (bet. 8th & 9th Aves.) | 212-397-7597 | www.becconyc.com

"Loosen" your belt for Joe Bastianich's "energetic" Restaurant Row Italian, which "continues to amaze" with its $21.95 all-you-can-eat "pasta-gasm" special and its "massive" cache of $20-and-under wines; given pre-theater mobs more suited to "Grand Central", "instant", "no-attitude" service is also a big plus.

Beccofino *Italian*   ▽ 22 | 19 | 19 | $32

Bronx | 5704 Mosholu Ave. (bet. Fieldston Rd. & Spencer Ave.) | 718-432-2604

Riverdale "finally" boasts a "neighborhood red-sauce" option courtesy of this "welcoming" Italian and its "plentiful" portions of "simply fabulous" "comfort food"; it's "intimate" and "not too pricey", but you'll have to "get there early" to "beat the crowds."

Bella Blu *Italian*   19 | 16 | 17 | $48

E 70s | 967 Lexington Ave. (bet. 70th & 71st Sts.) | 212-988-4624

To lose the blues, visit this Upper East Side Northern Italian, an "entertaining scene" serving "solid" pastas and wood-oven pizzas to a "loud", "bubbly" crowd; meanwhile curmudgeons cite "expensive" specials and a room that's due for an "extreme makeover."

Bella Via *Italian*   ▽ 23 | 18 | 20 | $31

LIC | 47-46 Vernon Blvd. (48th Ave.) | Queens | 718-361-7510 | www.bellaviarestaurant.com

With "terrific" "coal-oven" pizza and "authentic" pastas, this Long Island City Italian "competes with the best" for "everyday" eating at a "reasonable" cost; the pace is "relaxed", and the "outer-borough vibe" has visitors saying they "feel right at home."

Bellavitae ● *Italian*   22 | 18 | 20 | $52

G Village | 24 Minetta Ln. (bet. MacDougal St. & 6th Ave.) | 212-473-5121 | www.bellavitae.com

Aficionados of "rustic Italian" repasts "treasure" this Village enoteca for the "delectable" small-plate offerings, "well-selected" wines and "warm", "old-country" feel; though "a little haughty" and costing "a hefty sum", it's "one to remember" when Babbo's backed up.

Belleville ⊄ *French*   18 | 19 | 16 | $35

Park Slope | 350 Fifth St. (5th Ave.) | Brooklyn | 718-832-9777 | www.bellevillebistro.com

This "reasonable" Park Slope "replication" of a "Left Bank" bistro offers "comforting" French "classics" in *très belle* environs; "low-key" "without attitude", it's a "neighborhood favorite" especially for weekend brunch.

	FOOD	DECOR	SERVICE	COST

Bello ⑤ Italian
| | 20 | 16 | 20 | $46 |

W 50s | 863 Ninth Ave. (56th St.) | 212-246-6773 | www.bellorestaurant.com
"Convenience without too high prices" keeps "pre-theater" folks faithful to this Hell's Kitchen "oldie" and its "trustworthy" Italian fare; it's "spacious", "gracious" and offers "the plus of free parking" after 5 PM – "what else can you want?"

Bello Sguardo ● Mediterranean
| | 19 | 16 | 18 | $37 |

W 70s | 410 Amsterdam Ave. (bet. 79th & 80th Sts.) | 212-873-6252
For a "fresh take on Mediterranean standards", check out this Upper Westsider, where the "zesty" small plates "hit the spot" with fans who "feel like grazing" at a "moderate" cost; "attentive service" seals its appeal as a "comfortable" "neighborhood hangout."

Ben & Jack's Steak House Steak
| | 23 | 17 | 22 | $66 |

E 40s | 219 E. 44th St. (bet. 2nd & 3rd Aves.) | 212-682-5678 |
www.benandjackssteakhouse.com
Lots of "suits" steer to this Grand Central–area steakhouse, which "lives up to its" steakhouse pedigree with "ample" portions of "top-flight" beef served by "professionals"; critics cite the "forgettable decor" and "steep prices" as hard to swallow.

Ben Benson's Steak
| | 24 | 18 | 22 | $65 |

W 50s | 123 W. 52nd St. (bet. 6th & 7th Aves.) | 212-581-8888 |
www.benbensons.com
A "perennial favorite for the business" class, this "high-energy" Midtown meatery "holds its own" in the "upper tier" with *Flintstones*-scale steaks, "nearly fatal" martinis and service from "seasoned vets"; as for the "din", "sparse" decor and "brusque" attitude, "it's a guy thing."

NEW Benjamin Steak House Steak
| | ▽ 23 | 21 | 23 | $60 |

E 40s | 52 E. 41st St. (bet. Madison & Park Aves.) | 212-297-9177 |
www.benjaminsteakhouse.com
"If you're a steak person", this latest "Peter Luger knockoff" "sets itself apart" in Midtown with fine meats and "gentrified" digs with "high ceilings" and a fireplace; "top-notch" service matches the "sophisticated" setup, and though "expensive" it's "worth" all those benjamins.

Ben's Kosher Deli Deli
| | 17 | 10 | 14 | $23 |

Garment District | 209 W. 38th St. (bet. 7th & 8th Aves.) | 212-398-2367
Bayside | Bay Terrace | 211-37 26th Ave. (211th St.) | Queens |
718-229-2367
www.bensdeli.net
When "big mouths" "need to nosh", this low-budget Garment District-Bayside kosher deli duo does a "speedy" job supplying "heaping" sandwiches from a "broad" menu; service is "curt" and decor "dreary", but that comes with the territory – which also may require "Tums."

Beppe ⑤ Italian
| | 23 | 20 | 22 | $54 |

Flatiron | 45 E. 22nd St. (bet. B'way & Park Ave. S.) | 212-982-8422 |
www.beppenyc.com
"Go twice you're a regular" at this "comfy yet classy" Flatiron "find" for "lusty Tuscan" fare served by a "warm, smart staff"; combining "fresh" "culinary ideas" with a "homey feel", it maintains such "high quality" that few fret if the tabs get "a bit pricey."

	FOOD	DECOR	SERVICE	COST

Bereket ●₥ *Turkish*   18 | 3 | 12 | $12

LES | 187 E. Houston St. (Orchard St.) | 212-475-7700

To "cure" the "post-clubbing munchies" there's always this 24/7 Lower Eastsider, a "late-night fixture" vending "heartwarming" "Turkish eats" at "bargain" rates; sure, the "lunch-counter" setup is "spartan", but all those "taxi drivers can't be wrong."

Beso *Nuevo Latino*   19 | 12 | 14 | $25

Park Slope | 210 Fifth Ave. (Union St.) | Brooklyn | 718-783-4902

"Bright and cheerful", this Park Sloper "fills you up" with its "creative yet accessible", "excellent-value" Nuevo Latino dishes; despite "random" service and "garagelike" digs, local amigos "line up" for the "amazing brunch", but strangely it's a "sleeper" at night.

Bette ●☒ *European*   19 | 21 | 19 | $56

Chelsea | 461 W. 23rd St. (bet. 9th & 10th Aves.) | 212-366-0404 | www.betterestaurant.com

"Pretty" people "bet on" the "social atmosphere" at Amy Sacco's West Chelsea "hideaway", a mix of "mod" and "sexy" that's "*très* trendy" "in a good way"; many appreciate the "creative" European cuisine, but critics complain it's "pricey" – and say the novelty is "waning."

Better Burger *Hamburgers*   15 | 10 | 13 | $14

Chelsea | 178 Eighth Ave. (19th St.) | 212-989-6688 ●
Murray Hill | 561 Third Ave. (37th St.) | 212-949-7528
W 40s | 587 Ninth Ave. (bet. 42nd & 43rd Sts.) | 212-629-6622
www.betterburgernyc.com

At this "alternative fast-food" mini-chain, the organic beef burgers, "veggie options" and "air-baked fries" let "health-conscious" sorts "indulge without the guilt"; "inventive" sauces "add a nice touch", but dissenters dub them "blander burgers" – "sometimes you need the grease."

Bettola ● *Italian*   21 | 16 | 18 | $36

W 70s | 412 Amsterdam Ave. (bet. 79th & 80th Sts.) | 212-787-1660 | www.bettolanyc.com

There's "real Italian" "in the 'hood" thanks to this "quaint" Upper Westsider, where "amazing, crispy-thin" pizza leads a "solid" lineup of "rustic" fare; "sweet service", "alfresco" tables and "reasonable" tabs cement its rep as a "winning" bet.

Beyoglu ● *Turkish*   21 | 17 | 17 | $33

E 80s | 1431 Third Ave. (81st St.) | 212-650-0850

Even those with "no idea how to pronounce it" call this "upbeat" Upper East Side Turk a "keeper", adding that the "delish" "shareable" mezes are "the way to go"; "fair prices" ensure it's "always packed", and "sidewalk dining" offers relief from the sorta "cheesy" interior.

BG *American*   ▽ 20 | 23 | 20 | $48

W 50s | Bergdorf Goodman | 754 Fifth Ave., 7th fl. (bet. 57th & 58th Sts.) | 212-872-8977

"Well-coiffed shoppers" lunch in "high style" at this New American "tucked away" in Bergdorf's; it's "surprisingly good" culinarily and "even better" "aesthetically", so most don't let the "over-the-top prices" distract from the "people-watching" and "lovely view" of Central Park.

	FOOD	DECOR	SERVICE	COST

Bianca ⌇ *Italian*
▽ 22 | 16 | 20 | $33

NoHo | 5 Bleecker St. (bet. Bowery & Elizabeth St.) | 212-260-4666

"Hearty" "housemade" specialties from the Emilia-Romagnia region make this "spirited little" NoHo Italian an "excellent" pick; those "who know" "true value" are typically "clamoring for entry", so expect "tight" seating and a "wait", despite the efforts of an "efficient staff."

Bice ◑ *Italian*
20 | 19 | 19 | $60

E 50s | 7 E. 54th St. (bet. 5th & Madison Aves.) | 212-688-1999 | www.bicenewyork.com

Known for nonstop "action" by "good-looking", "Euro"-centric sorts, this Midtown Northern Italian provides "quality" fare along with "loud" "networking" and a super sidewalk "show"; there's also "hospitable service" (if you're "a VIP"), but it's "no bargain" and the "attitude" can be a "bice."

Big Nick's Burger Joint ◑ *Hamburgers*
17 | 5 | 14 | $16

W 70s | 2175 Broadway (77th St.) | 212-362-9238
W 70s | 70 W. 71st St. (Columbus Ave.) | 212-799-4444

Westsiders "craving" "greasy goodness" frequent these separately owned "dive diners", where "burgers rule" the "novel"-length menus supplying "monstrous portions" at "bargain" rates; they're longtime "go-to spots" (with 24/7 service on Broadway) even if the "seedy" digs are widely nixed.

Big Wong ⌇ *Chinese*
22 | 5 | 11 | $13

Chinatown | 67 Mott St. (bet. Bayard & Canal Sts.) | 212-964-0540

For "filling" Chinese "cheap eats", you can't go wong with the "traditional" congees and "BBQ meats" at this "no-nonsense" "C-town staple"; despite "perfunctory" service, "elbow-to-elbow" seating, "nonexistent" decor and an "unfortunate name", it's "always crowded" 'cause the food "rocks."

Biricchino ⌧ *Italian*
20 | 13 | 18 | $38

Chelsea | 260 W. 29th St. (8th Ave.) | 212-695-6690 | www.biricchino.com

"Known for" its "must-have" homemade sausages, this "steady" Northern Italian near Madison Square Garden is an "unexpected" source of "solid" cooking at "reasonable" prices; though "not much to look at", it's "handy" in an area "devoid of many choices."

Bistro Cassis *French*
20 | 17 | 16 | $42

W 70s | 225 Columbus Ave. (bet. 70th & 71st Sts.) | 212-579-3966 | www.bistrocassisnyc.com

To feed your "French jones" try this "authentic" West Side bistro, a "quaint" "neighborhood haunt" offering "flavorful" "classic" fare; though it's "always crowded" and "service-challenged" in "true Parisian style", its "popularity" and no-reservations rule make "a wait" de rigueur.

Bistro Citron *French*
21 | 19 | 20 | $40

W 80s | 473 Columbus Ave. (bet. 82nd & 83rd Sts.) | 212-400-9401 | www.bistrocitronnyc.com

Upper Westsiders "welcome" the "lively" "French experience" at this "well-priced" yearling that feels like "you could be in Paris"; given its "hearty" bistro "hits", "atmospheric" surroundings, "warm" service and "outdoor seating", it's no wonder it has *beaucoup* backers.

	FOOD	DECOR	SERVICE	COST

Bistro du Nord *French*   18 | 15 | 16 | $46
E 90s | 1312 Madison Ave. (93rd St.) | 212-289-0997
A "steady" haven for "the Carnegie Hill set", this petite bistro has a loyal "local" following for its "old-world French" cooking and "bargain" prix fixes; then again, "service is sketchy" and you may need a "shoe-horn" to get into the "narrow duplex" space.

Bistro Les Amis ◑ *French*   21 | 18 | 21 | $40
SoHo | 180 Spring St. (Thompson St.) | 212-226-8645 | www.bistrolesamis.com
Friends tend to "linger" at this "cozy" "little" SoHo bistro, where the "caring" service, French "comfort food" and moderate prices amount to the "perfect date"; it's "not too fancy", but admirers only "wish there were more of these."

Bistro Le Steak ◑ *French*   17 | 14 | 17 | $45
E 70s | 1309 Third Ave. (75th St.) | 212-517-3800 | www.bistrolesteak.com
With "no surprises", this Upper East Side "neighborhood" French bistro–steakhouse recalls the "'burbs" with its "straightforward" bites and "reasonable" prices; as for allegations of "tired" looks and "vari-able" service, its regulars shrug "*c'est la vie.*"

Bistro 61 *French*   20 | 15 | 19 | $37
E 60s | 1113 First Ave. (61st St.) | 212-223-6220 | www.bistro61.com
Amis "appreciate" the "authenticity" at this "compact" French bistro by the Queensboro Bridge, where the "caring" service and "ambitious" French fare "make one want to stay the night"; it claims a "loyal follow-ing", not least because "the price is right."

Bistro Ten 18 *American*   20 | 19 | 20 | $36
W 100s | 1018 Amsterdam Ave. (110th St.) | 212-662-7600 | www.bistroten18.com
Morningside Heights goes "upscale" at this pleasingly priced New American bistro with "surprisingly good" food and "warm" service; the "romantic fireplace" and St. John the Divine views make it "a real asset" for visiting Columbia "parents."

NEW **Bistro 33** *French/Japanese*   – | – | – | M
(fka Lil' Bistro 33)
Astoria | 19-33 Ditmars Blvd. (21st St.) | Queens | 718-721-1933 | www.bistro33nyc.com
Only the 'Lil' got lost in this Japanese-French bistro's recent move to roomier digs near Astoria Park; it has grown in other ways too, ex-panding its sushi menu and adding take-out service, a liquor license and sidewalk seating.

Black Duck *American/Seafood*   ▽ 20 | 19 | 20 | $46
Gramercy | Park South Hotel | 122 E. 28th St. (bet. Lexington Ave. & Park Ave. S.) | 212-448-0888 | www.blackduckny.com
It's easy to overlook, but this "intimate" New American in a Gramercy hotel is worth ducking into for its "lovingly prepared" seafood special-ties served "without attitude"; feathering the nest are a "working fire-place" and live jazz.

	FOOD	DECOR	SERVICE	COST

NEW Black Pearl *Seafood* | 17 | 14 | 17 | $37 |

Chelsea | 37 W. 26th St. (bet. B'way & 6th Ave.) | 212-532-9900 |
www.blackpearlonline.com

Fans of "proper lobster rolls" and other "classic" "New England clam-
bake" fare "look no further" than this "laid-back" "fish shack" newly
moored in Chelsea; a few complain about "lackluster" atmospherics
and "ordinary" eating, but supporters shrug "no frills necessary."

Blair Perrone Steakhouse ⓩ *Steak* | 21 | 23 | 22 | $69 |

E 40s | 885 Second Ave. (bet. 47th & 48th Sts.) | 212-796-8000 |
www.blairperrone.com

A "refreshing" "change of pace", this "beautifully appointed"
Midtowner features "first-rate" steak and "attentive service" from an
ex-Peter Luger/Mark Joseph team; "many suits" salute the "indulgence", even if hedgers hint it "falls a bit short" for the "hefty pricing."

Blaue Gans ⓓ *Austrian/German* | 20 | 18 | 19 | $46 |

TriBeCa | 139 Duane St. (bet. Church St. & W. B'way) | 212-571-8880 |
www.wallse.com

"*Wursthaus* meets TriBeCa" at this "casual" bistro from Wallsé's Kurt
Gutenbrunner offering "good old" Austro-German "staples" with "finesse"; maybe the "hip", spacious quarters are "not elegant", but "fair
pricing" and "unpretentious" staffers make it *gemütlich* all the same.

Blockheads Burritos *Mexican* | 17 | 10 | 15 | $18 |

E 50s | 954 Second Ave. (bet. 50th & 51st Sts.) | 212-750-2020
E 80s | 1563 Second Ave. (bet. 81st & 82nd Sts.) | 212-879-1999
Murray Hill | 499 Third Ave. (bet. 33rd & 34th Sts.) | 212-213-3332
W 50s | Worldwide Plaza | 322 W. 50th St. (bet. 8th & 9th Aves.) |
212-307-7029
www.blockheads.com

It's easy to satisfy "a big appetite" for a "little money" at this Mexican
mini-chain, where "zeppelin"-size burritos and "potent margaritas" are
the big "crowd-pleasers"; on the other hand, for many the "el blando"
surroundings make "fast delivery" "the way to go."

Blossom *Vegan/Vegetarian* | 21 | 19 | 21 | $38 |

Chelsea | 187 Ninth Ave. (bet. 21st & 22nd Sts.) | 212-627-1144 |
www.blossomnyc.com

"Fine vegan dining" that "doesn't scream 'bean curd'" is the forte of
this "cozy" Chelsea "haven" whose "wholesome" global fare is so "creative" it's "hard to believe it's good for you"; though it's a bit pricey "for
its type", the "organic wine list" alone makes it "worth considering."

NEW BLT Burger *Hamburgers* | 19 | 14 | 16 | $24 |

G Village | 470 Sixth Ave. (bet. 11th & 12th Sts.) | 212-243-8226 |
www.bltburger.com

For the "burger lover" in everyone, Laurent Tourondel's "casual" new
Villager does well with patties both "classic" and "postmodern"; all hail
the fair prices, if not the "confused service" and "unremarkable" decor.

BLT Fish ⓩ *Seafood* | 23 | 20 | 20 | $61 |

Flatiron | 21 W. 17th St. (bet. 5th & 6th Aves.) | 212-691-8888 |
www.bltfish.com

A "catch" "from top to bottom", Laurent Tourondel's Flatiron seafooder offers both a "classy" "skylit upstairs" room for "high-end" din-

ing and a "relaxed" "lively" downstairs beach bar for "casual" "surf fare"; wave off the "dent in your wallet" and you "can't go wrong."

NEW BLT Market *American* | - | - | - | VE |

W 50s | Ritz-Carlton | 1430 Sixth Ave. (CPS) | 212-521-6125 | www.bltmarket.com

Cross a farmer's market with the Ritz-Carlton and you get this pricey newcomer from Laurent Tourondel, where the focus is on seasonal, sometimes local ingredients that are the basis for its monthly changing menus and weekly specials; in the reconfigured former Atelier space, it's now done up in cheery agrarian chic, with big windows looking out onto the street and sidewalk seating in summer; N.B. there are even a few comestibles for sale up front.

BLT Prime *Steak* | 24 | 22 | 22 | $72 |

Gramercy | 111 E. 22nd St. (bet. Lexington Ave. & Park Ave. S.) | 212-995-8500 | www.bltprime.com

A "snazzy" steakhouse with a New American "twist", Laurent Tourondel's Gramercy "bovine bonanza" matches "expertly prepared" meat with a "palette" of à la carte sauces and sides in a "vibrant, modern" setting; it's a "top choice" for carnivores with "contemporary" tastes – "just bring lots of moo-la."

BLT Steak 🔏 *Steak* | 24 | 21 | 21 | $70 |

E 50s | 106 E. 57th St. (bet. Lexington & Park Aves.) | 212-752-7470 | www.bltsteak.com

As the progenitor of the "elite" BLT empire, this "dressed-up" East Midtown chophouse offers its "succulent" meats à la carte with "creative sides" and "VIP" service; it's "very 'in'" with "upscale", "high-decibel-level" "business" types who say it's "worth the premium" (if you can "get in the door").

bluechili 🌓 *Pan-Asian* | 19 | 16 | 17 | $37 |

W 50s | 251 W. 51st St. (bet. B'way & 8th Ave.) | 212-246-3330 | www.bluechilinyc.com

Something "different" for the Theater District, this Pan-Asian provides "lots of flavor for the buck" in "clublike", "futuristic" digs with "morphing" "mood lighting" and a "martini bar"; critics are chilly over "inattentive" service, but to most it's still "kinda cool."

Blue Fin 🌓 *Seafood* | 22 | 22 | 19 | $55 |

W 40s | W Times Sq. | 1567 Broadway (47th St.) | 212-918-1400 | www.brguestrestaurants.com

A Times Square "highlight", Steve Hanson's "splashy" seafooder is "jumping" with locals and sightseers lured by the "solid" "quality" fish and "upscale", bi-level space; despite the "din" and "erratic" service from "aspiring actors", "it works" for "the theatergoing masses" even "at those prices."

Blue Ginger *Japanese/Pan-Asian* | ▽ 22 | 18 | 19 | $36 |

Chelsea | 106 Eighth Ave. (bet. 15th & 16th Sts.) | 212-352-0911

Chelsea-ites "welcome" this Pan-Asian sushi purveyor after a "hype-free" arrival, notably for its "creative" "specialty rolls", "traditional entrees" and "gracious service"; as the "neighborhood" vibe implies, it's "reliable" for "a low-key" night.

	FOOD	DECOR	SERVICE	COST

Z Blue Hill *American*　　26 | 22 | 25 | $73

G Village | 75 Washington Pl. (bet. MacDougal St. & 6th Ave.) |
212-539-1776 | www.bluehillnyc.com

"I found my thrill" declare disciples at Dan Barber's gastronomic "temple" near Washington Square, whose "delectable" yet "unfussy" New American cuisine lets "the freshest" "organic" ingredients "shine through"; served with "genuine care" in a "subtly elegant" setting with a "quaint garden", it's an "artful" experience "for grown-ups."

Blue 9 Burger ●⊐ *Hamburgers*　　18 | 5 | 10 | $10

E Village | 92 Third Ave. (bet. 12th & 13th Sts.) | 212-979-0053

"Reminiscent of" California's "In-N-Out Burger", this "late-night" East Villager vends "sloppy" "bundles of joy" to "campus" refugees undergoing a "cash crunch"; "dingy" digs and "apathetic" counterfolk aside, it's a "super" "hangover" remedy.

Z Blue Ribbon ● *American*　　25 | 19 | 22 | $50

SoHo | 97 Sullivan St. (bet. Prince & Spring Sts.) | 212-274-0404
Park Slope | 280 Fifth Ave. (bet. 1st St. & Garfield Pl.) | Brooklyn |
718-840-0404
www.blueribbonrestaurants.com

First "prize" destinations, these "welcoming" SoHo–Park Slope New Americans from the Bromberg brothers stay "energized" into the "after hours" with an "interesting", "attractive" crowd; the cost runs "high" and waits "long", but "there's a reason" so many "love these places" – "astounding" food.

Blue Ribbon Bakery ● *American*　　24 | 19 | 20 | $39

G Village | 33 Downing St. (Bedford St.) | 212-337-0404 |
www.blueribbonrestaurants.com

Famed for "incredible" "fresh bread", this Village "winner" from the Bromberg brothers "pleases diverse tastes" with its "delightful" New American menu and "smart wine list"; no wonder "low-key" fans "line up for" the "limited" space, especially during the "awesome brunch."

Z Blue Ribbon Sushi ● *Japanese*　　25 | 19 | 21 | $54

SoHo | 119 Sullivan St. (bet. Prince & Spring Sts.) | 212-343-0404
Park Slope | 278 Fifth Ave. (bet. 1st St. & Garfield Pl.) | Brooklyn |
718-840-0408
www.blueribbonrestaurants.com

Surmounting the "summits" for sushi "verging on sublime", this SoHo–Park Slope pair purveys "exquisite" cuts of "mind-blowing" fish so "fresh" they "apparently swim to the plate"; the "Zen" "grotto" surroundings, "pleasant" service and "excellent sakes" are "soothing" enough to offset "top-dollar" tabs, but "go early or late" to "avoid crowds."

Blue Smoke *BBQ*　　22 | 17 | 19 | $41

Gramercy | 116 E. 27th St. (bet. Lexington Ave. & Park Ave. S.) |
212-447-7733 | www.bluesmoke.com

To "scratch the itch" for "pit BBQ", scoot over to this saucy Gramercy smokehouse and "pig out" on "meaty", "melt-in-your-mouth" ribs and "must-have" sides; sticklers say the "city-esque" setup sends a "mixed message", but it "holds its own" at "legit prices"; P.S. "sweet jazz" "beckons" in the club downstairs.

	FOOD	DECOR	SERVICE	COST

☑ Blue Water Grill ● *Seafood* **23 | 22 | 21 | $53**
Union Sq | 31 Union Sq. W. (16th St.) | 212-675-9500 |
www.brguestrestaurants.com
A "felicitous" island of "city chic", Steve Hanson's "Union Square anchor" serves "top-shelf" seafood in a "glossy" marble-clad "converted bank" boasting a "great veranda" and "jazz combo" sets downstairs; thanks to its "social" atmosphere and "excellent brunch", it's one of NYC's most popular, and though "too friggin' loud", at least it's "never dull."

Boathouse *American* **16 | 25 | 16 | $52**
E 70s | Central Park | Central Park Lake, enter on E. 72nd St. (Central Park Dr. N.) | 212-517-2233 |
www.thecentralparkboathouse.com
Like "dining in a postcard", Central Park's "enchanted" "pond-side" New American is "one of a kind" for "bucolic" tranquility and romance; the "marginal food" and "so-so service" stir sinking sensations at "this price point", but the "great escape" "is its own reward."

Bobby Van's Grill ●☑ *Steak* **22 | 19 | 21 | $64**
W 50s | 135 W. 50th St. (bet. 6th & 7th Aves.) | 212-957-5050
Bobby Van's Steakhouse *Steak*
E 40s | 230 Park Ave. (46th St.) | 212-867-5490 ☑
E 50s | 131 E. 54th St. (bet. Lexington & Park Aves.) |
212-207-8050
Financial District | 25 Broad St. (Exchange Pl.) | 212-344-8463 ☑
www.bobbyvans.com
"Meat-and-potatoes" mavens get "just what they want" from these "businessy" "standby" steakhouses, namely "quality cuts" and "solicitous service" in a "typical" "two-martini" milieu; they stay "up to par" with "no surprises" apart from the "intriguing" "bank vault" room at the Downtown outpost.

Boca Chica *Pan-Latin* **20 | 15 | 16 | $29**
E Village | 13 First Ave. (1st St.) | 212-473-0108
A "*muy caliente*" draw for "younger" compadres, this "bohemian" East Villager serves "addictive" Pan-Latin "cheap eats" and "deadly" *bebidas*; if the "lines", "noise" and "tight squeeze" don't "drive you loco", it's a "fun" "experience."

Bocca Lupo ●Ⓜ *Italian* **▽ 21 | 20 | 19 | $31**
Cobble Hill | 391 Henry St. (Warren St.) | Brooklyn | 718-243-2522
"Cool" but "neighborly", this Cobble Hill yearling "works big-time" for locals wolfing down "delicious" "tapas-style" Italian and "wonderful" vinos at "the right price"; its "smart" mix of "industrial" and "family" elements have proven predictably "popular" among Smith Street refugees.

Bocelli *Italian* **▽ 25 | 23 | 23 | $48**
Staten Island | 1250 Hylan Blvd. (bet. Clove & Old Town Rds.) |
718-420-6150 | www.bocellirest.com
Staten Islanders attest this Italian rises "above the usual" given the "high standards" of its cooking and staffers who see that "everyone is treated like family"; eye-catching Tuscan decor and weekend crooners also share the credit for making it "so satisfying."

	FOOD	DECOR	SERVICE	COST

Bogota Latin Bistro *Pan-Latin*   21 | 19 | 18 | $28

Park Slope | 141 Fifth Ave. (bet. Lincoln & St. Johns Pls.) | Brooklyn | 718-230-3805 | www.bogotabistro.com

"Say *hola*" to the "friendly" "fiesta" feeling at this "winning" Park Slope Pan-Latin, which plies its "refreshing" fare and "delicious drinks" at a "budget-conscious" cost; the "buzzing" premises include a "year-round" patio, and "you never leave hungry or thirsty."

Bôi *Vietnamese*   19 | 17 | 19 | $38

E 40s | 246 E. 44th St. (bet. 2nd & 3rd Aves.) | 212-681-6541

NEW Bôi to Go 🅿️🚫 *Vietnamese*

E 40s | 800 Second Ave. (bet. 42nd & 43rd Sts.) | 212-681-1122 www.boi-restaurant.com

"Oh, bôi" enthuse aficionados of the "exotic flavors" at this "minimalist" Midtown Vietnamese, known for the "subtlety" of its "solid" specialties; it generally assembles "the U.N. crowd", and the new take-out venue vends "great sandwiches" that make for a "unique" lunch.

Bolo *Spanish*   24 | 20 | 21 | $55

Flatiron | 23 E. 22nd St. (bet. B'way & Park Ave. S.) | 212-228-2200 | www.bolorestaurant.com

Fans cheer "*olé*" to Bobby Flay's "colorful" Flatiron Spaniard, which bowls 'em over "year after year" with "memorable" "nouvelle" Iberian cooking matched with well-chosen wines; "attentive staffers" help make it "worth the price tag", though contras contend it's starting to "show its age."

Bombay Palace *Indian*   18 | 16 | 17 | $41

W 50s | 30 W. 52nd St. (bet. 5th & 6th Aves.) | 212-541-7777 | www.bombay-palace.com

For a "reliable" "fix" of "the Raj", this Midtown Indian "standby" furnishes all the subcontinental "classics" in a "spacious", "unpretentious" setting; evenings boast an "extensive menu", but the best time to go is for the $14.95 lunch buffet spread – "your whole office will be there."

Bombay Talkie *Indian*   20 | 18 | 16 | $35

Chelsea | 189 Ninth Ave. (bet. 21st & 22nd Sts.) | 212-242-1900

Indian with a "hip" "twist" is the featured attraction at this "neat" Chelsea duplex, serving "imaginative riffs" on "street snacks" against a "Bollywood art" backdrop; while admirers talk up the "delicious" "concept", it bombs with critics who slam the "slackadaisical" staff.

Bond 45 ● *Italian*   20 | 18 | 19 | $50

W 40s | 154 W. 45th St. (bet. 6th & 7th Aves.) | 212-869-4545 | www.bond45.com

"Once a clothing store", this "expansive" Times Square space is now an "accommodating" pseudo-19th century outlet for "plentiful" helpings of "traditional Italian" steak and seafood; although "really loud" and "not exactly the Armani" of its kind, it fits the area to a T.

Bondi Road *Australian*   ▽ 21 | 18 | 20 | $31

LES | 153 Rivington St. (bet. Clinton & Suffolk Sts.) | 212-253-5311 | www.bondiroad.com

You're bound to bond with "friendly" "Oz" expats at this "laid-back", "great-value" LES Australian, "known for fish 'n' chips" and "solid" pub grub served in "kitschy" "beach getaway" digs; admirers of the "surfer cool" suggest that you "come for the fish and stay to booze."

Bond Street ● *Japanese* 25 | 22 | 19 | $60

NoHo | 6 Bond St. (bet. B'way & Lafayette St.) | 212-777-2500

Still a "hot spot" after recovering from a recent fire, this NoHo Japanese serves "fabulous designer sushi" in "sexy" environs complete with a "dark" downstairs lounge pouring "fancy drinks"; for better or worse, "hipper-than-thou" service and "expensive" tabs are just part of the "scene" that "never misses a beat."

Bonita ● *Mexican* 19 | 16 | 17 | $22

NEW **Fort Greene** | 243 DeKalb Ave. (Vanderbilt Ave.) | Brooklyn | 718-622-5300
Williamsburg | 338 Bedford Ave. (bet. S. 2nd & 3rd Sts.) | Brooklyn | 718-384-9500
www.bonitanyc.com

Peso-pinchers "never tire" of the "comforting" "homestyle Mexican" fare at this "down-to-earth" Williamsburg "staple" and its new Fort Greene sibling that's big with "hipster Pratt kids"; "cramped", "no-frills" digs and "so-so" service belie the name, but still the "crowds" keep coming.

Boqueria ● *Spanish* 23 | 18 | 19 | $46

Flatiron | 53 W. 19th St. (bet. 5th & 6th Aves.) | 212-255-4160 | www.boquerianyc.com

A *"fantastico"* take on Barcelona's tapas "tradition", this "energetic", "minimal"-size Flatiron fandango can get "crazy busy"; service "glitches" and tabs that tend to "creep up" on you do nothing to reduce the "ridiculous waits" that arise from its "no-reservations policy."

Borgo Antico ● *Italian* 19 | 17 | 20 | $41

G Village | 22 E. 13th St. (bet. 5th Ave. & University Pl.) | 212-807-1313 | www.borgoanticony.com

Don't expect fireworks at this Village Italian "sleeper", however, it's an "amenable" option with "serviceable" food, "comfortable" "rustic" surroundings and "capable service"; in sum, it "satisfies" at a "moderate" cost – "if you're in the neighborhood."

NEW Borough Food & Drink ● *American* – | – | – | M

Flatiron | 12 E. 22nd St. (bet. B'way & Park Ave. S.) | 212-260-0103 | www.chinagrillmgt.com

A collaboration of Zak Pelaccio (Fatty Crab) and Jeffrey Chodorow (China Grill), this new Flatironer celebrates old NY via a nostalgic American menu covering everything from fried chicken to herring and sausage plates, all via local purveyors; the space resembles a rural country store, albeit one packed with noisy city slickers.

Bottega del Vino *Italian* 22 | 20 | 20 | $62

E 50s | 7 E. 59th St. (bet. 5th & Madison Aves.) | 212-223-3028 | www.bottegadelvinonyc.com

Known for its vino list running to "biblical" length, this Midtown Italian wine bar is a "very Euro" "hideaway" for "excellent" pastas served amid "Tirolean decor"; the "jet-set" vibe is worthy of its Veronese parent, as is the "platinum-card" pricing.

	FOOD	DECOR	SERVICE	COST

Bottino *Italian* | 19 | 18 | 17 | $44

Chelsea | 246 10th Ave. (bet. 24th & 25th Sts.) | 212-206-6766 | www.bottinonyc.com

To take a "break from gallery-hopping", try this West Chelsea "art world" "mainstay", serving "fine" Tuscan bites in a "modern" space with a "fantastic back garden"; it's an area "best bet" even if some say there's "too much attitude" on exhibit.

Bouchon Bakery *American/French* | 23 | 13 | 17 | $28

W 60s | Time Warner Ctr. | 10 Columbus Circle, 3rd fl. (60th St. at B'way) | 212-823-9366 | www.bouchonbakery.com

Thomas Keller's "magic touches" lend a New American accent to French classics at this "elegant" cafe/patisserie specializing in "high-end" sandwiches and "exquisite pastries"; despite the "hectic" "mall setting" and "lackluster service", the majority deems it a "legitimate treat."

Bouillabaisse 126 *French* | 22 | 16 | 17 | $40

Carroll Gardens | 126 Union St. (bet. Columbia & Hicks Sts.) | Brooklyn | 718-855-4405 | www.bouillabaisse126.com

The name and owners have changed, but the "rich" "signature dish" remains a "must-try" at this Carroll Gardens joint, where "interesting" West African influences now add to the French menu; a "homey" interior and "charming garden" complement its "tastefully" "simple" style.

Z Bouley ◑ *French* | 28 | 26 | 27 | $94

TriBeCa | 120 W. Broadway (Duane St.) | 212-964-2525 | www.davidbouley.com

David Bouley's TriBeCa "mecca" "never ceases to amaze", carrying "class" to an "exemplary level" with "stunning" New French cuisine and "dazzling" but "unstuffy service"; the "opulent" space's "vaulted ceilings" and "soothing" lighting impart a "sense of contentment" that "memories are made of"; no, it's "not cheap"; N.B. watch for a 2008 move to gorgeous new digs down the block.

Z Bouley, Upstairs *Eclectic* | 26 | 17 | 20 | $46

TriBeCa | Bouley Bakery & Mkt. | 130 W. Broadway, 2nd fl. (Duane St.) | 212-608-5829 | www.davidbouley.com

David Bouley lets "his hair down" at this "lively", "informal" TriBeCan showcasing "impeccable" "open-kitchen" Eclectic "flights of fancy" paired with "phenomenal sushi"; "it's a terrific deal" to boot, but given the "tiny" space and "no-rez policy", the word is "come early or wait."

Brasserie ◑ *French* | 20 | 22 | 19 | $51

E 50s | 100 E. 53rd St. (bet. Lexington & Park Aves.) | 212-751-4840 | www.rapatina.com

A "way cool" "futuristic" layout is the backdrop for this East Midtown French brasserie that attracts the "business" set from breakfast through late dinner; while "the 'wow' factor" and "hopping" bar scene can "dazzle", there are "few surprises" by way of food or service.

Brasserie 8½ *French* | 22 | 24 | 22 | $56

W 50s | 9 W. 57th St. (bet. 5th & 6th Aves.) | 212-829-0812 | www.brasserie812.com

The "sweeping staircase" into this "submerged" Midtown brasserie is an "impressive" lead-in to "ambitious" French cooking that "lives up to

	FOOD	DECOR	SERVICE	COST

the promise" of the "spacious, chic" setting; "service is also first rate", rendering the "upscale experience" far more than half "inviting."

Brasserie Julien *French*

| | 19 | 20 | 17 | $44 |

E 80s | 1422 Third Ave. (bet. 80th & 81st Sts.) | 212-744-6327 | www.brasseriejulien.com

Yorkville denizens indulge "their inner Francophiles" at this "reliable" provider of "decent" French fare and a "funky art deco" mise-en-scène; with a "warm" vibe and "live jazz on weekends", it's ideal for a date.

Brasserie Ruhlmann *French*

| | 17 | 21 | 18 | $52 |

W 50s | 45 Rockefeller Plaza (enter on 50th St., bet. 5th & 6th Aves.) | 212-974-2020 | www.brasserieruhlmann.com

With a "striking" "deco interior", this "elegant" French brasserie offers "agreeable business" dining on "prime Rock Center" turf; though the "just fair" food and "spotty" service stir skepticism, fans feel it's "finding its way" since Laurent Tourondel took charge.

Bravo Gianni ● *Italian*

| | 23 | 13 | 21 | $63 |

E 60s | 230 E. 63rd St. (bet. 2nd & 3rd Aves.) | 212-752-7272

Ultra-"personable" chef-owner Gianni Garavelli leads a "capable staff" at this UES "mainstay", which still earns ovations for its "outstanding" Northern Italian food and "unpressured" vibe; the "dated decor" "needs work", but regulars might as well be "royalty here."

Bread Tribeca *Italian*

| | 19 | 16 | 16 | $38 |

TriBeCa | 301 Church St. (Walker St.) | 212-334-8282 | www.breadtribeca.com

Bread ● *Sandwiches*

NoLita | 20 Spring St. (bet. Elizabeth & Mott Sts.) | 212-334-1015

However you slice it, this "casual" TriBeCan is a "decent nosh stop" offering "fresh" "sandwich lunches" and "solid" "home-cooked" Italian fare for "reasonable" dough; "bustling" "young" clients keep the "minimalist" setting "crowded" and the staff often "overwhelmed"; N.B. there's a smaller, separately operated affiliate in NoLita.

Breeze *French/Thai*

| | ∇ 20 | 15 | 16 | $33 |

W 40s | 661 Ninth Ave. (bet. 45th & 46th Sts.) | 212-262-7777 | www.breezenyc.com

A "quick" crew dishes out the "tasty" Thai-French fusion fare at this modern Hell's Kitchen storefront; it can be "loud with music and videos" and looks "dinerlike", but for such "a good value" no one seems to mind.

Brennan & Carr ●⊟ *Sandwiches*

| | 19 | 10 | 15 | $17 |

Sheepshead Bay | 3432 Nostrand Ave. (Ave. U) | Brooklyn | 718-646-9559

This "long-lived institution" in Sheepshead Bay still "hits the spot" with au jus-"soaked" roast beef sandwiches that require "a ton of napkins" but not too many dollars; the "dingy" digs "haven't changed" in decades (ditto the servers), but you'll be too busy mopping up the "juice running down your chin" to notice.

NEW brgr *Hamburgers*

| | 18 | 14 | 14 | $16 |

Chelsea | 287 Seventh Ave. (bet. 26th & 27th Sts.) | 212-488-7500 | www.brgr.us

The idea is to "create your own" beef, turkey or veggie burger, or pick from a host of other "inventive combos" at this new David Rockwell-designed Chelsea patty palace; "great fries and shakes" round out the "McDonald's for grown-ups" menu, though surveyors say it's "slightly overpriced" and "disorganized."

Bricco *Italian*

19	17	18	$44

W 50s | 304 W. 56th St. (bet. 8th & 9th Aves.) | 212-245-7160 | www.bricconyc.com

"Warm and inviting", this "reliable", "fair-priced" Hell's Kitchen Italian works equally well for "business lunches" or "romantic dinners"; while brick-oven pizza is the menu "standout", fans also tout the "attentive yet unobtrusive" service.

Brick Cafe *French/Italian*

20	21	18	$31

Astoria | 30-95 33rd St. (31st Ave.) | Queens | 718-267-2735 | www.brickcafe.com

Patrons of this Astoria Franco-Italian bistro enthuse over its "cozy", "rustic" interior in the winter and "outdoor seating fabulous for people-watching" in summer; "quality" food for a "very fair price" and a "staff that works hard to please" make this a "local favorite."

Bridge Cafe *American*

22	18	21	$44

Financial District | 279 Water St. (Dover St.) | 212-227-3344

For a "truly old NY" experience, "seek out" this circa-1794 brick-walled tavern "under the Brooklyn Bridge"; besides the "excellent" New American menu, the "warm" staff does its best to be sure "you'll leave happy."

Brio *Italian*

18	14	17	$40

E 60s | 137 E. 61st St. (Lexington Ave.) | 212-980-2300 | www.brionyc.com

"Convenient to Bloomingdale's", this Italian is an "easy lunch" stop for shoppers seeking inexpensive, "delicious" pastas or thin-crust pizzas; however, "uncomfortable seating" and "too-modern" decor have regulars saying it was "better before" the last renovation.

Brioso *Italian*

▽ 25	20	23	$45

Staten Island | 174 New Dorp Ln. (9th St.) | 718-667-1700 | www.briosoristorante.com

"Excellent food, excellent service" give the brio to the DiMaggio brothers' Italian ristorante on Staten Island; while the "elegant" space can get "crowded and noisy" at peak hours, it's a "wonderful" dining experience overall, particularly "for the money."

Brooklyn Diner USA ● *Diner*

17	15	16	$31

NEW **W 40s** | 155 W. 43rd St. (bet. B'way & 6th Ave.) | 212-265-5400
W 50s | 212 W. 57th St. (bet. B'way & 7th Ave.) | 212-977-2280
www.brooklyndiner.com

Shelly Fireman's Midtown "re-creations of the city's diners of old" serve up "enormous portions" of American "comfort food" that are "worth a week of dieting"; they're also a "good value", which accounts for all of those "tourists" and "real NYers" who "crowd" in.

Brooklyn Fish Camp *Seafood*

23	14	19	$40

Park Slope | 162 Fifth Ave. (Degraw St.) | Brooklyn | 718-783-3264 | www.brooklynfishcamp.com

Mary Redding's Park Slope seafooder reels 'em in with "wonderful, fresh fish dishes" (including a famously "fabulous lobster roll") and "attentive, friendly" service; less happy campers crab about slightly "pricey" tabs and "bland" decor – unless you "eat out in the lovely garden."

Brother Jimmy's BBQ *BBQ*

16	10	14	$23

E 40s | Grand Central | lower level (42nd St. & Vanderbilt Ave.) | 212-661-4022
E 70s | 1485 Second Ave. (bet. 77th & 78th Sts.) | 212-288-0999 ●
E 90s | 1644 Third Ave. (92nd St.) | 212-426-2020 ●
NEW Garment District | 416 Eighth Ave. (31st St.) | 212-967-7603 ●
W 80s | 428 Amsterdam Ave. (bet. 80th & 81st Sts.) | 212-501-7515 ●
www.brotherjimmys.com

Basically a "big frat party", this low-budget "Southern-themed" BBQ quintet draws recent "college grads" with "cheap drinks" and "good grub" served by "scantily clad coed" types; while "family-friendly in the early evening", these joints get "rowdy" fast – luckily there's "delivery."

Brown Café *American*

▽ 25	19	19	$27

LES | 61 Hester St. (bet. Essex & Ludlow Sts.) | 212-477-2427

The "simple, delicious" American menu crafted from "top-notch" ingredients plus a "stellar brunch" draw a "relaxed twenty- and thirtysomething" crowd to this "delightful" Lower Eastsider; the "homey" vibe and "modest cost" make it "worth the wait" for a seat in the "little" available space.

Bruckner Bar & Grill ● *American*

▽ 21	18	17	$21

Bronx | 1 Bruckner Blvd. (3rd Ave.) | 718-665-2001 | www.brucknerbar.com

This "gritty" Mott Haven "beer and a burger joint" plays host to SoBro "artists" chowing down on "surprisingly good", "bargain"-priced American eats; weekly poetry readings, live music and a billiards table are a plus in an area where there's "not much around" yet.

Bryant Park Grill/Cafe *American*

17	21	17	$45

W 40s | behind NY Public Library | 25 W. 40th St. (bet. 5th & 6th Aves.) | 212-840-6500 | www.arkrestaurants.com

It's all about the "great location" at this "Midtown oasis" where on "sunny days" most "go for drinks" after work at the alfresco Cafe, and in winter sit "by a window" in the Grill's "pretty" dining room; just keep in mind it's really the "lovely setting" that "you're paying for" – the "so-so" American fare's "forgettable."

B. Smith's Restaurant Row *Southern*

19	19	18	$46

W 40s | 320 W. 46th St. (bet. 8th & 9th Aves.) | 212-315-1100 | www.bsmith.com

Theatergoing diners and "tourists" alike appreciate TV personality Barbara Smith's "upscale take" on "down-home" Southern food, calling her "feel-good" fixture on Restaurant Row "uniformly fine"; still, the sentiment isn't unanimous – a few find it "gimmicky" and "not what it once was."

Bubba Gump Shrimp Co. ● *American/Seafood*

14	16	17	$29

W 40s | 1501 Broadway (bet. 43rd & 44th Sts.) | 212-391-7100 | www.bubbagump.com

"Sure, it's a tourist trap", but this Times Square theme joint can be "really fun" and offers "delicious shrimp" cooked every which way; no surprise, there's "lots of Forrest Gump memorabilia" around, but

Forrest's quote, 'life's like a box of chocolates, you never know what you are going to get', could easily apply here.

Bubby's *American* | 18 | 14 | 14 | $28 |

TriBeCa | 120 Hudson St. (N. Moore St.) | 212-219-0666
Dumbo | 1 Main St. (bet. Plymouth & Water Sts.) | Brooklyn |
718-222-0666 Ⓜ
www.bubbys.com

You'd better "bring an appetite" for the "huge portions" of American "down-home cooking" at these underdecorated TriBeCa and Dumbo neighborhood havens; they're best known for their "fantastic brunch", but beware – it's "popular" with the "stroller set", so expect "kids everywhere" along with "long lines" and a little "attitude."

Ⓩ Buddakan ❶ *Asian Fusion* | 23 | 27 | 21 | $62 |

Chelsea | 75 Ninth Ave. (16th St.) | 212-989-6699 |
www.buddakannyc.com

Stephen Starr's "awe-inspiring" Chelsea "spectacle" "lives up to the hype" with a "bold, beautiful" space "like a movie set" and an equally appealing "young, chic" customer base, and the "feast for the eyes" is nearly matched by the "delicious", "pricey" Asian fusion fare; as "everyone" wants to "eat here" it gets "way crowded" and "loud", so "go early" if you want to avoid the "zoo."

Ⓩ Buddha Bar ❶ *Asian Fusion* | 19 | 26 | 17 | $60 |

Meatpacking | 25 Little W. 12th St. (bet. 9th Ave. & Washington St.) |
212-647-7314 | www.buddhabarnyc.com

"Wow" – this "cavernous" Meatpacking "club du jour's" "Disney-like" interior is a "must-see", with "jaw-dropping" features like a "giant" 17-ft. Buddha, semi-private pagodas, koi ponds and "amazing" jellyfish-filled aquariums; the Asian fusion fare is "surprisingly decent" – "if you ever get it" – but as the "everything big" approach includes the bill, it may be better "for a drink and a gander."

Buenos Aires ❶ *Argentinean* | 21 | 15 | 19 | $37 |

E Village | 513 E. Sixth St. (bet. Aves. A & B) | 212-228-2775

Operating in a "small, crowded" East Village space, this "down-to-earth" "taste of Argentina" purveys "delicious" steaks, empanadas and well-selected wines for "prices almost as affordable as Buenos Aires"; the atmosphere stays "lively" despite service on "Argentinean time."

Bukhara Grill *Indian* | 20 | 15 | 18 | $36 |

E 40s | 217 E. 49th St. (bet. 2nd & 3rd Aves.) | 212-888-2839 |
www.bukharany.com

Midtowners keep cumin to this "authentic" Indian serving "excellent tandoori" dishes and other well-priced, "dependable" fare, including a $13.95 lunch buffet; the "tranquil" atmosphere is abetted by a "charming" second-floor terrace and "pleasant" service.

Bull and Bear ❶ *Steak* | 19 | 20 | 19 | $58 |

E 40s | Waldorf-Astoria | 570 Lexington Ave. (49th St.) | 212-872-4900 |
www.waldorfastoria.com

"Clubby" and "masculine", this Waldorf-Astoria "throwback" evokes "old NY" and attracts "power-lunchers" with "hearty he-man steaks" and "excellent cocktails"; "attentive" service rounds out the experience, just "hope it's a bull market when paying the bill."

	FOOD	DECOR	SERVICE	COST

Bull Run *American* | 18 | 16 | 17 | $45 |

Financial District | Club Quarters Hotel | 52 William St. (Pine St.) |
212-859-2200 | www.bullrunwallstreet.com

A "calm spot" in the Financial District, this New American is "full of
suits" for lunch or after-market drinks; "ho-hum" decor and "reliable",
if "unspectacular", fare at "Wall Street prices" mean it might not do
such bullish business elsewhere.

Burger Heaven *Hamburgers* | 16 | 8 | 14 | $18 |

E 40s | 20 E. 49th St. (bet. 5th & Madison Aves.) | 212-755-2166
E 40s | 291 Madison Ave. (bet. 40th & 41st Sts.) | 212-685-6250
E 50s | 536 Madison Ave. (bet. 54th & 55th Sts.) | 212-753-4214
E 50s | 9 E. 53rd St. (bet. 5th & Madison Aves.) | 212-752-0340
E 60s | 804 Lexington Ave. (62nd St.) | 212-838-3580
E 80s | 1534 Third Ave. (bet. 86th & 87th Sts.) | 212-722-8292
www.burgerheaven.com

When "busy NY" needs a "boigah" "in a hurry" there's this "reliable" "local" chain of "coffee shop–style" joints serving "juicy" patties and other
"diner basics"; it's "not much in decor or service" but you get "great bang
for your buck" and it's still "a cut above" most other fast-fooders.

burger joint at
Le Parker Meridien ●☞ *Hamburgers* | 24 | 9 | 11 | $14 |

W 50s | Le Parker Meridien | 119 W. 56th St. (bet. 6th & 7th Aves.) |
212-708-7414 | www.newyork.lemeridien.com

"Don't let the line scare you" off this "hole-in-the-wall" hamburger
"heaven" "behind the curtain" in an "upscale hotel" lobby; many argue
that the "amazing" grilled patties here are "among the best in NYC",
but the waits for one of its "handful" of seats mean most Midtowners
will never know.

Burritoville *Tex-Mex* | 16 | 7 | 12 | $12 |

E 40s | 152 E. 43rd St. (bet. Lexington & 3rd Aves.) | 212-880-8300 🖂
E 50s | 866 Third Ave. (52nd St.) | 212-980-4111
E 70s | 1487 Second Ave. (bet. 77th & 78th Sts.) | 212-472-8800 ●
E Village | 141 Second Ave. (bet. 8th & 9th Sts.) | 212-260-3300 ●
Financial District | 80 Nassau St. (bet. Fulton & John Sts.) | 212-285-0070
Garment District | 352 W. 39th St. (9th Ave.) | 212-563-9088
TriBeCa | 116 Chambers St. (Church St.) | 212-566-2300
W 40s | 625 Ninth Ave. (44th St.) | 212-333-5352 ●
W 70s | 166 W. 72nd St. (bet. Amsterdam & Columbus Aves.) |
212-580-7700 ●
W Village | 298 Bleecker St. (7th Ave. S.) | 212-633-9249
www.burritoville.com
Additional locations throughout the NY area

"Huge burritos at a cheap price" draw the "super hungry" to this "addictive" Tex-Mex chain where "fresh ingredients" and "amazing vegetarian choices" mean you can actually eat "hearty" and "healthy"
simultaneously; if you'd rather pass on the "no-frills" eat-in experience, they "deliver a second after you hang up the phone."

Butai *Japanese* | ▽ 22 | 21 | 18 | $44 |

Gramercy | 115 E. 18th St. (bet. Irving Pl. & Park Ave. S.) | 212-387-8885 |
www.butai.us

Winning "kudos" for its midpriced Japanese robata dishes, this
"Gramercy gem" is also praised for its "calming" "loungelike" space;

subscribe to zagat.com

| | FOOD | DECOR | SERVICE | COST |

portions may be "small", but the "helpful, friendly staff keeps the plates coming", leaving fans wondering "why this place is often empty."

Butter ●☑ *American*
| | - | 19 | 23 | 19 | $56 |

E Village | 415 Lafayette St. (bet. Astor Pl. & 4th St.) | 212-253-2828 | www.butterrestaurant.com

While the New American "food is pretty good" at this bi-level East Villager, it's the "stylish" "sexy" vibe that butters up its "hip, pretty" crowd; if the place slips up, most fault staff "attitude" and "high prices."

Cabana ● *Nuevo Latino*
| | 21 | 18 | 17 | $35 |

E 60s | 1022 Third Ave. (bet. 60th & 61st Sts.) | 212-980-5678
Seaport | Pier 17 | 89 South St. (Fulton St.) | 212-406-1155
Forest Hills | 107-10 70th Rd. (bet. Austin St. & Queens Blvd.) | Queens | 718-263-3600
www.cabanarestaurant.com

"Always a fiesta", these "hopping" Cuban "hot spots" host "upbeat" crowds downing "delicious mojitos" and "full-flavored" Nuevo Latino fare; "pleasant" but "slow" service and "long waits" are part of the deal; P.S. the Seaport location offers a lovely "view of the water."

Cacio e Pepe *Italian*
| | 22 | 17 | 21 | $40 |

E Village | 182 Second Ave. (bet. 11th & 12th Sts.) | 212-505-5931 | www.cacioepepe.com

Those "addicted" to the namesake dish and other "creative", "fresh" offerings at this East Village "taste of Rome" also tout the "warm, genuine" service and moderate "price point"; it gets even better "in warm weather" when the "enchanting garden" is an option.

NEW Cacio e Vino ● *Italian*
| | ▽ 21 | 18 | 20 | $33 |

E Village | 80 Second Ave. (bet. 4th & 5th Sts.) | 212-228-3269 | www.cacioevino.com

From the Cacio e Pepe folks, this convivial East Village Sicilian *spuntino* specializes in pizzas from a wood-fired oven; besides being inexpensive, the menu reflects an artisan's pride; N.B. it's currently BYO.

NEW Cafe &
Wine Room, A Ⓜ *Caribbean/French*
| | - | - | - | I |

W 100s | 973 Columbus Ave. (bet. 107th & 108th Sts.) | 212-222-2033
Formerly called 'A', this bite-size Morningside Heights French-Caribbean has changed its name and moved a block north to slightly roomier digs (28 seats); its tiny kitchen turns out the same hearty menu of affordable, organic dishes and the BYO policy remains, but plans are afoot to start selling wine as well.

Cafe Asean ⇗ *SE Asian*
| | 21 | 13 | 18 | $26 |

G Village | 117 W. 10th St. (bet. Greenwich & 6th Aves.) | 212-633-0348
A "panoply" of "perfectly spiced" Southeast Asian fare is served by "sweet" staffers at this "bargain" Villager; inside, the "funky" digs are "cute but cramped", but in season the "tranquil refuge" of a patio "adds charm" to the experience

Cafe Bar ● *Greek/Mediterranean*
| | ▽ 20 | 20 | 17 | $21 |

Astoria | 32-90 36th St. (34th Ave.) | Queens | 718-204-5273
Part "coffeehouse", part "bar/lounge", this Astoria Greek-Med is a "comfy" local "hangout" with "mismatched" "'60s and '70s" furniture,

big-screen TVs and free WiFi; though "hipsters" hail the "simple" budget eats and "outdoor dining", for most it's about the "fun" scene.

⊠ Café Boulud *French*　　　| 27 | 23 | 26 | $79 |

E 70s | Surrey Hotel | 20 E. 76th St. (bet. 5th & Madison Aves.) | 212-772-2600 | www.danielnyc.com

Dining is "bliss" at "Daniel's Uptown sibling", where the "superb experiences" are "less formal" and less costly (if still "not cheap") than at the flagship; a "chic" UES clientele "savors each bite" of its "innovative" French fare served in "simple, elegant" environs by "pampering" pro staffers; P.S. lunch is a particularly "good buy."

Cafe Centro ⊠ *Mediterranean*　　| 20 | 18 | 19 | $46 |

E 40s | MetLife Bldg. | 200 Park Ave. (45th St.) | 212-818-1222 | www.patinagroup.com

"Meeting a need" just "steps from Grand Central", this midpriced purveyor of "surprisingly good" Med fare makes a "smart choice for a business lunch" or bite before "catching the train"; "quick service" and a "prime" location mean it's always "jumping", though less so at dinner.

Cafecito ⇗ *Cuban*　　| 21 | 14 | 17 | $24 |

E Village | 185 Ave. C (bet. 11th & 12th Sts.) | 212-253-9966

A slice of "Little Havana" on Avenue C, this "funky" East Village Cuban dishes up *"muy bueno"* eats plus mojitos that "rock"; on weekends there's "a hell of a line" and "tight seating" too, but amigos come for the "amazing value."

NEW Cafe Cluny ● *American/French*　| 19 | 18 | 18 | $50 |

W Village | 284 W. 12th St. (W. 4th St.) | 212-255-6900

West Villagers are "coming in droves" to this "adorable" newcomer done up in modern "country cottage" chic; "cheery service" and "delicious" (if "not adventurous") Franco-American fare are two reasons it's "so popular", though a puzzled few still wonder "what the hype's about."

Cafe Colonial *Brazilian*　　| ▽ 20 | 15 | 14 | $27 |

NoLita | 276 Elizabeth St. (Houston St.) | 212-274-0044 | www.cafecolonialny.com

It's been a local "favorite for years", and this NoLita Brazilian still "keeps it interesting" with a "something-for-everyone" menu and "dilapidated-chic" aesthetic; it's particularly popular at "breakfast and brunch", when devotees "brave the lines" and iffy service for "tasty" "hangover cures."

Cafe Con Leche *Cuban/Dominican*　| 18 | 11 | 16 | $23 |

W 80s | 424 Amsterdam Ave. (bet. 80th & 81st Sts.) | 212-595-7000
W 90s | 726 Amsterdam Ave. (bet. 95th & 96th Sts.) | 212-678-7000

"Ample-size breakfasts for economy-size" budgets are the big draws at these "crowded" UWS Cuban-Dominicans known for the "eponymous beverage"; however, "don't-look" interiors and an "air of chaos" have many opting for "convenient takeout."

Café d'Alsace ● *French*　　| 21 | 18 | 17 | $47 |

E 80s | 1695 Second Ave. (88th St.) | 212-722-5133 | www.cafedalsace.com

Upper Eastsiders "love" this "bustling" French brasserie's "you're-in-France" feel and "delicious, hearty" Alsace specialties supplemented by a 500-strong suds selection supervised by a "beer sommelier"; its "popularity" leads to "rushed" service and "crowded", "noisy" conditions – though you can escape to the "outdoor seats."

	FOOD	DECOR	SERVICE	COST

Café de Bruxelles ● Belgian

21 **15** **18** **$41**

W Village | 118 Greenwich Ave. (13th St.) | 212-206-1830

"If you want to feel like a Villager, eat at the bar" of this "gracious" Belgian "standby" where the "fabulous" moules frites and trappist beers go down well in "old Europe"–like digs; if trendoids find the vibe "staid", loyalists insist it has "charm" aplenty.

☑ Café des Artistes ● French

22 **26** **23** **$69**

W 60s | 1 W. 67th St. (bet. Columbus Ave. & CPW) | 212-877-3500 | www.cafenyc.com

George and Jenifer Lang's "NY icon" near Lincoln Center is "still one of the most beautiful, romantic places to dine" thanks to a space resplendent with "fresh flowers" and Howard Chandler Christy's "magical" "murals of nubile nymphs"; add "outstanding" French fare and "gracious" service, and it's "a superb evening every time" – "perfect for 'marry me' or 'I'm sorry!'"; N.B. dinner only, except for brunch on weekends.

Café du Soleil French/Mediterranean

19 **17** **14** **$38**

W 100s | 2723 Broadway (104th St.) | 212-316-5000

"Cheerful" and "sunny" as its name, this French-Med is "always full" thanks to "solid" bistro eats, sidewalk seats, proximity to Columbia and "value" specials; "amateur-hour" service is the only real storm cloud.

Cafe Español ● Spanish

20 **14** **19** **$32**

G Village | 172 Bleecker St. (bet. MacDougal & Sullivan Sts.) | 212-505-0657 | www.cafeespanol.com
G Village | 78 Carmine St. (bet. Bedford St. & 7th Ave. S.) | 212-675-3312

You "feel like you're in España", particularly after a few pitchers of sangria, at these separately owned Village Spaniards purveying "tasty tapas" and "terrific paella"; "affordable" prices (especially the Monday lobster deal), "friendly service" and outside seating keep locals loyal.

Café Evergreen Chinese

20 **13** **18** **$32**

E 60s | 1288 First Ave. (bet. 69th & 70th Sts.) | 212-744-3266

Saving Eastsiders a "trek to Chinatown", this Cantonese "godsend" is most appreciated for its "super dim sum" and surprisingly "extensive wine list"; "attentive service" enhances the dining here, though its dining room does the opposite.

Cafe Fiorello ● Italian

20 **16** **18** **$48**

W 60s | 1900 Broadway (bet. 63rd & 64th Sts.) | 212-595-5330 | www.cafefiorello.com

"Lincoln Center–goers" laud this across-the-street Italian for its "outstanding antipasto bar" and "thin-crust pizza"; it can be a "squeeze" pre-"curtain", but "pro waiters" will "get you to your performance on time"; P.S. the sidewalk seats are "the best in the house."

Café Frida Mexican

19 **16** **16** **$38**

W 70s | 368 Columbus Ave. (bet. 77th & 78th Sts.) | 212-712-2929 | www.cafefrida.com

"Terrific guac" stars at this "lively" UWS "hacienda" whose "awesome margaritas" and "gourmet Mexican" go for not too many pesos; it gets "loud" and service is "lackluster", but casanovas claim its "sexy", "dark" digs make an ideal "place to close" a deal.

NEW Cafe Fuego ● *Pan-Latin*   ▽ 19 | 18 | 17 | $28

E Village | 9 St. Marks Pl. (bet. 2nd & 3rd Aves.) | 212-677-7300 | www.cafefuego.com

Providing a respite "from the hustle and bustle of St. Marks", this East Village yearling is perfect for a "chill night" given its "flavorful" Pan-Latin fare dished up in cozy, "well-lit" digs; there's also a speakeasy-esque bar/lounge area, plus patio seating in warmer months.

Cafe Gitane ●≠ *French/Moroccan*   20 | 17 | 16 | $25

NoLita | 242 Mott St. (Prince St.) | 212-334-9552

It's worth paying "just to people-watch" at this Morocco-meets-Paris NoLita "hipster", where the "sunglasses-sporting" "Euro" "eye candy" is just as "delicious" as the "cheap" eats; if you'd rather skip the "constantly hopping" "scene", hit the take-out window instead.

Z Café Gray *French*   25 | 24 | 24 | $82

W 60s | Time Warner Ctr. | 10 Columbus Circle, 3rd fl. (60th St. at B'way) | 212-823-6338 | www.cafegray.com

Gray Kunz's Asian-accented French brasserie in the Time Warner Center is voted an all-around "wonderful experience" from the "palate-pleasing" cuisine and "spectacular wine list" to the "smooth" service; debate continues over David Rockwell's "glitzy" decor and the decision to "place the kitchen between diners and the view", but then "who looks out the window" with such "gorgeous food" on your plate?; P.S. it's a shame they "stopped lunch service", because dinner tabs tip to the "high-end."

Café Habana ● *Cuban/Mexican*   22 | 13 | 15 | $24

NoLita | 17 Prince St. (Elizabeth St.) | 212-625-2001

NEW Habana Outpost ≠ *Cuban/Mexican*

Fort Greene | 755-757 Fulton St. (S. Portland Ave.) | Brooklyn | 718-858-9500
www.ecoeatery.com

"It's easier to get into Cuba" than into this "tiny", "bursting-at-the-seams" NoLita "scenester", so you'd better "be willing to wait" for the "cheap", *"delicioso"* Cuban-Mexican dishes and drinks; if "ditsy" service and "cramped", "dingy" digs annoy, there's always the "next-door" take-out annex, not to mention the eco-conscious Fort Greene branch.

Cafe Joul *French*   18 | 13 | 17 | $44

E 50s | 1070 First Ave. (bet. 58th & 59th Sts.) | 212-759-3131

Just "what a bistro should be" say Sutton Place denizens of this "nothing-fancy" French "find"; the pricing gets mixed reactions ("affordable" vs. "expensive for what it is") but still most feel lucky to have such a "pleasant, reliable" neighbor.

Cafe Lalo ●≠ *Coffeehouse/Dessert*   19 | 19 | 13 | $20

W 80s | 201 W. 83rd St. (bet. Amsterdam Ave. & B'way) | 212-496-6031 | www.cafelalo.com

"Take a date" and try not to "drool" over the "sinful sweets" at this UWS "dessert staple"/"faux Parisian" cafe made famous (and "touristy") by *You've Got Mail*; there are "cheery lights in the trees outside", but once you're inside the "cramped" seating and "flaky" service aren't so charming.

	FOOD	DECOR	SERVICE	COST

Cafe Loup ◐ *French* — 18 | 16 | 19 | $43

G Village | 105 W. 13th St. (bet. 6th Ave. & 7th Ave. S.) | 212-255-4746
Village folks "love" this "neighborhood staple" for its "hearty", "reasonable" French bistro fare, "no-rush" vibe and "convivial" service; though it's "showing signs of wear", "happy patrons" say its "cozy" room "feels like home."

Cafe Luluc ◐⇄ *French* — 20 | 16 | 16 | $27

Cobble Hill | 214 Smith St. (Baltic St.) | Brooklyn | 718-625-3815
"*Très bon*" "basic" French bistro fare for half what you'd pay "on the other side of the river" endears "locals" to this "hip" Cobble Hiller; despite "modest" decor and a "cash-only" policy, it's "popular" enough to make it "hard to get a table" – though at least there's a "lovely" garden in which to "wait."

Cafe Luxembourg ◐ *French* — 20 | 18 | 19 | $50

W 70s | 200 W. 70th St. (bet. Amsterdam & West End Aves.) | 212-873-7411
"Still going strong" since 1982, this "timeless" UWS French bistro is always "jam-packed" with a "good-looking crowd" (including the occasional "celeb"); the "scene" gets "noisy", but *c'est la vie* – it's "perfect before or after Lincoln Center."

Cafe Mogador ◐ *Moroccan* — 21 | 16 | 17 | $27

E Village | 101 St. Marks Pl. (bet. Ave. A & 1st Ave.) | 212-677-2226 | www.cafemogador.com
A "neighborhood favorite" for almost 25 years thanks to its "cheap", "delectable" Moroccan tagines and other classics, this East Villager has the locals "leaving full and happy"; despite "pretty lax" service, the overall "warm", "laid-back" vibe keeps it "packed."

Café Pierre *Continental/French* — 23 | 25 | 24 | $69

E 60s | Pierre Hotel | 2 E. 61st St. (5th Ave.) | 212-940-8195
An "elegant" "retreat" from Midtown's "hustle and bustle", this Pierre Hotel "stalwart" offers "old-fashioned luxury" to "old-money" types with its "excellent" French-Continental cuisine that makes any meal, from breakfast to "special occasion" dinner; just make sure "Daddy Warbucks" is picking up the check, and remember jackets are required.

Café Ronda *Mediterranean/ S American* — 18 | 16 | 16 | $33

W 70s | 249-251 Columbus Ave. (bet. 71st & 72nd Sts.) | 212-579-9929 | www.caferonda.com
An "eclectic mix" of folks frequents this "reasonable" UWS Med–South American for "creative" tapas nibbled in "lively", often "noisy" environs; it's also a "great bunch place", if you can snag an "outside" seat, though "slow" service and a "small space" mean you may do some "waiting."

Café Sabarsky/Café Fledermaus *Austrian* — 22 | 24 | 19 | $40

E 80s | Neue Galerie | 1048 Fifth Ave. (86th St.) | 212-288-0665 | www.wallse.com
Kurt Gutenbrunner's "beautiful, old-world" Austrian cafe within the Neue Galerie makes a "charming" backdrop for "superb", "pricey" soups, sandwiches and "decadent desserts"; "long waits" are part of the deal, so if you're "in a hurry" try the "less-crowded Fledermaus."

	FOOD	DECOR	SERVICE	COST

Cafe Spice *Indian*
18 | 14 | 15 | $27

E 40s | Grand Central | lower level (42nd St. & Vanderbilt Ave.) | 646-227-1300
G Village | 72 University Pl. (bet. 10th & 11th Sts.) | 212-253-6999
W 50s | 54 W. 55th St. (bet. 5th & 6th Aves.) | 212-489-7444
www.cafespice.com

"If you can't make it to Curry Hill", try this "bargain" Indian trio that "satisfies" with "nicely spiced" basics and "well-poured drinks"; the "mod" sit-down branches are "busy" despite "slow service", while the "quick" Grand Central takeout–only counter is a hit with the "commuter crowd."

Cafe Steinhof *Austrian*
19 | 17 | 18 | $26

Park Slope | 422 Seventh Ave. (14th St.) | Brooklyn | 718-369-7776 | www.cafesteinhof.com

You'll be "full for days" after a "hearty" meal at this "funky" Park Slope "find" for simple "Austrian comfort food" at "value" rates; live music Wednesdays and film Sundays are draws, but "everybody seems to have fun" due to the "warm" service and "free-flowing beer."

Cafeteria ❶ *American*
18 | 16 | 14 | $30

Chelsea | 119 Seventh Ave. (17th St.) | 212-414-1717

The "air-kiss" and "eye-candy quotient" remains "high" at this "modern", "24/7" Chelsea American; whether it's for "weekend brunch", lunch after "shopping Loehmann's" or "post-clubbing", the "cheap", "tasty" "comfort" fare ensures there's "always a wait"; if it's "not as trendy as it used to be", the servers still have "'tude" aplenty.

Cafe Un Deux Trois ❶ *French*
16 | 14 | 16 | $41

W 40s | 123 W. 44th St. (bet. B'way & 6th Ave.) | 212-354-4148 | www.cafeundeuxtrois.biz

"Perfectly good" French bistro fare makes this "bustling" and "noisy" Times Square standby a "safe bet" for "midrange" "pre/post theater" eats; though it's "worn around the edges", it has a "family"-friendly atmosphere and "gets you in and out" in time for your show.

Caffe Bondi *Italian*
∇ 22 | 18 | 18 | $38

Staten Island | 1816 Hylan Blvd. (Dongan Hills Ave.) | 718-668-0100

There's no need for Staten Islanders to cross the Verrazano for "Sicilian food with plenty of character" thanks to this "delicious" "Manhattan transplant" "without the Manhattan prices"; the "relaxed" atmosphere and courteous service keep it a mainstay.

Caffe Buon Gusto *Italian*
18 | 14 | 17 | $32

E 70s | 236 E. 77th St. (bet. 2nd & 3rd Aves.) | 212-535-6884
Brooklyn Heights | 151 Montague St. (bet. Clinton & Henry Sts.) | Brooklyn | 718-624-3838

At these UES–Brooklyn Heights "mix-and-match" Italian "neighborhood favorites", the interiors are "homey" enough for a dinner "with friends" or other casual occasion; "solid" food and service and "inexpensive" tabs keep the regulars regular.

Caffe Cielo ❶ *Italian*
19 | 16 | 19 | $45

W 50s | 881 Eighth Ave. (bet. 52nd & 53rd Sts.) | 212-246-9555

It's a Hell's Kitchen "staple" that "changes little", which suits its regulars who cite "reliable", "reasonable" Northern Italian classics,

| | FOOD | DECOR | SERVICE | COST |

"pleasant" quarters and "fast service" as reasons to "go back"; its theater-"convenient" location and $12.95 brunch are two more.

NEW Caffe Emilia ●⊟ *Italian* — | — | — | I

E Village | 139 First Ave. (bet. 9th St. & St. Marks Pl.) | 212-388-1234
From the owners of Gnocco and Perbacco comes this new East Village Italian cafe providing espresso drinks and inexpensive artisanal sandwiches, salads and such; added virtues are a staff of beautiful Euro types and an informal, concrete-meets–art deco outdoor dining space.

Caffe Grazie *Italian* 19 | 17 | 20 | $48

E 80s | 26 E. 84th St. (bet. 5th & Madison Aves.) | 212-717-4407 | www.caffegrazie.com
"Lots of museum gift shop bags" tell the story of this UES Italian relied upon as a "convenient" choice "near the Met"; most tout its "tasty" fare, "relaxing" townhouse setting and "gracious" service, but a few find it a bit "ordinary" "for the price."

Caffe Linda ⊠ *Italian* 18 | 12 | 17 | $30

E 40s | 145 E. 49th St. (bet. Lexington & 3rd Aves.) | 646-497-1818
"Dependable pastas" and other Italiana lure Midtowners from their desks to this "unpretentious" trattoria; "friendly" (if "slow") service and "decent prices" add to the appeal, though it gets "loud" and "crowded at lunch."

Caffé on the Green ⊠ *Italian* 21 | 22 | 21 | $51

Bayside | 201-10 Cross Island Pkwy. (bet. Clearview Expwy. & Utopia Pkwy.) | Queens | 718-423-7272 | www.caffeonthegreen.com
Formerly home to Rudolph Valentino and Fiorello LaGuardia, this "charming" Bayside Italian's "lovely setting indoors and out" is "perfect for celebrating"; further justifying the "pricey" tabs are an "excellent" kitchen and service that's "so very nice."

Calle Ocho *Nuevo Latino* 22 | 22 | 19 | $46

W 80s | 446 Columbus Ave. (bet. 81st & 82nd Sts.) | 212-873-5025 | www.calleochonyc.com
Every bit as "boisterous" as its namesake street in Miami's Little Havana, this UWS Nuevo Latino entertains a "sexy", "young" crowd grazing on "pricey" but "creative" bites; factor in "spicy decor", "convivial" service and "exotic drinks", and you've got a "fun", high-"noise quotient" "night out."

CamaJe ☽ *American/French* ▽ 23 | 15 | 19 | $35

G Village | 85 MacDougal St. (bet. Bleecker & Houston Sts.) | 212-673-8184 | www.camaje.com
With the air of a "secret" find on an "out-of-the-way Paris street", this "terrific little" Village bistro's French-American fare comes via a "sweet" staff; it can be a "squeeze", but it's "romantic" for dining *à deux*; P.S. "try the cooking classes" or don a blindfold for one of their 'dark dining' events.

NEW Caminito ⊠ *Argentinean/Steak* — | — | — | M

Harlem | 1664 Park Ave. (bet. 117th & 118th Sts.) | 212-289-1343
Just about everything's grilled at this tiny, reasonable East Harlem hacienda serving up typical Argentinean steakhouse fare with wines from the motherland; although it's not a place to see and be seen, its

brick-lined interior and exterior Spanish tiles bring a welcome dash of charm to the area.

Campagnola ● *Italian*   23 | 17 | 21 | $66
E 70s | 1382 First Ave. (bet. 73rd & 74th Sts.) | 212-861-1102

At this East Side "old-school" Italian "scene", a "well-heeled clientele" (including a sprinkling of "celebrities") samples "simple" fare that's "delicious from start to finish"; "it pays to be a regular" when it comes to service, and as for the notable bill, it's "worth every penny" for the "people-watching" alone.

Canaletto *Italian*   ▽ 21 | 15 | 22 | $50
E 60s | 208 E. 60th St. (bet. 2nd & 3rd Aves.) | 212-317-9192

"Attentive" service and "delicious" "traditional" Northern Italian "chow" at "fair prices" have earned this Eastsider "standby" status; maybe there's "no wow factor" here, but to most it's just the kind of "relaxing" place a "neighborhood" eatery "should be."

Candle Cafe *Vegan/Vegetarian*   23 | 17 | 21 | $36
E 70s | 1307 Third Ave. (bet. 74th & 75th Sts.) | 212-472-0970

Candle 79 *Vegan/Vegetarian*
E 70s | 154 E. 79th St. (bet. Lexington & 3rd Aves.) | 212-537-7179
www.candlecafe.com

"Makes you proud to be veg" rave regulars of these "friendly" Upper Eastsiders purveying the "tastiest vegetarian/vegan food in the city"; they're places to "bring meat-eater friends without apologizing" – especially the Candle 79 location, whose "better decor" comes at only "slightly higher" rates.

Canyon Road *Southwestern*   19 | 16 | 16 | $36
E 70s | 1470 First Ave. (bet. 76th & 77th Sts.) | 212-734-1600 | www.arkrestaurants.com

Getting "happy" is the name of the game at this UES Southwestern "fiesta" filled with "young" partakers of "dynamite" margaritas that "do the trick" and "above-average" Tex-Mex; though often "crowded", its candlelit, O'Keeffe-worthy decor and "friendly" vibe make it an "excellent date" place.

Capital Grille *Steak*   23 | 22 | 23 | $63
E 40s | 155 E. 42nd St. (bet. Lexington & 3rd Aves.) | 212-953-2000 | www.thecapitalgrille.com

"Midtown business" types "power lunch" over "massive", "well-prepared" steaks at this chop chain link manned by staffers so "friendly", they "must be imported from the Atlanta home office"; quartered in "Philip Johnson's beautiful pyramid space" in the Chrysler Center, the "impressive" setting comes with matching prices.

Capsouto Frères *French*   24 | 23 | 24 | $55
TriBeCa | 451 Washington St. (Watts St.) | 212-966-4900 | www.capsoutofreres.com

"Visit Provence for a few hours" via this "out-of-the-way" TriBeCa "oasis" that "delights" with "nothing-flashy" French bistro classics "expertly done" (the "soufflés are a must"), "wonderful wines" and service to "make you feel like family"; its "lovely", "high-ceilinged" room works equally well for a "romantic" tête-à-tête or "brunch with friends."

	FOOD	DECOR	SERVICE	COST

Caracas Arepa Bar *Venezuelan* | 26 | 13 | 15 | $17 |

E Village | 93½ E. Seventh St. (bet. Ave. A & 1st Ave.) | 212-529-2314

Caracas to Go *Venezuelan*

E Village | 91 E. Seventh St. (1st Ave.) | 212-228-5062
www.caracasarepabar.com

This East Villager offers "something different", i.e. "wildly satisfying" Venezuelan street food, notably "dreamy", "addictive" stuffed arepas; eminently "affordable" prices ensure "the line never ceases" to get into its "closet-size" space – "thank goodness" there's "takeout."

Cara Mia *Italian* | 20 | 15 | 19 | $35 |

W 40s | 654 Ninth Ave. (bet. 45th & 46th Sts.) | 212-262-6767 | www.nycrg.com

Excelling at "fresh pastas" and other "reasonable" "basics", this "charming" Hell's Kitchen Italian can be a "tight fit", but "simpatico" staff and "value" pricing make it a "favorite" of locals and "pre-theater" eaters.

Caravan of Dreams *Vegan/Vegetarian* | ▽ 24 | 18 | 19 | $26 |

E Village | 405 E. Sixth St. (1st Ave.) | 212-254-1613 | www.caravanofdreams.net

"Healthy food" that's the stuff of dreams leaves even "meat eaters" "feeling satisfied" at this "hip" East Village kosher vegan, especially when washed down with "organic wine and beer"; the mood is "post-hippie earthy" (they even offer yoga classes), abetted by a "young, sincere" staff and prices as "wholesome" as the cooking.

Carl's Steaks *Cheese Steaks* | 22 | 6 | 13 | $11 |

Murray Hill | 507 Third Ave. (34th St.) | 212-696-5336 ◐
TriBeCa | 79 Chambers St. (bet. B'way & Church St.) | 212-566-2828
www.carlssteaks.com

"Forget the two-hour drive" – even City of Brotherly Love "natives" concede the "sublime cheese steaks" at these "cheap" Murray Hill-TriBeCa twins are just about "as good as the real" "South Philly" deal; "cramped" digs with "limited seating" and wadda ya want service have many getting it "to go."

☑ Carlyle Restaurant *French* | 21 | 26 | 24 | $77 |

E 70s | Carlyle Hotel | 35 E. 76th St. (Madison Ave.) | 212-744-1600 | www.thecarlyle.com

Impossibly "luxurious", this "elegant" UES hotel dining room has "dignified" diners "feeling pampered" thanks to "service of the first order" and "decadent" New French fare; the "tranquil", "handsome" space is ideal for "special occasions", so long as you wear a jacket (required at dinner) and come prepared to pay like "royalty"; N.B. your best buy is breakfast, brunch or afternoon tea.

☑ Carmine's *Italian* | 19 | 15 | 18 | $38 |

W 40s | 200 W. 44th St. (bet. B'way & 8th Ave.) | 212-221-3800 ◐
W 90s | 2450 Broadway (bet. 90th & 91st Sts.) | 212-362-2200
www.carminesnyc.com

"Bring your appetite" and "all your friends" to *mangia* "a lotta food" at these "glutton's delights" dishing up family-style Southern Italian "red sauce" at "bargain" rates; they're "overcrowded" and there's "always a wait", but "tourists" and "locals" alike consider that part of the "bustling", "party" vibe.

	FOOD	DECOR	SERVICE	COST

⚡ Carnegie Deli ◐≠ *Deli*   21 | 9 | 13 | $27

W 50s | 854 Seventh Ave. (55th St.) | 212-757-2245 | www.carnegiedeli.com
One sandwich could "feed an army" and the "classic" cheesecake "is the standard by which all others should be judged" at this Midtown "granddaddy of delis"; "true NYers" and "tourists" sit "shoulder-to-shoulder" in its "dumpy" quarters presided over by "fast", "surly servers" who've been on the job "since the beginning of time" – may this "quintessential NY" experience "never change."

NEW Carniceria *Steak*   - | - | - | M

Cobble Hill | 241 Smith St. (Douglass St.) | Brooklyn | 718-237-9100
Aside from the moose-antler lighting fixtures, little remains of Cobble Hill's short-lived Porchetta, whose owners have redone it as this low-key Latin American steakhouse; locals appreciate that its grass-fed beef (from chef Alex Garcia of Calle Ocho fame) comes for not a lot of green.

Carol's Cafe 🅢Ⓜ *Eclectic*   ▽ 26 | 18 | 21 | $56

Staten Island | 1571 Richmond Rd. (bet. Four Corners Rd. & Seaview Ave.) | 718-979-5600 | www.carolscafe.com
"'Delightful' best describes" chef Carol Frazzetta and her "ever-changing menu" of "imaginative" Eclectic dishes "served with TLC" in a "well-appointed" space; ardent admires insist "it's worth a trip" to SI, though the "Manhattan quality" comes complete with Midtown prices.

Casa 🅢 *Brazilian*   ▽ 22 | 18 | 20 | $40

W Village | 72 Bedford St. (Commerce St.) | 212-366-9410 | www.casarestaurant.com
Having mastered the art of "well-done simplicity", this "unassuming" Village Brazilian boasts a "cozy, casual" ambiance and "helpful", "charming" staff; however, it's the "strong caipirinhas", "terrific" "homestyle" dishes and moderate tabs that "make you want to eat here" again and again.

Casa Mono ◐ *Spanish*   25 | 18 | 20 | $50

Gramercy | 52 Irving Pl. (17th St.) | 212-253-2773
Muy delicioso small plates and "superb wines" star at Mario Batali's "better-than-Barcelona" Gramercy Spaniard; whether you "sit at the bar and watch the chefs work" or squeeze into the "sardine can"–size dining area, "be prepared to wait" for a seat and bring plenty of pesos because those "flavorful" bites "add up."

Cascina ◐ *Italian*   18 | 15 | 17 | $41

W 40s | 647 Ninth Ave. (bet. 45th & 46th Sts.) | 212-245-4422 | www.cascina.com
They sure "know how to cook" at this "reliable" Hell's Kitchen Italian, a "great pre-theater choice" for "moderately priced" pizza and pasta paired with "fine wines" from its own vineyard in The Boot; the "cozy", "rustic" space can get "crowded", but no matter what they'll "get you to the show on time."

Casimir ◐ *French*   19 | 18 | 15 | $36

E Village | 103-105 Ave. B (bet. 6th & 7th Sts.) | 212-358-9683 | www.casimirrestaurant.com
A great "first-date place", this "straight-out-of-Paris" Alphabet City bistro "sets the mood" with "dark", "romantic" atmosphere and a

"lovely garden"; the "wonderful" French fare comes with "attitude" as an unwanted "garnish", but "bargain prices" compensate.

NEW Catch 22 *Argentinean/Italian* — | — | — | M

Williamsburg | 312 Graham Ave. (Ainslie St.) | Brooklyn | 718-782-3199 | www.gocatch22.com

Catering to both the Neapolitan and Latin communities that straddle Williamsburg's Grand Street, chef Alex Garcia (Calle Ocho) crafts a beef-heavy Argentinean-Italian fusion menu at this newcomer; its old-fashioned decor isn't aimed at the area's younger crowd, but the varied sangrias hold multigenerational appeal.

Caviar Russe *American* 24 | 22 | 23 | $87

E 50s | 538 Madison Ave., 2nd fl. (bet. 54th & 55th Sts.) | 212-980-5908 | www.caviarrusse.com

To dine "like a Romanov", you only need to go one flight up at this Midtown "heaven for caviar lovers", where those "amazing" eggs and "outstanding sushi" are served in a "jewel-box" setting by "attentive" pros; while it's priced for "royals", even an "average Joe can afford" the prix fixe deals, and it's always a good bet for "special celebrations."

☑ Cávo ◐ *Greek* 21 | 26 | 19 | $42

Astoria | 42-18 31st Ave. (bet. 42nd & 43rd Sts.) | Queens | 718-721-1001 | www.cavocafelounge.com

An Astoria "surprise", this "modern Greek" scores points with its "sexy", "high-ceilinged" space, three-story waterfall and "beautiful" garden that "feels like Europe"; maybe the service "could be better", but the food is right up there with the "after-hours" "bar scene."

Cebu ◐ *Continental* ▽ 21 | 17 | 18 | $37

Bay Ridge | 8801 Third Ave. (88th St.) | Brooklyn | 718-492-5095

The Bay Ridge "after-hours crowd" frequents this "quaint" Continental "hideaway" for its solid "late-night" eats (open till 3 AM); the setup includes a bar area perfect for "people-watching" and an "intimate back room with fireplace"; P.S. it's also "worth a visit" for weekend brunch.

Celeste ⊄ *Italian* 24 | 11 | 16 | $33

W 80s | 502 Amsterdam Ave. (bet. 84th & 85th Sts.) | 212-874-4559

"Look for the crowd outside" to spot this "tiny" UWS Neapolitan famed for its "cheap" yet celestial fare; despite "no reservations", "long waits", "elbow-to-elbow tables" and "rushed" service, most surveyors "love it" all the same.

Cellini ☒ *Italian* 21 | 18 | 22 | $56

E 50s | 65 E. 54th St. (bet. Madison & Park Aves.) | 212-751-1555 | www.cellinirestaurant.com

Dealmakers "leave happy" from this "old faithful" for Midtown "business lunches", where "reliable", "old-school" Northern Italian fare is ferried by a "welcoming" staff; the decor's "dated" but "soothing", and "quiet" dinner hours can even be romantic – at least until the bill comes.

Cendrillon ☒ *Asian/Filipino* ▽ 20 | 17 | 20 | $40

SoHo | 45 Mercer St. (bet. Broome & Grand Sts.) | 212-343-9012 | www.cendrillon.com

"Intriguing", "flavorful" Filipino-Asian dishes "prepared with care" keep fans "coming back" to this SoHo "gem"; a "comfy", "low-key" setting and service that "makes you feel like family" have followers wondering why it's among the area's "best-kept secrets."

Centolire *Italian*   20 | 22 | 19 | $59

E 80s | 1167 Madison Ave. (bet. 85th & 86th Sts.) | 212-734-7711 | www.centolire.ypguides.net

Eastsiders get "dressed up" for "special-occasion" visits to Pino Luongo's "cut-above" Italian set in an "elegant townhouse"; the "upscale" Tuscan fare, "formal" service and glass elevator ride to the "lovely" upstairs dining room can run up, but the $24.50 "prix fixe lunch is a bargain."

Centovini *Italian*   ∇ 21 | 22 | 20 | $55

SoHo | 25 W. Houston St. (bet. Greene & Mercer Sts.) | 212-219-2113 | www.centovininyc.com

From the owners of I Trulli and the design gallery Moss comes this SoHo enoteca where "cool", "aggressively modern" decor meets first-class casual Italian fare paired with a "winning wine list"; it's "expensive", but from the "cordial service" to the "trendy" vibe, it's "right on the money."

Centrico *Mexican*   20 | 18 | 19 | $46

TriBeCa | 211 W. Broadway (Franklin St.) | 212-431-0700 | www.myriadrestaurantgroup.com

"Satisfy your Mexican craving" at Drew Nieporent's "much-needed" TriBeCan, where chef Aarón Sanchez's "vibrant", "nuevo" dishes are chased with "killer" margaritas; service is mostly "accommodating", and for those who find the interior "a little sterile", in summer there's always the outside seating.

NEW Centro Vinoteca ● *Italian*   - | - | - | M

W Village | 74 Seventh Ave. S. (Barrow St.) | 212-367-7470 | www.centrovinoteca.com

New to the bustling Seventh Avenue strip, this midpriced West Village Italian is luring a chic crowd with its small plates (called *piccolini*), as well as heartier pastas and such, via a former Felidia chef; the white-tiled space is warmed by vintage chandeliers and a curved wooden bar, and there's also a window-lined second-floor dining room.

'Cesca *Italian*   23 | 21 | 21 | $58

W 70s | 164 W. 75th St. (Amsterdam Ave.) | 212-787-6300 | www.cescanyc.com

At this "pricey" but "wildly popular" Westsider, "sumptuous", "hearty rustic" Southern Italian fare "warms the soul", as does the "inviting", "grown-up" interior (it's "roomy" enough to "actually have a private conversation") and "gracious" service; in a word, "bravo!"; N.B. Tom Valenti is no longer involved.

Chadwick's *American*   22 | 19 | 22 | $42

Bay Ridge | 8822 Third Ave. (89th St.) | Brooklyn | 718-833-9855 | www.chadwicksny.com

This "friendly" Bay Ridge American remains a neighborhood "favorite" for superior steaks and seafood enjoyed amid "homey", "publike" environs; it "caters to an older crowd" with specials like the $20.95 early-bird, but there's also a "decent bar scene" with an appealing "everyone-knows-everyone" vibe.

	FOOD	DECOR	SERVICE	COST

Chance *Pan-Asian*
▽ 21 | 18 | 20 | $32

Boerum Hill | 223 Smith St. (Butler St.) | Brooklyn | 718-242-1515 |
www.chancecuisine.com

At this "affordable" Boerum Hill Pan-Asian, "well-done" dishes are served in a "cool", modern space starring a "hypnotic waterfall behind the bar"; most find the service and back garden "lovely", but are particularly drawn to the $6.00 lunch deal.

⚡ Chanterelle *French*
27 | 26 | 27 | $119

TriBeCa | 2 Harrison St. (Hudson St.) | 212-966-6960 |
www.chanterellenyc.com

"Damn near perfect", David and Karen Waltuck's TriBeCa French "benchmark" keeps "getting better with age", providing a "regal dining experience" across "all categories"; "every bite of every course is heavenly", while the "elegant", "understated" interior is perfect for "special occasions" with "spot-on", "balletic" service to match; it's "oh so pricey", but "worth every dollar" to most; N.B. dinner is prix fixe only, but ordering à la carte is an option at Thursday-Saturday lunch.

Chanto *Japanese*
▽ 22 | 21 | 22 | $65

G Village | 133 Seventh Ave. S. (bet. Charles & W. 10th Sts.) | 212-463-8686 |
www.chantonyc.com

Making a strong "first impression" with its "contemporary" space spanning four "dramatic" levels, this Greenwich Village "haute" Japanese is the first stateside foray of an Osaka-based chain; its "flair" extends to the "refreshing" "fusion" fare and "helpful" service, and is priced accordingly.

Charles' Southern-Style Kitchen *Southern*
▽ 24 | 4 | 14 | $18

Harlem | 2839 Frederick Douglass Blvd. (151st St.) |
212-926-4313 Ⓜ

NEW Harlem | 308 Lenox Ave. (bet. 125th & 126th Sts.) |
212-722-7727 ●₱

"Skip a meal before" hitting this pair of "genuine" Harlem soul fooders in order to take best advantage of the "amazing" "bargain" all-you-can-eat buffet; the staff shows "Southern hospitality", but since the decor's "not much to look at" "takeout" might be the route to go.

Chat 'n Chew ● *American*
16 | 13 | 14 | $22

Union Sq | 10 E. 16th St. (bet. 5th Ave. & Union Sq. W.) | 212-243-1616 |
www.chatnchewnyc.com

As a fallback for "stick-to-your-ribs" "comfort" classics in "huge portions", this "funky", "family-friendly" Union Square American may be worth considering; the "staff isn't making a career" in service and the "hokey" decor is of the "knickknack-filled basement" variety, but it definitely "won't break the bank."

NEW Chat Noir *French*
18 | 16 | 19 | $52

E 60s | 22 E. 66th St. (bet. 5th & Madison Aves.) | 212-794-2428 |
www.bistrochatnoir.com

Off to a "promising start", this UES French 'gastro-bistro' is drawing "great-looking people" to its "hidden" townhouse lair manned by a "welcoming staff"; as a result, despite prices that "reflect the high-rent locale", most consider themselves lucky to cross its path and nab a seat.

	FOOD	DECOR	SERVICE	COST

Chef Ho's Peking Duck Grill *Chinese* `22 | 14 | 19 | $29`

E 80s | 1720 Second Ave. (bet. 89th & 90th Sts.) | 212-348-9444
Upper Eastsiders wonder "why go Downtown" when you can get "real-deal" Chinese for "reasonable" rates at this "local favorite" where the namesake dish is a "must-get"; its "quiet dining room", though a bit "drab", is "nice enough for an evening out" and the service is "pro" – hey, "it's packed for a reason."

NEW Chennai *Indian/Vegetarian* `_ | _ | _ | I`

E 80s | 1663 First Ave. (bet. 86th & 87th Sts.) | 212-831-1114
From the owners of Yorkville's Dakshin comes this unassuming white-tablecloth kosher vegetarian Indian; its low-cost menu is varied enough that diners shouldn't miss the meat as they dine in pleasant, exposed-brick environs.

Chennai Garden M *Indian/Vegetarian* `21 | 10 | 14 | $21`

Gramercy | 129 E. 27th St. (bet. Lexington Ave. & Park Ave. S.) | 212-689-1999
Diners "don't miss the meat" at this "solid" Curry Hill vegetarian kosher "must-try" for "South Indian classics"; though "service varies" and the decor is "nothing special", you get "great bang for your buck", particularly the $6.95 all-you-can-eat lunch buffet.

NEW Cheryl's Global Soul M *Soul Food* `∇ 22 | 21 | 20 | $28`

Prospect Heights | 236 Underhill Ave. (bet. Prospect Pl. & St. Marks Ave.) | Brooklyn | 347-529-2855
For soul food that "rocks your soul", plus "delicious baked goods", try TV personality Cheryl Smith's "excellent" Prospect Heights newcomer; "innovative", modern decor, "welcoming" service and praiseworthy prices make it an ideal "addition to the 'hood."

Chestnut M *American* `23 | 17 | 21 | $40`

Carroll Gardens | 271 Smith St. (bet. Degraw & Sackett Sts.) | Brooklyn | 718-243-0049 | www.chestnutonsmith.com
"Original", "well-prepared" seasonal dishes and "accommodating", "knowledgeable" service make this Carroll Gardens New American "stand out"; locals "feel right at home" in its "modern", "unpretentious" digs and "pretty garden", and the "deal" of a Tuesday–Wednesday prix fixe keeps 'em coming back.

Chez Jacqueline *French* `18 | 16 | 19 | $43`

G Village | 72 MacDougal St. (bet. Bleecker & Houston Sts.) | 212-505-0727
"Like a trip to" the "French country", this "sweet little" Gallic Villager offers bistro classics "done well" for a "fair price"; the "gracious" staff and "cozy", "relaxing" atmosphere ensure it remains a "neighborhood anchor."

Chez Josephine ● M *French* `20 | 21 | 21 | $50`

W 40s | 414 W. 42nd St. (bet. 9th & 10th Aves.) | 212-594-1925 | www.chezjosephine.com
You can "make a night of theater last two hours longer" at this "homage" to Josephine Baker overseen by her adopted son, "host-with-the-most" Jean-Claude; the decor is "bordello-romantic" meets "gay Paree" (*avec* "dynamite piano player"), the French bistro fare is "solid" and, *meilleur de tous,* you'll likely "leave with a story."

	FOOD	DECOR	SERVICE	COST

NEW Chez Lola *French* | - | - | - | M |

Clinton Hill | 387 Myrtle Ave. (bet. Clermont & Vanderbilt Aves.) | Brooklyn | 718-858-1484

The younger sibling of Fort Greene's Chez Oskar, this new French bistro is helping gentrify Clinton Hill's infamous 'Murder Avenue'; locals can't refuse the moderately priced eclectic menu served in sexy, art deco-ish digs, and there's a sizable heated garden to boot.

Chez Napoléon 🗷 *French* | 20 | 13 | 20 | $45 |

W 50s | 365 W. 50th St. (bet. 8th & 9th Aves.) | 212-265-6980 | www.cheznapoleon.com

"Old-fashioned" "Left Bank" charm evokes "times past" for the many longtime customers of this petite Theater District "classic"; its "well-prepared" French cooking, "warm" service, "old-school prices" and even its "dated" decor reinforce that feeling – loyalists laud "long may it last."

Chez Oskar ⏺ *French* | ▽ 19 | 18 | 17 | $29 |

Fort Greene | 211 DeKalb Ave. (Adelphi St.) | Brooklyn | 718-852-6250 | www.chezoskar.com

This "reliable" Fort Greene French bistro has become a local "favorite" thanks to its "tasty" classics ("amazing brunch"), "hip vibe" and low tabs; service can be overly "mellow", but that affords time to enjoy the "cozy" interior and "outdoor sidewalk seats."

Chiam Chinese Cuisine *Chinese* | 23 | 19 | 22 | $44 |

E 40s | 160 E. 48th St. (bet. Lexington & 3rd Aves.) | 212-371-2323

It's no wonder that this "high-end" Midtown Chinese "has held up over the years" given its "marvelous" food, "excellent" wine list, "superior" service" and "lovely space"; favored by "corporate" types, it's especially "bustling" at lunch.

Chianti 🅼 *Italian* | 21 | 17 | 19 | $39 |

Bay Ridge | 8530 Third Ave. (86th St.) | Brooklyn | 718-921-6300 | www.chianti86.com

"Fantastic family-style fare like mama used to cook" makes this "boisterous" midpriced Bay Ridge Italian "great for group" dining; the "casual" atmosphere and "delightful staff" keep "locals" "coming back for more" and more.

Chickpea ⏺ *Mideastern* | 19 | 8 | 13 | $10 |

E Village | 210 E. 14th St. (bet. 2nd & 3rd Aves.) | 212-228-3445
E Village | 23 Third Ave. (bet. 9th St. & St. Marks Pl.) | 212-254-1187

"Tasty" Middle Eastern "temptations" are the draw at this "quick, cheap" East Village duo; "pita fresh from the oven" and "really good falafel" particularly "hit the spot" "late-night", but just "don't expect much" decorwise – most maintain it's "better for takeout."

ChikaLicious 🅼 *Dessert* | 24 | 17 | 23 | $22 |

E Village | 203 E. 10th St. (bet. 1st & 2nd Aves.) | 212-995-9511 | www.chikalicious.com

To reach "sweet-tooth heaven", chick out this "exquisite" East Village dessert specialist where "edible art" takes the form of "oh-so-'licious" three-course, fixed-price lineups with optional wine pairings, served by a "stellar" staff; there's often a "line out the door", but "addicts" assure it's "worth the wait."

	FOOD	DECOR	SERVICE	COST

NEW Chiles & Chocolate
Oaxacan Kitchen *Mexican* ▽ 18 | 13 | 15 | $28

Park Slope | 54 Seventh Ave. (bet. Lincoln & St. John's Pls.) | Brooklyn | 718-230-7700

It's "just what Park Slope needed" enthuse eaters at this "delightful" Mexican arrival where the "authentic Oaxacan" menu is centered on the namesake ingredients (think "outrageous mole"); it manages to be both "delicious and inexpensive" – and complaints about its "minute space" have been answered with the post-Survey addition of an all-weather patio.

Chimichurri Grill ● *Argentinean/Steak* 21 | 14 | 20 | $46

W 40s | 606 Ninth Ave. (bet. 43rd & 44th Sts.) | 212-586-8655 | www.chimichurrigrill.com

You "can't beat the beef" at this Hell's Kitchen Argentinean where "big" steaks bathed in the "wonderful" eponymous sauce come in "cramped" quarters; still, "charming service" and not-too-bad tabs have most calling it an "excellent pre-theater" choice.

China Chalet *Chinese* 19 | 14 | 19 | $27

Financial District | 47 Broadway (bet. Exchange Pl. & Morris St.) | 212-943-4380
Financial District | 90 Broad St. (Stone St.) | 212-747-9099 🗷
Staten Island | 4326 Amboy Rd. (Armstrong Ave.) | 718-984-8044 ●
www.chinachalet.com

For three decades the "go-to Chinese lunch spots" for "Wall Street" workers, these affordable Financial District "survivors" (with a Staten Island outpost) "never fail to satisfy"; service is "pleasant" too, but given decor that's "a bit faded", many go the "takeout" or "fast delivery" route.

NEW China de Puebla *Mexican* - | - | - | M

Harlem | 3143 Broadway (LaSalle St.) | 212-222-8666 | www.chinadepuebla.com

As the name suggests, this Harlem newcomer offers Asian-accented Mexican cuisine, with a decor palette that pays homage to its native country with white walls, red cushions and a green-accented oak bar; moderate prices and artfully prepared cocktails abet the festive vibe.

China Fun ● *Chinese* 16 | 10 | 13 | $23

E 60s | 1221 Second Ave. (64th St.) | 212-752-0810
W 70s | 246 Columbus Ave. (bet. 71st & 72nd Sts.) | 212-580-1516

Maybe these "no-frills" crosstown Chinese have been slipping, but they remain "quick and cheap", if "not exactly gourmet", and they also serve sushi; "they know how to turn the tables", so they're good for a "quick pre-movie or weeknight meal."

China Grill *Asian* 22 | 20 | 18 | $55

W 50s | 60 W. 53rd St. (bet. 5th & 6th Aves.) | 212-333-7788 | www.chinagrillmgt.com

This "great big" Midtown "staple" for Asian fare "hasn't lost its lus-ter", attracting a "steady parade" of "corporate" types for "pricey" "power" meals, plus a smattering of "tourists"; the lure is "sophisti-cated" food and drink that's "perfect for groups" and enjoyed in "lively", "noisy" environs.

	FOOD	DECOR	SERVICE	COST

Chinatown Brasserie ⏺ *Chinese* | 21 | 23 | 19 | $49 |

NoHo | 380 Lafayette St. (Great Jones St.) | 212-533-7000 | www.chinatownbrasserie.com

At this "trendy" NoHo Chinese, the "upscale" menu runs the gamut from "excellent" renditions of standards like Peking duck and BBQ ribs to all-day dim sum; true, it comes at "double the price of Chinatown", but if you factor in the "grandiose", "Shanghai-glam" interior, it's probably "worth the premium."

Chin Chin ⏺ *Chinese* | 22 | 18 | 21 | $48 |

E 40s | 216 E. 49th St. (bet. 2nd & 3rd Aves.) | 212-888-4555 | www.chinchinny.com

For "gourmet Chinese" in Midtown, you can't do much better than this veteran whose fare is "excellent no matter what the dish", and served in "stylish", "calm" digs; maybe it's "pricey", but most are "happy to pay."

Chino's *Asian* | ▽ 22 | 15 | 19 | $30 |

Gramercy | 173 Third Ave. (bet. 16th & 17th Sts.) | 212-598-1200 | www.chinosnyc.com

It's "fun to share" at this "delicious" Gramercy Asian specializing in "interesting" small plates and "creative" cocktails; "friendly" service and "value" pricing (e.g. the "bargain $12 lunch special") make the "tiny", "cramped" setting easy to overlook.

Chipotle *Mexican* | 18 | 10 | 14 | $12 |

E 40s | 150 E. 44th St. (bet. Lexington & 3rd Aves.) | 212-682-9860
E 50s | 150 E. 52nd St. (bet. Lexington & 3rd Aves.) | 212-755-9754
E Village | 19 St. Marks Pl. (bet. 2nd & 3rd Aves.) | 212-529-4502
Financial District | 2 Broadway (Whitehall St.) | 212-344-0941
Flatiron | 680 Sixth Ave. (bet. 21st & 22nd Sts.) | 212-206-3781
Garment District | 304 W. 34th St. (8th Ave.) | 212-268-4197
G Village | 55 E. Eighth St. (bet. B'way & University Pl.) | 212-982-3081
SoHo | 200 Varick St. (bet. Houston & King Sts.) | 646-336-6264
W 40s | 9 W. 42nd St. (bet. 5th & 6th Aves.) | 212-354-6760
Brooklyn Heights | 185 Montague St. (Court St.) | Brooklyn | 718-243-9109
www.chipotle.com

It "used to be owned by McDonald's", but this "assembly-line Mexican" chain is "not your typical fast-fooder" given its "comparatively healthy" "choose-your-own" ingredients; at lunch it's "bustling with business folks" in need of a "burrito fix", so expect "lines out the door."

ChipShop *British* | 18 | 13 | 16 | $20 |

Brooklyn Heights | 129 Atlantic Ave. (bet. Clinton & Henry Sts.) | Brooklyn | 718-855-7775
Park Slope | 383 Fifth Ave. (bet. 6th & 7th Sts.) | Brooklyn | 718-832-7701 ⏘
www.chipshopnyc.com

British expats "hankering for" a taste of home hit these "friendly" Park Slope–Brooklyn Heights chippies, where the "artery-clogging" fare (from "fish 'n' chips" to "deep-fried Twinkies") goes well with "imported" suds; it's as "authentic as you can get", but "just don't tell your internist."

Chiyono ⏺Ⓜ *Japanese* | ▽ 23 | 15 | 19 | $32 |

E Village | 328 E. Sixth St. (bet. 1st & 2nd Aves.) | 212-673-3984 | www.chiyono.com

Chef-owner Chiyono Mirano's "Japanese home cooking" sans sushi "dazzles" at her "unique" East Village namesake; the "friendly com-

| | FOOD | DECOR | SERVICE | COST |

"munal" setup and "hospitable service" lend "charm" to a "small" space, ditto the low prices.

Chocolate Room, The Ⓜ *Dessert* — 25 | 19 | 20 | $17
Park Slope | 86 Fifth Ave. (bet. St. Marks Pl. & Warren St.) | Brooklyn | 718-783-2900 | www.thechocolateroombrooklyn.com

"Talk about dying and going to heaven" – this Park Slope dessert destination presents a "chocoholic's dream" menu of "cocoas" and "sweets", plus "wines to drink with them"; its "boîtelike" interior is ideal for "cozying up with a date."

Cho Dang Gol *Korean* — ▽ 21 | 15 | 16 | $28
Garment District | 55 W. 35th St. (bet. 5th & 6th Aves.) | 212-695-8222 | www.chodanggolny.com

So dang "good" is what satisfied samplers say about the "fresh" "housemade" tofu at this Garment District Korean, where the "authentic" specialties can be "tough to decipher" without help from the "pleasant" staff; low prices seal the deal.

Chola *Indian* — 23 | 17 | 20 | $37
E 50s | 232 E. 58th St. (bet. 2nd & 3rd Aves.) | 212-688-4619 | www.fineindiandining.com

The "flavorful" Indian fare will bring you "closer to Nirvana" according to acolytes of this "authentic" Eastsider; "couldn't-be-nicer" service plus a "popular" $13.95 lunch "buffet bargain" are two more reasons it's a "favorite."

Chop't Creative Salad *American* — 20 | 9 | 14 | $13
E 50s | 165 E. 52nd St. (bet. Lexington & 3rd Aves.) | 212-421-2300 Ⓢ
E 50s | 60 E. 56th St. (bet. Madison & Park Aves.) | 212-750-2467 Ⓢ
Union Sq | 24 E. 17th St. (bet. B'way & 5th Ave.) | 646-336-5523 www.choptsalad.com

You can "invent your own" leafy creation at these "quick" salad shops boasting lots of "fresh ingredients" and "tasty dressings" "chopped to perfection"; though some suggest "prices should be chop't too", the fact that it's "mobbed at lunch" speaks for itself.

Chow Bar *Asian Fusion* — 21 | 17 | 18 | $40
W Village | 230 W. Fourth St. (W. 10th St.) | 212-633-2212

Thanks to its "ingenious" Asian Fusion menu and "creative" cocktails, this West Villager "still feels fresh"; the "vibrant" atmosphere, central "location" and moderate prices draw "young" types who go both for "group" get-togethers and "dates."

Christos Steak House ❶ *Steak* — 22 | 17 | 21 | $57
Astoria | 41-08 23rd Ave. (41st St.) | Queens | 718-777-8400 | www.christossteakhouse.com

The "melt-in-your-mouth meat" plus appetizers and sides "with a Greek twist" at this Astoria surf 'n' turfer stand up to the Manhattan competition; though it may be "pricey", most maintain "you get what you pay for."

Churrascaria Plataforma ❶ *Brazilian* — 23 | 19 | 21 | $67
W 40s | 316 W. 49th St. (bet. 8th & 9th Aves.) | 212-245-0505 | www.churrascariaplataforma.com

(continued)

Churrascaria TriBeCa ◑ *Brazilian*

TriBeCa | 221 W. Broadway (bet. Franklin & White Sts.) | 212-925-6969 | www.churrascariatribeca.com

"Go hungry" and "wear loose pants" to these "all-you-can-eat", prix fixe–only Brazilian meatfests where "sword"-happy staffers serve "skewer after skewer" of "superb" cuts to a "rapacious clientele"; the "bustling" milieu is most "fun for groups", and though the bill can run up, your "food coma" keeps you from caring.

Cibo *American/Italian*   20 | 18 | 20 | $45

E 40s | 767 Second Ave. (41st St.) | 212-681-1616

"Well-prepared" Tuscan–New American fare and a "cheery staff" have made a "neighborhood classic" of this East Midtowner; for "business lunches" or "pleasant" dinners, its "comfortable" space and "bargain prix fixe" deals produce reliably "satisfying" experiences.

Cilantro ◑ *Southwestern*   17 | 14 | 17 | $28

E 70s | 1321 First Ave. (71st St.) | 212-537-4040
E 80s | 1712 Second Ave. (bet. 88th & 89th Sts.) | 212-722-4242
www.cilantronyc.com

"Crunchy chips", "spicy salsa" and "marvelous margaritas" make these UES family-style Southwesterners a good bet (especially given their big portions and fair prices); Monday's $10 fajita special – "Holy frijoles, Batman!" – keeps the neighbors coming.

Cipriani Dolci ◑ *Italian*   18 | 20 | 16 | $49

E 40s | Grand Central | West Balcony (42nd St. & Vanderbilt Ave.) | 212-973-0999 | www.cipriani.com

The "impressive view" overlooking Grand Central Station makes this "sophisticated" balcony Italian a no-brainer for "drinks" or a "convenient" meal "en route to a train"; though it's a "little pricey", its "elegant setting" is worth visiting at least once, especially with "visitors" in tow.

Cipriani Downtown ◑ *Italian*   20 | 19 | 18 | $67

SoHo | 376 W. Broadway (bet. Broome & Spring Sts.) | 212-343-0999 | www.cipriani.com

"It's all about" the "models, moguls" and other "famous faces" at this "super-glam" SoHo Italian where "beautiful" types come to sip "Bellinis to die for" and "play, not eat" (though the fare is "delish"); maybe it's "more show than substance", with prices to match, but as a place to "see and be seen" it's hard to beat.

Circus *Brazilian*   20 | 19 | 20 | $54

E 60s | 132 E. 61st St. (bet. Lexington & Park Aves.) | 212-223-2965 | www.circusrestaurante.com

A "departure from the same-old", this "upbeat" East Side Brazilian plies "imaginative" dishes and "must-have caipirinhas" in "cheerful" circus-like digs; with "accommodating" service and tabs "reasonable" for the zip code, "well-heeled" regulars wonder why it's not better known.

Citrus Bar & Grill *Asian/Nuevo Latino*   20 | 19 | 17 | $39

W 70s | 320 Amsterdam Ave. (75th St.) | 212-595-0500 | www.citrusnyc.com

"Young" things who pack this "upbeat" UWS Asian–Nuevo Latino say it's "awesome" to find "margaritas and sushi" in one "cool" place; the edibles, service and setting are "decent" enough, but most come for the "party" powered by "potent" cocktails and "outdoor" seating.

City Bakery *Bakery*

21 | 13 | 13 | $19

Flatiron | 3 W. 18th St. (bet. 5th & 6th Aves.) | 212-366-1414 | www.thecitybakery.com

Its buffet/salad bar is a "knockout", but for most it's "all about" the "decadent" desserts at Maury Rubin's Flatiron "winner"; it would all be "divine" but for the "overcrowded", underdecorated bi-level "cafeteria-style" setting and "sticker shock at the register."

City Crab & Seafood Co. *Seafood*

17 | 14 | 16 | $42

Flatiron | 235 Park Ave. S. (19th St.) | 212-529-3800 | www.citycrabnyc.com

Though crabby critics feel it's "faded", this "lively" Flatiron "seafood joint" seems to do swimmingly thanks to its "ample portions" of "fresh" fin fare; "modest prices" for the genre ensure it remains a "busy" "port of call."

City Hall ⓢ *Seafood/Steak*

21 | 21 | 20 | $54

TriBeCa | 131 Duane St. (bet. Church St. & W. B'way) | 212-227-7777 | www.cityhallnyc.com

"Bankers, brokers and barristers" blatently broach "business" at Henry Meer's "masculine" TriBeCa surf 'n' turf "classic"; sure, it's costly to be part of "power at play", but the place is "quality" top-to-bottom, and the "soaring space" exudes "old NY."

City Lobster & Crab Co. *Seafood*

18 | 15 | 16 | $49

W 40s | 121 W. 49th St. (bet. 6th & 7th Aves.) | 212-354-1717 | www.citylobster.com

A "well-situated" standby for "business lunches" or "pre-theater", this "decent" Radio City–area seafooder serves up "fresh" shore fare at "reasonable" prices; though service is just "ok" and the feel a bit "cookie cutter", it fills the bill for a "decent" "Midtown bite."

Clinton St. Baking Co. *American*

24 | 14 | 18 | $25

LES | 4 Clinton St. (bet. Houston & Stanton Sts.) | 646-602-6263 | www.greatbiscuits.com

It feels like "the whole city" lines up for brunch at this "homey" LES bakery/cafe, where "pancakes to die for" and other "comfort staples" keep wait times "crazy" on weekends; service is "friendly" despite the "mob", but for the "crowd"-averse there's always less-busy dinner.

Coals ⓢ *Pizza*

▽ 22 | 17 | 19 | $19

Bronx | 1888 Eastchester Rd. (Morris Park Ave.) | 718-823-7002 | www.coalspizza.com

"Every pizza-lover should know about" this "unique", "friendly" Bronx joint, which "breaks the mold" with "grilled" pies (sounds strange, but "it works") served "quick"; the "limited" but "delicious" menu also includes soups, panini and such, washed down with "first-rate" brews.

Coco Pazzo *Italian*

22 | 20 | 21 | $66

E 70s | 23 E. 74th St. (bet. 5th & Madison Aves.) | 212-794-0205 | www.cocopazzonewyork.ypguides.net

"Refined" and "very UES", this Northern Italian "perennial favorite" draws a "mature" mix of "locals" and "celebs" for a taste of "old NY glamour" and Mark Strausman's "elegant" cooking; its "pleasant" space is manned by a surprisingly "unstuffy" staff, and though it's "pricey", the regulars couldn't care less.

Cocotte Ⓜ *American/French* ▽ 20 | 18 | 18 | $36
Park Slope | 337 Fifth Ave. (4th St.) | Brooklyn | 718-832-6848 | www.cocotterestaurant.com

Considered one of Park Slope's "gems" among those in-the-know, this "cozy" French–New American remains a "best-kept secret" despite its fine fare and service; "reasonable prices" (especially on "bargain" "two-for-one Thursdays") are the crowning touch.

Coffee Shop ☻ *American/Brazilian* 15 | 12 | 11 | $29
Union Sq | 29 Union Sq. W. (16th St.) | 212-243-7969

This "bustling" Union Square "institution" is best known for its "reliable" Brazilian-American grub, "campy" "diner-style" decor and "snooty", "model"-turned-waitress staff; maybe it's not quite the "scene" it used to be, but it stays "packed" into "the wee hours."

Colors Ⓜ *Eclectic* 19 | 19 | 21 | $49
E Village | 417 Lafayette St. (bet. Astor Pl. & 4th St.) | 212-777-8443 | www.colors-nyc.com

The idea behind this East Villager was to establish a "cooperative owned by the staff" (many of them "former Windows on the World" workers), and their "investment shows" in the thoughtful "global" menu and "sincere service" ; a "warm" deco space and Public Theater–handy location make it doubly "worth a visit."

Columbus Bakery *Bakery* 18 | 11 | 10 | $17
W 80s | 474 Columbus Ave. (bet. 82nd & 83rd Sts.) | 212-724-6880 | www.arkrestaurants.com

"Terrific" baked goods and "healthy" lunch options ensure this Westside bakery/cafe is usually "packed"; despite "bumper-to-bumper strollers", a "confusing ordering system" and "service without a smile", there's no shortage of fans.

Comfort Diner *Diner* 16 | 12 | 15 | $21
E 40s | 214 E. 45th St. (bet. 2nd & 3rd Aves.) | 212-867-4555
Flatiron | 25 W. 23rd St. (bet. 5th & 6th Aves.) | 212-741-1010
www.comfortdiner.com

"Truly comforting", this "time-capsule" twosome dishes up a "slice of Americana" via its "large" menu of low-priced "home-cooking" classics and "kitschy" "'50s decor"; enough enjoy the "nostalgia" trip that it's "terribly busy on weekends."

⊠ Compass *American* 22 | 22 | 22 | $58
W 70s | 208 W. 70th St. (bet. Amsterdam & West End Aves.) | 212-875-8600 | www.compassrestaurant.com

"Pointed in the right direction" under a "talented" new chef, this "attractive", "modern" UWS New American turns out "creative", "delicious" fare at "reasonable" prices "for the quality"; the "gracious" service also "doesn't disappoint", ditto the convenience to Lincoln Center.

Congee ☻ *Chinese* 21 | 14 | 14 | $20
Chinatown | 98 Bowery (bet. Grand & Hester Sts.) | 212-965-5028 | www.congeeinc98.com

(continued)

(continued)

Congee Bowery ◐ *Chinese*
LES | 207 Bowery (bet. Delancey & Rivington Sts.) | 212-766-2828

Congee Village ◐ *Chinese*
LES | 100 Allen St. (bet. Broome & Delancey Sts.) | 212-941-1818

The "secret's out" about the "amazing" namesake rice porridge at these separately owned LES-Chinatown Cantonese whose committed converts consider "crazy lines" and "noisy, crowded" conditions well "worth" it given the "high quality" at "tremendous-value" prices; P.S. the "ridiculously kitschy" Congee Village branch is fun "for a party."

Convivium Osteria *Mediterranean* 25 | 23 | 21 | $48
Park Slope | 68 Fifth Ave. (bet. Bergen St. & St. Marks Ave.) | Brooklyn | 718-857-1833 | www.convivium-osteria.com

Groupies gladly "travel to eat" at this Park Slope Med "hideaway" that remains "excellent all around", from the "simple, delicious" food and wine to the "transporting" "rustic" environs and "charming" service; the only rub is the "price"; P.S. "don't miss" the "romantic" garden.

Cookshop ◐ *American* 23 | 19 | 21 | $51
Chelsea | 156 10th Ave. (20th St.) | 212-924-4440 | www.cookshopny.com

"Fresh", "locally grown" "ingredients are king" at this "hip" West Chelsea American serving "well-executed" seasonal dishes; the "always-changing menu", "lovely staff" and "smart", "modern" space make a "winning combo", so it's no wonder tables are "hard to get."

Coppola's ◐ *Italian* 19 | 15 | 17 | $35
Gramercy | 378 Third Ave. (bet. 27th & 28th Sts.) | 212-679-0070
W 70s | 206 W. 79th St. (bet. Amsterdam Ave. & B'way) | 212-877-3840
www.coppolas-nyc.com

These "neighborhood joints" offering "huge portions" of "traditional" Italian "basics done well" offer "solid" value; the service is "a little uneven" and the "homey" spaces can get "tight", but there's always the "delivery option."

Cornelia Street Cafe ◐ *American/French* 19 | 15 | 17 | $32
G Village | 29 Cornelia St. (bet. Bleecker & W. 4th Sts.) | 212-989-9319 | www.corneliastreetcafe.com

With "reliable" French-American fare, "cheerful" service and "frequent events" in the "downstairs performance space", this "darling" "vintage Village" "favorite" keeps it "lively"; it's particularly popular for brunch, though the $21 prix fixe dinner is an "excellent value" too.

Corner Bistro ◐⇥ *Hamburgers* 22 | 9 | 12 | $16
W Village | 331 W. Fourth St. (Jane St.) | 212-242-9502

Despite the notoriously "long waits", some of the "best burgers in town" and $2.50 "pints of McSorley's" keep this ancient "Village tavern" hopping; you eat on "paper plates with plastic forks" and service can be "surly", but it's the "juicy", "cheap" patties that keep 'em coming.

Cortina *Italian* ∇ 18 | 15 | 17 | $35
E 70s | 1448 Second Ave. (bet. 75th & 76th Sts.) | 212-517-2066 | www.ristorantecortina.com

Eastsiders "save their carbs" for this "friendly neighborhood stop" serving "basic, dependable" Northern Italian favorites; the "low-lit room" is "pleasant" enough and allows for "quiet conversation", while "modest prices" mean "locals" can stay within their budgets.

Cosette *French*
21 | 14 | 20 | $39

Murray Hill | 163 E. 33rd St. (bet. Lexington & 3rd Aves.) | 212-889-5489
Though "a little frayed", this "tiny", "Left Bank"-like Murray Hill French bistro is a "wonderful find" for "buttery" classic fare and service "warm" enough to "make you feel like a long-lost" relative; "affordable" tabs further boost the "charm" factor.

Così *Sandwiches*
16 | 10 | 11 | $14

E 50s | 60 E. 56th St. (bet. Madison & Park Aves.) | 212-588-1225
Financial District | World Financial Ctr. | 200 Vesey St. (West St.) | 212-571-2001
Flatiron | 700 Sixth Ave. (bet. 22nd & 23rd Sts.) | 212-645-0223
Garment District | 498 Seventh Ave. (bet. 36th & 37th Sts.) | 212-947-1005
G Village | 504 Sixth Ave. (13th St.) | 212-462-4188 ●
NEW G Village | 53 E. Eighth St. (bet. Greene & Mercer Sts.) | 212-260-1507
G Village | 841 Broadway (13th St.) | 212-614-8544 ●
W 40s | 11 W. 42nd St. (bet. 5th & 6th Aves.) | 212-398-6662
W 50s | Paramount Plaza | 1633 Broadway (51st St.) | 212-397-9838
W 70s | 2160 Broadway (76th St.) | 212-595-5616
www.getcosi.com
Additional locations throughout the NY area
"Fantabulous" "fresh" flatbread and "flavorful" fillings find favor at this "solid" sandwich chain; decor and service quality "depend on the location", but "slow-moving lines" are a constant during "jam-packed" lunch hours – and "good luck finding a seat."

Counter ● *Vegan/Vegetarian*
22 | 21 | 22 | $38

E Village | 105 First Ave. (bet. 6th & 7th Sts.) | 212-982-5870 | www.counternyc.com
"Common ground" for "devoted carnivores" and "vegans" alike, this "upscale" East Village vegetarian serves up its "flavorful" fare in "chic", "contemporary" quarters; "attentive", "unpretentious service" and reasonable rates are other reasons eaters of all stripes consider it "cool."

Country Ⓩ *American*
23 | 23 | 21 | $127

Gramercy | Carlton Hotel | 90 Madison Ave., 2nd fl. (29th St.) | 212-889-7100

Café at Country ● *American*

Gramercy | Carlton Hotel | 90 Madison Ave. (29th St.) | 212-889-7100
www.countryinnewyork.com
There's "certainly nothing rural" about Geoffrey Zakarian's "sophisticated" "winner" in the "revamped Carlton Hotel" – it "wows" with "sumptuous" prix fixe-only New American fare, an "elegant" dining room and "formal service" that together "make it feel like a special occasion"; "bargain"-seekers tout the "more casual" downstairs Café at Country, where you can get a "delicious" meal minus the "high-end" tab.

Cowgirl *Southwestern*
16 | 17 | 16 | $27

W Village | 519 Hudson St. (W. 10th St.) | 212-633-1133 | www.cowgirlnyc.com
You'd better "check your diet at the door" of this "kitschy", "festive" (read: "noisy") "Western-themed" Villager whose "hearty"

Southwestern "comfort food" comes via staffers with a "sense of humor"; "fun" for "kiddie cowpokes" by day, later on it morphs into a "singles scene" fueled by "knock-your-socks-off" margaritas.

Cozy Soup & Burger ● *Hamburgers/Soup*　　　　18 | 8 | 14 | $17

G Village | 739 Broadway (Astor Pl.) | 212-477-5566

"Huge burgers", "legendary split-pea soup" and other "classic diner" staples make this 24/7 Villager a "godsend to the NYU students" who "pack" in for "midnight snacks"; sure, it's a "dive", but service is "quick" enough to satisfy the 3 AM "urge to nosh."

Ⓩ Craft *American*　　　　25 | 23 | 24 | $74

Flatiron | 43 E. 19th St. (bet. B'way & Park Ave. S.) | 212-780-0880 | www.craftrestaurant.com

"Simple food perfectly prepared" and a "mix-and-match" ordering routine are keys to the success of Tom Colicchio's "original" Flatiron New American "masterpiece", where diners "love" the "chic" ("not stuffy") setting and "attentive but not intrusive" service; just remember to bring your "platinum card."

Craftbar *American*　　　　22 | 18 | 19 | $49

Flatiron | 900 Broadway (bet. 19th & 20th Sts.) | 212-461-4300 | www.craftrestaurant.com

Craft's "delightful", "more casual" Flatiron sibling offers "simpler fare but with comparable" quality to its namesake's – perfect if you want Tom Colicchio's New American cooking "on a [relative] budget"; an "upbeat staff" abets the overall "exciting", "unpretentious" feel.

Craftsteak *Steak*　　　　22 | 23 | 22 | $79

Chelsea | 85 10th Ave. (bet. 15th & 16th Sts.) | 212-400-6699 | www.craftsteaknyc.com

At Tom Colicchio's Chelsea steakhouse, a "knowledgeable staff" "guides" guests through the "mouthwatering" selection of steaks (grass-fed, corn-fed, Wagyu) and "scrumptious" sides; the "sophisticated", "soaring space" wins wows, but a "disappointed" contingent finds that overall it "lacks finesse", especially given the "over-the-top" price point.

🆕 Crave Ceviche Bar *Pan-Latin*　　　　- | - | - | M

E 50s | 946 Second Ave. (bet. 50th & 51st Sts.) | 212-355-6565 | www.craveceviche.com

Serving up an innovative, midpriced menu focused on fish and meat 'cooked' Latin American–style in citrus juices, this tiny Eclectic East 50s boîte creates a decidedly downtown vibe with its clean, white decor; N.B. until late-night, the seats at the bar are for diners, not winers.

Crema Ⓜ *Mexican*　　　　21 | 18 | 17 | $44

Chelsea | 111 W. 17th St. (bet. 6th & 7th Aves.) | 212-691-4477 | www.cremarestaurante.com

Just about the "crema the crop" for "upscale" Nuevo Mexican, chef Julieta Ballesteros' Chelsea "favorite" is rated a "taste sensation" thanks to its "creative" cuisine and "dynamite" drinks; the "brightly colored", "narrow" dining area is "welcoming", but some say the staff could be "a bit more" so.

	FOOD	DECOR	SERVICE	COST

Crispo ● *Italian*
23 | 19 | 19 | $45

W Village | 240 W. 14th St. (bet. 7th Ave. S. & 8th Ave.) | 212-229-1818 | www.crisporestaurant.com

"Once a neighborhood secret", this Village Northern Italian is now downright "bustling" thanks to "delicious" cuisine, "warm" service and "comfortable", "rustic" space that includes a "year-round garden"; though not cheap, it probably "could charge twice what it does."

☑ Cru ☒ *European*
26 | 23 | 26 | $108

G Village | 24 Fifth Ave. (9th St.) | 212-529-1700 | www.cru-nyc.com

It's the "right place for wine lovers", but don't let this Villager's "bible"-length list of *vins* overshadow the "equally impressive" modern European cuisine; yes, its prix fixe–only menus start at $78, but to most they're "worth the expense" considering the "five-star service" and "charming", "special occasion"-worthy decor; N.B. the casual no-reserving front room is à la carte.

Cuba *Cuban*
21 | 19 | 17 | $36

G Village | 222 Thompson St. (bet. Bleecker & W. 3rd Sts.) | 212-420-7878 | www.cubanyc.com

Fans "can't say enough" about this "boisterous" Village Cuban, a "mojito heaven" where "inexpensive" "flavorful food", live jazz and "free, hand-rolled cigars" make it feel like "you've landed in Havana"; it's no wonder the "tiny space" often gets "crowded" and "noisy."

Cuba Cafe *Cuban*
18 | 16 | 18 | $31

Chelsea | 200 Eighth Ave. (bet. 20th & 21st Sts.) | 212-633-1570 | www.chelseadining.com

With a "lively" "Latin flair", this Chelsea Cuban "staple" serves "heaps" of "fresh" fare and "tasty mojitos" amid "festive" island-themed decor; an affable staff and "fair" prices add to the overall "good vibe."

Cubana Café ●⇥ *Cuban*
20 | 16 | 16 | $21

G Village | 110 Thompson St. (bet. Prince & Spring Sts.) | 212-966-5366
Carroll Gardens | 272 Smith St. (bet. Degraw & Sackett Sts.) | Brooklyn | 718-858-3980.
www.cubanacafeelchulo.com

These "laid-back" Carroll Gardens-Village "slices of Havana" boast "friendly" staffers serving up *muy bueno* Cuban "cheap eats"; "tables are so close" that their "colorful" quarters almost feel "crowded when empty", but "fantastic" cocktails "make the squeeze" quite "bearable."

Cube 63 ● *Japanese*
21 | 15 | 17 | $34

LES | 63 Clinton St. (bet. Rivington & Stanton Sts.) | 212-228-6751 Ⓜ
Cobble Hill | 234 Court St. (bet. Baltic & Warren Sts.) | Brooklyn | 718-243-2208
www.cube63.com

You'll "save big bucks" at this LES-Cobble Hill Japanese duo that slices "value sushi" and has a "BYO policy" to keep the bill down; it's a "favorite" for "fresh fish", so be prepared to "get there super-early" or "wait."

Cucina di Pesce ● *Italian*
17 | 14 | 17 | $28

E Village | 87 E. Fourth St. (bet. Bowery & 2nd Ave.) | 212-260-6800 | www.cucinadipesce.com

This "reliable" East Village Italian "does the trick" for "tasty" "basics" that leave diners feeling "well fed" for "a bargain" – especially "before

| | FOOD | DECOR | SERVICE | COST |

"6:30 PM", when the "unbeatable" $11.95 early-bird is an option; a "fine garden" and "cheerful" service further explain why it's such a hit.

Curry Leaf *Indian*
20 | 10 | 16 | $25

Gramercy | 99 Lexington Ave. (27th St.) | 212-725-5558 | www.curryleafnyc.com

"The spice is right" – and so is the price – at Kalustyan's "traditional Indian" in Gramercy, where "big servings" of "mouthwatering" dishes place it "a step up" from its neighbors; though the decor is strictly "no-frills", "polite" service compensates.

Da Andrea *Italian*
24 | 16 | 22 | $36

W Village | 557 Hudson St. (bet. Perry & W. 11th Sts.) | 212-367-1979 | www.biassanot.com

At this "local legend", West Village "regulars" swear by the "exceptional", "authentic" Emilian dishes; add "delightful" staffers, a "quaint" "tiny" space and unpretentious prices, and most agree it's "worth" the inevitable "killer wait."

Da Ciro *Italian/Pizza*
21 | 16 | 20 | $43

Murray Hill | 229 Lexington Ave. (bet. 33rd & 34th Sts.) | 212-532-1636 | www.daciro.com

Brick-oven "gourmet pizzas" to "make you weak at the knees" plus other "fine" Italian standards have earned this "low-key" Murray Hiller "local favorite" status; it can get "noisy" and "a little pricey", but "repeat customers" find it more than "worthwhile."

Dae Dong ● *Korean*
18 | 12 | 15 | $29

Garment District | 17 W. 32nd St. (bet. B'way & 5th Ave.) | 212-967-1900

Bayside | 220-15 Northern Blvd. (220th St.) | Queens | 718-631-7100

BBQ that's "tasty", "plentiful" and "inexpensive" is the deal at this Bayside–Garment District Korean-Japanese pair; tabletop cooking makes for a "fun" time "with friends" (even if you come away "smelling like your meal") – as for the service and setting, the ratings speak for themselves.

Da Filippo *Italian*
19 | 15 | 19 | $53

E 60s | 1315 Second Ave. (bet. 69th & 70th Sts.) | 212-472-6688 | www.dafilipporestaurant.com

"Colorful" owner Carlo Meconi and his "friendly" staff "know their regulars by name" at this "high-end" East Side Northern Italian that collects a "neighborhood crowd" for "solid" "basics" in "generous portions"; though some bemoan "rising prices", for most it's a "favorite" all the same.

☑ Daisy May's BBQ USA *BBQ*
24 | 6 | 13 | $22

W 40s | 623 11th Ave. (46th St.) | 212-977-1500 | www.daisymaysbbq.com

"BBQ heaven" dwells in Hell's Kitchen at this "budget-friendly" "pit" stop whose "smoky, delicious" meats include "the best ribs north of the Mason-Dixon", joined by "addictive" "Southern sides"; if the "picnic table" seating isn't your thing, check out their squadron of street carts.

Dakshin Indian Bistro *Indian*
∇ 20 | 10 | 19 | $25

E 80s | 1713 First Ave. (bet. 88th & 89th Sts.) | 212-987-9839

"Better-than-average" Indian delivered by staffers who "make you feel like a family member" explains why this UES "hole-in-the-wall" is a local "favorite"; even those put off by the "cramped", "no-decor" digs find the $7.95 lunch buffet hard to pass up.

Dallas BBQ ● *BBQ*

15	9	14	$21

Chelsea | 261 Eighth Ave. (23rd St.) | 212-462-0001
E 70s | 1265 Third Ave. (bet. 72nd & 73rd Sts.) | 212-772-9393
E Village | 132 Second Ave. (St. Marks Pl.) | 212-777-5574
Washington Heights | 3956 Broadway (166th St.) | 212-568-3700
W 40s | 241 W. 42nd St. (bet. 7th & 8th Aves.) | 212-221-9000
W 70s | 27 W. 72nd St. (bet. Columbus Ave. & CPW) | 212-873-2004
Downtown | 180 Livingston St. (bet. Hoyt & Smith Sts.) | Brooklyn | 718-643-5700
www.dallasbbq.com

"You don't leave hungry" from this "no-frills" chain known for its "humongous portions" of "decent" BBQ washed down with "jumbo" drinks; the "loud", "cafeterialike" digs may have you feeling like one of the herd, but hey, it's "super-fast" and "cheap."

Danal *French/Mediterranean*

22	21	20	$37

E Village | 90 E. 10th St. (bet. 3rd & 4th Aves.) | 212-982-6930

"Idiosyncratic and charming" as ever, this affordable East Village "hideaway" presents a "limited" but "delicious" French-Med lineup; the "funky" "thrift store–chic" aesthetic appeals to locals, as do the "casual but attentive" servers and "lovely back garden."

Dani 🗷 *Italian*

▽ 20	20	19	$50

SoHo | 333 Hudson St. (Charlton St.) | 212-633-9333 |
www.danirestaurant.com

"Creative Sicilian" fare draws fans to Don Pintabona's "wonderful" Italian in way West SoHo; a "pleasant" crew, "inviting" room and sidewalk seating seal the deal; N.B. it's now open for weekday lunch only.

Da Nico *Italian*

21	17	19	$37

Little Italy | 164 Mulberry St. (bet. Broome & Grand Sts.) | 212-343-1212 |
www.danicoristorante.com

On a "warm summer night", a table in the "wonderful" garden of this Italian eatery is truly "Little Italy at its finest"; the modestly priced food is "fresh", portions "solid" and service "attentive."

Z Daniel 🗷 *French*

28	28	28	$132

E 60s | 60 E. 65th St. (bet. Madison & Park Aves.) | 212-288-0033 |
www.danielnyc.com

An "unparalleled dining experience" awaits at Daniel Boulud's "impeccable" UES namesake, the "standard" for "luxe" prix fixe–only New French fare and rated NYC's No. 1 for Food; add an "amazing" wine list, "breathtaking" decor and "flawless", "white-glove service" and it's easy to see why this is at the "top of the NY dining food chain"; of course, the tab is equal to a "mortgage payment", but "if you're going to splurge", splurge on "perfection"; N.B. you can order à la carte in the lounge; jackets required.

Da Noi *Italian*

24	20	22	$44

NEW **Staten Island** | 138 Fingerboard Rd. (Tompkins Ave.) | 718-720-1650
Staten Island | 4358 Victory Blvd. (Westshore Expwy.) | 718-982-5040

Insiders gladly "travel to eat" at this "top-rate" SI Northern Italian (now with a new "happening" Fingerboard Road location), which cooks up "some of the best food on the Island"; service is "friendly" and the rates "reasonable", so, no surprise, it's "popular" enough to draw "crowds" and "long waits."

☑ Danube ❶☒ *Austrian* | 26 | 27 | 26 | $86 |

TriBeCa | 30 Hudson St. (bet. Duane & Reade Sts.) | 212-791-3771 | www.davidbouley.com

At David Bouley's "transporting" "TriBeCa gem", the "Klimt"-inspired dining room (among the "most beautiful in NYC") takes you back to "a more elegant time", while "sensational" French-accented Viennese fare, an "outstanding wine list" and "seamless", "pampering" service complete the "magical" experience; as one would expect, tabs also are "opulent"; P.S. for a "very special" private party, check out the downstairs.

Darbar *Indian* | ▽ 20 | 15 | 18 | $34 |

E 40s | 152 E. 46th St. (bet. Lexington & 3rd Aves.) | 212-681-4500 | www.darbarny.com

It's "dependably delicious" as well as "affordable", so it's no wonder that this East Midtown Indian "packs in the crowds", particularly for the $10.95 lunch buffet; its "understated" space is "pleasant" (especially upstairs) and service "friendly" – what more could you ask?

Da Silvano ❶ *Italian* | 20 | 15 | 17 | $62 |

G Village | 260 Sixth Ave. (bet. Bleecker & Houston Sts.) | 212-982-2343 | www.dasilvano.com

At Silvano Marchetto's Tuscan "scene" in the Village, "A-listers" up the "air-kiss count" at "charming", "hard-to-get" sidewalk tables, though to many the "real star is the cooking" here; opinions are split on service ("snooty" vs. "down to earth"), and prices ("stratospheric" vs. less than you'd pay to see your fellow diners on stage).

Da Tommaso ❶ *Italian* | 20 | 14 | 19 | $45 |

W 50s | 903 Eighth Ave. (bet. 53rd & 54th Sts.) | 212-265-1890

It plies "tasty" Northern Italian "standards" and gets you "in and out" with "minimal fuss", so it's no wonder show-goers "depend" on this "convenient" Theater District vet; the decor "could use updating", but regulars just "don't look at anything but the food."

Da Umberto ☒ *Italian* | 25 | 18 | 23 | $60 |

Chelsea | 107 W. 17th St. (bet. 6th & 7th Aves.) | 212-989-0303

Seekers of "old-fashioned Italian dining at its best" collect at this "dignified" Chelsea "institution" where the "superb" Tuscan fare comes via "solicitous" "pro" waiters; most agree it "still has it" after all these years, though there are a few complaints about "tired" decor and "formidable" tabs.

☑ davidburke & donatella *American* | 25 | 23 | 23 | $75 |

E 60s | 133 E. 61st St. (bet. Lexington & Park Aves.) | 212-813-2121 | www.dbdrestaurant.com

Chef David Burke's East Side New American never fails to "impress" with its "innovative", "whimsical" cuisine "served impeccably" with oh-so-"chic" co-owner Donatella Arpaia's oversight; the "funky" townhouse setting and "flamboyant" extras like a limo for smokers parked out front mean meals here are just plain "fun", except possibly the prices – but then there's always the $24 prix fixe lunch "bargain."

	FOOD	DECOR	SERVICE	COST

David Burke at Bloomingdale's *American* | 18 | 13 | 14 | $30 |

E 50s | Bloomingdale's | 159 E. 59th St. (bet. Lexington & 3rd Aves.) |
212-705-3800 | www.burkeinthebox.com

"Two favorite things" – "shopping and eating" – merge in "delicious"
fashion at chef David Burke's "affordable" New American pit stop inside Bloomie's, featuring a cafe and adjacent "self-serve" "gourmet
fast-food" shop; downsides are "discombobulated" service and an
"awkward", "cramped" setting.

Dawat *Indian* | 23 | 18 | 21 | $46 |

E 50s | 210 E. 58th St. (bet. 2nd & 3rd Aves.) | 212-355-7555
"Curry queen" Madhur Jaffrey's East Midtowner reigns as a "favorite"
for "first-rate" Indian ferried by an "attentive" staff; maybe the prices
are a bit "high" and the setting could use a little "sprucing up", but
most subjects say it's "still one of the best in town."

☑ db Bistro Moderne *French* | 25 | 21 | 22 | $63 |

W 40s | City Club Hotel | 55 W. 44th St. (bet. 5th & 6th Aves.) |
212-391-2400 | www.danielnyc.com

For the "ultimate" in Theater District dining, patrons pick Daniel
Boulud's "snazzy French bistro" where the "top-notch" fare (including
that "legendary" $32 hamburger) tastes even better thanks to
"charming" staffers who are "prompt" "without being pushy"; sure,
"prices are steep", but then again the $45 dinner prix fixe is a "bargain
for a Boulud place."

Deborah Ⓜ *American* | 21 | 14 | 20 | $36 |

G Village | 43 Carmine St. (bet. Bedford & Bleecker Sts.) | 212-242-2606 |
www.deborahlifelovefood.com

"Comfort food" embodying an "interesting mix" of "haute and homey"
is the deal at Deborah Stanton's "lovely little" Village New American;
"fair prices" compensate for the "narrow" space's slightly "claustro-
phobic" feel, and in summer there's always the "secret back garden."

Dee's Brick Oven Pizza Ⓜ *Mediterranean/Pizza* | 22 | 17 | 18 | $27 |

Forest Hills | 107-23 Metropolitan Ave. (74th Ave.) | Queens |
718-793-7553 | www.deesnyc.com

"Dee-licious pizza" and a "plethora" of "tasty", "affordable" Med
dishes make this "festive" (read: noisy) Forest Hills eatery a favorite
of "families with young kids"; despite "constant crowds", there's always "room to breathe" in its "comfy, casual" space.

DeGrezia ☒ *Italian* | 22 | 20 | 22 | $60 |

E 50s | 231 E. 50th St. (bet. 2nd & 3rd Aves.) | 212-750-5353 |
www.degreziaristorante.com

"A delightful surprise" hidden "partially underground", this Eastsider's
"delicious" Italian "classics" come on the high side via an "attentive"
pro staff; perhaps trendsters find it "slightly stuffy", but mature "regulars" "love" the "wonderful" "old-world" vibe.

Degustation ☒ *French/Spanish* | 26 | 21 | 25 | $56 |

E Village | 239 E. Fifth St. (bet. 2nd & 3rd Aves.) | 212-979-1012
Foodies "yearning to try something new" hit Jack and Grace Lamb's
16-seat, "no-reservations" East Village tasting bar to "watch the inventive chef" prepare "stellar" French-Spanish small plates full of

	FOOD	DECOR	SERVICE	COST

"clean, bold flavors"; it's exciting culinary "theater" with "luxurious service" to boot, leaving just "one problem" – "long waits."

☑ Del Frisco's ◐ Steak
25 | 22 | 22 | $70

W 40s | 1221 Sixth Ave. (48th St.) | 212-575-5129 | www.delfriscos.com
"Boisterous" after-work types collect at this "snazzy", "hangar"-size Midtown "he-man's" steakhouse for "generous" pours and "gigantic", "first-rank" cuts via a "good-looking" crew; the "Texas"-scale tabs don't faze "deep-pocketed" "movers and shakers", but wallet-watchers stick to the $39.95 prix fixe; N.B. there are several luxe party rooms.

Delmonico's ☒ Steak
22 | 22 | 21 | $61

Financial District | 56 Beaver St. (S. William St.) | 212-509-1144 | www.delmonicosny.com
A Financial District "landmark" (circa 1827), this rehabbed steakhouse draws "Wall Street carnivores and cashivores" for "mighty slabs" and "classic" sides tendered by an "unflappable" staff; its setting of "sumptuous simplicity" continues to serve the 21st century's versions of Diamond Jim Brady or John D.

☑ Del Posto Italian
25 | 26 | 24 | $88

Chelsea | 85 10th Ave. (16th St.) | 212-497-8090 | www.delposto.com
"Dazzled" disciples of the "dress-up dining" at this Batali-Bastianich "instant classic" in Chelsea "come out reeling" after savoring its "sublime", "authentic" Italian cuisine, "phenomenal wine list" and service as polished as the "beautiful marble floors" and dark-wood paneling in its grand main dining room; yes, tabs here can "suck expense accounts dry", but there's always the "less-formal", "less-expensive" enoteca.

Delta Grill ◐ Cajun/Creole
19 | 15 | 17 | $32

W 40s | 700 Ninth Ave. (48th St.) | 212-956-0934 | www.thedeltagrill.com
"Wickedly good" Cajun-Creole eats keep patrons "marching in" to this Hell's Kitchen "dive" for "mammoth", "spicy", "stick-to-your-ribs" repasts; service seems "uninterested", but the "cheap" rates and live music on weekends create a "down-home" New Orleans mood.

Demarchelier French
17 | 15 | 15 | $47

E 80s | 50 E. 86th St. (bet. Madison & Park Aves.) | 212-249-6300 | www.demarchelierrestaurant.com
"Still drawing a crowd" after all these years, this "bustling" UES French balances "reliable" fare, a "lively bar" and "people-watching" galore against "sardine seating", "worn" decor and "haughty" service; in a "food-challenged" area, it easily qualifies as a "neighborhood favorite."

Demetris ◐ Greek
▽ 21 | 15 | 19 | $34

Astoria | 32-11 Broadway (bet. 32nd & 33rd Sts.) | Queens | 718-278-1877
It's "nothing fancy", but for "huge portions" of "fresh", "simple", "delish" fish and other "conventional Greek" favorites, put this Astoria seafood house on your list to try; "cheery, bright" decor, a "friendly", "family"-oriented vibe and "good prices" round out the endorsement.

Denino's Pizzeria ⊋ Pizza
25 | 10 | 18 | $19

Staten Island | 524 Port Richmond Ave. (bet. Hooker Pl. & Walker St.) | 718-442-9401
Maybe "it's not much to look at", but that "all melts away" when this "been-there-forever" Staten Island pie purveyor presents its "fa-

| | FOOD | DECOR | SERVICE | COST |

mous", "delicious" pizzas and "pitchers of cold beer" at "low, low prices"; bring your bowling team and a "huge appetite."

NEW Dennis Foy ⑤ *American*   ▽ 24 | 22 | 24 | $64

TriBeCa | 313 Church St. (bet. Lispenard & Walker Sts.) | 212-625-1007 | www.dennisfoynyc.com

An "understated addition" to the TriBeCa dining scene, this "inviting" New American from Dennis Foy (Mondrian, EQ) has outgrown any start-up "kinks" and is winning "wows" with its "wonderful" cuisine, "lovely" service and "serene", "modern interior" hung with "the chef's own paintings"; tabs are a "comparative bargain" for a "foodie restaurant."

Dervish Turkish ● *Turkish*   19 | 15 | 19 | $35

W 40s | 146 W. 47th St. (bet. 6th & 7th Aves.) | 212-997-0070 | www.dervishrestaurant.com

A Theater District "change of pace", this Turkish "delight" dispenses a "delectable array" of dishes via waiters who'd willingly "whirl around to get you out on time"; it's "low on ambiance" but "the price is right", especially the $23 early-bird prix fixe.

NEW DeStefano's Steakhouse Ⓜ *Steak*   – | – | – | E

Williamsburg | 89 Conselyea St. (Leonard St.) | Brooklyn | 718-384-2836

Unlike most of Williamsburg's youthfully oriented newcomers, this steakhouse honors its deep-rooted Italian community with old-style pastas and chops; the *Moonstruck* and *Saturday Night Fever* posters outside add some kitsch, but the snug interior keeps it simple with wood wainscoting and family photos.

Destino ● *Italian*   18 | 18 | 16 | $56

E 50s | 891 First Ave. (50th St.) | 212-751-0700 | www.destinony.com

The "jet set" rubs elbows with "quieter" Sutton Place denizens at this "jumping" "upscale" Italian where the "best meatballs" lead an otherwise "hit-or-miss" "red-sauce" lineup; the fact that Justin Timberlake is a backer adds "glitz", but "steep" prices and "bored" staffers don't.

Deux Amis *French*   19 | 16 | 20 | $50

E 50s | 356 E. 51st St. (bet. 1st & 2nd Aves.) | 212-230-1117

A "welcoming" owner adds a "convivial" feel to this "unpretentious" East Midtown favorite; "don't expect fireworks", just "appealing", "abundant" French bistro fare in a "low-key" setting, and maybe the "mid-summer night" bonus of "sidewalk seating."

Devin Tavern *American*   18 | 22 | 19 | $53

TriBeCa | 363 Greenwich St. (bet. Franklin & Harrison Sts.) | 212-334-7337 | www.devintavern.com

There's "space for all" in this "big", "gorgeous" TriBeCa New American whose "modern ski-chalet"-like space is augmented with a "warm" and "clubby" downstairs lounge; surveyors split on the "pricey", "pleasantly varied" offerings ("amazing" vs. "passable"), but a post-Survey chef change should help.

NEW Dieci ●⑤ *Italian*   ▽ 23 | 20 | 26 | $39

E Village | 228 E. 10th St. (bet. 1st & 2nd Aves.) | 212-387-9545 | www.diecinyc.com

The chef, owners, architect and "outstanding" staff may all be Japanese, but this "tiny" new sub-sidewalk East Villager trades in "wonderful", well-priced Italian small plates; its sleek, "low-key" space reflects the designer's minimalist Asian aesthetic.

☒ Di Fara ⊅ *Pizza* | 27 | 4 | 7 | $13

Midwood | 1424 Ave. J (bet. 14th & 15th Sts.) | Brooklyn | 718-258-1367
It "looks like hell" and waits can be "timed with a calendar", but Dominic De Marco's "legendary" circa-1963 Midwood "mecca of pizza" creates pies that are pure "heaven"; in sum, they're "all they're cracked up to be" – i.e. No. 1 in NYC.

Dim Sum Go Go *Chinese* | 20 | 11 | 14 | $22

Chinatown | 5 E. Broadway (Chatham Sq.) | 212-732-0797
"Made-to-order" "delicate, flavorful" dim sum comes "fresh out of the kitchen" at this "white-tablecloth" Chinatown "standout"; it's "cheap" and, despite "abrupt" service, more "peaceful" than the "hustle-bustle" trolly type, even if some say "no pushcarts mean no fun."

Diner ◐ *Diner* | 22 | 18 | 17 | $31

Williamsburg | 85 Broadway (Berry St.) | Brooklyn | 718-486-3077 | www.dinernyc.com
The "place that defined cool" in Williamsburg, this "lovingly renovated diner" draws "arty" locals for "creative", "elevated" (yet affordable) New American grub dished up by a "relaxed" "hipster" staff; just know "it's a jungle on weekends" when "waits can be grueling", especially for the "incredible brunch."

Dinosaur Bar-B-Que Ⓜ *BBQ* | 22 | 16 | 17 | $29

Harlem | 646 W. 131st St. (12th Ave.) | 212-694-1777 | www.dinosaurbarbque.com
"Lip-smacking", "dino-size" BBQ and "good fixin's" washed down with "amazing" microbrews make it "worth the hike" to this "cavernous" West Harlem "faux" "roadhouse"; prices are "cheap to boot", so no wonder it's often "crowded bedlam" here and a reservation is essential.

Dirty Bird to-go *American* | 17 | 5 | 12 | $15

W Village | 204 W. 14th St. (bet. 7th Ave. S. & 8th Ave.) | 212-620-4836 | www.dirtybirdtogo.com
A "welcome break from" the norm, this Village take-out joint serves "succulent" free-range chicken, fried and rotisserie, plus "fresh" sides; still, critics squawk about "small portions" and seriously basic digs.

Dishes *Sandwiches* | 22 | 13 | 12 | $17

E 40s | 6 E. 45th St. (bet. 5th & Madison Aves.) | 212-687-5511
E 40s | Grand Central | lower level (42nd St. & Vanderbilt Ave.) | 212-808-5511
E 50s | Citigroup Ctr. | 399 Park Ave. (54th St.) | 212-421-5511 ☒
"Killer lines" form at lunchtime for this Midtown trio's "unbelievable selection" of "terrific sandwiches", "can't-go-wrong" soups and "gourmet" salads rated "way above the competitors'"; the answer to anyone who claims "it's on the pricey side" is that "you're paying for quality."

District *American* | 20 | 19 | 20 | $57

W 40s | Muse Hotel | 130 W. 46th St. (bet. 6th & 7th Aves.) | 212-485-2999 | www.districtnyc.com
At this New American pre-curtain "favorite" within the Muse Hotel, David Rockwell's "clever" "theater"-esque decor creates a "calm oa-

sis" amid the Times Square "frenzy"; "satisfying", "imaginative" fare, "personal service" and a "get-your-money's-worth" prix fixe should put it center stage.

Ditch Plains ● *Seafood*

17	16	17	$37

G Village | 29 Bedford St. (Downing St.) | 212-633-0202 | www.ditch-plains.com

"Named after a Montauk surf break", Marc Murphy's "sceney" Village seafooder offers "interesting" "twists on traditional" shore favorites; it exudes a "mellow" vibe that makes it a "lovely place to loiter", though a few shrug "solid" but "forgettable."

Divino *Italian*

18	15	19	$41

E 80s | 1556 Second Ave. (bet. 80th & 81st Sts.) | 212-861-1096 | www.divinoristorante.net

A "gracious host" sets the tone at this "relaxed" UES Northern Italian whose "reliable" cuisine holds "no surprises" but has you leaving "full and happy"; the "cute", candlelit setting may need "fixing up", but "attentive" staffers and "weekend music" keep locals "loyal" all the same.

Diwan *Indian*

▽ 21	17	18	$33

E 40s | Helmsley Middletowne | 148 E. 48th St. (bet. Lexington & 3rd Aves.) | 212-593-5425

"Delicious, aromatic" Indian cuisine at modest prices makes this an East Midtown mainstay; it's particularly "busy" at lunch time, when business types pile in for the $13.95 "top-of-the-line buffet."

Django ⑤ *French/Mediterranean*

20	23	20	$52

E 40s | 480 Lexington Ave. (46th St.) | 212-871-6600 | www.djangorestaurant.com

"Drinks after work" have special "allure" in the "sea-of-suits" downstairs lounge at this "exotic" Midtowner, while "inventive", "tasty" French-Med cuisine holds sway in the "relatively tranquil" upstairs; all that jangles is "the price."

Docks Oyster Bar *Seafood*

19	16	17	$47

E 40s | 633 Third Ave. (40th St.) | 212-986-8080
W 80s | 2427 Broadway (bet. 89th & 90th Sts.) | 212-724-5588
www.docksoysterbar.com

"Briny-fresh" fish, a "terrific raw bar" and "quality martinis" lure "oyster heads" and others to this "big, loud", "no-frills" pair of midpriced seafood "standbys"; admirers advise "for best results, keep it simple" – and remember that service is "catch as catch can."

Do Hwa *Korean*

21	19	17	$38

G Village | 55 Carmine St. (bet. Bedford St. & 7th Ave. S.) | 212-414-1224 | www.dohwanyc.com

"K-town" comes to Greenwich Village via this "cool", "minimalist" Korean specializing in "high-quality" BBQ meats; it's "a bit of a scene", where even "hit-or-miss service" doesn't dampen the "nightclub" vibe, abetted by "original cocktails" from a "sleek" bar, all at a modest cost.

Dok Suni's ●⊟ *Korean*

▽ 21	14	17	$29

E Village | 119 First Ave. (bet. 7th St. & St. Marks Pl.) | 212-477-9506

"Calling all spicy-food lovers": this "dimly lit" East Village Korean attracts a "youngish crowd" with "consistently fine" eats, "potent martinis", "sweet", if distracted, service and a "funky vibe"; overall, it's a "comfy" place for a date, as well as a "cash-only" "bargain."

Dominick's 🍽 Italian · 22 | 9 | 16 | $35
Bronx | 2335 Arthur Ave. (bet. Crescent Ave. & E. 187th St.) | 718-733-2807
"Go with friends" to best enjoy the "delicious" "red-sauce" Italian served "rough and tumble" at the elbow-to-elbow communal tables of this "quirky" Bronx "time warp"; there are no reservations, no menu ("let the waiter order") and no bill (they "make up a price" and you pay in cash) – i.e. it's "a real NY experience"; N.B. a recent redo isn't reflected in the above Decor score.

Don Giovanni 🌑 Italian · 17 | 12 | 15 | $26
Chelsea | 214 10th Ave. (bet. 22nd & 23rd Sts.) | 212-242-9054
W 40s | 358 W. 44th St. (bet. 8th & 9th Aves.) | 212-581-4939
www.dongiovanni-ny.com
"Out-of-control" portions ensure "you won't walk out hungry" from these "hopping" West Side Italian "carbfests" that locals "depend" on for "pleasing" pastas and brick-oven pizzas; service is "lackluster" and the decor a bit "tired", but sidewalk seating is redeeming in season.

Donguri Ⓜ Japanese · ∇ 27 | 15 | 24 | $62
E 80s | 309 E. 83rd St. (bet. 1st & 2nd Aves.) | 212-737-5656 | www.dongurinyc.com
Now specializing in soba and udon noodle dishes, this UES Japanese "jewel" gets high ratings for the "artistic quality and precision" of its cooking (which excludes sushi); the staff presiding over its "Tokyo apartment"–size space is "beyond excellent", and while tabs are "expensive", they're "not exorbitant" for such a "treat."

Don Pedro's Caribbean/S American · 23 | 17 | 19 | $35
E 90s | 1865 Second Ave. (96th St.) | 212-996-3274 | www.donpedros.net
This "slightly upscale" UES Caribbean–South American brings "artistic flair" to its "excellent", "savory" dishes, while "amiable service" keeps the atmosphere "warm" – as do the "wonderful cocktails"; all in all, it's counted as a "gem" in an underserved neighborhood.

Don Peppe Ⓜ🍽 Italian · 25 | 10 | 18 | $44
Ozone Park | 135-58 Lefferts Blvd. (149th Ave.) | Queens | 718-845-7587
"Noisy, celebratory" dining is the style at this "old-fashioned", cash-only Ozone Park Italian "icon" dishing up "outstanding", "garlic"-laden classics on "huge" "family-style platters" plus "house wine in unmarked bottles"; just "don't expect white-glove service" or a "fancy setting."

Dos Caminos Mexican · 20 | 20 | 18 | $43
E 50s | 825 Third Ave. (50th St.) | 212-336-5400
Gramercy | 373 Park Ave. S. (bet. 26th & 27th Sts.) | 212-294-1000
SoHo | 475 W. Broadway (Houston St.) | 212-277-4300
www.brguestrestaurants.com
There's "never a dull moment" at Steve Hanson's "energetic" trio of "dressed-up" midpriced Mexicans; starting with the "made-at-your-table guacamole", the menu still "dazzles", while "knockout margs" take the edge off of "so-so" service and the "noise" kicked up by all those "singles and yuppies."

	FOOD	DECOR	SERVICE	COST

Downtown Atlantic Ⓜ *American* 　　19 | 16 | 19 | $32
Boerum Hill | 364 Atlantic Ave. (bet. Bond & Hoyt Sts.) | Brooklyn |
718-852-9945 | www.downtownatlantic.com

At this "friendly" Boerum Hill New American, there's "straight-ahead"
fare plus "out-of-this-world" desserts from a "cute little front bakery";
factor in "cozy" digs and tabs "easy on the pocketbook", and you've
got the "perfect neighborhood restaurant."

Doyers Vietnamese *Vietnamese* 　　20 | 6 | 13 | $16
Chinatown | 11-13 Doyers St., downstairs (Chatham Sq.) | 212-513-1521

In a "subterranean" "secret den" on a "movie set-like" Chinatown
street there's this "dirt-cheap" producer of "fresh", "terrific" Vietnamese
dishes; given the "value", those "in-the-know" shrug "who cares"
about "erratic" service or "tacky", "dungeon"-like digs?

Dressler *American* 　　24 | 25 | 23 | $47
Williamsburg | 149 Broadway (bet. Bedford & Driggs Aves.) | Brooklyn |
718-384-6343 | www.dresslernyc.com

"Making a hell of an entrance", Williamsburg's "upscale but not up-
tight" New American "new kid on the block" is voted "fabulous" all
around, mixing a "gorgeous" space (full of "handcrafted" "decorative
details") with "spot-on" service and "stylish", "well-executed" cuisine
you'd "pay double for in Manhattan"; advice: go "while you still can."

Duane Park Cafe *American* 　　24 | 19 | 23 | $52
TriBeCa | 157 Duane St. (bet. Hudson St. & W. B'way) | 212-732-5555 |
www.duaneparkcafe.com

"Elegant" New American food "perfectly served" is the forte of this
"tranquil" TriBeCa "find"; maybe it's "dwarfed by the big boys" nearby,
but "aficionados" report that it "never fails to please."

Due ⚫ *Italian* 　　22 | 17 | 21 | $45
E 70s | 1396 Third Ave. (bet. 79th & 80th Sts.) | 212-772-3331

"Every neighborhood should be so lucky" gloat groupies of this "congenial" UES "staple" serving "solid" Northern Italian at "decent prices"
for the area; it's a "kitchen away from home" for an "older crowd"
seeking "low-key" meals that are "always on the mark."

Duke's *Southern* 　　16 | 13 | 14 | $24
Gramercy | 99 E. 19th St. (Park Ave. S.) | 212-260-2922
NEW **Murray Hill** | 560 Third Ave. (37th St.) | 212-949-5400
www.dukesnyc.com

"Mouthwatering pulled pork" and "juicy burgers" are among the
Southern-style "cheap eats" that come with "strong drinks" at these
"rowdy" "frat parties"; most like the "damn fine trashy food" and "hot"
waitresses, but others suggest you "tie your arteries closed" first.

DuMont *American* 　　23 | 17 | 17 | $27
Williamsburg | 432 Union Ave. (bet. Devoe St. & Metropolitan Ave.) |
Brooklyn | 718-486-7717 | www.dumontrestaurant.com
DuMont Burger ⚫ *American*
Williamsburg | 314 Bedford Ave. (bet. S. 1st & 2nd Sts.) | Brooklyn |
718-384-6127

"Edgy and hipster-laden", this "cozy" Williamsburg New American
"packs 'em in" with its "appealing" "comfort" fare, which tastes better

with some elbow room out in the "wonderful garden"; "insanely good" burgers and sandwiches are served until the wee hours at the Bedford Avenue offshoot.

Dumplin Man ❷ Chinese

	FOOD	DECOR	SERVICE	COST
	19	7	13	$11

E Village | 100 St. Marks Pl. (bet. Ave. A & 1st Ave.) | 212-505-2121 | www.dumplingman.com

"Marvelous", "chubby dumplings" in "exciting flavors" are made "hypnotically" before your eyes at this East Village Chinese; its "barebones" space is "teeny", meaning for most it's "strictly takeaway", and happily "not many pennies are needed" for a "fast fix."

Dylan Prime Steak

	FOOD	DECOR	SERVICE	COST
	24	23	22	$64

TriBeCa | 62 Laight St. (Greenwich St.) | 212-334-4783 | www.dylanprime.com

"Not your grandpa's steakhouse", this "suave" TriBeCa version goes well beyond red meat as it attracts "suits" and "young singles" with its first-class fare, "solicitous" service and a next-door "bar scene that's a blast"; no wonder it's a "bit expensive."

NEW Earthen Oven Indian

	FOOD	DECOR	SERVICE	COST
	21	12	19	$34

W 70s | 53 W. 72nd St. (Columbus Ave.) | 212-579-8888

"Terrifically tasty" dishes (via ex Tamarind chefs) come out of the tandoor at this "friendly", "high-end" Indian newcomer near Lincoln Center that has already won a loyal following; despite a lackluster "long, narrow" space that has seen "quite a lot of turnover" over the years, this one seems to be here to stay.

East Buffet Eclectic

	FOOD	DECOR	SERVICE	COST
	20	14	12	$27

Flushing | 42-07 Main St. (Maple Ave.) | Queens | 718-353-6333 | www.eastusa.com

The "elaborate" "all-you-can-eat" buffet boasting every taste "you can imagine" (200-plus dishes) is the thing at this "enormous" Asian-Eclectic Flushing "palace", though you can go à la carte too; expect a "madhouse on weekends", when "value"-seekers come to "chow down."

East Manor Chinese

	FOOD	DECOR	SERVICE	COST
	▽ 19	14	13	$24

Flushing | 46-45 Kissena Blvd. (Laburnum Ave.) | Queens | 718-888-8998

"Sunday morning dim sum" is the ticket at this big, "busy" Flushing Chinese, but it also offers the same wide "variety" of "delicious", "cheap", "cart"-borne tidbits daily at lunch; it's "crowded" and has subpar service, so think of it as an "adventure" and "be prepared to wait."

East of Eighth ❷ Eclectic

	FOOD	DECOR	SERVICE	COST
	16	15	18	$31

Chelsea | 254 W. 23rd St. (bet. 7th & 8th Aves.) | 212-352-0075 | www.eastofeighth.com

"Hot scene downstairs, quieter dining upstairs" and a "relaxing outdoor garden" are the highlights of this "low-budget" Chelsea Eclectic cafe; for "best value" join the neighbors at the "$18 early-bird special - and don't forget brunch."

NEW East Village Yacht Club 🛇 American

	FOOD	DECOR	SERVICE	COST
	–	–	–	M

E Village | 42 E. First St. (bet. 1st & 2nd Aves.) | 212-777-5617 | www.evyc.com

This new East Village duplex replicates an upper-crust country club via its ample use of nautical memorabilia; the Cape Cod-esque downstairs dining room features suitably Waspy American fare (think Cobb salad, spinach dip, icebox cake) priced to please parsimonious preppies.

E.A.T. *American*

FOOD	DECOR	SERVICE	COST
19	11	14	$39

E 80s | 1064 Madison Ave. (bet. 80th & 81st Sts.) | 212-772-0022 | www.elizabar.com

"Handy" as a "shopping" or museum-hopping "reenergizer", Eli Zabar's beloved "chaotic" UES "emporium" is renowned for "fabulous sandwiches" and other "stylish" choices; it draws a "chic" local crowd that doesn't blink at "iffy service", "zero" decor and record-breaking rates – at this point it's a "NY fixture."

Eatery ● *American*

FOOD	DECOR	SERVICE	COST
19	16	16	$32

W 50s | 798 Ninth Ave. (53rd St.) | 212-765-7080 | www.eaterynyc.com

The look is "*Mad Max* minimalist" at this Hell's Kitchen New American, where a "cool", "elbow-to-elbow" crowd creates "quite the scene" while munching "inventive home cooking" (e.g. "slammin'" mac 'n' jack); service is overly "relaxed", but at least the prices are too.

Ecco 🗷 *Italian*

FOOD	DECOR	SERVICE	COST
21	17	20	$52

TriBeCa | 124 Chambers St. (bet. Church St. & W. B'way) | 212-227-7074

"Traditional" is the word for this "reliable" TriBeCa Italian offering "well-prepared" favorites in an "old-school", "Sinatra"-worthy setting; most agree it's "pricey" but "worth it", especially when the "weekend piano bar" is in session and the mood gets "romantic."

Edgar's Cafe ●🗷➿ *Coffeehouse*

FOOD	DECOR	SERVICE	COST
18	18	15	$20

W 80s | 255 W. 84th St. (bet. B'way & West End Ave.) | 212-496-6126

A raven couldn't find a more "dizzying array of desserts" than at this "bohemian" UWS coffeehouse-cum–Edgar Allan Poe homage; it's a "pleasant hangout" and good for an affordable "late-night nosh", but given the "not-so-special" service, "don't be in a rush."

Edison Cafe ➿ *Coffee Shop*

FOOD	DECOR	SERVICE	COST
15	8	13	$21

W 40s | Edison Hotel | 228 W. 47th St. (bet. B'way & 8th Ave.) | 212-840-5000

Widely known as "the Polish Tea Room" or the Shubert Cafeteria, this "kitschy", "cheap" Theater District coffee shop has become a "legend" thanks to its Broadway "celebrity-sighting" and "old-fashioned Jewish" staples like matzo ball soup and blintzes; maybe it's in line for a "rehab", but most feel "they should landmark the interior."

NEW Ed's Lobster Bar Ⓜ *Seafood*

FOOD	DECOR	SERVICE	COST
▽ 23	15	16	$42

NoLita | 222 Lafayette St. (bet. Kenmare & Spring Sts.) | 212-343-3236 | www.lobsterbarnyc.com

"Sensational" "lobster roll fixes" can now be had in NoLita thanks to this "excellent" "New England–style" seafood arrival from an ex-Pearl Oyster Bar sous-chef; despite "amateurish service" and other "newness" "kinks", its counter seats and handful of tables are already a squeeze.

Edward's ● *American*

FOOD	DECOR	SERVICE	COST
16	14	17	$29

TriBeCa | 136 W. Broadway (bet. Duane & Thomas Sts.) | 212-233-6436 | www.edwardsnyc.com

"Part diner, part bistro", this "welcoming", well-priced TriBeCa American is where "locals gather" to "unwind" over "reliable" comfort fare, including "fantastic breakfasts"; by day there are "tons of kids", but nighttime brings a "swinging" "bar scene" and even "an occasional celeb" sighting.

	FOOD	DECOR	SERVICE	COST

Eight Mile Creek ● *Australian* ▽ 20 | 15 | 19 | $40

Little Italy | 240 Mulberry St. (bet. Prince & Spring Sts.) | 212-431-4635 | www.eightmilecreek.com

"G'day, mate" – at this Little Italy taste of "Down Under", the "mid-priced" Aussie grub includes some "exotic" choices like kangaroo; it's "overrun with expats" so expect appealing "Oz attitude" and "energy", whether upstairs, in the casual downstairs pub or in the "cool garden."

EJ's Luncheonette ∅ *American* 15 | 9 | 14 | $22

E 70s | 1271 Third Ave. (73rd St.) | 212-472-0600
W 80s | 447 Amsterdam Ave. (bet. 81st & 82nd Sts.) | 212-873-3444

"Darn-good breakfasts" star at these crosstown "retro-'50s" diners that proffer a "giant menu" of "homespun" affordable Americana; they're "havens" for the "mommy brigade" and "mobbed on weekends", despite "dumpy" digs and "get 'em in, get 'em out" service.

Elaine's ● *American/Italian* 13 | 14 | 13 | $54

E 80s | 1703 Second Ave. (bet. 88th & 89th Sts.) | 212-534-8103

Among "the last of the old NY haunts with old NYers still haunting it", Elaine Kaufman's "playground" hosts an UES crowd of "characters" and "literary folk" who don't mind that the Italian-American fare is "mediocre", the service "surly" and the "tavern" digs in need of an "update"; Page Six mentions notwithstanding, ordinary joes wonder "what's all the fuss about?"

El Centro ● *Mexican* 18 | 17 | 18 | $27

W 50s | 824 Ninth Ave. (54th St.) | 646-763-6585 | www.elcentro-nyc.com

A "cut above" "your usual Mexican", this "happening" Hell's Kitchen cantina plies a "young" crowd with "cheap eats" delivered by a "chirpy" staff; its "kitschy", "cramped" space gets "loud", but patrons "chugging the house margaritas" don't seem to mind.

El Charro Español *Spanish* 22 | 15 | 22 | $40

G Village | 4 Charles St. (bet. Greenwich Ave. & 7th Ave. S.) | 212-242-9547 | www.el-charro-espanol.com

Offering a "hospitable bit of old Spain" since 1925, this "off-the-beaten-path" Villager turns out "surprisingly good" "Spanish classics" ferried by "genuine, kind" staffers; as for the "cozy" subterranean space, you'll feel you took "a time machine to an earlier era."

El Cid ⑤Ⓜ *Spanish* 21 | 13 | 19 | $35

Chelsea | 322 W. 15th St. (bet. 8th & 9th Aves.) | 212-929-9332

"Wonderful tapas" "pile up fast and furious" at this "unassuming" Chelsea Spaniard serving "all the old reliables" plus "knockout sangria" in the "smallest piece of real estate" around; just "ignore the silly, outdated" decor and "elbow your way to a table."

Elephant, The ● *French/Thai* ▽ 21 | 16 | 15 | $36

E Village | 58 E. First St. (bet. 1st & 2nd Aves.) | 212-505-7739 | www.elephantrestaurant.com

You couldn't even think about "fitting an elephant" into the "tiny" quarters of this "funky", "raucous" Thai-French East Villager; still, "crowds" "squeeze in" for "knock-your-socks-off" Thai-French fare and "fancy cocktails", never mind the "lackluster service" and "noisy" acoustics.

	FOOD	DECOR	SERVICE	COST

Elephant & Castle ● *Pub Food* | 17 | 14 | 17 | $26 |

G Village | 68 Greenwich Ave. (bet. Perry St. & 7th Ave. S.) | 212-243-1400 | www.elephantandcastle.com

"Dependable" for "comforting" American "pub grub" and an "exceptional brunch", this "lively" Villager has been a "neighborhood hangout" going way back; space is "tight", but the "sweet" (if sometimes "frazzled") staff and "moderate prices" compensate.

NEW eleven B. ● *Italian/Pizza* | - | - | - | I |

E Village | 174 Ave. B (11th St.) | 212-388-9811 | www.11Bexpress.com

Old-school with a 21st-century edge, this new East Village Italian boasts rustic tables and an antique fireplace, plus plasma TVs; its "thin-crust" pizzas and other affordable standards are served by a "personable" crew, and are available to-go at the next-door annex.

Z Eleven Madison Park *French* | 26 | 26 | 26 | $104 |

Gramercy | 11 Madison Ave. (24th St.) | 212-889-0905 | www.elevenmadisonpark.com

Now with a "brilliant" New French menu from executive chef Daniel Humm, Danny Meyer's "magical" Madison Square Park "triumph" is "better than ever"; "it's posh", with "polished service" in a "huge", "gorgeous" "vaulted room", and although the prix fixe "price tags equal" its "high culinary" standard and a few mutter about "midget portions", most "blather on" about "blissdom."

El Faro ●M *Spanish* | 23 | 11 | 18 | $38 |

W Village | 823 Greenwich St. (Horatio St.) | 212-929-8210 | www.elfaronyc.com

"Age does no harm" to this "convivial" Village Spaniard and the "fantastic paella" and other "delicious", "garlicky" standards it's been serving for 80 years; its "shoebox" digs are beyond "faded" and even the "old-time" waiters "seem the same" from decade to decade, but that's all "part of the charm."

Eliá M *Greek* | ▽ 25 | 19 | 23 | $46 |

Bay Ridge | 8611 Third Ave. (bet. 86th & 87th Sts.) | Brooklyn | 718-748-9891 | www.eliarestaurant.com

"Fabulous" "fresh seafood" "prepared with a light touch" is the forte of this "charming", "no-fuss" Bay Ridge Hellenic; the "wonderful" staff "treats you like family", while the whitewashed walls and flower-filled deck have you imagining "you're in Greece."

Elias Corner ●⊄ *Greek/Seafood* | 22 | 8 | 13 | $36 |

Astoria | 24-02 31st St. (24th Ave.) | Queens | 718-932-1510

To say it's "nothing fancy" is an understatement, but this affordable Astoria Greek "dive" is nevertheless a source for first-rate grilled fish and other "remarkable" Hellenic classics; service is "brusque", "napkins are paper" and it's cash-only, but go once, you'll go again.

Elio's ● *Italian* | 23 | 16 | 19 | $59 |

E 80s | 1621 Second Ave. (bet. 84th & 85th Sts.) | 212-772-2242

"Getting a table is always a challenge" at this "chic" UES Italian known as much for its clientele of "famous faces" and "'in' crowd" types as for its "consistently delicious" fare; service is "professional" enough, but you may "feel a little left out" if "you're not a regular."

	FOOD	DECOR	SERVICE	COST

El Malecon *Dominican*

21 | 8 | 14 | $17

Washington Heights | 4141 Broadway (175th St.) | 212-927-3812 ◐
W 90s | 764 Amsterdam Ave. (bet. 97th & 98th Sts.) | 212-864-5648
Bronx | 5592 Broadway (231st St.) | 718-432-5155 ◐
www.maleconrestaurants.com

"Hearty", "honest" eats ("heavenly" rotisserie chicken) at minimal cost have kept these "lively", "friendly" Uptown Dominicans perpetually "packed"; decor is strictly "bare-bones", but "lightning-fast delivery" is the way to avoid it.

elmo ◐ *American*

15 | 17 | 15 | $32

Chelsea | 156 Seventh Ave. (bet. 19th & 20th Sts.) | 212-337-8000 | www.elmorestaurant.com

"Chelsea boys" "show off their muscles" amid a nonstop "party" at this "retro"-"trendy" New American "upscale diner"; some say it's "better for the drinks than the grub" (though brunch is a standout), but "hot waiters" and "decent prices" keep it humming.

El Parador Cafe *Mexican*

20 | 16 | 21 | $42

Murray Hill | 325 E. 34th St. (bet. 1st & 2nd Aves.) | 212-679-6812 | www.elparadorcafe.com

"Still flying under the radar", this Murray Hill Mexican standby makes a "delightful break from the nuevo invasion" with its "surprisingly decent" dishes and a "hospitable" staff; digs are so "dated" it's "soothing" – ditto the "fabulous sangria" and margaritas.

El Paso ◐ *Mexican/Spanish*

- | - | - | M

G Village | 134 W. Houston St. (bet. MacDougal & Sullivan Sts.) | 212-673-0828 | www.elpasonyc.com

Modest prices and generous portions keep the trade brisk at this venerable Villager offering a large array of Spanish-Mexican dishes in a small setting; it's a quiet refuge from the trendier neighbors nearby, drawing in loyal supporters and curious passersbys.

El Paso Taqueria *Mexican*

22 | 11 | 17 | $23

E 100s | 1642 Lexington Ave. (104th St.) | 212-831-9831 ◐
E 90s | 64 E. 97th St. (Park Ave.) | 212-996-1739
NEW **Harlem** | 237 E. 116th St. (bet. Lexington & 3rd Aves.) | 212-860-4875 ◐
www.elpasotaqueria.com

"Gringos are made to feel welcome" at this "terrific" "far UES" trio serving "super-good", "real-deal" Mexican "prepared with heart"; the "homey" surroundings are "not much to look at" and "slow service is a downside" but "bargain" rates trump all.

El Pote ⊠ *Spanish*

21 | 14 | 21 | $41

Murray Hill | 718 Second Ave. (bet. 38th & 39th Sts.) | 212-889-6680

Don't judge this "gracious" Murray Hill Spaniard by its facade, because "waiting within" is a "lively clientele" partaking of "pleasing paella" and other "*bueno*" "down-to-earth" dishes; maybe it could use a "face-lift", but most just "focus on the food."

El Quijote ◐ *Spanish*

19 | 14 | 17 | $39

Chelsea | 226 W. 23rd St. (bet. 7th & 8th Aves.) | 212-929-1855

You half expect "Ricky Ricardo will walk in" to this "cheerful" Chelsea "golden oldie" (circa 1930) famed for its "classic" "lobster-driven"

	FOOD	DECOR	SERVICE	COST

Spanish cooking and "strong sangria"; portions are "ample" and prices "fair", so most "look past" "siesta-paced service" and "campy" decor.

Embers *Steak*
22 | 13 | 17 | $44

Bay Ridge | 9519 Third Ave. (bet. 95th & 96th Sts.) | Brooklyn | 718-745-3700
"Nothing beats the T-bone for two" at this "casual" Bay Ridge steakhouse claim carnivores who don't let "long waits" or "crowded", "run-down" digs dampen the fire; further fanning the ardor are "valet parking" and prices that "won't break the bank."

Empanada Mama ● *S American*
20 | 10 | 14 | $15

W 50s | 763 Ninth Ave. (bet. 51st & 52nd Sts.) | 212-698-9008
"Myriad" "cheap" empanadas with "assorted fillings" (even dessert options) are the draw at this "funky" Hell's Kitchen South American storefront; it's a "tiny place" where "cooked-to-order" means "slow service", so "bring your patience."

Empire Diner ● *Diner*
15 | 15 | 14 | $24

Chelsea | 210 10th Ave. (22nd St.) | 212-243-2736
"Possibly the hippest diner on earth", this Chelsea vet is "still going strong", dishing up "reliable comfort food" 24/7; its "black-and-chrome" "art deco" digs (circa 1929), long hours and sidewalk seating are long-standing lures that become irresistible to club-goers after 2 AM.

Empire Szechuan ● *Chinese*
15 | 9 | 14 | $22

G Village | 15 Greenwich Ave. (bet. Christopher & W. 10th Sts.) | 212-691-1535 | www.empiretogo.com
G Village | 173 Seventh Ave. S. (bet. Perry & W. 11th Sts.) | 212-243-6046
Washington Heights | 4041 Broadway (bet. 170th & 171st Sts.) | 212-568-1600
W 60s | 193 Columbus Ave. (bet. 68th & 69th Sts.) | 212-496-8778
W 100s | 2642 Broadway (100th St.) | 212-662-9404 | www.empiretogo.com
Around "just about every corner", this "Empire of cheap Chinese" cooking can be "counted on" for its "huge menu" that drifts over to sushi at times; the food is "pretty good" but "the decor isn't appetizing", leading many to consider it more of a "delivery standby."

Employees Only ● *European*
18 | 21 | 18 | $42

W Village | 510 Hudson St. (bet. Christopher & W. 10th Sts.) | 212-242-3021 | www.employeesonlynyc.com
"Outstanding mixology" and a "gorgeous faux-speakeasy" setting make for "fantastic bar" action at this "cocktail-centric" West Villager; though secondary to the "scene", its "surprisingly good" European food is served until "late night" and out in an "adorable garden."

Energy Kitchen *Health Food*
18 | 6 | 14 | $13

Chelsea | 307 W. 17th St. (bet. 8th & 9th Aves.) | 212-645-5200
E 40s | 300 E. 41st St. (2nd Ave.) | 212-687-1200
E 50s | 1089 Second Ave. (bet. 57th & 58th Sts.) | 212-888-9300
W 40s | 417 W. 47th St. (bet. 9th & 10th Aves.) | 212-333-3500
W Village | 82 Christopher St. (bet. Bleecker St. & 7th Ave. S.) | 212-414-8880
www.energykitchen.com
"Who knew healthy could taste so good?" pant partakers of the bison burgers, "creative wraps" and other "nutritious" "fast food" dispensed

by this "quick" quintet; costs are "low", but given the "sterile environment", "post-gym" types may opt "for takeout" or energetic delivery.

EN Japanese Brasserie Japanese   22 | 25 | 20 | $56

W Village | 435 Hudson St. (Leroy St.) | 212-647-9196 | www.enjb.com
The "high-design", "large, open" quarters at this "chic" West Villager
threaten to "outshine" the "delicious" Japanese small plates (including "outstanding housemade tofu"); it gets bonus points for a "helpful"
staff and a "sake lover's dream" bar, if not its high-EN tabs.

Ennio & Michael Italian   21 | 16 | 21 | $42

G Village | 539 La Guardia Pl. (bet. Bleecker & W. 3rd Sts.) | 212-677-8577 |
www.ennioandmichael.com
Loyal locals rely on this "comforting" Village Italian for its "peaceful
ambiance" and "warm hospitality", not to mention "wholesome"
"classic" cuisine; maybe the decor's "a little plain-Jane", but in summer there's dining on the "nicest" terrace.

Enzo's Italian   23 | 14 | 20 | $35

Bronx | 1998 Williamsbridge Rd. (Neill Ave.) | 718-409-3828 M
Bronx | 2339 Arthur Ave. (bet. Crescent Ave. & E. 186th St.) | 718-733-4455
These Bronx "crowd-pleasers" prepare "standard Italian to perfection"
and "don't mess it up" with newfangled ideas; everything comes via a
"warm", "hustling" staff at "more than fair" prices, but beware – "no
reserving" equals "long waits", and once inside, the decor is "blah."

Epices du Traiteur Mediterranean/Tunisian   21 | 16 | 20 | $42

W 70s | 103 W. 70th St. (Columbus Ave.) | 212-579-5904
"Vive la différence!" declare diners "enjoying" the "interesting", "delicious" Med-Tunisian fare at this "popular" (i.e. sometimes "overcrowded") Lincoln Center–area "find"; "competent service" is a plus,
as are "affordable" rates and the garden when open.

Erawan Thai   22 | 20 | 19 | $37

Bayside | 213-41 39th Ave. (Bell Blvd.) | Queens | 718-229-1620
Bayside | 42-31 Bell Blvd. (bet. 43rd Ave. & Northern Blvd.) | Queens |
718-428-2112
www.erawan-seafoodandsteak.com
"Getting more popular all the time" (i.e. more "crowded"), these
good-buy Bayside Thais offer "top-notch" dishes running "from
traditional to exotic", with the 39th Avenue branch specializing in
Siamese takes on steak and seafood; service with a "smile" overcomes
any "language problems."

Erminia 🅱 Italian   25 | 24 | 25 | $63

E 80s | 250 E. 83rd St. (bet. 2nd & 3rd Aves.) | 212-879-4284
Romance practically "seeps from the walls" at this UES Italian "hideaway", where an "attentive staff" dispenses "delizioso" Roman dishes
in a "small, well-appointed" candlelit room; it "sets the stage" for "lovers" "to get engaged", but even old married couples suggest celebrating "happy anything" here.

Esca ● Italian/Seafood   25 | 20 | 21 | $67

W 40s | 402 W. 43rd St. (9th Ave.) | 212-564-7272 | www.esca-nyc.com
A Batali-Bastianich-Pasternak production, this "airy" Theater District
Italian seafooder has "true foodies swooning" over its "piscatory

	FOOD	DECOR	SERVICE	COST

excellence" – and "the pastas are no slouch either"; add a "solicitous"
staff and a "splurge"-size tab seems quite reasonable.

Esperanto ● *Nuevo Latino*

| | 20 | 17 | 18 | $29 |

E Village | 145 Ave. C (9th St.) | 212-505-6559 | www.esperantony.com
"Food as hot as the patrons" plus "powerful drinks" and low prices
mean this "perky" East Village Nuevo Latino speaks the language of
"young, vibrant" types who pack in for a "sultry meal" and a "good
time"; service may be "lackadaisical", but not the "lively" music.

ESPN Zone *American*

| | 12 | 19 | 14 | $29 |

W 40s | 1472 Broadway (42nd St.) | 212-921-3776 | www.espnzone.com
You can be certain "your game will be on" and the "kids will have a
blast" at this "oversized" Times Square American that's the "ultimate
in sports bars"; it's "crazy loud" and "you don't go for the food" or
the "spotty" service, but "real fans" and "tourists" give it a rousing
"rah rah" nonetheless.

Ess-a-Bagel *Deli*

| | 23 | 6 | 13 | $10 |

E 50s | 831 Third Ave. (bet. 50th & 51st Sts.) | 212-980-1010
Gramercy | 359 First Ave. (21st St.) | 212-260-2252
www.ess-a-bagel.com
"Not for carbophobes", these "rushed" East Side delis proffer "fresh,
hot, chewy" "doughy" bagels "bigger than your head", crowned with
"every topping known to man"; service is "crusty", decor "not pretty"
and lines "long", but the price is right.

Essex ● Ⓜ *American*

| | 20 | 17 | 15 | $29 |

LES | 120 Essex St. (Rivington St.) | 212-533-9616 | www.essexnyc.com
This "funky" LES New American is "packed on weekends" when
"young" locals and "Uptown tourists" mingle for the "killer" "liquid
brunch", and nobody notices "patchy" service; cognoscenti say the affordable Jewish-Latin–accented eats are "even better for dinner."

NEW Estancia 460 *Argentinean/Italian*

| | ▽ 21 | 18 | 20 | $41 |

(fka Sosa Borella)

TriBeCa | 460 Greenwich St. (bet. Desbrosses & Watts Sts.) | 212-431-5093 |
www.estancia460.com
Despite its new moniker, this TriBeCa Italian-Argentinean still feels
like the same "laid-back", "homey" place that chic "neighborhood regulars" have been coming to for years; a "winning" menu of "consistent" fare, decent prices and "friendly" service are the reasons why.

Etats-Unis *American*

| | 25 | 16 | 22 | $57 |

E 80s | 242 E. 81st St. (bet. 2nd & 3rd Aves.) | 212-517-8826
A "relaxed" UES "charmer", this "pint-size" New American offers
"consistently interesting", sometimes "inspired" dishes delivered by
"pleasant" staffers in "minimalist" digs; those seeking "the same great
food at lower prices" cross the street to its "tiny", "happening" wine bar.

etcetera etcetera ● Ⓜ *Italian*

| | 20 | 19 | 20 | $48 |

W 40s | 352 W. 44th St. (bet. 8th & 9th Aves.) | 212-399-4141 |
www.etcrestaurant.com
"Personable" waiters preside over the "stylish" setting of this "nifty"
Theater District Italian offering "inventive", "beautifully presented"
dishes, including many available in "half portions"; if the "harsh

acoustics" are irksome, keep in mind "upstairs is much quieter than down" at this "worthy spin-off of ViceVersa."

Ethiopian Restaurant *Ethiopian*

FOOD	DECOR	SERVICE	COST
17	12	17	$26

E 80s | 1582 York Ave. (bet. 83rd & 84th Sts.) | 212-717-7311

"Basic decor and basic service" accompany the "authentic Ethiopian eats" at this "informal" UES "cubbyhole"; the "vegetarian-friendly" (and wallet-friendly) fare may be an "acquired taste", but "who doesn't love eating with their hands?"

Ethos ● *Greek*

FOOD	DECOR	SERVICE	COST
22	16	19	$37

Murray Hill | 495 Third Ave. (bet. 33rd & 34th Sts.) | 212-252-1972 | www.ethosnyc.com

NEW **Astoria** | 33-04 Broadway (bet. 33rd & 34th Sts.) | Queens | 718-278-1001

"Fantastic" fish is "grilled to perfection" at this "busy" Murray Hill Greek, where the "traditional cooking" has surveyors shouting *"opa!"* and the prices have them "dancing in the aisles" – never mind the "uninspiring" decor and "slow" service; N.B. the Astoria location opened post-Survey.

NEW E.U., The ● *European*
(aka European Union)

FOOD	DECOR	SERVICE	COST
▽ 20	23	19	$43

E Village | 235 E. Fourth St. (bet. Aves. A & B) | 212-254-2900 | www.theeunyc.com

"Bringing sophistication to the gastropub model", this "ambitious", "good-looking" European done up in "signature AvroKO" style turns out an "eclectic" range of "buzzworthy" "morsels"; its "low-key" vibe suits its "young" "Alphabet City crowd", leaving "sporadic" service as its only demerit.

Euzkadi *Spanish*

FOOD	DECOR	SERVICE	COST
▽ 21	19	17	$37

E Village | 108 E. Fourth St. (bet. 1st & 2nd Aves.) | 212-982-9788 | www.euzkadirestaurant.com

"Unpronounceable" though it may be, admirers aver the name of this "fun" East Village Basque "should be on everyone's lips" given its "wonderful tapas"; an "artistic setting" and "friendly prices" attract "young" types, who add Tuesday flamenco as "another reason to come."

Evergreen Shanghai *Chinese*

FOOD	DECOR	SERVICE	COST
19	12	16	$23

Murray Hill | 10 E. 38th St. (bet. 5th & Madison Aves.) | 212-448-1199

The "genuine" "Shanghainese cuisine" at this Murray Hill Chinese includes dishes "rarely found on menus in English", as well as "marvelous dim sum" and "soup dumplings", all "priced right"; there's almost "no atmosphere" but service is "super fast" – a good thing because it's often "nuts at lunchtime."

Excellent Dumpling House ⊄ *Chinese*

FOOD	DECOR	SERVICE	COST
21	5	11	$15

Chinatown | 111 Lafayette St. (bet. Canal & Walker Sts.) | 212-219-0212

"True to its name", this usually "mobbed" Chinatowner turns out "transcendent dumplings" as well as Shanghai-style "staples" like "delicious" noodle dishes; its prices are so "low", most happily "forget" the "eat-and-run" pace, "awful decor" and "cafeteria seating" next to "strangers on jury duty."

	FOOD	DECOR	SERVICE	COST

Extra Virgin *Mediterranean* | 21 | 17 | 18 | $40 |

W Village | 259 W. Fourth St. (bet. Charles & Perry Sts.) | 212-691-9359 | www.extravirginrestaurant.com

"Pretty people" populate this "loud" West Villager serving "tempting" midpriced Med fare and a "sumptuous Sunday brunch"; those who "survive the wait" to get in find sometimes "scatterbrained" staffers and tables in "close proximity", though "sidewalk seating" is an "enjoyable" warm weather option.

NEW Fabio Piccolo Fiore *Italian* | – | – | – | M |

E 40s | 230 E. 44th St. (bet. 2nd & 3rd Aves.) | 212-922-0581

The underserved area around Grand Central gets a boost with the arrival of this "cheery" new Italian, a "grown-up" enclave that's surprisingly upscale given the down-to-earth pricing; the twist here is that the chef is willing to go beyond the menu to "prepare special requests."

Fairway Cafe *American* | 18 | 8 | 11 | $28 |

W 70s | 2127 Broadway, 2nd fl. (74th St.) | 212-595-1888
Red Hook | 480-500 Van Brunt St. (Reed St.) | Brooklyn | 718-694-6868 | www.fairwaymarket.com

"A haven" from the "hubbub" of the supermarkets they're part of, these budget-friendly "pit stops" deliver "surprisingly good" "simple" American fare, plus steaks at dinnertime in the UWS original; service is "crazy confusion" in digs "low on ambiance", though the Red Hook site boasts "priceless views" of the "harbor and Miss Liberty."

Falai ⓜ *Italian* | 25 | 19 | 21 | $53 |

LES | 68 Clinton St. (bet. Rivington & Stanton Sts.) | 212-253-1960 | www.falainyc.com
Falai Panetteria *Italian*
LES | 79 Clinton St. (Rivington St.) | 212-777-8956
NEW Caffe Falai ⮺ *Italian*
SoHo | 265 Lafayette St. (Prince St.) | 917-338-6207 | www.falainyc.com

"Outstanding" "modern" Italian fare from chef Iacopo Falai is the hallmark of this "hip", "sophisticated", minimalist" Lower Eastsider; its nearby Panetteria offshoot affords a casual alternative, while the latest progeny in SoHo, Caffe Falai, proffers "divine pastries and bread" (both serve breakast and lunch).

F & B *Hot Dogs* | 18 | 9 | 13 | $11 |

Chelsea | 269 W. 23rd St. (bet. 7th & 8th Aves.) | 646-486-4441
E 50s | 150 E. 52nd St. (bet. Lexington & 3rd Aves.) | 212-421-8600 🗷
www.gudtfood.com

"Combos for every taste" grace the lineup of "cheap" "designer franks" and "enticing toppings" proffered by this "no-guilt dog" duo, as do frites, beignets and other "interesting" Euro-style "street food"; they're certainly "nothing fancy" (champagne splits notwithstanding), so most get it "to go."

F & J Pine Restaurant ⮺ *Italian* | 20 | 19 | 19 | $34 |

Bronx | 1913 Bronxdale Ave. (bet. Morris Park Ave. & White Plains Rd.) | 718-792-5956

"Baseball fans" and others seeking "extra inning-size portions" of "red-sauce" Italian fare in the "Boogie Down" hit this "big and bustling" "Yankee hangout"; it's something of a "mob scene" with "long waits" on weekends and game days, despite scattered quibbles about "quantity over quality."

Farm on Adderley *American*   23 | 19 | 20 | $36

Ditmas Park | 1108 Cortelyou Rd. (bet. Stratford & Westminster Rds.) | Brooklyn | 718-287-3101 | www.thefarmonadderley.com

Greeted as a "godsend" to Ditmas Park, this "gracious" New American yearling "fills up quickly" with diners out to harvest "smart", "satisfying" fare cooked with "fresh, seasonal ingredients"; "cheerful" staffers, "comfortable" digs (including a back patio) and "1990 prices" brand it an oasis in a "restaurant desert."

Fatty Crab ● *Malaysian*   21 | 12 | 15 | $39

W Village | 643 Hudson St. (bet. Gansevoort & Horatio Sts.) | 212-352-3590 | www.fattycrab.com

"Bold", "no-holds-barred" Malaysian "street food" that "rocks" is the reason to "fight the crowds" at Zak Pelaccio's "hugely loud" West Village "shoebox"; service is on the "hipster-doofus" side, plus "there's the wait", but it's the "best 2 AM snack ever" – and a good buy at any time.

⊠ Felidia *Italian*   25 | 21 | 23 | $73

E 50s | 243 E. 58th St. (bet. 2nd & 3rd Aves.) | 212-758-1479 | www.lidiasitaly.com

Lidia Bastianich's "class act" is even "better than on TV" at her East Side "heavenly haute Italian", where the "exquisite" cuisine is "anything but predictable"; a "spectacular" wine list, "beautiful townhouse" setting and "stellar" staff contribute to the "memorable evenings" out, and though "you really pay", it's "worth every penny."

Félix ● *French*   16 | 17 | 15 | $41

SoHo | 340 W. Broadway (Grand St.) | 212-431-0021 | www.felixnyc.com

A "playground" for the "beautiful", "international" set, this "loud, lively", "very SoHo" French bistro delivers "decent" eats in "airy" digs with "two walls of open doors"; "brunch is a highlight", but the "rowdy patrons and inevitable dancing" always steal the show.

Ferrara ● *Bakery*   22 | 16 | 16 | $20

Little Italy | 195 Grand St. (bet. Mott & Mulberry Sts.) | 212-226-6150 | www.ferraracafe.com

With its *delizioso* pastries and espresso, this "charming", modestly priced Little Italy "landmark" has been a "heavenly dessert" haven since 1892; service may be "brassy" and the "out-of-control crowd" "touristy", but "lines move quickly", making it "a must" – "calories be damned!"

NEW Fette Sau *BBQ*   ∇ 19 | 19 | 11 | $25

Williamsburg | 354 Metropolitan Ave. (bet. Havemeyer & Roebling Sts.) | Brooklyn | 718-963-3404

At this new Williamsburg "roadhouse" from the owners of Spuyten Duyvil, you order your BBQ "by the pound", choose from an "impressive" list of whiskeys and beers on tap, and park it at a "communal" picnic table; just "get there early" because the food really does "run out."

	FOOD	DECOR	SERVICE	COST

Fiamma Osteria *Italian*   `25` `23` `23` `$66`

SoHo | 206 Spring St. (bet. 6th Ave. & Sullivan St.) | 212-653-0100 |
www.brguestrestaurants.com

"Excellent from start to finish", Steve Hanson's "gorgeous", "pricey"
SoHo triplex blends "sublime" Italian cuisine and "smooth", "pampering service" to produce an atmosphere of "simple sophistication"
that's "wonderfully romantic"; N.B. a recent renovation and a new
chef put the above ratings in question.

NEW 15 East 🅔 *Japanese*   ▽ `26` `22` `23` `$73`

Union Sq | 15 E. 15th St. (bet. 5th Ave. & Union Sq. W.) | 212-647-0015 |
www.15eastrestaurant.com

They've "done it again" swoon sushiphiles of this "exceptional" Union
Square arrival from the owners of Tocqueville; the modern Japanese
fare (via ex-Jewel Bako chef Masato Shimizu) has early fans calling it
"comparable to" the genre's top players, while "fab" service and a "relaxing" vibe help diners forget how much it all costs.

57 *American*   `22` `24` `23` `$74`

E 50s | Four Seasons Hotel | 57 E. 57th St. (Madison Ave.) | 212-829-3859 |
www.fourseasons.com

"Easy for business meetings", this "three-meal" New American dining
room off the Four Seasons' soaring I.M. Pei–designed lobby makes a
low-key "alternative" to the hotel's main eatery, L'Atelier de Joël
Robuchon; most consider it a "comfortable" choice, except when it
comes to paying.

Fig & Olive *Mediterranean*   `20` `20` `18` `$44`

E 60s | 808 Lexington Ave. (bet. 62nd & 63rd Sts.) | 212-207-4555
NEW Fig & Olive Downtown 🌙 *Mediterranean*

Meatpacking | 420 W. 13th St. (bet. 9th Ave. & Washington St.) |
212-924-1200
www.figandolive.com

"Olive oil–infused everything" is the signature of this "lively"
Mediterranean duo offering "fresh, flavorful" "little plates" as well as
"oils, tapenades" and such to buy; the newer Meatpacking District
branch "is bigger and prettier", but both suffer from "erratic service."

F.illi Ponte 🅔 *Italian*   `21` `20` `21` `$63`

TriBeCa | 39 Desbrosses St. (West St.) | 212-226-4621 |
www.filliponte.com

The "traditional Italian" fare is a tremendous, theatrical "treat" at this
way West TriBeCan, where the vibe is "old-school" (think "Brooklyn in
Manhattan"), the pace "slow" and the "wiseguys-and-wannabes"
crowd isn't the kind you joke about; the "mighty-fine view of the Hudson"
is good enough to trump "expensive" tabs, especially at sunset.

Fino 🅔 *Italian*   ▽ `20` `17` `21` `$47`

Financial District | 1 Wall Street Ct. (Pearl St.) | 212-825-1924 |
www.finony.com
Murray Hill | 4 E. 36th St. (bet. 5th & Madison Aves.) | 212-689-8040
"Old-style" Italian "with service to match" can be found at this "consistent" twosome offering "well-prepared" standards in a "soothing,
quiet atmosphere" conducive to "business lunches or dinners"; the
Murray Hill original loses points for digs that are not so fino anymore.

	FOOD	DECOR	SERVICE	COST

Fiorentino's *Italian* — 19 | 13 | 18 | $32

Gravesend | 311 Ave. U (bet. McDonald Ave. & West St.) | Brooklyn | 718-372-1445

"Large portions" of "zesty", "homey", "authentic Brooklyn" Neapolitan fare and "generous, cheap" pours keep this Gravesend "favorite" "mobbed" and "noisy"; maybe the "1974 decor" "needs a face-lift", but the "family atmosphere" and big "bang for your buck" justify "long waits" on weekends.

NEW Fiorini 🛇 *Italian* — - | - | - | M

E 50s | 209 E. 56th St. (bet. 2nd & 3rd Aves.) | 212-308-0830 | www.fiorinirestaurant.com

Longtime restaurateur Lello Arpaia returns to East Midtown with this elegant, moderately priced (for the neighborhood) arrival serving up old-school Italian favorites and wines from The Boot; its cream-colored quarters clad with cherry-red booths are presided over by accommodating, *Italiano*-speaking servers.

FireBird Ⓜ *Russian* — 18 | 25 | 20 | $62

W 40s | 365 W. 46th St. (bet. 8th & 9th Aves.) | 212-586-0244 | www.firebirdrestaurant.com

You'll "feel like Russian royalty" at this "lush", "atmospheric" Restaurant Row duplex "full of artwork" "from the czarist era"; "solid standbys like blini with caviar" and "honey-infused vodka" served by "attentive", "tunic-clad" staffers keep up the illusion, but "boy, you pay for it."

Firenze ◑ *Italian* — 21 | 20 | 22 | $44

E 80s | 1594 Second Ave. (bet. 82nd & 83rd Sts.) | 212-861-9368

Though "barely bigger than a breadbox", this "tempting" Tuscan trattoria on the UES is a favorite for "romance", turning out "super" Tuscan dishes via a "friendly" staff; "she'll be smiling through the candlelight", especially after the "free grappa" that rounds out the "memorable experience."

NEW Fireside *Eclectic* — ▽ 21 | 19 | 18 | $57

E 50s | Omni Berkshire Place Hotel | 19 E. 52nd St. (bet. 5th & Madison Aves.) | 212-754-5011 | www.fireside-nyc.com

At this "trendy" Midtown newcomer in the Omni Berkshire Place, a dramatic floor-to-ceiling hearth is the focal point, and the crowd a mix of tourists and nearby business types; the draw is the "pricey" but "remarkably good" lineup of Eclectic small plates that chef Sam DeMarco (ex First) terms 'cocktail cuisine.'

Fish *Seafood* — 20 | 14 | 18 | $39

G Village | 280 Bleecker St. (Jones St.) | 212-727-2879

A "fishmonger on the premises" hints at the "quality" at this "laid-back" yet "energetic" faux "New England fish shack" in the Village; the chef's "wizardry with seafood" far outweighs the "sketchy service" and "cool hovel" digs, while "fair prices" are the catch of the day.

Five Front *American* — 21 | 19 | 19 | $39

Dumbo | 5 Front St. (Old Fulton St.) | Brooklyn | 718-625-5559 | www.fivefrontrestaurant.com

Something of a "hidden gem", this "unpretentious" Dumbo "neighborhood bistro" turns out "serious" New American fare in "pretty" quarters; for a "magical evening", "grab a seat" in the "gorgeous" bamboo garden with the "Brooklyn Bridge yawning above" – occasional "slow" service is the "only flaw", but moderate prices compensate.

NEW Five Guys *Hamburgers*

| – | – | – | I |

Brooklyn Heights | 138 Montague St. (bet. Clinton & Henry Sts.) | Brooklyn | 718-797-9380
College Point | 132-01 14th Ave. (132nd St.) | Queens | 718-767-6500
www.fiveguys.com

The first NYC links of a chain voted one of the most popular in our DC Survey, these outer-borough burger joints are set to be joined soon by three Manhattan locations; the service is strictly assembly-line and the ketchup-red digs geared mostly for takeout, but low prices encourage return visits.

5 Ninth ● *Eclectic*

| 19 | 21 | 18 | $53 |

Meatpacking | 5 Ninth Ave. (bet. Gansevoort & Little W. 12th Sts.) | 212-929-9460 | www.5ninth.com

Though its founding chef has left, this "hip" Meatpacking District townhouse carries on with "bold" Eclectic fare served to a "pretty" crowd; the "sweet back garden" wins raves, but a few say it doesn't make up for the "uneven service" and "expensive" tabs.

Five Points ● *American/Mediterranean*

| 22 | 21 | 20 | $47 |

NoHo | 31 Great Jones St. (bet. Bowery & Lafayette St.) | 212-253-5700 | www.fivepointsrestaurant.com

A "stream running through" the room to "a skylit nook" in back brings a touch of "soothing" "Zen" to this otherwise "thunderous" NoHo Med–New American; "hordes" gather for its "talented cooking", including a "spectacular" brunch, served by a "cheerful" staff.

NEW Flatbush Farm *American*

| ∇ 19 | 19 | 18 | $37 |

Park Slope | 76 St. Marks Ave. (bet. Flatbush & 6th Aves.) | 718-622-3276 | www.flatbushfarm.com

The mood is always "easygoing" at this "friendly" Park Slope yearling whose New American fare comes in "minimalist" quarters done up with "rustic farm implements"; though some cite "inconsistency" as a problem, all agree they're "trying hard" and a new chef post-Survey shows promise.

Flea Market Cafe ● *French*

| 19 | 17 | 16 | $28 |

E Village | 131 Ave. A (bet. 9th St. & St. Marks Pl.) | 212-358-9282

Apart from its "transporting" "Tompkins Square Park view", this "cheery" East Village bistro has a real "Parisian feel", with "cheap", "simple French food", "funky" decor ("everything's for sale") and generally "no-attitude" service; given all that, most "put up with dense seating" and high decibels.

Fleur de Sel *French*

| 25 | 21 | 23 | $91 |

Flatiron | 5 E. 20th St. (bet. B'way & 5th Ave.) | 212-460-9100 | www.fleurdeselnyc.com

"Petite and charming", Cyril Renaud's "transcendent" prix fixe-only Flatiron French blooms with "extraordinary" Breton dishes that are "creative without being outlandish"; a "splendid" if "high-end" "wine selection" and "unobtrusive" service make dinner a "special occasion", albeit a "stiffly priced" one, while the $29 prix fixe lunch is "a swell deal."

	FOOD	DECOR	SERVICE	COST

Flor de Mayo ◐ *Chinese/Peruvian*   20 | 9 | 16 | $21

W 80s | 484 Amsterdam Ave. (bet. 83rd & 84th Sts.) | 212-787-3388
W 100s | 2651 Broadway (101st St.) | 212-663-5520

Diners "come out raving" about the "celestial" rotisserie chicken at these "busy" UWS Chinese-Peruvians; despite "run-down" digs, they're favorites with those on "a shoestring budget", so there's "almost always a wait."

Flor de Sol ☒ *Spanish*   20 | 20 | 19 | $42

TriBeCa | 361 Greenwich St. (bet. Franklin & Harrison Sts.) | 212-366-1640 | www.flordesolnyc.com

"Tops for tapas", this "flirty" TriBeCa Spaniard's "seductive", candlelit ambiance also makes it a perfect "date" place, "noisy" acoustics notwithstanding; the midweek "flamenco music" livens things up, as does the "killer sangria" and "hot" staff.

Florent ◐ *French*   20 | 14 | 16 | $31

Meatpacking | 69 Gansevoort St. (bet. Greenwich & Washington Sts.) | 212-989-5779 | www.restaurantflorent.com

"Good, honest" French bistro fare "shines" 24/7 at this Meatpacking District "original"; it's the "come-as-you-are eclectic" clientele, "kitschy" diner digs and "entertainingly snippy staff" that make it "a hoot in the middle of the night" – though it's "one cool hang" at any time, and a bargain too.

Flor's Kitchen *Venezuelan*   ▽ 16 | 13 | 18 | $28

G Village | 170 Waverly Pl. (Christopher St.) | 212-229-9926 | www.florskitchen.com

Greenwich Villagers flock to this "cute", "tiny" Venezuelan for "satisfying arepas" and such; the "simple" eats are a rare "easy-on-the-wallet" option in these parts, while the "lovely" staff contributes to its "warm, neighborhood" feel.

Food Bar ◐ *American*   16 | 15 | 16 | $31

Chelsea | 149 Eighth Ave. (bet. 17th & 18th Sts.) | 212-243-2020

"Cool, hip, trendy, cute – but enough about the waiters" at this "festive", *"très gay"* Chelsea New American; "no one comes for the food", but happily "hanging with friends" while taking in the "eye candy" comes at "reasonable" rates.

Fornino *Pizza*   22 | 14 | 17 | $22

Williamsburg | 187 Bedford Ave. (N. 7th St.) | Brooklyn | 718-384-6004

"Subtle flavors" from the "freshest ingredients" (including herbs from the back garden) make the "fancy" brick-oven pizza at this Williamsburg emporium just about "as good as it gets"; the decor is "not as inspired", though, so "delivery and takeout" should be kept in mind.

44 & X Hell's Kitchen ◐ *American*   21 | 18 | 19 | $45

W 40s | 622 10th Ave. (44th St.) | 212-977-1170 | www.44andX.com

"Delicious" "spins" on comfort classics (e.g. "kickin' mac 'n' cheese"), "sassy" "model/waiters" and "fresh, bright" digs make this Hell's Kitchen American "stand out"; "extra-loud" acoustics and a "gas station" view don't stop the "crowds" from coming.

	FOOD	DECOR	SERVICE	COST

Z Four Seasons ☑ *Continental* — 25 | 27 | 26 | $91

E 50s | 99 E. 52nd St. (bet. Lexington & Park Aves.) | 212-754-9494 | www.fourseasonsrestaurant.com

Still a "stunner" after nearly 50 years, this "timeless" Midtown "classic" (led by suave host-owners Alex von Bidder and Julian Niccolini) delivers "first-class" Continental cuisine to an "oh-so-urbane crowd" that's practically a "who's who of the city", while service is "superior" and the "NY landmark" surroundings famously "sleek and sumptuous"; regulars tout lunching among "power players" in the Grill room or in the "serene" Pool Room at night, allowing that, yes, it's "expensive", but "if it's awesome you want, this is the place"; N.B. jackets required.

Fragole *Italian* — 23 | 17 | 20 | $29

Carroll Gardens | 394 Court St. (bet. Carroll St. & 1st Pl.) | Brooklyn | 718-522-7133 | www.fragoleny.com

"Simple", "flavorful" Italian dishes that stand out in the "red-sauce neighborhood" of Carroll Gardens make this "unassuming little hole-in-the-wall" one "popular" place; the "long list of blackboard specials", "warm" service and "gentle prices" are other reasons it's a "winner."

Francisco's Centro Vasco *Spanish* — 22 | 13 | 18 | $45

Chelsea | 159 W. 23rd St. (bet. 6th & 7th Aves.) | 212-645-6224

"It's all about" the "succulent, gargantuan lobsters" at this "festive" (read: noisy) Chelsea Spanish "old-timer", so "strap on a bib" and make allowances for "servers doing their best" in digs that "could use sprucing up"; after all, the "deals" are almost as "mouthwatering" as the crustaceans.

Frank ●⊟ *Italian* — 24 | 14 | 16 | $33

E Village | 88 Second Ave. (bet. 5th & 6th Sts.) | 212-420-0202 | www.frankrestaurant.com

"They ain't lining up outside all night for nothin'" say fans of this "homey" East Village Italian and its "cheap", "robust, bristling-with-flavor" eats; frankly, service is "rushed, even brusque", and space "unbelievably tight" – "it should be annoying, but instead it's wonderful."

Frankie & Johnnie's Steakhouse ☑ *Steak* — 21 | 14 | 19 | $59

Garment District | 32 W. 37th St. (bet. 5th & 6th Aves.) | 212-947-8940
W 40s | 269 W. 45th St. (bet. B'way & 8th Ave.) ● www.frankieandjohnnies.com

"Hungry carnivores" get their fixes at these "old-fashioned" chophouses where super steaks are "prepared with care" and served by "pro" staffers; the "tired" Times Square mezzanine original shows its 1926 "speakeasy beginnings", while the newer Garment District spin-off in John Barrymore's onetime townhouse has "charm."

Frankies Spuntino *Italian* — 24 | 19 | 19 | $33

LES | 17 Clinton St. (bet. Houston & Stanton Sts.) | 212-253-2303 ●
Carroll Gardens | 457 Court St. (bet. 4th Pl. & Luquer St.) | Brooklyn | 718-403-0033 ⊟
www.frankiesspuntino.com

"Rustic Italian" small plates with "robust flavors" and "sophisticated twists" come out of "teeny kitchens" at this "low-key" duo; it lacks the "wonderful garden" of the Carroll Gardens original, but the newer LES "walk-in closet" is still "charming", and both boast "gentle prices."

	FOOD	DECOR	SERVICE	COST

Frank's *Italian/Steak* — 19 | 13 | 17 | $52

Chelsea | 410 W. 16th St. (bet. 9th & 10th Aves.) | 212-243-1349
A real "guy's place", this "casual", "old-style" Italian steakhouse proffers aged beef and "great beers" within a "sparsely decorated" Chelsea Market space behind the family-run butcher shop; service is "friendly", if "slow", so most just sit back and enjoy the "camaraderie."

Franny's Ⓜ *Pizza* — 23 | 17 | 19 | $34

Prospect Heights | 295 Flatbush Ave. (bet. Prospect Pl. & St. Marks Ave.) | Brooklyn | 718-230-0221 | www.frannysbrooklyn.com
The "sophisticated", "crispy-crust" pies come with "local, seasonal", "housemade" credentials at this "upscale" Prospect Heights pizza place that also does "divine" "apps", pastas and "innovative cocktails"; "pleasant" service and a "date"-worthy backyard hit a high note, but some feel the prices are relatively "steep" "for what you get."

Fratelli *Italian* — ▽ 21 | 17 | 20 | $34

Bronx | 2507 Eastchester Rd. (Mace Ave.) | 718-547-2489
Turning out "typical" standards but "delicious" specials, this "quaint, romantic" white-tablecloth Bronx Italian earns its status as a "popular neighborhood place"; service is "good", prices "affordable" and it's "quiet" enough to "have a conversation", so really "you can't go wrong."

Fraunces Tavern Ⓢ *American* — 15 | 21 | 18 | $43

Financial District | 54 Pearl St. (Broad St.) | 212-968-1776 |
www.frauncestavern.com
You "dine with the ghosts of the Colonial army" at this "charming" "landmark" tavern dating back to 1762; the Traditional American fare is "only so-so" (hopefully "George Washington had better luck"), so most consider it good for a drink when in the Financial District but otherwise "strictly for history buffs" and "out-of-towners."

NEW Frederick's — 19 | 16 | 17 | $58

Downtown ❶ *French/Mediterranean*
W Village | 637 Hudson St. (Horatio St.) | 212-488-4200
Frederick's Madison *French/Mediterranean*
E 60s | 768 Madison Ave. (bet. 65th & 66th Sts.) | 212-737-7300
www.fredericksnyc.com
The French-Med fare is "good" at these "trendy" "magnets" for "Gucci and Prada"-clad "Euros", but they're mostly about the "fun scene"; sidewalk seats are a plus at the UES branch, while the new Villager is "working out kinks" – if they're "expensive", that's the price of "chic."

Fred's at Barneys NY *American/Italian* — 20 | 18 | 17 | $46

E 60s | Barneys NY | 660 Madison Ave., 9th fl. (60th St.) | 212-833-2200
"Fashionistas" "rest from the rigors of shopping" at this "frenetic" Midtown Tuscan–New American serving "solid", predictably "expensive" fare; "hearty" portions "can feed two people (or four models)", and though service is merely "middling", at dinner there's "less turmoil."

Freemans ❶ *American* — 21 | 23 | 19 | $42

LES | Freeman Alley (off Rivington St., bet. Bowery & Chrystie St.) | 212-420-0012 | www.freemansrestaurant.com
"Hidden" down a "narrow alley", this "eccentric" LES New American earns its "high hipness quotient" with a blend of "amazing" "comfort

	FOOD	DECOR	SERVICE	COST

food" and "lodgelike", "taxidermy-chic" looks; a recent expansion has shortened waits, but the "friendly" staff still can get "overwhelmed" by the "beautiful" "throngs."

French Roast ● *French* — 14 | 14 | 13 | $27

G Village | 78 W. 11th St. (6th Ave.) | 212-533-2233
W 80s | 2340 Broadway (85th St.) | 212-799-1533
www.frenchroastny.com

Stick with "something simple" and this "pseudo-French" pair providing "passable" eats will suffice; hey, they're "cheap" and "open 24/7", so even with "somnambulant service" and "squished" "fake bistro" digs, they're "a godsend when you need a midnight snack."

Fresco by Scotto ⊠ *Italian* — 23 | 19 | 21 | $61

E 50s | 34 E. 52nd St. (bet. Madison & Park Aves.) | 212-935-3434

Fresco on the Go ⊠ *Italian*

E 50s | 40 E. 52nd St. (bet. Madison & Park Aves.) | 212-754-2700
www.frescobyscotto.com

"Local news and TV celebs" show up at the "hospitable" Scotto family's Midtown Tuscan "powerhouse", a "lively, bright" setting for "fabulous" food and "attentive" service; for less of a "wallet buster", the take-out annex offers "Fresco food at deli prices" – "what's not to like?"

fresh *Seafood* — 24 | 20 | 22 | $60

TriBeCa | 105 Reade St. (bet. Church St. & W. B'way) | 212-406-1900 | www.freshrestaurantnyc.com

A "seafood lover's" "paradise", this "out-of-the-way" "upscale" TriBeCan "doesn't get enough attention" declare devotees of its "superbly fresh" fin fare; a "lovely staff" presides over its "spacious" "serene room", so its "loud" acoustics at prime times and high prices all the time are the only downsides.

Friend of a Farmer *American* — 17 | 18 | 16 | $29

Gramercy | 77 Irving Pl. (bet. 18th & 19th Sts.) | 212-477-2188

"Escape the city" at this "cheerful" "little country inn" transplanted to Gramercy, complete with "exposed beams", "comfy fireplace" and "tasty", modestly priced homespun American fare; the "snail's-pace" service doesn't help the "huge lines" that form at weekend brunch, but for most it's "worth the wait."

NEW FR.OG ⊠ *Eclectic/French* — ▽ 21 | 16 | 15 | $59

SoHo | 71 Spring St. (bet. Crosby & Lafayette Sts.) | 212-966-5050 | www.frognyc.com

Its name stands for 'France Origine', the thread uniting all of chef Didier Virot's "excellent" global dishes, which dart from Morocco to Vietnam and are served in a "stark-white" SoHo duplex accented with "over-the-top" splashes of color; exotic libations from bars both upstairs and down fuel the scene.

Fuleen Seafood ● *Chinese/Seafood* — ▽ 24 | 9 | 16 | $26

Chinatown | 11 Division St. (bet. Bowery & E. B'way) | 212-941-6888

"Truly singular tastes" swim your way at this "excellent" Chinatown seafooder where fish "directly from the tanks" is "masterfully prepared" "Hong Kong–style" way into the wee hours; "dull" decor and "language-related confusion" are swept away by the prices – "what a deal!"

	FOOD	DECOR	SERVICE	COST

Fushimi *Japanese* ▽ 26 | 24 | 22 | $48

Staten Island | 2110 Richmond Rd. (Lincoln Ave.) | 718-980-5300
An "evening of pleasure" awaits at this Staten Island Japanese "standout" known for its "wonderful array" of "consistently excellent" sushi as well as for its "hectic", "trendy" "Manhattan"-esque ambiance; even its "city prices" don't slow the "happening bar scene."

Gabriela's *Mexican* 17 | 17 | 16 | $32

W 90s | 688 Columbus Ave. (bet. 93rd & 94th Sts.) | 212-961-0574 | www.gabrielas.com
"Spacious" and "cheery", this UWS "everyday Mexican" is usually "filled to overflowing" – just like the "big" plates of "tasty" eats; nostalgists claim it's "not the same" since moving to more "upscale" digs last year, but no one complains about the "fab patio" or "amazing margaritas."

Gabriel's ☒ *Italian* 22 | 19 | 22 | $60

W 60s | 11 W. 60th St. (bet. B'way & Columbus Ave.) | 212-956-4600 | www.gabrielsbarandrest.com
Gabriel Aiello's "gracious touch" is in evidence at his "delightful", "understated" Tuscan "stalwart" near Lincoln Center, where an always "interesting crowd" convenes for "terrific" fare ferried by a "cordial" staff "choreographed to curtain-time"; an "impressive, reasonably priced wine list" caps it all off.

Gahm Mi Oak ● *Korean* ▽ 22 | 13 | 16 | $21

Garment District | 43 W. 32nd St. (bet. B'way & 5th Ave.) | 212-695-4113
"Magnificent" "Korean soul food" fixes can be found 24/7 at this "inexpensive", "dependable" Garment Districter beloved for its "famed hangover cure", "heavenly *sollongtang*" soup; as for the "spartan" digs, "after a long night of partying" most hardly notice.

Gallagher's Steak House ● *Steak* 20 | 17 | 18 | $62

W 50s | 228 W. 52nd St. (bet. B'way & 8th Ave.) | 212-245-5336 | www.gallaghersnysteakhouse.com
"Classic NY" from its "top-quality", top-dollar steaks to its "ornery waiters", this "honest-to-goodness, old-time chophouse" has been a Theater District "mainstay" since 1927; yes, it's "a little run-down" but the "gritty", sports-memorabilia-and-checkered-tablecloth atmosphere is part of its "manly" charm.

☒ Garden Cafe ☒Ⓜ *American* 27 | 20 | 25 | $50

Prospect Heights | 620 Vanderbilt Ave. (Prospect Pl.) | Brooklyn | 718-857-8863
There must be "magic" in the "postage-stamp kitchen" at John and Camille Policastro's "petite" Prospect Heights New American for it to conjure food this "fabulous"; a "convivial", "romantic" vibe, "personal attention" and all-around "understated class" ensure that customers "dress nicely" and "keep coming back" "for those special nights" here.

Gargiulo's *Italian* 21 | 18 | 21 | $43

Coney Island | 2911 W. 15th St. (bet. Mermaid & Surf Aves.) | Brooklyn | 718-266-4891 | www.gargiulos.com
"Take your nonny" and "your appetite" to this "cavernous" circa-1907 Coney Island Southern Italian "landmark" for "satisfying" fare straight

outta the "heyday of cuisine in Brooklyn", delivered by "outstanding", "old-time" waiters; the "fun part" is "rolling the dice" after dinner – "if you get lucky" the meal's free.

	FOOD	DECOR	SERVICE	COST

☑ **Gari** *Japanese* | 26 | 14 | 20 | $73 |

W 70s | 370 Columbus Ave. (bet. 77th & 78th Sts.) | 212-362-4816

☑ **Sushi of Gari** Ⓜ *Japanese*

E 70s | 402 E. 78th St. (bet. 1st & York Aves.) | 212-517-5340

☑ NEW **Sushi of Gari 46** Ⓜ *Japanese*

W 40s | 347 W. 46th St. (bet. 8th & 9th Aves.) | 212-957-0046

Gari Sugio's Japanese empire continues to grow, with a new Restaurant Row outpost joining his "wonderful" UES and UWS locations; no matter where you taste it, his "right-out-of-the-ocean" sushi is "exquisite" and "totally unique", and the omakase option an opportunity for "multiple novel treats" – though a "trip to Japan may be less expensive."

Gascogne *French* | 22 | 19 | 21 | $49 |

Chelsea | 158 Eighth Ave. (bet. 17th & 18th Sts.) | 212-675-6564 | www.gascognenyc.com

Its "warm farmhouse feel" "transports you to SW France", while this Chelsea "sleeper's" "terrific cassoulet" and other "solid" bistro classics "warm" the soul; a few claustrophobes chafe in the "cramped space", but all agree "for a sure thing, take a date" to the "*très romantique*" back garden.

NEW **Gaucho Steak Co.** *Argentinean/Steak* | - | - | - | M |

W 50s | 752 10th Ave. (bet. 51st & 52nd Sts.) | 212-957-1727 | www.gauchosteakco.com

On a rapidly gentrifying Hell's Kitchen strip, chef Alex Garcia (Calle Ocho) has opened this gaucho-themed, wood and leather-adorned Argentinean steakhouse; it dishes up good-value offerings – none of the sizable cuts of grass-fed Uruguayan beef top $20 – that can be washed down with sangria or South American wines.

Gavroche *French* | 19 | 16 | 19 | $42 |

W Village | 212 W. 14th St. (bet. 7th Ave. S. & 8th Ave.) | 212-647-8553 | www.gavroche-ny.com

A "beautiful garden" makes this West Village French bistro an "oasis" on a busy street; its "no-nonsense" offerings – including a "high-value" $20 early-bird – are served "without pretense" under the supervision of a "friendly, attentive" owner; in short, it's an overall "comfortable" choice.

Geisha Ⓢ *Japanese* | 23 | 21 | 20 | $61 |

E 60s | 33 E. 61st St. (bet. Madison & Park Aves.) | 212-813-1112 | www.geisharestaurant.com

"Innovative", "jewel-bright" French-influenced Japanese cuisine comes "with a side of beautiful people" at this East 60s duplex; the David Rockwell-designed space is "hip" yet "lovely", though tight tables and "nouvelle portions" at "nouvelle prices" may be problems.

NEW **Gemma** ☻ *Italian* | - | - | - | E |

E Village | Bowery Hotel | 335 Bowery (E. 3rd St.) | 212-505-9100 | www.theboweryhotel.com

In the chic new Bowery Hotel comes this buzzy Italian with an open kitchen, wood-fired pizza oven and a serious chef behind the burners;

the warm room resembles a rustic farmhouse, with windowed doors that open to the street in warm weather – something unthinkable in these parts just a few years back.

	FOOD	DECOR	SERVICE	COST

Gennaro ⧸ *Italian*

25 | 14 | 17 | $38

W 90s | 665 Amsterdam Ave. (bet. 92nd & 93rd Sts.) | 212-665-5348 | www.gennarorestaurant.com

Upper Westsiders gennar-ally gush over this "unassuming" cash-only Italian "gem", citing "sophisticated" preparations at "bargain" prices; to cope with "awful lines", "crapshoot" service and a room "packed tighter than a box of pasta", go at off-hours.

NEW Georgia's Eastside BBQ Ⓜ⧸ *BBQ*

– | – | – | I

LES | 192 Orchard St. (bet. Houston & Stanton Sts.) | 212-253-6280

Mounds of barbecued ribs on the cheap, beer-steamed before grilling, Georgia-style, are the deal at this rib-thin LES roadhouse; it has but a modicum of kitsch and even fewer tables – but if you can't find a seat there's always takeout as an option.

Ghenet *Ethiopian*

▽ 22 | 14 | 16 | $31

NoLita | 284 Mulberry St. (bet. Houston & Prince Sts.) | 212-343-1888 | www.ghenet.com

At this "low-key" NoLita Ethiopian, the "terrific combinations" of "spicy", family-style Ethiopian eats are "scooped and blended" with traditional injera bread rather than fork and spoon; "somewhat slow" service is outweighed by very "fair" rates for the chance to "amaze your taste buds."

Giambelli ● *Italian*

21 | 17 | 22 | $59

E 50s | 46 E. 50th St. (bet. Madison & Park Aves.) | 212-688-2760 | www.giambelli50th.com

For "a trip down memory lane" *amici* meander over to this 50-year-old Midtown ristorante, where "civilized" staffers who've "been there forever" serve up "delicious" Italian standards; never mind if trendier types rate the experience "tired" and "overpriced."

Gigino at Wagner Park *Italian*

20 | 19 | 19 | $42

Financial District | 20 Battery Pl. (West St.) | 212-528-2228 | www.gigino-wagnerpark.com

Gigino Trattoria *Italian*

TriBeCa | 323 Greenwich St. (bet. Duane & Reade Sts.) | 212-431-1112 | www.gigino-trattoria.com

TriBeCa families flock to this "rough-hewn", midpriced "Roman trattoria" for "solid", "casual" favorites like "thin and crispy pizzas"; its sleeker, smaller Battery Park sibling – whose "marvelous" patio offers "breathtaking" views of Lady Liberty and the harbor – not surprisingly draws a more "touristy" crowd.

Gilt Ⓢ Ⓜ *American*

▽ 25 | 26 | 25 | $109

E 50s | NY Palace Hotel | 455 Madison Ave. (bet. 50th & 51st Sts.) | 212-891-8100 | www.giltnewyork.com

"Living up to its name", this "elegant" Midtown showplace is a "sublime" foil for new chef Christopher Lee's "divine" yet "user-friendly" New American cuisine offered via a $78 (and up) prix fixe-only menu; its "stunning" "mural and statue"-adorned space meets the gold standard, as do its 1,500-strong wine list and "impeccable" service, adding up to undeniably "decadent" experiences that leave luxury-loving loyalists "feeling no guilt."

Ginger Chinese

∇ 21 | 19 | 18 | $29

Harlem | 1400 Fifth Ave. (116th St.) | 212-423-1111 | www.gingerexpress.com

Specializing in heart-healthy Chinese-style dishes, this East Harlem standout makes its "neighborhood crowd" "happier and happier"; the room's "loungelike" look also elevates it above the average Sino spot; N.B. a recent chef change may outdate the above Food score.

Gin Lane ● Continental

17 | 24 | 19 | $54

Chelsea | 355 W. 14th St. (bet. 8th & 9th Aves.) | 212-691-0555 | www.ginlanenyc.com

"Cool", "classy" quarters crowned with a "huge", "unexpected" skylight give this Chelsea Continental yearling a "dramatic" look; many find its "standard" eats "underwhelming" and "overpriced", but "divine" specialty cocktails made by "cute, savvy" mixologists help compensate.

Gino ⊄ Italian

21 | 13 | 20 | $48

E 60s | 780 Lexington Ave. (bet. 60th & 61st Sts.) | 212-758-4466

From the "hearty" Southern Italian "home cooking" to the "funky zebra" wallpaper and "gentlemanly" "career waiters", this "institution" near Bloomingdale's is a "throwback to the '50s"; critics call it "cramped" and "shabby", but *amici* who adore its "utter lack of pretension" assert "some things should never change."

Giorgione Italian

23 | 19 | 20 | $49

SoHo | 307 Spring St. (bet. Greenwich & Hudson Sts.) | 212-352-2269

Giorgione 508 Italian

SoHo | 508 Greenwich St. (bet. Canal & Spring Sts.) | 212-219-2444

Touting "top-notch ingredients" from owner and eminent grocer Giorgio DeLuca, this "hip" West SoHo trattoria is a "fun place" to savor "delicious" Italian fare and vino while "taking in the scene"; servers are "charming but harried" amid the "bustle", so some opt for the nearby cafe/mini-market 508 instead.

Giorgio's of Gramercy American

22 | 17 | 21 | $47

Flatiron | 27 E. 21st St. (bet. B'way & Park Ave. S.) | 212-477-0007 | www.giorgiosofgramercy.com

"Cozy" and "intimate", this Flatiron "hidden treasure" offers terrific, "something-for-everyone" New American cuisine delivered by a staff that "knows its food and wine"; it may not be cheap, but its "hefty portions" make for "great value."

Giovanni Venticinque Italian

∇ 22 | 19 | 22 | $61

E 80s | 25 E. 83rd St. (bet. 5th & Madison Aves.) | 212-988-7300

"Just a hop-step away from the Met", this UES Italian refreshes "weary museumgoers" with its "excellent", albeit "expensive", Tuscan fare ferried by "efficient" staffers; its "quiet", candlelit quarters allow diners to "actually converse", making it a fallback for many a mature local.

Girasole ● Italian

20 | 15 | 20 | $56

E 80s | 151 E. 82nd St. (bet. Lexington & 3rd Aves.) | 212-772-6690

It's "not exactly trendy", but this "reliable" UES ristorante still draws crowds of "wealthy over-50" types with its "satisfying", "inventive" cucina and "professional" service; at dinnertime the "understated" environs are "full of life" (read: "noisy").

	FOOD	DECOR	SERVICE	COST

Gnocco Caffe ● Italian — ▽ 21 | 16 | 18 | $37

E Village | 337 E. 10th St. (bet. Aves. A & B) | 212-677-1913 | www.gnocco.com

The namesake fried-dough appetizer "will gnocc your socks off" and the pizzas are "delicious" too at this "quaint" East Villager; the "lovely" garden and low prices have locals calling it a "major sleeper."

Gobo Vegan/Vegetarian — 22 | 18 | 18 | $32

E 80s | 1426 Third Ave. (81st St.) | 212-288-5099
G Village | 401 Sixth Ave. (bet. 8th St. & Waverly Pl.) | 212-255-3242 ●
www.goborestaurant.com

"For the sophisticated vegan" and curious carnivore alike, this "upscale" Village-UES pair delivers "creative", Asian-accented vegetarian fare via a "chef with imagination"; other appeals are "calming" settings that are somehow "both bustling and Zen" and "budget"-friendly rates.

Golden Unicorn Chinese — 20 | 12 | 13 | $24

Chinatown | 18 E. Broadway, 2nd fl. (Catherine St.) | 212-941-0911

A "dim sum bonanza" awaits at this "big, loud" Chinatown vet where "locals and visitors alike" "eat themselves silly" on "sumptuous, lip-smacking" morsels from "swift" rolling carts; the weekend scene gets "wild and crazy", but "get there before noon and the wait's minimal."

NEW Gold St. ● Eclectic — ▽ 15 | 17 | 18 | $26

Financial District | 2 Gold St. (bet. Maiden Ln. & Platt St.) | 212-747-0797 | www.goldstnyc.com

"Finally a 24-hour joint in the Financial District" cheer customers of this "diner"-inspired newcomer whose "huge variety" of affordable Eclectic fare spans everything from sushi to Kobe sliders to breakfast classics served round the clock; its sprawling setup includes a full bar and outdoor seating, with "accommodating" service to ice the cake.

Gonzo Italian/Pizza — 21 | 17 | 18 | $45

G Village | 140 W. 13th St. (bet. 6th Ave. & 7th Ave. S.) | 212-645-4606

"Delicious grilled pizzas" with "razor-thin" crusts and "toppings that change seasonally" are the trademark of this "friendly" Village Italian; the "lovely" back dining room with its high "painted-wood ceiling" "gets pretty noisy", but "easy-on-the-pocketbook" prices compensate.

good American — 20 | 16 | 18 | $33

W Village | 89 Greenwich Ave. (bet. Bank & W. 12th Sts.) | 212-691-8080 | www.goodrestaurantnyc.com

The "epitome of a neighborhood eatery", this "friendly, down-to-earth" West Village New American "lives up to its name" with "superior baked goods" and other "comfort" dishes "prepared with care"; it's known especially as a "brunch-lover's heaven", so "get there early" or face "lines."

goodburger Hamburgers — 18 | 8 | 12 | $13

E 40s | 800 Second Ave. (43rd St.) | 212-922-1700
NEW E 50s | 636 Lexington Ave. (54th St.) | 212-838-6000
www.goodburgerny.com

Its name represents "truth in advertising" declare devotees of this "funky" East Midtown duo's "juicy", "made-to-order" patties; "when

	FOOD	DECOR	SERVICE	COST

you want the grease", its "tiny" burgers – along with "crispy" fries and "diet-blowing" shakes – "hit the spot", though a budget-minded few cite prices a bit "high" for "fast food."

Good Enough to Eat *American* | 20 | 15 | 16 | $25 |

W 80s | 483 Amsterdam Ave. (bet. 83rd & 84th Sts.) | 212-496-0163 | www.goodenoughtoeat.com
It slings "down-home", "affordable" Americana "like you wish you had the energy to cook", so this Upper Westsider's "cramped", "country-kitsch" digs and "distracted" service are easy to ignore; its brunch draws "outrageous" lines, but to regulars it's "good enough to wait."

Z Good Fork M *Eclectic* | 26 | 20 | 22 | $40 |

Red Hook | 391 Van Brunt St. (bet. Coffey & Van Dyke Sts.) | Brooklyn | 718-643-6636 | www.goodfork.com
A "bright star" in Red Hook, this "cozy", "pocket-size" yearling is "always packed" with fans of its "innovative" Eclectic eats with "inspired Korean touches" and "sophisticated" drinks; run by an "adorable husband-and-wife team", it's developing a reputation for "trying hard to please."

Goodies *Chinese* | 20 | 7 | 14 | $17 |

Chinatown | 1 E. Broadway (bet. Catherine & Oliver Sts.) | 212-577-2922
"Addictive", "dirt-cheap" soup dumplings plus "tasty housemade noodles" draw aficionados to this no-frills Shanghainese standby; its "off-the-strip" location for many is a "relief from" Chinatown "madness."

Z NEW Gordon Ramsay *French* | 25 | 24 | 25 | $126 |

W 50s | The London NYC | 151 W. 54th St. (bet. 6th & 7th Aves.) | 212-468-8888 | www.gordonramsay.com
"Crusty" TV chef Gordon Ramsay "leaves the terror in the kitchen" at this "sublime" New French arrival in Midtown's London NYC hotel, his first U.S. foray, which "lives up to the hype" with "meticulously prepared", prix fixe–only cuisine full of "complex and layered" flavors; service is "flawless without being stuffy", though the "modern", neutral-toned decor gets mixed reviews ("elegant" and "refined" vs. "bland" and "sterile"); naturally, all of this "understated" "excellence" is "not for the faint of pocketbook"; N.B. jackets required.

Z Gotham Bar & Grill *American* | 27 | 25 | 26 | $72 |

G Village | 12 E. 12th St. (bet. 5th Ave. & University Pl.) | 212-620-4020 | www.gothambarandgrill.com
At this Village culinary "temple", "grand master" Alfred Portale continues to "excite" enthusiasts with his "soigné" "skyscrapers" of "spectacular" New American fare, while staffers "grant your wishes before you even know what to ask for" in a room that's "urbane" but "never pretentious"; to a few it "feels dated", but the majority declares this "quintessential NYC" experience still "vibrant after all these years."

Grace's Trattoria *Italian* | 18 | 16 | 18 | $43 |

E 70s | 201 E. 71st St. (bet. 2nd & 3rd Aves.) | 212-452-2323 | www.gracestrattoria.com
An adjunct to the "famous grocery store next door", this "cozy", "casual" Italian "standby" is "always crowded" with UES local "regulars" filling up on "fresh, simple" Pugliese specialties; though "nothing spectacular", it's "reliable for a quiet lunch or dinner."

	FOOD	DECOR	SERVICE	COST

Gradisca *Italian*
▽ 21 | 17 | 17 | $47

G Village | 126 W. 13th St. (bet. 6th Ave. & 7th Ave. S.) | 212-691-4886 | www.gradiscanyc.com

"Amazing housemade pastas" and other "hearty" Italian classics earn this "cozy" Villager local "favorite" status; its grottolike digs are doubly "inviting on a cold night", though critics find them "too dark" and "noisy", also citing "folksy", "inattentive" service.

☒ Gramercy Tavern *American*
27 | 25 | 27 | $92

Flatiron | 42 E. 20th St. (bet. B'way & Park Ave. S.) | 212-477-0777 | www.gramercytavern.com

Supporters of this "superb-in-all-respects" Flatiron New American hail the new chef – Michael Anthony, formerly of Blue Hill at Stone Barns – and salute his "spellbinding" market-centric cuisine, matched with an "extraordinary wine list"; the flower-filled, "rustic-yet-refined" main room "puts diners at ease", as does the "quicksilver" staff that's "on top of everything without being on top of you"; prix fixe–only tabs are "costly" and reservations "tough" ("getting into Harvard is easier"), but there's always the "lower-priced", "drop-in" front tavern.

Grand Café ● *Eclectic*
▽ 17 | 22 | 16 | $23

Astoria | 37-01 30th Ave. (37th St.) | Queens | 718-545-1494

"Athens meets South Beach" at this "glitzy", "energetic" Astorian, a "weekend hot spot" in a "prime location" for "chatting and people-watching over brunch"; the Eclectic eats are "light" and "reasonable", but be ready to "hang out" for a while, since service can be "slow."

Grand Sichuan *Chinese*
22 | 7 | 12 | $23

Chelsea | 229 Ninth Ave. (24th St.) | 212-620-5200 ●
Chinatown | 125 Canal St. (Chrystie St.) | 212-625-9212 ⊟
E 50s | 1049 Second Ave. (bet. 55th & 56th Sts.) | 212-355-5855
E Village | 19-23 St. Marks Pl. (bet. 2nd & 3rd Aves.) | 212-529-4800
Murray Hill | 227 Lexington Ave. (bet. 33rd & 34th Sts.) | 212-679-9770
Rego Park | 98-108 Queens Blvd. (bet. 66th & 67th Aves.) | Queens | 718-268-8833
www.thegrandsichuan.com

"Spices that'll kick you all the way to China" are in liberal use at this "genuine-article" Szechuan mini-chain where even the less "assertive" dishes have "loads of flavor"; it's "low on decor" and "service could be warmer", but no one seems to mind much.

Grand Tier Restaurant ☒ *American/Continental*
19 | 24 | 22 | $77

W 60s | Metropolitan Opera House | Lincoln Center Plaza, 2nd fl. (bet. 63rd & 65th Sts.) | 212-799-3400 | www.patinagroup.com

When attending "that special opera" or any Lincoln Center performance, ticket-holders can dine at this "beautiful" Met venue; its "luxury" and "convenience" are the main attraction, as the American-Continental fare is "predictable" – and you "may hit high C" when you "see the bill."

Gray's Papaya ●⊟ *Hot Dogs*
20 | 4 | 12 | $5

Garment District | 539 Eighth Ave. (37th St.) | 212-904-1588
G Village | 402 Sixth Ave. (8th St.) | 212-260-3532
W 70s | 2090 Broadway (72nd St.) | 212-799-0243

"These puppies hit the spot" howl lovers of the "snappy", "juicy", "dirt-cheap" links washed down with "refreshing" tropical juice drinks at this 24/7 trio of "stand-up" "hot dog heavens"; "loved" by everyone from "bankers" to eaters "on a pauper's pension", it should be registered as a "NY landmark."

NEW Grayz *Eclectic*

| - | - | - | E |

W 50s | 13-15 W. 54th St. (bet. 5th & 6th Aves.) | 212-262-4600 | www.grayz.net

Cocktails and hors d'oeuvres get the Gray Kunz treatment at this new Midtown Eclectic set to open in the Rockefeller townhouse that was formerly home to Aquavit; the meandering space (a series of cozy chambers leading to a transporting atrium) will offer a full lunch menu, and after dark, haute drinks and snacks; it's also available for private parties.

Great Jones Cafe ◐ *Cajun*

| 19 | 12 | 16 | $27 |

NoHo | 54 Great Jones St. (bet. Bowery & Lafayette St.) | 212-674-9304 | www.greatjones.com

Revelers recover from "long nights out" over "amazing Bloody Mary"-fueled "killer brunch" at this "cheap" NoHo Cajun "dive", a "down-to-earth" scene with "friendly" staffers and "zydeco on the jukebox"; "be prepared to wait for a table", though, 'cause the space is "infinitesimal."

Great NY Noodle Town ◐⇝ *Noodle Shop*

| 22 | 5 | 12 | $16 |

Chinatown | 28½ Bowery (Bayard St.) | 212-349-0923

This "basic" C-towner churns out "fantastic" salt-baked seafood and noodle dishes into the wee hours for those willing to sit "elbow to elbow with strangers"; ignore the "nonexistent" decor and "gruff" service and focus on the "cheap" tabs.

Greek Kitchen *Greek*

| 19 | 13 | 17 | $28 |

W 50s | 889 10th Ave. (58th St.) | 212-581-4300 | www.greekkitchennyc.com

Cheap and "authentic" enough to draw droves of "native Greeks", this decidedly "unpretentious" Hellenic in way West Hell's Kitchen proffers "delicious" meze and other "fresh", "simple" fare; a "friendly" vibe makes it a "pleasant" change of pace before or after Lincoln Center.

Green Field Churrascaria *Brazilian*

| 19 | 14 | 19 | $36 |

Corona | 108-01 Northern Blvd. (108th St.) | Queens | 718-672-5202

It's "gluttony gone wild" at this "noisy" all-you-can-eat Corona "palace" where the "meat, meat and more meat" "keeps coming" via "skewer"-wielding waiters – and the salad bar "ain't no joke either"; the fact that this football field–size Brazilian rodizio is "run by Koreans" just typifies "Queens in all its ethnic glory."

Greenhouse Café *American*

| 19 | 18 | 19 | $34 |

Bay Ridge | 7717 Third Ave. (bet. 77th & 78th Sts.) | Brooklyn | 718-833-8200 | www.greenhousecafe.com

Turning out "tasty", "affordable" eats, this "family-oriented" Bay Ridge New American remains a "staple" for its "pretty" glass-clad back room, 40-ft. mahogany bar and live entertainment on Saturday nights; "friendly" service further boosts the "wonderful" vibe.

Grifone ⊠ *Italian*

| 23 | 18 | 24 | $59 |

E 40s | 244 E. 46th St. (bet. 2nd & 3rd Aves.) | 212-490-7275 | www.grifonenyc.com

"Old-world charm and class abound" at this "intimate" U.N.-area ristorante where "wealthier locals" and "diplomats" "savor the flavors" of "terrific" Northern Italian classics; staffers "treat you like family" and the "kitchen is happy to accommodate", but just be sure to budget for the "pricey" tabs.

Z Grimaldi's ⊘ Pizza 25 | 10 | 14 | $20

Dumbo | 19 Old Fulton St. (bet. Front & Water Sts.) | Brooklyn | 718-858-4300 | www.grimaldis.com

"Thin, crispy crusts" and "perfect sauce" make the "sublime" coal-oven pizzas at this cash-only Dumbo "landmark" "craveable" enough to inspire interborough "pilgrimages"; plan on "lines", crowds and "brusque" service, but then "you're not there for the ambiance."

Z Grocery, The ⑤ American 26 | 16 | 24 | $60

Carroll Gardens | 288 Smith St. (bet. Sackett & Union Sts.) | Brooklyn | 718-596-3335

"Success hasn't spoiled" this "brilliant" "mom-and-pop" Carroll Gardens New American, whose "haute cuisine with humility" lets its "supremely fresh" seasonal ingredients "shine through"; given the "teeny" confines (augmented in summer with a "lovely garden") and the staff's "personal attention", an evening here feels a bit "like being at a friend's for dinner", i.e. a friend who's a great cook.

Grotta Azzurra ● Italian 18 | 16 | 17 | $41

Little Italy | 177 Mulberry St. (Broome St.) | 212-925-8775 | www.grottaazzurrany.com

"The fish aren't the only ones wearing sharkskin" at this Little Italy eatery, a reincarnation of the 1908 original; *amici* applaud "honest" Southern Italian fare and "bargain prix fixe menus", but nostalgists who deem this redux a "shadow of its former self" come away feeling blue.

NEW Guadalupe Mexican ▽ 19 | 19 | 16 | $29

Inwood | 597 W. 207th St. (bet. B'way & Vermilyea Ave.) | 212-304-1083 | www.guadaluperestaurant.com

At this new Inwood Mexican, "approachable" south-of-the-border specialties and "marvelous margaritas" materialize in a "loftlike" space that "feels like an old-world church"; service "needs work", but neighbors "happy to have this new choice" nearby are "really rooting" for it.

Guantanamera ● Cuban ▽ 22 | 15 | 19 | $36
(fka Azucar)

W 50s | 939 Eighth Ave. (bet. 55th & 56th Sts.) | 212-262-5354 | www.guantanameranyc.com

"Delicious", "lively Latin" dishes and "sugarcane spear"-adorned mojitos ensure everyone's "Havana great meal" at this affordable West Midtown Cuban; other pluses are an "entertaining cigar roller" and nightly live music – though all that "fun" can get "loud."

NEW Gus' Place ● Greek/Mediterranean 20 | 16 | 20 | $37

G Village | 192 Bleecker St. (bet. MacDougal St. & 6th Ave.) | 212-777-1660

"New location, same warm welcome" report Village Gus-tomers "thrilled" by the return (after two years) of this longtime source for "savory" Greek-Med fare; boosting the "charm" factor of its "tiny", "rustic" digs is a small sidewalk patio, not to mention the presence of the "genial" owner and namesake.

	FOOD	DECOR	SERVICE	COST

Gusto *Italian* | 22 | 21 | 19 | $53
G Village | 60 Greenwich Ave. (Perry St.) | 212-924-8000 |
www.gustonyc.com
New chef Amanda Freitag is "coming into her own" at this "hip" but
"friendly" Greenwich Village Italian, turning out "skillful" *cucina* full of
"bright, distinctive" flavors; its "snazzy" black-and-white *La Dolce
Vita* decor has a "glamorous" feel, as does the "buzzy, beautiful",
"high-energy" crowd.

Gyu-Kaku *Japanese* | 21 | 20 | 20 | $43
NEW **E 40s** | 805 Third Ave., 2nd fl. (50th St.) | 212-702-8816
E Village | 34 Cooper Sq. (bet. Astor Pl. & 4th St.) | 212-475-2989
www.gyu-kaku.com
"NYC lounge meets Asian BBQ" at these "chic" East Village–Midtown
links of a Japanese chain where diners grill "high-quality" marinated
meats, seafood and veggies on their own charcoal braziers; it's great
for groups, though the "costs can add up" and a few wonder "why pay"
to "do all the work"?

Hacienda de Argentina ● *Argentinean/Steak* | 21 | 21 | 19 | $51
E 70s | 339 E. 75th St. (bet. 1st & 2nd Aves.) | 212-472-5300 |
www.haciendadeargentina.com
Carnivores have a cow over the "tender" grass-fed beef at this "very
Buenos Aires" UES steakhouse that's cheap for the genre; "polite"
staffers and "dark", "hacienda"-style environs with glowing candles
lend date-worthy "romantic" overtones.

Hakata Grill *Japanese* | 20 | 15 | 18 | $35
W 40s | 230 W. 48th St. (bet. B'way & 8th Ave.) | 212-245-1020
Show-goers "squeeze in a bite of sushi" pre-curtain at this Theater
District Japanese "secret", appreciated for its "tasty", "fresh" fish;
sure, seating is "elbow-to-elbow" and the pace often "hurried", but
few fret much given the "inexpensive" tabs.

Hale & Hearty Soups ⊘ *Sandwiches/Soup* | 19 | 7 | 12 | $11
Chelsea | Chelsea Mkt. | 75 Ninth Ave. (bet. 15th & 16th Sts.) |
212-255-2400
E 40s | 685 Third Ave. (43rd St.) | 212-681-6460 🎟
E 40s | Grand Central | lower level (42nd St. & Vanderbilt Ave.) |
212-983-2845
E 60s | 849 Lexington Ave. (bet. 64th & 65th Sts.) | 212-517-7600
Financial District | 55 Broad St. (Beaver St.) | 212-509-4100 🎟
Garment District | 462 Seventh Ave. (35th St.) | 212-971-0605 🎟
W 40s | Rockefeller Plaza | 30 Rockefeller Plaza (49th St.) | 212-265-2117 🎟
W 40s | 49 W. 42nd St. (bet. 5th & 6th Aves.) | 212-575-9090 🎟
W 50s | 55 W. 56th St. (bet. 5th & 6th Aves.) | 212-245-9200 🎟
Brooklyn Heights | 32 Court St. (Remsen St.) | Brooklyn |
718-596-5600 🎟
www.haleandhearty.com
Additional locations throughout the NY area
Given its "bewildering" "variety" of "hit-the-spot" potages, this ubiq-
uitous "cafeteria-style" chain is like the "Baskin-Robbins of soup"; it
gets "hectic" during "prime lunch hours" and "inattentive" staffers can
be "as cold as the gazpacho", but at least the "pace is quick" and the
price is right.

| | FOOD | DECOR | SERVICE | COST |

Hallo Berlin *German* | 17 | 8 | 12 | $21

W 40s | 626 10th Ave. (bet. 44th & 45th Sts.) | 212-977-1944
Cheap, "hearty" Teutonic "peasant food" and "good German beers on tap" are what this West Hell's Kitchen "bratwurst central" is all about; frank fans figure the "sausages and brew are worth" enduring "nonexistent ambiance" and "surly", "painfully slow" service.

Hampton Chutney Co. *Indian* | 20 | 10 | 15 | $15

SoHo | 68 Prince St. (bet. Crosby & Lafayette Sts.) | 212-226-9996
W 80s | 464 Amsterdam Ave. (bet. 82nd & 83rd Sts.) | 212-362-5050
www.hamptonchutney.com
So "huge" they're "shareable", the bargain "nouvelle dosas" at these "casual" storefront siblings "light up your mouth" with "refreshing" Indian fusion flavors; though the SoHo "hipster" magnet is short on seats, its roomier UWS offshoot is "paradise for mothers with strollers."

Hangawi *Korean* | 23 | 24 | 21 | $46

Murray Hill | 12 E. 32nd St. (bet. 5th & Madison Aves.) | 212-213-0077 | www.hangawirestaurant.com
"Exit a busy street" in Murray Hill and enter a "temple of tranquility" at this vegetarian Korean where the "intriguing", "high-end" fare "goes way beyond kimchi" and the staff is "lovely" and "attentive"; just be sure to "wear nice socks" because you have to "check your shoes at the door."

Hard Rock Cafe ❷ *American* | 13 | 20 | 14 | $30

W 40s | 1501 Broadway (43rd St.) | 212-343-3355 | www.hardrock.com
"Tourists, teens" and types who "really like being surrounded by gold records and guitars" groove on this "loud", "hectic", "kitschy" Times Square "rock mall"; admittedly, "you come for the show", not the "so-so" American grub, but "you'll be safe with a burger and a shake."

Harrison, The *American* | 24 | 21 | 23 | $61

TriBeCa | 355 Greenwich St. (Harrison St.) | 212-274-9310 | www.theharrison.com
"Sophisticated" but "not stuffy", this "welcoming" TriBeCan turns out "bold" New American fare paired with "excellent wines" to "young CEO types" and other "grown-ups"; "mellow" "pro" staffers "serve with class", ensuring that, despite the "high" tab, "you can't go wrong here."

Harry Cipriani ❷ *Italian* | - | - | - | VE

E 50s | Sherry Netherland | 781 Fifth Ave. (bet. 59th & 60th Sts.) | 212-753-5566 | www.cipriani.com
Serving pasta and Bellinis again after a lengthy face-lift, this haute Venetian in the Sherry Netherland with a polished new look is still attracting enough Euro jet-setters and society types to make it a people-watching paradise; comically high pricing doesn't mean a thing to this crowd since it's all about the scene here.

Harry's Cafe ❷🗺 *Eclectic* | 22 | 21 | 22 | $52

Financial District | 1 Hanover Sq. (bet. Pearl & Stone Sts.)
Harry's Steak 🗺 *Steak*
Financial District | 97 Pearl St. (bet. Broad St. & Hanover Sq.)
212-785-9200 | www.harrysnyc.com
This Financial District twofer within the "beautiful", "historic" 1875 India House ministers "attentively" to area bulls and bears; the "un-

	FOOD	DECOR	SERVICE	COST

pretentious" upstairs Eclectic cafe features a "great, friendly bar", while the steakhouse proffers "excellent" beef and wines in a setting so "clubby" you may "forget you're in a basement."

Haru *Japanese*

| 21 | 17 | 17 | $40 |

E 40s | 280 Park Ave. (48th St.) | 212-490-9680
E 70s | 1327 Third Ave. (76th St.) | 212-452-1028 ◐
E 70s | 1329 Third Ave. (76th St.) | 212-452-2230 ◐
Flatiron | 220 Park Ave. S. (18th St.) | 646-428-0989 ◐
W 40s | 205 W. 43rd St. (bet. B'way & 8th Ave.) | 212-398-9810 ◐
W 80s | 433 Amsterdam Ave. (bet. 80th & 81st Sts.) | 212-579-5655 ◐
www.harusushi.com

"Haray" cheer fans of this "lively" Japanese chain that reels in "young" types who "crave a scene" with their modestly priced, "whale-size sushi"; it's "reliable" for a "quick" bite, but don't plan on "settling in for a chat", as the staff "works to turn over tables" and noise can be "haruble."

Hasaki ◑ *Japanese*

| 23 | 14 | 18 | $41 |

E Village | 210 E. Ninth St. (bet. 2nd & 3rd Aves.) | 212-473-3327

"Excellent" classic Japanese fare, including "quality" sushi, gives "value" at this East Village "gem"; there's little "elbow room", but sentimental sorts claim "cozy" confines and a "jazzy soundtrack" render it "improbably romantic", that is if you "arrive early" to avoid the "legendary" lines.

Hatsuhana ⊠ *Japanese*

| 24 | 15 | 20 | $50 |

E 40s | 17 E. 48th St. (bet. 5th & Madison Aves.) | 212-355-3345
E 40s | 237 Park Ave. (46th St.) | 212-661-3400
www.hatsuhana.com

For "power lunches" or "after-work dinners", Midtowners count on these longtime sushi siblings likened to "Toyotas that never break down"; maybe the ambiance is "austere" and "pedestrian concoctions outweigh creative ones", but for "consistently fresh" (if "expensive") fish, most consider them "toro-tastic."

Havana Alma de Cuba *Cuban*

| 21 | 17 | 19 | $34 |

W Village | 94 Christopher St. (bet. Bedford & Bleecker Sts.) | 212-242-3800 | www.havanavillagenyc.com

With its "amazing" mojitos, "authentic" Cuban food and "cheerful" service, not to mention "wonderful live music", this "welcoming", well-priced West Villager has "first-date place" written all over it; the "tiny" digs are often "crowded", but the "outside garden is a plus."

Havana Central *Cuban*

| 17 | 15 | 16 | $30 |

Union Sq | 22 E. 17th St. (bet. B'way & 5th Ave.) | 212-414-2298
W 40s | 151 W. 46th St. (bet. 6th & 7th Aves.) | 212-398-7440 ◐
NEW W 100s | 2911 Broadway (bet. 113th & 114th Sts.) | 212-662-8830
www.havanacentral.com

These three amigos boast "decent" "nuevo" Cuban basics in "festive" quarters; "under-par" service can detract, but it's made up for by the lively bar scene and "affordable" tabs; there's "often live music" at the UWS branch on Broadway, housed in the former West End bar.

Haveli ◐ *Indian*

| 23 | 16 | 20 | $32 |

E Village | 100 Second Ave. (bet. 5th & 6th Sts.) | 212-982-0533

"Fabulous spicing without the grease" ensures this East Village Indian "stalwart" remains a "league above" its Curry Row neighbors; its rela-

	FOOD	DECOR	SERVICE	COST

tively "upscale" (yet still affordable) approach costs "a little more", but it's "reliable", with "attentive" service and "no disco lights."

NEW Hawaiian Tropic Zone ● *American* ▽ 16 | 18 | 15 | $43

W 40s | 729 Seventh Ave. (49th St.) | 212-626-7312 | www.hawaiiantropiczone.com

"*Baywatch* meets Manhattan" at this "eye-popping" new Theater District themer, a three-level, 16,000-sq.-ft. party where "cute" waitresses "not wearing much" steal the show from David Burke's just-"good" New American fare; critics put off by the "frat-house-for-suits" vibe dismiss it as "Hooter's goes to the beach."

Hearth *American/Italian* 25 | 21 | 24 | $63

E Village | 403 E. 12th St. (1st Ave.) | 646-602-1300 | www.restauranthearth.com

Chef Marco Canora's "informal" but culinarily "serious" Tuscan-accented East Village New American features "no trendy cooking", just "exquisite", "imaginative" dishes from an open kitchen; it also boasts a "well-chosen" wine list and "top-notch service", ensuring it's a "hit on every level", "big prices" aside.

Heartland Brewery *Pub Food* 14 | 13 | 15 | $28

Garment District | Empire State Bldg. | 350 Fifth Ave. (34th St.) | 212-563-3433
Seaport | South Street Seaport | 93 South St. (Fulton St.) | 646-572-2337
Union Sq | 35 Union Sq. W. (bet. 16th & 17th Sts.) | 212-645-3400
W 40s | 127 W. 43rd St. (bet. B'way & 6th Ave.) | 646-366-0235 ●
W 50s | 1285 Sixth Ave. (51st St.) | 212-582-8244
www.heartlandbrewery.com

With five locations around Manhattan, this microbrewery chain "not unexpectedly produces good beer", but also offers "surprisingly" "tasty" and "inexpensive" pub fare; accordingly, it's usually packed after work with a "young crowd", though critics pan its "generic" eats and say it feels "remarkably like a corporate restaurant in a suburban mall."

Heidelberg *German* 17 | 16 | 16 | $34

E 80s | 1648 Second Ave. (bet. 85th & 86th Sts.) | 212-628-2332 | www.heidelbergrestaurant.com

A "throwback" to the heyday of Yorkville's Germantown, this "everything-Deutsch" "charmer" produces hard-to-find classics served by a lederhosen-clad staff; some find the "biergarten" setting "cheesy", but most embrace the "festive" spirit and low prices.

Hell's Kitchen *Mexican* 23 | 16 | 19 | $43

W 40s | 679 Ninth Ave. (bet. 46th & 47th Sts.) | 212-977-1588 | www.hellskitchen-nyc.com

Look for "inventive", "spicy" dishes washed down with "delightfully toxic" margaritas at this "small", "friendly" Hell's Kitchen Mexican; maybe its "stark" interior "needs flavor", but the prices are "gentle" and it "works well for pre-theater."

Henry's End *American* 25 | 14 | 23 | $45

Brooklyn Heights | 44 Henry St. (Cranberry St.) | Brooklyn | 718-834-1776 | www.henrysend.com

"If game is your thing", the hunt ends at this "hearty" Brooklyn Heights New American beloved for its "creative dishes" and "varied" wine list, as well as for its modest prices and "pleasant" staff; the "tight quarters" have "zero ambiance", but otherwise it's a "first-rate" experience.

Highline ◐ *Thai*

19	22	17	$36

Meatpacking | 835 Washington St. (Little W. 12th St.) | 212-243-3339 | www.nychighline.com

A "funky", "manageable alternative" to more "flashy" Meatpacking District neighbors, this sprawling, tri-level source for solid, "affordable" Thai fare is lots of "fun"; the soundtrack "can be loud" and the service variable, but its "very cool" "modern" space trumps all.

NEW Hill Country *BBQ*

–	–	–	M

Chelsea | 30 W. 26th St. (bet. B'way & 6th Ave.) | 212-255-4544 | www.hillcountryny.com

Taking you to Texas Hill Country by way of Chelsea, this big, boisterous, bi-level newcomer features three in-house smokers manned by a seasoned pit master (Robbie Richter) and decor right out of a back country roadhouse; the meats and sides are ordered from a counter, then carried on trays to long communal tables, and the result is a place that tastes, looks and smells as good as anything in the Lone Star state.

Hispaniola ◐ *Dominican*

▽ 21	21	17	$42

Washington Heights | 839 W. 181st St. (bet. Cabrini Blvd. & Pinehurst St.) | 212-740-5222 | www.hispaniolarestaurant.com

"Breathtaking views of the GW Bridge" are the thing at this "upscale" Washington Heights Dominican, though the "delicious" Asian-inflected fare is also a draw; it's a "must-try" for an Uptown adventure.

HK ◐ *American*

▽ 16	16	15	$29

Garment District | 523 Ninth Ave. (39th St.) | 212-947-4208

Despite its "dreary location" behind the Port Authority, this "reliable" Garment District American serves "decent", comforting "diner fare" in starkly modern digs; service is "spotty" and the "decibels" "loud", but it's a "terrific bargain", and in warmer weather, you can escape to the patio.

Holy Basil ◐ *Thai*

22	19	19	$31

E Village | 149 Second Ave., 2nd fl. (bet. 9th & 10th Sts.) | 212-460-5557 | www.holybasilrestaurant.com

"Dark", "atmospheric" digs boost the "romance" factor at this East Village "upstairs hideaway" that's popular for "inexpensive" but high-rated Thai dishes; "gracious" service and prime "people-watching" from the balcony round out the endorsement.

Home *American*

20	15	19	$40

G Village | 20 Cornelia St. (bet. Bleecker & W. 4th Sts.) | 212-243-9579 | www.recipesfromhome.com

Who knew "home cooking" could be "gourmet", but the "expertly prepared" "inventive spins" on comfort classics at this "welcoming", "true Village joint" keep folks coming back; its "quaint", "narrow" space gets "crowded", but the garden gives diners needed "elbow room."

Hope & Anchor *Diner*

18	15	18	$20

Red Hook | 347 Van Brunt St. (Wolcott St.) | Brooklyn | 718-237-0276 | www.hopeandanchordiner.com

The staff and owners of this "funky", "laid-back" Red Hook diner make patrons "feel at home", as does the kitchen's "satisfying", low-budget output; between the "excellent" brunch and "drag queen"-hosted karaoke nights, it's no wonder this "remote outpost" keeps the locals coming.

NEW House, The ● *Mediterranean* ▽ 22 | 27 | 21 | $52

Gramercy | 121 E. 17th St. (bet. Irving Pl. & Park Ave. S.) | 212-353-2121 | www.thehousenyc.com

Set in an "exquisite" 1850s Gramercy Park carriage house, this "elegant", pricey Med "hideaway" strikes a "romantic" chord with its dark woods, fireplace and flickering candles; the menu of "mostly small plates" veers toward Italy and is calibrated to a "fabulous" list of vinos.

Houston's *American* 20 | 18 | 19 | $36

E 50s | Citigroup Ctr. | 153 E. 53rd St. (enter at 3rd Ave. & 54th St.) | 212-888-3828

Gramercy | NY Life Bldg. | 378 Park Ave. S. (27th St.) | 212-689-1090

www.hillstone.com

"In a sea of upscale bar grub", this "dependable" American chain stands out with "surprisingly good" food, service and prices; not surprisingly, "killer waits" are common, but "slammin' drinks", a "huge happy-hour scene" and that "to-die-for spinach dip" are your reward.

HQ *American* ▽ 19 | 18 | 18 | $42

SoHo | 90 Thompson St. (bet. Prince & Spring Sts.) | 212-966-2755

A "refreshing change" from the usual "SoHo scene", this "unpretentious", relatively inexpensive New American offers "tasty" bistro fare via an "attentive", "witty" staff; its "cozy", "warm" HQ features a frontage of French doors ideal for "people-watching."

HSF ⊟ *Chinese* 20 | 9 | 12 | $23

Chinatown | 46 Bowery (bet. Bayard & Canal Sts.) | 212-374-1319

"Carts galore" brimming with "delicious", reasonably priced dim sum explain the everlasting popularity of this Chinatown Cantonese "institution"; it's "a zoo, plain and simple", with "off-putting" service and decidedly downscale digs, but get there early to avoid the "maddening crowds."

Hudson Cafeteria ● *American/Eclectic* 19 | 22 | 18 | $47

W 50s | Hudson Hotel | 356 W. 58th St. (bet. 8th & 9th Aves.) | 212-554-6000 | www.chinagrillmgt.com

"Hearty", "stylish" comfort fare served in "pseudo" college dining hall digs ("high ceilings", "Gothic" lighting, "wooden communal tables") is the drill at this hotel American-Eclectic; most agree it's "not trendy anymore", but it's still a good bet before or after "Lincoln Center" or if you get a room upstairs.

NEW Hudson River Café ● *American/Seafood* - | - | - | M

Harlem | 697 W. 133rd St. (12th Ave.) | 212-491-9111 | www.hudsonrivercafe.com

Under the steel trusses just north of Harlem's Fairway Market, a former mechanic's shop has been transformed into this airy New American seafooder with a California-winery look; inside wrought-iron gates there's bi-level patio seating and an outdoor bar pouring until the wee hours.

	FOOD	DECOR	SERVICE	COST

Hummus Place ⬤ *Israeli/Vegetarian*   `23` `11` `17` `$14`
E Village | 109 St. Marks Pl. (bet. Ave. A & 1st Ave.) | 212-529-9198
G Village | 99 MacDougal St. (bet. Bleecker & W. 3rd Sts.) | 212-533-3089
NEW **W 70s** | 305 Amsterdam Ave. (bet. 74th & 75th Sts.) |
212-799-3335
www.hummusplace.com
As the name suggests, this Israeli trio is a "one-note Johnny" – but oh,
"what a note" sing "addicts" of its "out-of-this-world hummus" and other
"amazing", "cheap" vegetarian snacks; the setups are "small and
cramped", but "pleasant" (if "uncoordinated") service compensates.

NEW **Hurapan Kitchen** *Thai*   ▽ `20` `19` `20` `$43`
G Village | 29 Seventh Ave. S. (bet. Bedford & Morton Sts.) |
212-727-2678
"Inventive", "delicious" spins on Thai standards are the specialty of this
Village newcomer, whose "attentive" crew presides over a "pretty",
somewhat "upscale" room; it's a little "expensive" for the genre, but
after an "innovative sake cocktail" or two, most hardly notice.

Ichimura 🅱 *Japanese*   ▽ `24` `11` `17` `$84`
E 50s | 1026 Second Ave. (bet. 54th & 55th Sts.) | 212-355-3557
Sushi-seekers retreat from the hustle of Midtown at this "undiscovered"
Japanese where the monastic decor allows diners to focus on the fresh
fish; yes, it all comes at a "high-end" price – it would be a challenge not
to exceed the $30 minimum – but enthusiasts aren't deterred.

Ichiro ⬤ *Japanese*   `20` `12` `18` `$32`
E 80s | 1694 Second Ave. (bet. 87th & 88th Sts.) | 212-369-6300 |
www.ichi-ro.com
"Ample", "consistently fresh" sushi that "couldn't be much cheaper",
doled out by an "able" staff, keeps this UES "neighborhood" Japanese
"crowded"; most everyone agrees it's a "solid" bet for everything but
the "plain" setting.

Ici Ⓜ *American/French*   `22` `19` `19` `$39`
Fort Greene | 246 DeKalb Ave. (bet. Clermont & Vanderbilt Aves.) |
Brooklyn | 718-789-2778 | www.icirestaurant.com
With Franco-American "seasonal dishes that always shine" and appealing decor and pricing, this Fort Greene spot has Brooklynites wondering "why go into Manhattan?"; there are a few gripes about
"uneven" service, but all agree that the garden is "lovely."

I Coppi *Italian*   `23` `20` `20` `$43`
E Village | 432 E. Ninth St. (bet. Ave. A & 1st Ave.) | 212-254-2263 |
www.icoppinyc.com
"Happiness" is the "spectacular" year-round back garden of this "rustic" East Village Tuscan "standout"; there's "no attitude here", just
"excellent" "classic" pastas and "wood-fired" entrees perfect for pair-
ing with its "fabulous" Tuscan wines.

Ideya *Caribbean*   ▽ `20` `15` `17` `$36`
SoHo | 349 W. Broadway (bet. Broome & Grand Sts.) | 212-625-1441 |
www.ideya.net
A "welcome escape" from the usual SoHo hot spots, this "casual",
"welcoming" Caribbean dishes up "flavorful" fare and "killer" mojitos

at surprisingly "affordable" prices given the zip code; the mood is "festive" (read: "loud") and the staff "friendly" if sometimes "harried."

Il Bagatto ●Ⓜ *Italian* | 23 | 16 | 16 | $36 |

E Village | 192 E. Second St. (bet. Aves. A & B) | 212-228-0977
"Loyal regulars" frequent this "small", "down-to-earth" East Village Italian for its "high-quality" classic cuisine and wines offered at "reasonable" rates; despite "Christmas-light" decor, "curt" service and occasional "waits", "you don't mind once you taste the food."

Il Bastardo ● *Italian/Steak* | 19 | 18 | 18 | $40 |

Chelsea | 191 Seventh Ave. (bet. 21st & 22nd Sts.) | 212-675-5980 | www.ilbastardonyc.com
The "sensuous" room at this Chelsea Tuscan steakhouse has a "lounge feel" left over from its nightclub days, complete with "loud" acoustics and a "happening" "after-work" scene; most find the "basic" fare to be "well prepared", and the $15 prix fixe lunch to be a deal.

NEW Il Brigante *Italian* | ▽ 21 | 17 | 17 | $29 |

Seaport | 214 Front St. (bet. Beekman St. & Peck Slip) | 212-285-0222
Set in the historic South Street Seaport, this new Italian trattoria has made itself welcome with a rustic space warmed by a wood-burning oven churning wonderful pizzas and "fresh" pastas at budget-friendly prices; service and decor are more debatable.

Il Buco ● *Italian/Mediterranean* | 25 | 23 | 22 | $59 |

NoHo | 47 Bond St. (bet. Bowery & Lafayette St.) | 212-533-1932 | www.ilbuco.com
"Sublime", "seasonal" Italian-Med cuisine as "utterly fabulous" as the "*molto bello*" clientele is the hallmark of this NoHo "hipster"; its "tight" but "charming", "antiques"-adorned digs and "big prices" can be a "squeeze", but overall, you'll be glad you went.

Il Cantinori *Italian* | 22 | 20 | 21 | $59 |

G Village | 32 E. 10th St. (bet. B'way & University Pl.) | 212-673-6044 | www.ilcantinori.com
Adorned with "over-the-top flowers" and the "occasional celeb", this Village "standby" manages to combine "sophisticated" aesthetics with an "unpretentious" vibe, while the "classic" Northern Italian fare is "terrific"; in sum, "when money doesn't matter", it's "superb."

Il Corallo Trattoria *Italian* | 22 | 12 | 19 | $27 |

SoHo | 176 Prince St. (bet. Sullivan & Thompson Sts.) | 212-941-7119
The menu's "endless" choices "make it difficult to decide" among the many "well-prepared" pastas this "friendly", usually "packed" SoHo Italian is known for; most overlook the bland setting because "you can't find a better deal."

Il Cortile ● *Italian* | 23 | 20 | 20 | $50 |

Little Italy | 125 Mulberry St. (bet. Canal & Hester Sts.) | 212-226-6060 | www.ilcortile.com
Made for those who "love garlic" and "phenomenal red sauce", this "old-world" Little Italy vet's "delicious" edibles are delivered by "personable" waiters; sure, it's a bit "pricey", but the atmosphere is "lively" and there's an "elegant" back "garden room" perfect for "romance."

	FOOD	DECOR	SERVICE	COST

Il Fornaio *Italian*
21 | 14 | 18 | $34

Little Italy | 132A Mulberry St. (bet. Grand & Hester Sts.) | 212-226-8306
In a neighborhood full of "touristy" spots, this "dependable", "reasonably priced" Little Italy "favorite" is deemed an "island of authenticity"; "to-die-for" meatballs, "al dente" pasta and, of course, "fresh" red sauce are its forte – "don't look for frills, just bring an appetite."

Il Gattopardo ● *Italian*
23 | 18 | 23 | $61

W 50s | 33 W. 54th St. (bet. 5th & 6th Aves.) | 212-246-0412 | www.ilgattopardonyc.com
Boasting an "ideal" Midtown location, this "unheralded" "gem" also proffers "sublime" Neapolitan dishes and "outstanding" service; it's "pricey" and the decor gets mixed reactions ("minimalist and chic" vs. simply "stark"), but for the area, it's a "blessing."

Ⓩ Il Giglio Ⓢ *Italian*
26 | 18 | 24 | $76

TriBeCa | 81 Warren St. (bet. Greenwich St. & W. B'way) | 212-571-5555 | www.ilgigliorestaurant.com
Don't "fill up on the freebie appetizers" lest you miss out on the full "first-rate", "explosion-of-flavors" experience at this "old-world", "up-scale" TriBeCa Tuscan, presided over by a staff that "couldn't be better"; though you may "need a loan" to settle the check, most surveyors say it's "worth every penny."

Il Mattone Ⓢ *Italian/Pizza*
▽ 21 | 13 | 17 | $30

TriBeCa | 413 Greenwich St. (Hubert St.) | 212-343-0030
"Terrific" brick-oven pizzas have those in-the-know calling this "reasonable" TriBeCa Italian "joint" a solid "staple" in a "neighborhood that needs it"; still, it flies somewhat under the radar, perhaps because of its "small quarters" and nonexistent decor.

Il Menestrello Ⓢ *Italian*
▽ 22 | 18 | 22 | $60

E 50s | 50 E. 50th St. (bet. Madison & Park Aves.) | 212-421-7588
Its "new location is a winner" declare "business-lunch" regulars and the other necessarily well-heeled devotees of this "old-world" East Midtown Italian; maybe the "cozy" setting is only "so-so", but it's got the same "wonderful" food and "friendly" pro service as ever – "glad they're back."

Ⓩ Il Mulino Ⓢ *Italian*
27 | 18 | 24 | $83

G Village | 86 W. Third St. (bet. Sullivan & Thompson Sts.) | 212-673-3783 | www.ilmulinonewyork.com
"Age has not diminished" the "one-of-a-kind" experience at this "outstanding", "crowded" Village Italian "classic", where nearly "every dish is a masterpiece", and the "white-glove" service has patrons feeling "like royalty"; while some insist "it's the best meal you'll ever have", it's also among "the hardest to book and the hardest to pay for" – to improve your chances in both respects, go for lunch.

Il Nido Ⓢ *Italian*
23 | 18 | 22 | $66

E 50s | 251 E. 53rd St. (bet. 2nd & 3rd Aves.) | 212-753-8450 | www.ilnidonyc.com
The "fantastic", "traditional" Northern Italian cuisine and "first-rate" service at this "old-school" Midtown "standby" "still pass muster", but the setting "reminiscent of a bygone era" is getting "as tired as

| | FOOD | DECOR | SERVICE | COST |

Paris Hilton on a Monday morning"; still, for most the "well-spaced tables allowing for conversation" alone justify the "pricey" tabs.

Il Palazzo *Italian*   ▽ 23 | 19 | 21 | $46
Little Italy | 151 Mulberry St. (bet. Grand & Hester Sts.) | 212-343-7000
The seafood dishes are "particularly recommended" at this "festive"
Little Italy stalwart, but of course "you can get some fantastic pasta"
here too; its "friendly" service and "pleasant" glass-enclosed garden
place it "a cut above" most others on Mulberry Street.

Il Postino ◑ *Italian*   22 | 19 | 20 | $62
E 40s | 337 E. 49th St. (bet. 1st & 2nd Aves.) | 212-688-0033 |
www.ilpostinorestaurant.com
A staff of "theatrical" waiters who recite a lengthy "specials list" are
the "corporate" crowd's "guide" to this "understated" Midtown
Italian's "terrific", "traditional" fare; just "be careful to ask for prices",
lest your tab "creep up."

Il Riccio ◑ *Italian*   21 | 15 | 19 | $54
E 70s | 152 E. 79th St. (bet. Lexington & 3rd Aves.) | 212-639-9111
"Tiny and crowded" it may be, but given its "delicious" Southern
Italian fare, UES "locals" don't mind sitting "elbow to elbow" at this
"unpretentious" trattoria; besides, there's a "welcoming" staff, relatively "reasonable" rates for a "high-priced neighborhood" and the
chance to spy the occasional "celeb."

❷ Il Tinello ☒ *Italian*   26 | 21 | 26 | $66
W 50s | 16 W. 56th St. (bet. 5th & 6th Aves.) | 212-245-4388
"Tuxedoed waiters" serve the "sumptuous" Northern Italian dishes
with "courtesy" and "elegance" at this "serene" "white-tablecloth"
Midtown "classic"; it "caters to an older crowd" that "loves its old-
fashioned feel" and doesn't blink at the up-to-date prices.

Il Vagabondo *Italian*   19 | 15 | 18 | $43
E 60s | 351 E. 62nd St. (bet. 1st & 2nd Aves.) | 212-832-9221 |
www.ilvagabondo.com
It "says a lot" that this "reliable" East Side Italian is praised for "never
changing" after 50 years – and given its "terrific" pastas and other
"bargain"-priced "standards", thank goodness it hasn't; it even boasts
a "bocce ball court" for killing time "between courses."

Inagiku *Japanese*   23 | 19 | 22 | $60
E 40s | Waldorf-Astoria | 111 E. 49th St. (bet. Lexington & Park Aves.) |
212-355-0440 | www.inagiku.com
"Meticulous", "kimono-clad" staffers lend a "refined" air to this
"quiet" Midtown sushi specialist that offers "top-of-the-line" rolls at
similar prices; some find the atmosphere a bit "lacking", but the "tran-
sient" "business" crowd doesn't seem to notice.

Indochine ◑ *French/Vietnamese*   20 | 19 | 18 | $50
E Village | 430 Lafayette St. (bet. Astor Pl. & 4th St.) | 212-505-5111 |
www.indochinenyc.com
"Convenient" before a show at the Public, this "hopping" East Village
French-Vietnamese standby features "delicious" cuisine ferried by
"modelicious waitresses"; it's an overall "sexy" scene, though been-
there-done-that types assert the "colonial"-themed decor is "dated."

	FOOD	DECOR	SERVICE	COST

Industria Argentina ◐ *Argentinean/Steak* ▽ 20 | 19 | 19 | $47

TriBeCa | 329 Greenwich St. (bet. Duane & Jay Sts.) | 212-965-8560 |
www.iatribeca.com

"Beautiful people" boost the "buzz" at this "sophisticated" TriBeCa
Argentinean steakhouse; it can get "a bit expensive", but then
again, considering the "swish" surroundings and zip code, most feel it
delivers "decent value."

Indus Valley *Indian* 23 | 16 | 20 | $31

W 100s | 2636 Broadway (100th St.) | 212-222-9222

Upper Westsiders are all aglow about the "fascinating spicing" at
this "top-shelf" Indian, where the "fresh" dishes are "cooked to
your palate"; the "charming" staff and "modest prices" more than
compensate for its "small", "crowded" space; P.S. the $12.95 lunch
prix fixe is "unbeatable."

NEW Inn LW12 ◐ *American* ▽ 19 | 24 | 18 | $48

Meatpacking | 7 Ninth Ave. (Little W. 12th St.) | 212-206-0300

This attractive, "ski lodge"-esque new Meatpacking District triple-
decker showcases a "pricey" American gastropub menu that's "actually very good"; definitely "a scene", it's still "working out the kinks",
but it gets points for "originality" – and for serving till 3 AM.

'ino ◐ *Italian* 24 | 15 | 19 | $27

G Village | 21 Bedford St. (bet. Downing St. & 6th Ave.) | 212-989-5769 |
www.cafeino.com

Diners are "cramped" enough to "feel like pressed panini" themselves
at this "teeny" Village Italian wine bar, but its "cheap", "hauntingly"
"marvelous" sandwiches make up for the "squeeze" – as well as the
"waits"; for "small bites", "nobody does it better."

'inoteca ◐ *Italian* 23 | 18 | 19 | $37

LES | 98 Rivington St. (Ludlow St.) | 212-614-0473 |
www.inotecanyc.com

Like its smaller sibling, 'ino, this "vibrant", "friendly" LES Italian is a
"grazer's paradise" of *fantastico* salumi, cheeses and panini paired
with "terrific" wines; those "tidbits" can "easily rack up a big bill", but
after sampling them, "you'll know why you waited so long" for a seat.

NEW Insieme *Italian* ▽ 26 | 20 | 24 | $72

W 50s | The Michelangelo Hotel | 777 Seventh Ave. (bet. 50th & 51st Sts.) |
212-582-1310 | www.restaurantinsieme.com

Marco Canora (Hearth) "has outdone himself" at this new
Midtown "winner" where half of the "terrific" Italian dishes are "traditional" and the other half "modern", and all are high-priced; service is
"relaxed", but the contemporary room draws mixed reactions
("classy" vs. "ice palace").

Intermezzo ◐ *Italian* 18 | 16 | 17 | $32

Chelsea | 202 Eighth Ave. (bet. 20th & 21st Sts.) | 212-929-3433 |
www.intermezzony.com

"Wedged in among the local trendies", this "reasonable" Chelsea
Italian offers "no surprises", just an "attentive" staff doling out "large
portions" of "reliable" pastas with "zesty sauces"; the "live DJ" music
is "loud", but that suits the "young, lively crowd."

	FOOD	DECOR	SERVICE	COST

Iron Sushi *Japanese*
19 | 13 | 18 | $28

E 70s | 355 E. 78th St. (bet. 1st & 2nd Aves.) | 212-772-7680
Murray Hill | 440 Third Ave. (bet. 30th & 31st Sts.) | 212-447-5822
"Huge slabs" of "fresh" fish grace the "larger-than-life", "creative" rolls at this "no-frills" East Side sushi duo deemed a "superb value"; the "attentive staff" makes the "mundane surroundings" easy to overlook, but there's also "speedy delivery" as an option.

Isabella's ● *American/Mediterranean*
20 | 19 | 18 | $42

W 70s | 359 Columbus Ave. (77th St.) | 212-724-2100 | www.brguestrestaurants.com
"They have the formula down pat" at this "deservedly popular" longtime Med–New American, an UWS "oasis" for "unrushed", "delicious" meals overseen by "pleasant" staffers; outdoor seating and prime "people-watching" make it "hard to beat", especially at Sunday brunch.

NEW Isabella's Oven ●⊄ *Pizza*
– | – | – | M

LES | 365 Grand St. (Essex St.) | 212-529-5206 | www.isabellasoven.com
This new LES Italian turns out simple salads, pastas and sandwiches, but the real stars are its brick-oven pizzas cooked to slightly charred perfection; the storefront space seats about 10, but there's a big patio in back where locals linger over beer and wine and take in occasional live jazz.

Ise *Japanese*
22 | 12 | 18 | $38

E 40s | 151 E. 49th St. (bet. Lexington & 3rd Aves.) | 212-319-6876
Financial District | 56 Pine St. (bet. Pearl & William Sts.) | 212-785-1600 ⊠
W 50s | 58 W. 56th St. (bet. 5th & 6th Aves.) | 212-707-8702
It's a good sign that this "reliable" *izakaya* trio is "filled" at lunch "with Japanese businessmen" who come for "excellent", "affordable" katsu, sushi and sashimi; the "fluorescent-lit" setups are "forgettable", but "you can't go wrong with anything on the menu."

NEW Island *Mediterranean*
∇ 18 | 21 | 18 | $32

Astoria | 35-15 36th St. (bet. 35th & 36th Aves.) | Queens | 718-433-0690 | www.islandcafebar.com
At this easily affordable, Euro-chic oasis set in a sea of Astoria warehouses, the specialty is Med small plates; it's easy to get lost in its "huge" clublike space, which includes two levels of dining areas, canopied lounges with settees, several bars and a fully decked-out DJ suite.

Island Burgers & Shakes ⊄ *Hamburgers*
22 | 8 | 14 | $16

W 50s | 766 Ninth Ave. (bet. 51st & 52nd Sts.) | 212-307-7934
"Divine" shakes and "hearty burgers" with a "mind-boggling variety" of toppings set this "cheap", "surf"-themed Hell's Kitchen "shack" apart from the pack; most don't care about its "hole-in-the-wall" setup, but the "no-fries" situation is an "Achilles heel."

Ithaka ● *Greek/Seafood*
20 | 16 | 19 | $43

E 80s | 308 E. 86th St. (bet. 1st & 2nd Aves.) | 212-628-9100 | www.ithakarestaurant.com
If you're in a "Greek isles mood", travel to this Yorkville "favorite" proffering "flavorful" seafood in "traditional" taverna environs enhanced by "lovely" live guitar music; "warm" service and "reasonable" prices are two more reasons it "deserves to be more popular."

subscribe to zagat.com

	FOOD	DECOR	SERVICE	COST

I Tre Merli ☾ *Italian* — 18 | 18 | 17 | $43

SoHo | 463 W. Broadway (bet. Houston & Prince Sts.) | 212-254-8699
W Village | 183 W. 10th St. (W. 4th St.) | 212-929-2221
www.itremerli.com

Oozing "Italian chic" and "trendy" bar "action", this "breezy", mid-priced SoHo trattoria has a "smaller" Village "brother" that's more on the "cute and romantic" side; at both, the food's "good", if "not memorable", and the servers, though not so good, are memorable.

I Trulli *Italian* — 22 | 20 | 20 | $56

Gramercy | 122 E. 27th St. (bet. Lexington Ave. & Park Ave. S.) |
212-481-7372 | www.itrulli.com

Whether you sit "inside by the fire or out on the patio", this "classy" Gramercy Italian's "earthy" Pugliese cuisine is "trulli" *delizioso*; some say it's "overpriced", but the "inviting" staff and an "incredible wine list" (also poured at the "attached enoteca") have most saying this "well-orchestrated act" is "worth it."

Itzocan ⊞ *Mexican* — 23 | 12 | 18 | $33

E 100s | 1575 Lexington Ave. (101st St.) | 212-423-0255
E Village | 438 E. Ninth St. (bet. Ave. A & 1st Ave.) | 212-677-5856 ☾
French-influenced "Mexican haute cuisine" is the specialty of the UES branch of this "friendly", "reasonable" pair, while the East Village original offers straightforward south-of-the-border cooking; the "tight" digs "aren't much to look at", but given the "jazzy" tastes and low prices, "who cares?"

Ivo & Lulu ⊠⊞ *Caribbean/French* — ▽ 22 | 13 | 18 | $27

SoHo | 558 Broome St. (bet. 6th Ave. & Varick St.) | 212-226-4399
"Wonderful", "organic" French-Caribbean fare at "out-of-this-world-inexpensive" prices (abetted by a BYO policy) keeps this "charming", "cash-only" West SoHo "shoebox" "packed"; it changed hands recently, but early reports say it's as "friendly" as ever.

NEW Izakaya Ten ☾ *Japanese* — ▽ 19 | 20 | 18 | $40

Chelsea | 207 10th Ave. (bet. 22nd & 23rd Sts.) | 212-627-7777
Its slim Chelsea space was first D'or Ahn, then briefly, Anzu, and now it's been remade again as this less-expensive "publike" Japanese *izakaya* specializing "tasty little plates"; a wild exterior paint job and wide sake selection distinguishes what's otherwise basically a neighborhood joint.

Jack Bistro ☾ *French* — 17 | 16 | 18 | $36

G Village | 80 University Pl. (11th St.) | 212-620-5544
"Pleasant" and "unpretentious", this "well-rounded" Villager makes a "dependable" local "hangout" for a "casual" French bistro bite "that won't break the bank"; it's "nothing earth-shattering", but the overall "relaxing dining experience" "fills a void" in the area.

Jack's Luxury — ▽ 24 | 17 | 21 | $63
Oyster Bar ☾⊠ *Continental/French*

E Village | 101 Second Ave. (bet. 5th & 6th Sts.) | 212-979-1012
The "luxurious" French-Continental fare remains "out-of-this-world" and the service pleasingly "low-key" at this recently relocated East Villager; nonetheless, nostalgists noting its new "postage-stamp

space" lament the loss of its "original townhouse" digs that were "so much a part" of its "romantic" charm.

Jackson Diner ⊅ Indian
FOOD	DECOR	SERVICE	COST
22	10	14	$22

Jackson Heights | 37-47 74th St. (bet. Roosevelt & 37th Aves.) | Queens | 718-672-1232

Maybe it "looks like a canteen", but this Indian vet is a "reigning rajah" of Jackson Heights thanks to its "stupendously delicious" dishes; yes, its high quality and low prices can lead to total "bedlam", but the $8.95 buffet brunch is "a steal" that leaves everyone "stuffed and happy."

Jackson Hole American
FOOD	DECOR	SERVICE	COST
17	9	14	$20

E 60s | 232 E. 64th St. (bet. 2nd & 3rd Aves.) | 212-371-7187 ●
E 80s | 1611 Second Ave. (bet. 83rd & 84th Sts.) | 212-737-8788 ●
E 90s | 1270 Madison Ave. (91st St.) | 212-427-2820
Murray Hill | 521 Third Ave. (35th St.) | 212-679-3264 ●
W 80s | 517 Columbus Ave. (85th St.) | 212-362-5177
Bayside | 35-01 Bell Blvd. (35th Ave.) | Queens | 718-281-0330 ●
Jackson Heights | 69-35 Astoria Blvd. (70th St.) | Queens | 718-204-7070 ●
www.jacksonholeburgers.com

"Don't plan on running a marathon" after consuming one of the "colossal" burgers this "cheap", "child-friendly" "diner-style" chain is famous for; "you can smell the grease" in its "often-crowded" quarters and the "desultory waiters" aren't much help, but you won't find a better "hangover" cure.

Jack the Horse Tavern American
FOOD	DECOR	SERVICE	COST
20	20	19	$38

Brooklyn Heights | 66 Hicks St. (Cranberry St.) | Brooklyn | 718-852-5084 | www.jackthehorse.com

The "creative" New American cooking at this "charming" Brooklyn Heights "tavern" is gaining a "solid fan base", despite "smallish portions" and tabs "slightly pricey" for the genre; still, most surveyors are won over by the "chic" ambiance and "responsive" staff.

Jacques French
FOOD	DECOR	SERVICE	COST
18	17	17	$42

E 80s | 206 E. 85th St. (bet. 2nd & 3rd Aves.) | 212-327-2272
NoLita | 20 Prince St. (bet. Elizabeth & Mott Sts.) | 212-966-8886
www.jacquesnyc.com

"Must-try" moules frites are the star at these "pleasant", "very French" brasseries that also offer a menu of "decent" Gallic "standards" (with a slight North African "flair" at the NoLita branch); the prices are "reasonable" enough so that most don't mind the "spotty" service.

Jacques-Imo's NYC Cajun/Creole
FOOD	DECOR	SERVICE	COST
17	14	16	$32

W 70s | 366 Columbus Ave. (77th St.) | 212-799-0150 | www.jacquesimosnyc.com

"It's not Mardi Gras", but this "funky", low-budget UWS "N'Awlins" transplant offers plenty of "fun", not to mention "darn good" Cajun-Creole fare (try the "kickin'" fried chicken); the setting is "stripped-down" and service "can be slow", but you may "end up dancing on your chair" anyway.

Jaiya Thai Thai
FOOD	DECOR	SERVICE	COST
22	10	13	$27

Gramercy | 396 Third Ave. (28th St.) | 212-889-1330 | www.jaiya.com

"Not for the faint of heart", the "fiery hot" dishes at this "authentic" Gramercy Thai are so "stunningly delicious" and their price tags so

	FOOD	DECOR	SERVICE	COST

"gentle", the "bossy" service and "lacking" decor are beside the point; "just be careful", because "hot means inferno."

Jake's Steakhouse *Steak*
24 | 19 | 21 | $49

Bronx | 6031 Broadway (242nd St.) | 718-581-0182 | www.jakessteakhouse.com

Somewhat "unexpected" for the zip code, this "friendly", "special-occasion" Riverdale steakhouse owned by meat wholesalers "rivals the best in Manhattan" but is "considerably cheaper"; the "second-floor view of Van Cortlandt Park" makes for "fond memories."

Jane ● *American*
21 | 18 | 19 | $41

G Village | 100 W. Houston St. (bet. La Guardia Pl. & Thompson St.) | 212-254-7000 | www.janerestaurant.com

"Satisfying all around", this "casual" Village New American is "deserv-edly packed", especially during its "top-notch brunch"; "everyone can find something to like" on its midpriced menu, delivered by "pro" serv-ers in "large, open" quarters.

Japonais ☒ *Japanese*
20 | 23 | 18 | $58

Gramercy | 111 E. 18th St. (bet. Irving Pl. & Park Ave. S.) | 212-260-2020 | www.japonaisnewyork.com

Maybe "it's all about the scene" at this "crowded", "cavernous" Gramercy Japanese fusion specialist, but they "do pay attention to" the "tasty" fare too; its "beautiful", "other-worldly", red-lacquered space (complete with two "hip" lounges) helps justify "pricey" tabs, if not occasionally "snobby" service.

Japonica *Japanese*
22 | 14 | 20 | $45

G Village | 100 University Pl. (12th St.) | 212-243-7752 | www.japonicanyc.com

The "crowds confirm the quality" at this "tried-and-true" Village Japanese "institution", where devotees swear by the "huge" pieces of "fresh" (practically "still flapping") sushi served by "attentive" staff-ers; just try not to notice the "cramped", "lackluster" setup.

Jarnac ⓜ *Mediterranean*
22 | 19 | 23 | $52

W Village | 328 W. 12th St. (Greenwich St.) | 212-924-3413 | www.jarnacny.com

"Charming" waiters tend to a "restaurant full of regulars" at this "cozy" West Village "hideaway", where the Med menu boasts a "fab-ulous cassoulet" and the "very visible" owner ensures even "first-timers aren't neglected"; it's a "definite find" and "great for a date", slightly "pricey" tabs notwithstanding.

Jasmine *Thai*
19 | 15 | 16 | $25

E 80s | 1619 Second Ave. (84th St.) | 212-517-8854

"For your Thai cravings on the Upper East Side", this vet "hits the mark" with "quick fixes" of "solid" "standards"; it "can get loud" and "crowded", but those "inexpensive" prices ensure that, for most lo-cals, it's the "perfect standby."

Jean Claude ⊘ *French*
▽ 22 | 16 | 20 | $43

SoHo | 137 Sullivan St. (bet. Houston & Prince Sts.) | 212-475-9232

"If you can't live in Paris", there's this "charming" SoHo French bistro whose "intimate", "candlelit" quarters make a "romantic" backdrop for "expertly prepared" "classic" offerings; it's a "perennial date place for the young and budget-conscious" – just remember it's "cash only."

⚡ Jean Georges 🔄 *French*   28 | 26 | 27 | $126

W 60s | Trump Int'l Hotel | 1 Central Park W. (bet. 60th & 61st Sts.) | 212-299-3900 | www.jean-georges.com

"From start to finish", expect "profound dining experiences" at Jean-Georges Vongerichten's "stunning", jackets-required New French "temple to gastronomy" at Columbus Circle, where the regularly changing, prix fixe–only menus based on fresh seasonal ingredients are probably the "most creative" in town; add "flawless" formal service (supervised by the chef's brother, Philippe), "elegant", recently redone rooms overlooking Central Park and alfresco seating, and it's no wonder it's voted one of the city's most popular places; P.S. for "NYC's best bargain", the Nougatine Room offers "ethereal" $24 prix fixe lunches.

Jewel Bako ●🔄 *Japanese*   25 | 22 | 22 | $74

E Village | 239 E. Fifth St. (bet. 2nd & 3rd Aves.) | 212-979-1012

A "jewel indeed", this "tiny", dinner-only East Village Japanese cuts "perfect" sushi (including "exotic" choices "flown in from all over the world") presented in "the coolest" bamboo-lined space abetted by "delightful" service overseen by "amazing" hosts Jack and Grace Lamb; however, wallet-watchers beware: "someone has to foot that FedEx bill."

Jewel of India *Indian*   20 | 18 | 19 | $37

W 40s | 15 W. 44th St. (bet. 5th & 6th Aves.) | 212-869-5544 | www.jewelofindiarestaurant.com

"It's all about the $15.95 lunch buffet" at this "friendly" Midtown Indian standby dishing up "authentic" eats to "continuous" crowds of "bargain"-hunters and business types; although it's quite comfortable, critics contend that the decor has become "dull" and could use "a little zip."

J.G. Melon ●⊄ *Pub Food*   21 | 12 | 15 | $25

E 70s | 1291 Third Ave. (74th St.) | 212-744-0585

An UES crowd "heavy on Lillys and Lacostes" counts on this "dark, noisy" "burger champ" for "cheap" pub grub; "rude" staffers, "jam-packed", "worn" digs and a "cash-only" policy are all "part of the experience" – and all "worth it" for those "unmatchable" patties and cottage fries.

Jing Fong *Chinese*   19 | 13 | 13 | $21

Chinatown | 20 Elizabeth St. (bet. Bayard & Canal Sts.) | 212-964-5256

"Chase after those carts" cry devotees of this "gigantic" Chinatown dim sum emporium evoking the floor of the "NYSE" (lots of "noise", lots of "pointing"); "shared tables", "long waits" and "not-so-charming" service make for a "zoo"-like vibe, but hey, "take a risk – it'll only cost a few yuan."

JJ's Asian Fusion Ⓜ *Asian Fusion*   ▽ 25 | 15 | 20 | $28

Astoria | 37-05 31st Ave. (bet. 37th & 38th Sts.) | Queens | 718-626-8888 | www.myjjs.com

"Delicious, stylish fusion" fare and "solid", "fresh" sushi at incredibly "reasonable prices" make this "friendly" Astorian a contender for the

| | FOOD | DECOR | SERVICE | COST |

"best Asian food in Queens award"; the space is "nothing spectacular", but there's always "super-fast delivery"; P.S. the "edamame potstickers are a must."

Joe Allen ● *American* 　　　　　17 | 15 | 18 | $42

W 40s | 326 W. 46th St. (bet. 8th & 9th Aves.) | 212-581-6464 | www.joeallenrestaurant.com

For a "boffo" pre- or post-show "experience", hit this "longtime" Theater District "tradition" for "unpretentious" American "comfort" fare at "reasonable" rates; for most, the likelihood of "rubbing elbows with Broadway stars" outweighs the "sketchy" service and "pub"-like digs that "need a face-lift."

Joe & Pat's *Italian/Pizza* 　　　∇ 22 | 13 | 18 | $20

Staten Island | 1758 Victory Blvd. (Manor Rd.) | 718-981-0887

"Now you're talking pizza" cry surveyors smitten with this "old-style" Staten Islander's "excellent thin-crust" pies; it also proffers "typical" red-sauce "staples" in dinerlike digs – i.e. it's a "basic Italian" joint like they were "way back when."

Joe's Pizza *Pizza* 　　　　　　　23 | 5 | 11 | $8

G Village | 7 Carmine St. (bet. Bleecker St. & 6th Ave.) | 212-255-3946 ●
NEW **Midwood** | 1621 Kings Hwy. (Ocean Ave.) | Brooklyn | 718-339-4525 ⊄
Park Slope | 137 Seventh Ave. (bet. Carroll St. & Garfield Pl.) | Brooklyn | 718-398-9198

"Locals and tourists alike" line up for "fabulous" slices of "cheap" "classic NY pizza" with the "perfect balance of cheese and crispiness" at these separately owned, "standing-room-only" Village-Brooklyn joints; "fast delivery" is one way to avoid "the wait."

Joe's Shanghai *Chinese* 　　　　22 | 9 | 13 | $23

Chinatown | 9 Pell St. (bet. Bowery & Mott St.) | 212-233-8888 ⊄
W 50s | 24 W. 56th St. (bet. 5th & 6th Aves.) | 212-333-3868
Flushing | 136-21 37th Ave. (bet. Main & Union Sts.) | Queens | 718-539-3838 ⊄
www.joeshanghairestaurants.com

"Ethereal soup dumplings" are the claim to fame of this "no-frills" Shanghainese trio; getting in requires "waiting (and waiting)", "sharing tables with strangers" and enduring "erratic service", but those "off-the-charts good" morsels make it all "worthwhile."

NEW Johnny Utah's ● *BBQ/Southwestern* 　　- | - | - | M

W 50s | 25 W. 51st St., downstairs (bet. 5th & 6th Aves.) | 212-265-8824 | www.johnnyutahs.com

NYC now has a mechanical bull to call its own thanks to this upscale saloon that just rode into Rock Center; its rib-sticking, midpriced Southwestern fare, backed by impressive tequilas and whiskeys poured at a lengthy bar, can be savored in banquettes with views of the ring, or in private dining rooms.

John's of 12th Street ⊄ *Italian* 　　　19 | 14 | 18 | $34

E Village | 302 E. 12th St. (2nd Ave.) | 212-475-9531

"Fuhgeddaboutit" – for "huge portions" of "cheap" Italian fare "oozing cheese and red sauce", East Villagers hit this 100-year-old "staple" where "friendly" staffers make "everyone feel like a regular"; its dark, "dripping candles"–adorned space is great for "first dates", while disguising the fact that it "needs a face-lift."

John's Pizzeria ● *Pizza* | 22 | 12 | 15 | $22

E 60s | 408 E. 64th St. (bet. 1st & York Aves.) | 212-935-2895
G Village | 278 Bleecker St. (bet. 6th Ave. & 7th Ave. S.) | 212-243-1680 ⊟
W 40s | 260 W. 44th St. (bet. B'way & 8th Ave.) | 212-391-7560
www.johnspizzerianyc.com

"I'll be eating here as long as I have teeth" vow die-hard fans of this "coal-oven" pizzeria trio turning out "fantastic" "crispy, thin-crust" pies – "no slices!" – that leave you "wondering how you ate it all"; most prefer the circa-1929 Village original, but prepare for "long lines" at all three locations.

JoJo *French* | 24 | 22 | 22 | $67

E 60s | 160 E. 64th St. (bet. Lexington & 3rd Aves.) | 212-223-5656 | www.jean-georges.com

"Sample a great chef's wizardry" in "romantic" townhouse quarters at Jean-Georges Vongerichten's "elegant" East Side French bistro, presided over by a "warm", "polished" staff; surveyors split allegiances between upstairs and downstairs, but no matter where you sit it's "consistently excellent"; P.S. the $24 prix fixe lunch is "a steal."

Jolie *French* | 20 | 20 | 20 | $38

Boerum Hill | 320 Atlantic Ave. (bet. Hoyt & Smith Sts.) | Brooklyn | 718-488-0777 | www.jolierestaurant.com

A "delightful" Boerum Hill "surprise", this "smooth" French "boîte" enjoys a loyal local following for its "authentic", "beautifully prepared" dishes delivered by an "unrushed" staff; it's "lovely for a romantic night out", especially when you can "sit out in the garden."

Josephina ● *American* | 18 | 16 | 18 | $47

W 60s | 1900 Broadway (bet. 63rd & 64th Sts.) | 212-799-1000 | www.josephinanyc.com

"The waiters know how to use a watch" at this "huge", "hectic" New American across from Lincoln Center, where the staff "handles theater and music audiences" "seamlessly", i.e. "in plenty of time for the curtain"; the menu's "not exciting", but it's "satisfying" and "decently priced" too.

Joseph's Restaurant ⑤ *Italian* | ▽ 21 | 17 | 22 | $52

Financial District | 3 Hanover Sq. (Pearl St.) | 212-747-1300

To uncover this "old-world" Hanover Square Italian, descend "below street level" where you'll find a "pricey" "treasure" that's become a "staple in the financial community" for its "authentic" fare, "pro" service and "clubby" vibe; "dated" decor notwithstanding, most would bank on it as a "no-fail choice."

Josie's *Eclectic* | 19 | 15 | 16 | $33

Murray Hill | 565 Third Ave. (37th St.) | 212-490-1558
W 70s | 300 Amsterdam Ave. (74th St.) | 212-769-1212
NEW Josie's Kitchen *Eclectic*
E 80s | 1614 Second Ave. (84th St.) | 212-734-6644
www.josiesnyc.com

The "wholesome", "budget"-friendly New American fare is "health-conscious" enough to appease "granola-and-veggie" types at this

	FOOD	DECOR	SERVICE	COST

Eclectic trio, and fortunately it has the "flavor" to satisfy "taste-seekers" too; given the prices, most don't mind that the decor and service are "uninspiring", but a few wonder "where are the guys?"

Joya ⌖ Thai
23 | 17 | 18 | $22

Cobble Hill | 215 Court St. (bet. Warren & Wycoff Sts.) | Brooklyn | 718-222-3484

"Super-cheap", "out-of-this-world" fare is the reason that this "friendly" Cobble Hill Thai is "perpetually packed"; its "rock 'n' roll atmosphere" complete with "LaGuardia"-worthy "noise" levels is "not great for conversation", but the "lovely garden" is a quieter option.

Jubilee French
22 | 15 | 18 | $48

E 50s | 347 E. 54th St. (bet. 1st & 2nd Aves.) | 212-888-3569 | www.jubileeny.com

"Mmm-ussels" headline the "perfect bistro" menu at this relatively "reasonable" Sutton Place "favorite" that's as "French as French gets"; despite uneven service and dated decor, it's still good enough and cozy enough to stay "crowded" with "knowing locals."

Jules ◑ French
19 | 19 | 17 | $37

E Village | 65 St. Marks Pl. (bet. 1st & 2nd Aves.) | 212-477-5560 | www.julesbistro.com

"Live jazz is what makes it special" say surveyors of this "charming" East Village French bistro, where the "reliable" fare plays second fiddle to the "fun scene"; "nothing will blow you over" here – including the "reasonable" check – but to most it's a "neighborhood asset."

Junior's Diner
18 | 11 | 15 | $23

E 40s | Grand Central | lower level (42nd St. & Vanderbilt Ave.) | 212-983-5257

W 40s | Shubert Alley | 1515 Broadway (enter on 45th St., bet. B'way & 8th Ave.) | 212-302-2000 ◑

Downtown | 386 Flatbush Ave. Ext. (DeKalb Ave.) | Brooklyn | 718-852-5257 ◑

www.juniorscheesecake.com

"It's the cheesecake, stupid" – beyond the "heavenly" signature dessert at this Downtown Brooklyn "institution", the "classic" NY deli eats are deemed "just ok" and the "nostalgic" decor "cheesy"; the Manhattan branches are "good bets" when you "need to make a train" or a curtain.

Kai ⬛Ⓜ Japanese
▽ 25 | 23 | 24 | $74

E 60s | Ito En | 822 Madison Ave., 2nd fl. (bet. 68th & 69th Sts.) | 212-988-7277 | www.itoen.com

"Delicious", "meticulously prepared" Japanese kaiseki is the hallmark of this "refined" "secret" above the tea boutique Ito En; its "serene" setting is a "respite from the frenzy" of UES shopping, but just remember "peace" can be "pricey."

NEW Kaijou Japanese
- | - | - | M

Financial District | 21 South End Ave. (W. Thames St.) | 212-786-9888 | www.kaijounewyork.com

The main attraction at this new Battery Park City eatery is its idyllic waterfront location, but well-priced Japanese classics also make it a welcome find; its Hudson River views with the Statue of Liberty in the distance can be enjoyed from inside or out on the spacious patio.

	FOOD	DECOR	SERVICE	COST

NEW Kampuchea *Cambodian* ▽ 20 | 18 | 19 | $28

LES | 78 Rivington St. (Allen St.) | 212-529-3901 |
www.kampucheanyc.com

NYC "could use more Cambodian places", and this "funky" LES arrival
is filling the void with noodle dishes, sandwiches and other "flavorful"
Khmer "street food" at the "right" price; "loud" music, "hip crowds"
and "communal tables" make for a "lively" scene.

Kang Suh ● *Korean* ▽ 20 | 12 | 16 | $34

Garment District | 1250 Broadway (32nd St.) | 212-564-6845

"Always tasty (and always open)", this big, budget-friendly 24/7
Korean BBQ "fixture" in the Garment District allows you to "cook your
own" "meltingly tender beef" or order from a menu that includes
sushi; just "eat fast" because "they rush you out the door."

Z Kanoyama ● *Japanese* 27 | 16 | 19 | $51

E Village | 175 Second Ave. (11th St.) | 212-777-5266 | www.kanoyama.com

A "seat at the sushi bar is a beautiful thing" at this "friendly", "moderately priced" East Village Japanese where you can watch "pristine"
fish that "you've never heard of" get "lovingly" sliced and rolled; "word
is getting out", though, so "go early before the place fills up."

Kati Roll Co. *Indian* 20 | 5 | 11 | $12

G Village | 99 MacDougal St. (bet. Bleecker & W. 3rd Sts.) | 212-420-6517 ●
W 40s | 140 W. 46th St. (bet. 6th & 7th Aves.) | 212-730-4280

This Delhi duo is always "packed to bursting", and so are its "cheap,
delicious" "Indian burritos" (aka kati rolls); Midtown office types seek
it out for "quick lunches", while in the Village "college kids" hit it
"post-partying", but "hole-in-the-wall" setups and "poor" service
mean many tout it "to go."

Katsu-Hama *Japanese* 20 | 9 | 15 | $24

E 40s | 11 E. 47th St. (bet. 5th & Madison Aves.) | 212-758-5909 |
www.katsuhama.com

"Sushi isn't the only Japanese food" note fans of the "light, crispy"
fried pork cutlets that are the mainstay of this Midtown katsu specialist; the decor "isn't fancy" by any means and service is "slightly uneven", but it's a "reliable" "bargain" that's "filling" and "flavorful."

Katz's Delicatessen *Deli* 23 | 9 | 11 | $21

LES | 205 E. Houston St. (Ludlow St.) | 212-254-2246 | www.katzdeli.com

As "quintessential NY" as the "yellow taxi", this "last-of-its-kind" LES
deli is famed for its "orgasmic" (see *When Harry Met Sally*) corned
beef and pastrami sandwiches dispensed in "fluorescent-and-
linoleum" digs worthy of a "prison mess hall"; it's "intimidating the
first time you go" given the "loud" crowds and "gruff" countermen, but
that's "all part of the charm"; N.B. this may well be the best museum
of American history in the country.

Keens Steakhouse *Steak* 24 | 22 | 22 | $62

Garment District | 72 W. 36th St. (bet. 5th & 6th Aves.) | 212-947-3636 |
www.keens.com

The ultimate "old-school boy's club" is this circa-1885 Garment District
steakhouse where the "unique and heavenly mutton chops" and other
"fantastic meats" come via an "attentive" crew; its "ancient" clay

pipe-adorned quarters (complete with "elegant" private rooms) "reek of history and show business", but prices are strictly up-to-date.

NEW Kefi ⇄ Greek — 23 | 16 | 17 | $36

W 70s | 222 W. 79th St. (bet. Amsterdam Ave. & B'way) | 212-873-0200

Formerly Onera, this "lively" UWS nook from Michael Psilakis scores well for "delicious, inventive" Greek food and wines at "value" prices; less popular are its "cramped" digs, "long waits", "rushed service", "no-rez" and "cash-only" policies, but the fact that most "keep coming back" speaks volumes.

Kellari Taverna ● Greek — 23 | 23 | 21 | $48

W 40s | 19 W. 44th St. (bet. 5th & 6th Aves.) | 212-221-0144 | www.kellari.us

The "fantastically simple" whole grilled fish is "a must" at this "upscale" Theater District Greek, where "fabulously prepared" cuisine comes in "lush", "airy" quarters via a "pleasant" crew; it's a bit on the "expensive" side, but "bargain" prix fixe deals ensure it's usually affordable.

Kelley & Ping Pan-Asian — 16 | 13 | 12 | $24

E Village | 325 Bowery (2nd St.) | 212-475-8600
SoHo | 127 Greene St. (bet. Houston & Prince Sts.) | 212-228-1212
www.eatrice.com

"Reliable" for "quick, tasty" Pan-Asian "comfort food", this East Village-SoHo noodle duo is self-serve "cafeteria by day", "candlelit" restaurant by night; the service "could use some work", ditto the "hard seats" in "crowded, noisy" quarters, but "cheap" prices keep 'em "bustling."

Killmeyer's Old Bavaria Inn German — ▽ 21 | 21 | 21 | $32

Staten Island | 4254 Arthur Kill Rd. (Sharrotts Rd.) | 718-984-1202 | www.killmeyers.com

You can "linger in the old world" for a while at this *"gemütlich"* SI German, where "substantial", well-priced classics plus brews from a "phone book-size menu" are "best when the biergarten is open"; quite simply, it's "worth the trip."

Kings' Carriage House American — 21 | 26 | 22 | $60

E 80s | 251 E. 82nd St. (bet. 2nd & 3rd Aves.) | 212-734-5490 | www.kingscarriagehouse.com

Located in an "intimate" "English manor"-like house, this UES New American draws "special-occasion" diners and "ladies who lunch" with its "ravishing" decor and "graciously served", prix fixe-only fare; it's favored for "elegant" afternoon tea, but just "prepare to shell out" for all that *"très romantique"* charm.

King Yum Chinese — ▽ 17 | 15 | 19 | $25

Fresh Meadows | 181-08 Union Tpke. (181st St.) | Queens | 718-380-1918 | www.kingyumrestaurant.com

"Since the '50s", this "kitschy" Fresh Meadows veteran has dished up "quality" Cantonese-Polynesian fare with a heaping side of "nostalgia"; sure, "tacky lives" on in its "tiki" trappings, "drinks with umbrellas" and karaoke nights, but "for cheap Chinese food as you remember it, it's the king."

	FOOD	DECOR	SERVICE	COST

Kin Khao *Thai* — 22 | 17 | 18 | $37

SoHo | 171 Spring St. (bet. Thompson St. & W. B'way) | 212-966-3939 |
www.eatrice.com

"Still sexy and tasty after all these years", this "funky" SoHo Thai plies
its "trendy", youthful crowd with "phenomenal cocktails" and "solid",
"affordable" fare; it's a good pick for dates and groups, but since it
takes no reservations, expect to "wait."

NEW Ki Sushi *Japanese* — ▽ 25 | 22 | 23 | $33

Boerum Hill | 122 Smith St. (bet. Dean & Pacific Sts.) | Brooklyn |
718-935-0575

Some say the "fresh, creative" sushi at this "tranquil" new Boerum Hill
Japanese is some of the "best in Brooklyn"; insiders advise "sit at the
bar", where the "skilled", "gracious chefs" "know just what to recommend"; P.S. the "lunch specials are a steal."

Kitchen Club *French/Japanese* — ▽ 22 | 18 | 22 | $47

NoLita | 30 Prince St. (Mott St.) | 212-274-0025 | www.thekitchenclub.com
"You'll make fast friends" with the "warm" owner and her "precious
pooch" at this "quaint" NoLita French-Japanese, where "eager-to-
please" staffers dispense "divine dumplings" and other "high-quality"
fare; it's "not particularly inexpensive", but regulars don't mind given
the "unpretentious" vibe and handy "adjoining sake bar."

Kitchenette *Southern* — 19 | 15 | 15 | $22

TriBeCa | 156 Chambers St. (bet. Greenwich St. & W. B'way) | 212-267-6740
W 100s | 1272 Amsterdam Ave. (bet. 122nd & 123rd Sts.) |
212-531-7600

You'd better "loosen your belt" before taking on the cheap comfort
dishes doled out at these "no-frills, retro" Southerners; "strollers and po-
seurs" alike crowd the "shabby-chic" digs, though "ungodly waits" and
"harried service" are often the norm, especially at the "zoolike" brunch.

Z Kittichai *Thai* — 23 | 27 | 20 | $59

SoHo | 60 Thompson Hotel | 60 Thompson St. (bet. Broome & Spring Sts.) |
212-219-2000 | www.kittichairestaurant.com

"Sleek and sexy", this SoHo Thai dishes up "divine", "innovative" cuisine in a Zen-like, "drop-dead gorgeous" setting; sure, "it's a scene",
and the "high impress-a-date factor" comes steep, but then "what
did you expect?"

NEW Klee Brasserie *American/European* — 21 | 19 | 19 | $52

Chelsea | 200 Ninth Ave. (bet. 22nd & 23rd Sts.) | 212-633-8033 |
www.kleebrasserie.com

There's a "buzz around" this Chelsea yearling that was "just what the
neighborhood needed", with "terrific" Euro-American fare, "low-key,
classy" environs and "friendly service"; downsides include "lots of
noise", "close seating" and upmarket tabs.

Klong �½ *Thai* — 19 | 18 | 16 | $25

E Village | 7 St. Marks Pl. (bet. 2nd & 3rd Aves.) | 212-505-9955 |
www.klongnyc.com

Despite looking expensive, this "trendy" East Village Thai's "street
food" makes for "good cheap eating"; however, "on busy nights" you
may feel "rushed", and the noise can rise to "club scene" levels.

	FOOD	DECOR	SERVICE	COST

Knickerbocker Bar & Grill ◐ *American*   20 | 18 | 19 | $46

G Village | 33 University Pl. (9th St.) | 212-228-8490 |
www.knickerbockerbarandgrill.com

Best known for its "solid" New American steakhouse fare in "hefty
portions", this "friendly" "Village staple" also provides "live jazz on
weekends"; it gets "noisy", and the "'70s decor" borders on "tired",
but there's a reason it's been a local "fixture" for three decades.

Knife + Fork Ⓜ *European*   ▽ 23 | 18 | 21 | $52

E Village | 108 E. Fourth St. (bet. 1st & 2nd Aves.) | 212-228-4885 |
www.knife-fork-nyc.com

"Exceptionally well-prepared", "innovative" modern European fare
and first-rate "personal service" are earning this "tiny", "quaint" yearling a rep as an "East Village foodie heaven"; it's "pricey à la carte", so
insiders recommend the $45 six-course tasting menu and booking
ahead since "getting a table is a chore."

NEW Kobe Club ◐Ⓢ *Steak*   20 | 22 | 18 | $146

W 50s | 68 W. 58th St. (bet. 5th & 6th Aves.) | 212-644-5623 |
www.kobeclubny.com

A "mind-blowing" variety of Wagyu beef (domestic, Australian and Japanese) "like butter" is the thing at this slick new Midtowner from restaurateur Jeffrey Chodorow; "happening" types gladly "risk their lives"
beneath a ceiling hung with 2,000 "samurai swords" in its "cool", moody
space, but the real danger may be the "out-of-this-world" tabs.

Kodama ◐ *Japanese*   19 | 9 | 16 | $30

W 40s | 301 W. 45th St. (bet. 8th & 9th Aves.) | 212-582-8065

Specializing in "delicious", moderately priced sushi at a pace that'll
get you "in and out in time" for your show, this Theater District
Japanese "stalwart" is usually "busy"; it doesn't matter that the "minimalist" digs definitely "aren't fancy."

Koi *Japanese*   23 | 23 | 19 | $62

W 40s | Bryant Park Hotel | 40 W. 40th St. (bet. 5th & 6th Aves.) |
212-921-3330 | www.koirestaurant.com

A "very swank" sister to the LA eatery of the same name, this Midtown
Japanese "hot spot" attracts "young 'in'" types with its "brilliant" sashimi, sushi and cooked fare; "variable" service and "scary prices" are easily overlooked since the "achingly hip" vibe "makes you feel like a star."

Korea Palace Ⓢ *Korean*   18 | 14 | 16 | $33

E 50s | 127 E. 54th St. (bet. Lexington & Park Aves.) | 212-832-2350 |
www.koreapalace.com

It's a "typical Korean BBQ house", but this bright neon Midtowner does
sushi too, and comes as a "pleasant surprise" with its "courteous" service and "tasty" chow nearly "as good as you'll find in K-town"; expect
"dinerlike" decor and modest prices, especially at the $17.95 lunch.

Ko Sushi *Japanese*   19 | 14 | 19 | $31

E 70s | 1329 Second Ave. (70th St.) | 212-439-1678
E 80s | 1619 York Ave. (85th St.) | 212-772-8838 |
www.newkosushi.com

Though separately owned, both of these "neighborly" UES sushi
"standbys" offer an "incredible variety" of "fresh fish" and "innova-

tive" rolls at "value prices"; they're "nothing fancy", but the "hospitable staff" and "tasty" offerings ensure they're "always crowded."

Kuma Inn Ⓜ🗗 *Filipino/Thai*

▽ 24 | 15 | 19 | $34

LES | 113 Ludlow St., 2nd fl. (bet. Delancey & Rivington Sts.) | 212-353-8866 | www.kumainn.com

"Foodies in-the-know" flock to this LES Filipino-Thai "hole-in-the-wall" to sample its "delectable" and eminently "affordable" Asian-inspired tapas and bask in the warmth of its "gracious hosts"; the "secret upstairs location" and "tiny" size make it "good for a tryst" – that is, "if you can find it."

Kum Gang San ● *Korean*

21 | 14 | 16 | $32

Garment District | 49 W. 32nd St. (bet. B'way & 5th Ave.) | 212-967-0909

Flushing | 138-28 Northern Blvd. (bet. Bowne & Union Sts.) | Queens | 718-461-0909

The Korean "equivalent of the Greek diner", down to its 24/7 hours and "diverse menu", this Garment District–Flushing duo dishes out "delicious BBQ" and plenty more; despite "spotty" service, "elbow-to-elbow crowds" and "awesomely cheesy" decor, they're "terrific fun."

Kuruma Zushi Ⓢ *Japanese*

▽ 28 | 15 | 21 | $138

E 40s | 7 E. 47th St., 2nd fl. (bet. 5th & Madison Aves.) | 212-317-2802

Sushi "as elegant as raw fish can get" is the province of this mezzanine Midtown Japanese that caters to the connoisseur with "divine" sashimi, "very formal" service and an "extraordinary omakase"; the "spartan" setup is easily outweighed by the "heavenly" cuisine, although "Tokyo prices" will surely "bring you back to earth."

Kyma *Greek*

18 | 15 | 18 | $41

W 40s | 300 W. 46th St. (8th Ave.) | 212-957-8830

A "welcome surprise" in the Theater District, this "reliable" Greek proffers the "usual standards done with finesse", including "simple grilled fish", all at "reasonable" rates; the interior strikes some as "a little too bright", but never mind – "fast service" means you "make your curtain."

🆕 Kyotofu ●Ⓜ *Dessert*

▽ 23 | 21 | 21 | $26

W 40s | 705 Ninth Ave. (bet. 48th & 49th Sts.) | 212-974-6012 | www.kyotofu-nyc.com

"You'll never look at tofu the same way" after visiting this "small", "sleek" Midtown Japanese dessert specialist where "sublime", mostly soy-based creations "take sweet nothings to a higher level"; insiders suggest "skip the savory" options and "go straight to dessert" with the advice of the "knowledgeable staff."

La Baraka *French*

21 | 17 | 23 | $41

Little Neck | 255-09 Northern Blvd. (2 blocks e. of Little Neck Pkwy.) | Queens | 718-428-1461 | www.labarakarest.com

"Family-owned" for nearly 30 years, this Little Neck "treasure" is as renowned for its "caring proprietors" (and hostess "Lucette's kisses") as for its "bargain"-priced "country French" menu; some find it a bit "dated", but ultimately the proprietor's "charm" obliterates any possible complaint.

	FOOD	DECOR	SERVICE	COST

La Bergamote *Bakery/French*
24 | 15 | 15 | $14

Chelsea | 169 Ninth Ave. (20th St.) | 212-627-9010

For "glorious pastries" and other "fabulous" Gallic goods, this "small" Chelsea bakery/cafe is a natural for breakfast or lunch; "surly service" makes it feel all the more "like being in Paris", though that doesn't make it any less "tempting."

La Boîte en Bois *French*
21 | 15 | 20 | $50

W 60s | 75 W. 68th St. (bet. Columbus Ave. & CPW) | 212-874-2705 | www.laboitenyc.com

This "sweet little" Lincoln Center–area bistro features a "wonderful" French menu "unspoiled by modernity", backed up by "attentive service" and an "excellent" $36 early-bird prix fixe; show-goers say its "close quarters prepare one for the theater seats" to come.

La Bonne Soupe *French*
18 | 13 | 15 | $28

W 50s | 48 W. 55th St. (bet. 5th & 6th Aves.) | 212-586-7650 | www.labonnesoupe.com

You'll cross the "final fondue frontier" at this "old-fashioned" Midtown bistro where "delicious onion soup" and other "hearty" Gallic offerings prove there's still some "truth in advertising"; though service can be "indifferent" and the quarters "a bit too cozy", its "budget-friendly" prix fixes are always appreciated.

La Bottega ● *Italian/Pizza*
18 | 21 | 15 | $42

Chelsea | Maritime Hotel | 88 Ninth Ave. (17th St.) | 212-243-8400 | www.themaritimehotel.com

Thanks to a "popular" outdoor terrace and the "glam crowd" it attracts, this "festive" Chelsea Italian is a "scene with a capital S" come summertime; few seem to mind the "lackluster" service since most of the young diners are principally here to cruise.

L'Absinthe *French*
22 | 22 | 20 | $65

E 60s | 227 E. 67th St. (bet. 2nd & 3rd Aves.) | 212-794-4950 | www.labsinthe.com

Done up like a "Parisian brasserie in all its art nouveau glory", this "sophisticated" Eastsider serves first-rate French fare to a "clientele that's as haute as the food"; "heart-stopping" prices may be a downside, but most feel the place is worth every euro.

La Cantina Toscana *Italian*
▽ 24 | 14 | 21 | $50

E 60s | 1109 First Ave. (bet. 60th & 61st Sts.) | 212-754-5454

A "sleeper" for "wonderful" Tuscan cooking, this "authentic" East Side Italian offers "excellent homemade pastas" and "superb wild game" paired with a "first-rate wine list"; "tiny" digs and somewhat "pricey" tabs are fully offset by "helpful" service and "old-world charm."

Lady Mendl's Ⓜ *American*
22 | 26 | 24 | $43

Gramercy | Inn at Irving Pl. | 56 Irving Pl. (bet. 17th & 18th Sts.) | 212-533-4466 | www.ladymendls.com

"Edith Wharton is alive" and well at this "dignified" Gramercy tea salon where the "lovely service", Victorian atmosphere and tasty finger sandwiches make you "feel like royalty"; for best results, "bring your mother" and don't fret over the prices – "it's really all about the experience."

La Esquina ● *Mexican*   21 | 21 | 16 | $39

Little Italy | 106 Kenmare St. (bet. Cleveland Pl. & Lafayette St.) |
646-613-7100 | www.esquinanyc.com

There are three dining options at this "ultracool" Little Italy Mexican:
a 24-hour taqueria, a "funky" sit-down cafe and a subterranean, semi-
secret "grotto"; catering to the "über-trendy", the latter's "infuriating"
reservation policy and "Stalin-era bouncers" make normal folks stay
upstairs where there's "less fuss."

La Flor Bakery & Cafe ⊋ *Bakery*   ▽ 24 | 16 | 19 | $24

Woodside | 53-02 Roosevelt Ave. (53rd St.) | Queens | 718-426-8023

"*Muy delicioso*" Mexican-Eclectic sweet and savory items prove the
kitchen really "knows its stuff" at this Woodside bakery/cafe; "don't
be fooled by the exterior" or the sometimes "spotty service" – what it
"lacks in looks", it "makes up for in taste" and "value."

La Focaccia ● *Italian*   ▽ 20 | 18 | 18 | $37

W Village | 51 Bank St. (W. 4th St.) | 212-675-3754

"Romantic at night and friendly all day", this "old-style" Village Italian
"charmer" offers "tasty, fresh" pasta plus "affordable" meat and fish
"grilled to perfection"; service is "attentive", but the "small" space
means you're apt to share the experience with whoever sits next to you.

La Giara *Italian*   19 | 16 | 18 | $35

Murray Hill | 501 Third Ave. (bet. 33rd & 34th Sts.) | 212-726-9855 |
www.lagiara.com

"Pleasant" and "reliable", this Murray Hill Italian is known for its
"wholesome" "homemade pastas" and "bargain" $19.95 early-bird;
"simple" decor, sidewalk seats and "friendly service" make for "solid
but not extraordinary" dining.

La Gioconda *Italian*   20 | 13 | 19 | $41

E 50s | 226 E. 53rd St. (bet. 2nd & 3rd Aves.) | 212-371-3536 |
www.lagiocondany.com

"Smiling" staffers serve "homey" Italian vittles at this Turtle Bay
"sleeper" that's well regarded for its "fair" prices, a "rare thing in
Manhattan"; sure, the "exposed-brick" decor is "dull" and the
"postage-stamp" dimensions "too small for comfort", but regulars report it's "like going home."

La Goulue ● *French*   20 | 19 | 18 | $62

E 60s | 746 Madison Ave. (bet. 64th & 65th Sts.) | 212-988-8169 |
www.lagouluerestaurant.com

"Fashionable" Euros and other "10021 fixtures" tout the "above-
average" French fare (at way above-average cost) and "chic Parisian
feel" at this UES bistro that's known for its "lively" "kissy-kissy scene";
service may be "sporadic", but there's no denying that "zing in the air."

☑ La Grenouille ⊠ *French*   27 | 28 | 27 | $120

E 50s | 3 E. 52nd St. (bet. 5th & Madison Aves.) | 212-752-1495 |
www.la-grenouille.com

NY's "last great haute French" restaurant, the Masson family's "timeless" Midtowner is "superlative" in every way, boasting "done-to-
perfection" cuisine, "impeccable service" and an "enchanting" room
filled with "flowers galore" (even the "diners exude class"); yes, you

may need to "raid your piggy bank" to foot the prix fixe–only bill at this "*magnifique* grande dame", but all concur it's "worth the splash"; N.B. jackets required.

La Grolla *Italian*   20 | 13 | 19 | $42

W 70s | 413 Amsterdam Ave. (bet. 79th & 80th Sts.) | 212-496-0890 | www.lagrolla.us

"Authentic" dishes from Italy's Val d'Aosta region fill out the "relatively inexpensive" menu of this "solid" UWS trattoria where the "welcoming" staffers have "real accents"; it may be "cramped" and "lacking lighting", but at least the "food is beautiful."

Lake Club *Continental/Seafood*   ▽ 21 | 24 | 21 | $46

Staten Island | 1150 Clove Rd. (Victory Blvd.) | 718-442-3600 | www.lake-club.com

A "gorgeous venue" for a "classy evening" out, this Staten Island Continental seafooder overlooking "pretty" Clove Lake is all about "fine dining" and "courteous" service; it's "a little pricey", but bargain-hunters tout "Sunday brunch" as a more affordable alternative.

La Lanterna di Vittorio ● *Italian*   20 | 23 | 18 | $28

G Village | 129 MacDougal St. (bet. W. 3rd & 4th Sts.) | 212-529-5945 | www.lalanternacaffe.com

"Nothing beats the ambiance" of this "romantic" Village Italian, a "paradise on rainy nights" thanks to its "roaring fireplaces", "live jazz" and "covered garden"; the "limited menu" leans toward pizzas and "heavenly" desserts, but most are too busy "snuggling" to notice the food.

La Locanda dei Vini *Italian*   ▽ 21 | 14 | 20 | $44

W 40s | 737 Ninth Ave. (bet. 49th & 50th Sts.) | 212-258-2900 | www.lalocandadeivinirestaurant.com

Ok, maybe the "modest" storefront exterior suggests that this mid-priced Hell's Kitchen Italian is just another "local haunt", but proponents praise its "hearty, well-prepared" food, "charming" service and "amiable" vibe; it's also a "good bet pre-theater."

La Lunchonette *French*   22 | 14 | 19 | $41

Chelsea | 130 10th Ave. (18th St.) | 212-675-0342

A "welcome relief from Chelsea trendiness", this "slice of beatnik France" is a "foie-gras-and-cassoulet kind of place" with "delicious" Gallic grub; though the digs "could use a face-lift", its "diverse" clientele couldn't care less as it all comes without a bank-breaking bill.

La Mangeoire *French*   19 | 19 | 19 | $47

E 50s | 1008 Second Ave. (bet. 53rd & 54th Sts.) | 212-759-7086 | www.lamangeoire.com

"Like an old friend", this East Midtown bistro is a "steady standby" for classic French fare, "fine house wines" and "gracious service"; throw in a "romantic", "Provençal setting" with "gorgeous flowers", and "you might be dining in France" – though "without the Paris prices."

La Masseria ● *Italian*   22 | 19 | 21 | $53

W 40s | 235 W. 48th St. (bet. B'way & 8th Ave.) | 212-582-2111 | www.lamasserianyc.com

With a "perfect location" for pre-show dining, this "upscale" Theater District Southern Italian "gets you in and out on time" with "high-quality cooking" served in a "spacious", "farmhouse"-esque setting; though it's "expensive", "the secret's out", so be ready for "noise" and "crowds."

La Mediterranée *French*   19 | 17 | 19 | $48

E 50s | 947 Second Ave. (bet. 50th & 51st Sts.) | 212-755-4155 | www.lamediterraneeny.com

"Good old-style French food", "gracious service" and a nightly pianist have made this "casual" Midtown bistro a local "fixture"; it's a "favorite" among "mature" folks who like the fair prices and "time-warp" decor.

La Mela ● *Italian*   18 | 12 | 17 | $35

Little Italy | 167 Mulberry St. (bet. Broome & Grand Sts.) | 212-431-9493 | www.lamelarestaurant.com

Expect "minimal decision making" at this "shut-up-and-eat" Little Italy Italian where five-course, "family-style" meals can be had for a flat $32 price; it's especially "fun with a group" that doesn't mind "touristy" neighbors and an emphasis on "quantity over quality."

La Mirabelle *French*   22 | 18 | 23 | $48

W 80s | 102 W. 86th St. (bet. Amsterdam & Columbus Aves.) | 212-496-0458

There's "nothing trendy or gimmicky" going on at this "old-fashioned" UWS French bistro where a "delectable" menu is served by a "treat-you-like-family" staff; maybe the decor hovers between "homey" and "fusty", but that's how its "mature following" likes it.

Lan ● *Japanese*   ▽ 25 | 18 | 20 | $47

E Village | 56 Third Ave. (bet. 10th & 11th Sts.) | 212-254-1959 | www.lan-nyc.com

"Not your typical sushi/sashimi place", this "attractive" East Village Japanese also offers "awesome cooked food" like shabu-shabu paired with an "extensive sake list"; though a bit "expensive" and "dark" inside, it's "still going strong" after a decade in business.

Land *Thai*   23 | 16 | 18 | $25

NEW **E 80s** | 1565 Second Ave. (bet. 81st & 82nd Sts.) | 212-439-1847
W 80s | 450 Amsterdam Ave. (bet. 81st & 82nd Sts.) | 212-501-8121
www.landthaikitchen.com

"When they say spicy they mean it" at this crosstown duo where the "authentic" Thai dishes "seem a lot more upscale than they cost"; the tiny digs are "chic" in a "downtown" way, but service seems "rushed."

L & B Spumoni Gardens *Dessert/Pizza*   22 | 10 | 14 | $21

Bensonhurst | 2725 86th St. (bet. 10th & 11th Sts.) | Brooklyn | 718-449-6921 | www.spumonigardens.com

This Bensonhurst Italian "tradition" serves what could be the "best Sicilian squares in the universe" along with "luscious" spumoni; there's "no decor to speak of" and frequent "long waits", but it's got "tons of character" and picnic tables for alfresco dining.

Landmarc ● *French*   23 | 19 | 21 | $49

TriBeCa | 179 W. Broadway (bet. Leonard & Worth Sts.) | 212-343-3883
NEW **W 60s** | Time Warner Ctr. | 10 Columbus Circle, 3rd fl. (60th St. at B'way) | 212-823-6123
www.landmarc-restaurant.com

Marc Murphy's "informal" bistros serve "spot-on" French fare but are best known for their wine lists with "gentle markups"; the more rustic

TriBeCa original is smaller than its sprawling Time Warner Center sibling, but the "no-reservations" policy spells a "rush for tables" at both.

Landmark Tavern *American/Irish*   18 | 20 | 20 | $38

W 40s | 626 11th Ave. (46th St.) | 212-247-2562 |
www.thelandmarktavern.org

A "landmark indeed", this circa-1868 Hell's Kitchen tavern is complete with "ghosts of dock workers at the bar"; its Irish-American "upscale pub grub" may be "generic", but it's worth a visit for the "history" alone.

La Paella *Spanish*   20 | 18 | 17 | $34

E Village | 214 E. Ninth St. (bet. 2nd & 3rd Aves.) | 212-598-4321 |
www.lapaellanyc.com

"Delicious" tapas and "potent" sangria at "great prices" make for "satisfying" repasts at this "atmospheric" East Village Spaniard that draws a "hip" "hodgepodge" of a crowd; though service is only "adequate" and the room sometimes "loud", it still enjoys a "romantic" reputation.

La Palapa ● *Mexican*   20 | 17 | 18 | $34

E Village | 77 St. Marks Pl. (bet. 1st & 2nd Aves.) | 212-777-2537
G Village | 359 Sixth Ave. (bet. Washington Pl. & W. 4th St.) | 212-243-6870
www.lapalapa.com

Celebrated for "dressed-up" but priced-down Mexicana, this "festive" cross-Village duo's "multiflavored margs" can keep anyone happy; their daytime "laid-back" vibe turns *mucho* sexy after dark, when the "loud and frenetic" pace can transform them into "a bit of a madhouse."

La Petite Auberge *French*   20 | 15 | 21 | $45

Gramercy | 116 Lexington Ave. (bet. 27th & 28th Sts.) | 212-689-5003 |
www.lapetiteaubergeny.com

It "hasn't changed in 30 years", but this "welcoming" Gramercy bistro "keeps chugging along" on the strength of its "solid" French fare, "old-school" staffers and "inexpensive" price point; "nouvelle it's not", but the "dated" setting has a pleasing "Paris-in-the-'50s" feel.

La Pizza Fresca Ristorante *Italian*   22 | 17 | 17 | $38

Flatiron | 31 E. 20th St. (bet. B'way & Park Ave. S.) | 212-598-0141 |
www.lapizzafrescaristorante.com

Behind an "unassuming facade", this "simple yet sophisticated" Flatiron Italian dishes out "delicious" brick-oven Neapolitan pizza and pastas accompanied by an "outstanding wine list"; just "bring a lot of lira" and some patience, as the service can be "leisurely."

La Ripaille *French*   ▽ 23 | 20 | 21 | $48

W Village | 605 Hudson St. (bet. Bethune & W. 12th Sts.) | 212-255-4406 |
www.laripailleny.com

"For a true taste of small-town French cuisine", this venerable Villager features "perfectly done" traditional dishes in an "old-school" setting complete with sidewalk seating; it's best known for an "ever-present owner" who sees to it that "everyone leaves with a smile."

La Rivista ●☒ *Italian*   18 | 15 | 19 | $46

W 40s | 313 W. 46th St. (bet. 8th & 9th Aves.) | 212-245-1707 |
www.larivistanyc.com

"Definitely convenient" if "not terribly original", this midpriced Restaurant Row Italian offers "plentiful" portions of "better-than-average" grub in "pleasant" albeit "simple" environs; bonuses include a nightly pianist and the "real money saver" of "discounted parking."

Las Ramblas ● *Spanish* ▽ 23 | 17 | 22 | $36

G Village | 170 W. Fourth St. (bet. Cornelia & Jones Sts.) | 646-415-7924 | www.lasramblasnyc.com

Thankfully still "under the radar", this "charming" Village Spaniard combines "modern tapas", "super sangria" and "enthusiastic" service in one "tiny" space at one modest price; fans say it's the "closest you'll get to Barcelona in NY" given food "so good, it's hard to stop ordering."

La Taqueria *Mexican* 19 | 11 | 14 | $15

Park Slope | 74 Seventh Ave. (bet. Berkeley & Lincoln Pls.) | Brooklyn | 718-398-4300

Rachel's Taqueria ⊘ *Mexican*

Park Slope | 408 Fifth Ave. (bet. 7th & 8th Sts.) | Brooklyn | 718-788-1137 | www.rachelstaqueria.com

"Colossal burritos" and other Mexican standards fill out the menu of these "down-to-earth" Park Slope taqueria twins; though "schlumpy" decor makes them "better for takeout", they're "quick and inexpensive" enough to be local "staples."

La Taza de Oro ⊠⊘ *Diner* 18 | 6 | 16 | $14

Chelsea | 96 Eighth Ave. (bet. 14th & 15th Sts.) | 212-243-9946

The "lunch counter lives on" at this Chelsea Puerto Rican that "gives greasy spoons a good name" with its "authentic" renditions of "old-school rice and beans"; sure, it's "funky" and has "been around for a million years", but those "cheapo" tabs can't be beat.

☑ L'Atelier de Joël Robuchon *French* 27 | 24 | 26 | $131

E 50s | Four Seasons Hotel | 57 E. 57th St. (bet. Madison & Park Aves.) | 212-350-6658 | www.fourseasons.com

From the "brilliant" Robuchon comes this "off-the-charts" "consolidation of French technique and Japanese style", where "decadent" dishes in "tapas-style" portions come with a "perfectly designed wine list" and "impeccable service"; although there are comfortable tables, "counter seating is the way to go" in the "minimalist", "casually elegant" space, as the "theater of the open kitchen" is almost as "memorable" as the "eye-popping prices."

Lattanzi ●⊠ *Italian* 22 | 18 | 21 | $53

W 40s | 361 W. 46th St. (bet. 8th & 9th Aves.) | 212-315-0980 | www.lattanzinyc.com

Although "always a winner pre-theater", this Restaurant Row Italian is best "after 8 PM" when there's more time to savor the menu's Roman-Jewish specialties (e.g. the "superb fried artichokes"); a "lovely back garden" and "welcoming service" add to the "romantic", if "expensive", experience.

Lavagna *Italian* 24 | 18 | 20 | $43

E Village | 545 E. Fifth St. (bet. Aves. A & B) | 212-979-1005 | www.lavagnanyc.com

This little Alphabet City "neighborhood favorite" "hits all the right notes" with an "inventive" Italian menu, "friendly service" and a "reasonable price-to-quality ratio"; the "cozy" space is often "crowded", but still "sophisticated" enough to be a "great date restaurant."

			FOOD	DECOR	SERVICE	COST

La Vela *Italian*

19 | 14 | 19 | $34

W 70s | 373 Amsterdam Ave. (bet. 77th & 78th Sts.) | 212-877-7818
"Warm welcomes" combine with "well-prepared", "moderately priced" Tuscan fare at this "family-friendly" Westsider where dining is "pleasant" and "relaxed"; it's a "good standby", so long as you ignore the "uninspiring decor."

La Villa Pizzeria *Italian*

21 | 14 | 17 | $26

Mill Basin | Key Food Shopping Ctr. | 6610 Ave. U (bet. 66th & 67th Sts.) | Brooklyn | 718-251-8030
Park Slope | 261 Fifth Ave. (bet. 1st St. & Garfield Pl.) | Brooklyn | 718-499-9888 | www.lavillaparkslope.com
Howard Bch | Lindenwood Shopping Ctr. | 82-07 153rd Ave. (82nd St.) | Queens | 718-641-8259
It's "fun for the whole gang" at this outer-borough Italian trio where "extra-good" pizza and "heaping portions" of "Sunday family favorites" keep things "bustling"; easy pricing trumps the "bland" decor.

La Vineria *Italian*

∇ 20 | 13 | 18 | $43

W 50s | 21 W. 55th St. (bet. 5th & 6th Aves.) | 212-247-3400 | www.lavineriarestaurant.com
Despite one of the "tiniest" rooms in town, this "sweet" Midtown trattoria is "big on taste", supplying "delightful" thin-crust pizzas and other Italian dishes "made with love"; regulars ignore the "loud", "cramped" settings in favor of the "midrange" prices and "charming staff."

NEW Le Barricou ☞ *French*

- | - | - | M

Williamsburg | 533 Grand St. (bet. Lorimer St. & Union Ave.) | Brooklyn | 718-782-7372
Williamsburg is home to this airy new Gallic arrival that plays to a young clientele with a funky, brick-walled setting and a foosball table; its usual-suspects French bistro menu is tweaked with some Asian flavors and priced for the hipster audience.

☑ Le Bernardin ☒ *French/Seafood*

28 | 27 | 28 | $129

W 50s | 155 W. 51st St. (bet. 6th & 7th Aves.) | 212-554-1515 | www.le-bernardin.com
All the "accolades are well deserved" at Maguy LeCoze's Midtown French "phenomenon" where "piscatorial fantasy" meets "culinary perfection" via chef Eric Ripert's "beyond sublime" seafood, abetted by "smooth-as-silk service" and a "quietly elegant" setting; to get around the "sky-high", prix fixe-only prices, try the $64 lunch, or go for broke and chalk it up as a "must-do experience"; N.B. jackets required.

Le Bilboquet *French*

20 | 16 | 15 | $55

E 60s | 25 E. 63rd St. (bet. Madison & Park Aves.) | 212-751-3036
"Waiflike Euros" wiggle into this "tight" East Side bistro where the "fine" French cuisine struggles for attention with the "noisy", "buzzy" scene; on the downside, "if you don't know the staff, don't expect great service."

Le Boeuf à la Mode *French*

21 | 19 | 21 | $54

E 80s | 539 E. 81st St. (bet. East End & York Aves.) | 212-249-1473
There's "no rush" at this Yorkville "golden oldie" that's been serving "reliable" French bistro standards for 45-plus years; "seasoned wait-

ers" and a "circa-1953 Paris" setting appeal to its "mature" crowd, not the "inflated" tabs or "worn-around-the-edges" decor.

Le Cirque ☒ French
23 | 25 | 23 | $94

E 50s | One Beacon Court | 151 E. 58th St. (bet. Lexington & 3rd Aves.) | 212-644-0202 | www.lecirque.com

Midtown's third incarnation of Sirio Maccioni's literally "movable circus" is as "haute as ever", from the "sumptuous" French cuisine, "cosmopolitan" crowd and "fabulous" service to its "smashing modern look"; despite "arm-and-a-leg" pricing, it "can be hard to book", so "reserve in advance" and dress appropriately ("Chanel" suggested for ladies, jackets required for men); N.B. the less formal front cafe is being turned into a wine lounge with a small-plates menu.

L'Ecole ☒ French
23 | 19 | 22 | $52

SoHo | French Culinary Institute | 462 Broadway (Grand St.) | 212-219-3300 | www.frenchculinary.com

"Student chefs" cook for "extra credit" at the French Culinary Institute's SoHo lab/eatery that offers an "ever-changing menu" of Gallic standards at a "haute bargain" $39.95 tab; "consistency may not be 100 percent", but service is "sweet" and it's "all in the name of education."

Le Colonial French/Vietnamese
20 | 22 | 19 | $51

E 50s | 149 E. 57th St. (bet. Lexington & 3rd Aves.) | 212-752-0808 | www.lecolonialnyc.com

Think "colonial-era" Saigon to get the gist of this "sexy" Eastsider where "delicious" French-Vietnamese dishes are served in a cross between a "tiki lounge" and a "Far East movie set"; except for the "spotty" service and distinctly "Manhattan prices", most feel "positively transported."

Leela Lounge Indian
▽ 22 | 18 | 16 | $33

G Village | 1 W. Third St. (bet. B'way & Mercer St.) | 212-529-2059 | www.leelalounge.com

Putting a "modern spin on traditional" dishes, this "chic" Village Indian employs "no butter or heavy cream" for more "healthy" repasts; though the "eager" service sometimes wobbles, "pittance" prices and a "relaxed" ambiance compensate.

Le Gamin French
19 | 16 | 15 | $25

E Village | 536 E. Fifth St. (bet. Aves. A & B) | 212-254-8409 ☽
G Village | 132 W. Houston St. (bet. MacDougal & Sullivan Sts.) | 212-475-1543 ☗
W Village | 522 Hudson St. (bet. Charles & W. 10th Sts.) | 212-807-7357 ☽
Prospect Heights | 556 Vanderbilt Ave. (bet. Bergen & Dean Sts.) | Brooklyn | 718-789-5171
www.legamin.com

"Inexpensive" Gallic grub graces the menus of these "laid-back" bistros where many report "brunch is the standout" meal; they're so "markedly French" that you'll need the "patience of a saint" to deal with the "absentminded" service.

Le Gigot ☒ French
24 | 19 | 23 | $53

G Village | 18 Cornelia St. (bet. Bleecker & W. 4th Sts.) | 212-627-3737 | www.legigotrestaurant.com

"When homesick for Paris", expats head for this "miniature" Village bistro specializing in "delicious" Provençal cooking served by a "won-

	FOOD	DECOR	SERVICE	COST

derful" crew; there's agreement on the "expensive" tabs, but debate over the dimensions: "cozy" vs. "cramped."

Le Grainne Cafe ● *French*   ▽ 19 | 15 | 13 | $23

Chelsea | 183 Ninth Ave. (21st St.) | 646-486-3000 | www.legrainnecafe.com

Chelsea's "literati and artisti" tout this "pleasant" French cafe for its "fantastic" lattes and crêpes, not to mention the low cost; allow yourself "plenty of time", however, and "make sure you like your dinner guest": service can be "slooow."

Le Jardin Bistro *French*   18 | 17 | 18 | $42

NoLita | 25 Cleveland Pl. (bet. Kenmare & Spring Sts.) | 212-343-9599 | www.lejardinbistro.com

"Lingering is welcome" at this affordable NoLita French bistro where "awesome alfresco" dining is embellished by a "romantic" grapevine-covered trellis; admirers avow it's "great year-round", citing "tasty" vittles and "pleasant" (if "slow") service.

Le Madeleine *French*   20 | 18 | 19 | $46

W 40s | 403 W. 43rd St. (bet. 9th & 10th Aves.) | 212-246-2993 | www.lemadeleine.com

Beloved for its "charming", glass-enclosed garden room, this long-running Hell's Kitchen French bistro is also known for "reliable" cooking that "won't break the bank"; it's currently "battling to keep its space", so regulars suggest "visit while you still can."

Le Marais *French/Steak*   20 | 15 | 16 | $51

W 40s | 150 W. 46th St. (bet. 6th & 7th Aves.) | 212-869-0900 | www.lemarais.net

Giving glatt kosher a "French spin", this Theater District steakhouse features "excellent quality meats" either on the plate or from its "in-house butcher shop up front"; even though it's "pricey", "loud" and underserviced, it still "packs 'em in" nightly.

Le Miu ● *Japanese*   ▽ 25 | 16 | 19 | $55

E Village | 107 Ave. A (bet. 6th & 7th Sts.) | 212-473-3100 | www.lemiusushi.com

"Classing up" Alphabet City, this "not-what-you'd-expect" Japanese offers both "superb sushi" and "sophisticated" cooked dishes; though "pricey for the location", wags tag it "Nobu for less", citing a five-course, $55 prix fixe that's actually a "good value."

Le Monde ● *French*   17 | 18 | 14 | $32

W 100s | 2885 Broadway (bet. 112th & 113th Sts.) | 212-531-3939 | www.lemondenyc.com

"Decent French-flavored cuisine" and a chance to "relax" and "actually enjoy reading" have Columbia students touting this Morningside Heights bistro; the $24 lunch prix fixe is another reason it's a neighborhood "favorite", though the principal downside is "mediocre" service.

Lemongrass Grill *Thai*   17 | 13 | 15 | $23

Financial District | 84 William St. (Maiden Ln.) | 212-809-8038
G Village | 9 E. 13th St. (bet. 5th Ave. & University Pl.) | 646-486-7313
Murray Hill | 138 E. 34th St. (bet. Lexington & 3rd Aves.) | 212-213-3317
W 90s | 2534 Broadway (bet. 94th & 95th Sts.) | 212-666-0888

(continued)

(continued)

Lemongrass Grill

Cobble Hill | 156 Court St. (bet. Dean & Pacific Sts.) | Brooklyn | 718-522-9728

Park Slope | 61A Seventh Ave. (bet. Berkeley & Lincoln Pls.) | Brooklyn | 718-399-7100

For a "quick fix", try out this "budget-friendly", "Thai-for-beginners" chain, even if the food's strictly "by the numbers"; since the settings tend to "lack atmosphere", aesthetes opt for their "lightning-fast delivery."

Lenny's *Sandwiches*

19 | 9 | 15 | $13

E 50s | 1024 Second Ave. (54th St.) | 212-355-5700

NEW **E 60s** | 1269 First Ave. (68th St.) | 212-288-0852

E 70s | 1481 Second Ave. (77th St.) | 212-288-5288

Financial District | 108 John St. (bet. Cliff & Pearl Sts.) | 212-385-2828

Flatiron | 16 W. 23rd St. (5th Ave.) | 212-462-4433

NEW **G Village** | 418 Sixth Ave. (9th St.) | 212-353-0300

W 40s | 60 W. 48th St. (bet. 5th & 6th Aves.) | 212-871-6677

NEW **W 40s** | 613 Ninth Ave. (43rd St.) | 212-957-7800

W 70s | 302 Columbus Ave. (74th St.) | 212-580-8300

W 80s | 489 Columbus Ave. (84th St.) | 212-787-9368

www.lennysnyc.com

"Well-oiled machines", this "proliferating" low-budget chain vends "substantial" sandwiches via an "assembly-line" staff that gets you "in and out in minutes"; even so, the "school cafeteria vibe" leads some to opt for "no-hassle delivery."

L'Entrecote ⑤ *French*

▽ 19 | 14 | 21 | $49

E 50s | 1057 First Ave. (bet. 57th & 58th Sts.) | 212-755-0080

Harking back to "pre-nouvelle cuisine" days, this Sutton Place "time-tripper" is a "very French" source for Gallic classics; the "pocket-size" space is "inviting" thanks to owners who "take hospitality seriously."

Leo's Latticini Ⓜ *Deli/Italian*

▽ 28 | 10 | 25 | $12

(aka Mama's of Corona)

Corona | 46-02 104th St. (46th Ave.) | Queens | 718-898-6069

A longtime Corona "cornerstone", this 1920-vintage Italian deli is re-nowned as a "great workingman's lunch spot" with "excellent sand-wiches" and "fab fresh mozzarella"; it may be "nothing fancy", but "smiling" staffers and bargain prices "take you back to the old country."

Le Pain Quotidien *Bakery/Belgian*

19 | 15 | 14 | $21

E 60s | 833 Lexington Ave. (bet. 63rd & 64th Sts.) | 212-755-5810

E 70s | 252 E. 77th St. (bet. 2nd & 3rd Aves.) | 212-249-8600

E 80s | 1131 Madison Ave. (bet. 84th & 85th Sts.) | 212-327-4900

Flatiron | ABC Carpet & Home | 38 E. 19th St. (bet. B'way & Park Ave. S.) | 212-673-7900

G Village | 10 Fifth Ave. (8th St.) | 212-253-2324

NEW **G Village** | 801 Broadway (11th St.) | 212-677-5277

SoHo | 100 Grand St. (bet. Greene & Mercer Sts.) | 212-625-9009

W 50s | 922 Seventh Ave. (58th St.) | 212-757-0775

W 60s | 60 W. 65th St. (bet. B'way & CPW) | 212-721-4001

W 70s | 50 W. 72nd St. (bet. Columbus Ave. & CPW) | 212-712-9700

www.painquotidien.com

Additional locations throughout the NY area

This "informal" Belgian bakery/cafe chain is noted for its "scrump-tious" breads, sandwiches and other light, "mostly organic" fare; the "pleasant formula" features "communal tables" and "farmhouse-cool" settings, marred only by "unpredictable" service at prime times.

Le Perigord French

FOOD	DECOR	SERVICE	COST
24	20	24	$76

E 50s | 405 E. 52nd St. (bet. FDR Dr. & 1st Ave.) | 212-755-6244 | www.leperigord.com

"One of the last of the classics", this "old-line" Sutton Place "bastion of France" exudes "elegance" with its "superb" "cordon bleu cuisine" and "seamless", "tuxedoed" service overseen by owner Georges Briguet; *mais oui*, you'll pay for this "step back in time", but its "well-heeled" following agrees it's "worth every franc", especially once former chef Antoine Bouterin returns to the kitchen.

NEW Le Petit Bistro ● French

FOOD	DECOR	SERVICE	COST
-	-	-	I

Chelsea | 258 W. 15th St. (bet. 7th & 8th Aves.) | 212-929-3270

Despite new owners and a new name, little has changed at this former Chelsea branch of Le Gamin, where traditional French bistro items are served in casual, petite quarters; laid-back service and tabs that don't add up to more than a few euros contribute to the sanguine vibe.

NEW Le Petit Marché French

FOOD	DECOR	SERVICE	COST
▽ 22	20	21	$44

Brooklyn Heights | 46 Henry St. (bet. Cranberry & Middagh Sts.) | Brooklyn | 718-858-9605

Bringing some Gallic flair to Brooklyn Heights, this new French bistro is already "bustling" thanks to a "solid" kitchen, "warm", exposed-brick decor and "welcoming" service; though tables are "packed together", the pricing is *bon marché*.

Le Refuge French

FOOD	DECOR	SERVICE	COST
21	20	20	$54

E 80s | 166 E. 82nd St. (bet. Lexington & 3rd Aves.) | 212-861-4505 | www.lerefugenyc.com

There's "no pretension" at this "quiet" UES "fixture" that's been "popular for years" given its French *campagne* cooking, "country inn" feel and "great little garden"; though "a touch pricey", to most it's "well worth it."

Le Refuge Inn Ⓜ 🏠 French

FOOD	DECOR	SERVICE	COST
▽ 24	26	24	$58

Bronx | Le Refuge Inn | 586 City Island Ave. (bet. Beach & Cross Sts.) | 718-885-2478 | www.lerefugeinn.com

Set in a landmark Bronx waterfront inn, this "lovely" French "oasis" offers "outstanding" cuisine along with "warm service" in a "white-tablecloth" Victorian setting; sure, this "unique experience" comes at a price, but "romantic" folk spring for a "room for the night" after dinner.

Le Rivage French

FOOD	DECOR	SERVICE	COST
19	16	20	$43

W 40s | 340 W. 46th St. (bet. 8th & 9th Aves.) | 212-765-7374 | www.lerivagenyc.com

"Raising predictability to an art form", this venerable Restaurant Row "staple" is still as "convenient" as it is "tasty"; though the room may be a bit "tired", the "well-prepared" French dishes are "reasonably priced", especially the "terrific" $35 post-theater prix fixe.

Les Enfants Terribles ● African/French

FOOD	DECOR	SERVICE	COST
▽ 19	18	16	$34

LES | 37 Canal St. (Ludlow St.) | 212-777-7518 | www.lesenfantsterriblesnyc.com

An "out-of-the-way" *boîte* in a "turning-trendy" neighborhood, this "lively", low-cost Lower Eastsider fields a "flavorful" French-African menu served by a staff that's "happy" if "too relaxed"; naughty night owls come for the "cool bar scene", complete with DJs and "exotic cocktails."

Les Halles ❶ *French* | 20 | 17 | 16 | $44 |

Financial District | 15 John St. (bet. B'way & Nassau St.) | 212-285-8585
Gramercy | 411 Park Ave. S. (bet. 28th & 29th Sts.) | 212-679-4111
www.leshalles.net

Even if "rock star chef" Anthony Bourdain is "nowhere in sight", his "hearty" hallmarks (steaks "like butta", "stellar fries") keep these "energetic" French bistros "jammed" with fans; in spite of "off-handed service" and an "earsplitting din", they still "hit the spot" for "affordable" grazing.

Le Singe Vert ❶ *French* | 19 | 16 | 16 | $40 |

Chelsea | 160 Seventh Ave. (bet. 19th & 20th Sts.) | 212-366-4100 |
www.lesingevert.com

"Hip locals" dig this "very French" Chelsea bistro where "straight-ahead", midpriced Gallic fare is served by an "inconsistent" crew in a "cramped", "backstreets-of-Paris" setting; sidewalk tables are just the ticket during warm weather, but there's lots of "noise in all seasons."

Le Tableau *French* | 24 | 16 | 20 | $45 |

E Village | 511 E. Fifth St. (bet. Aves. A & B) | 212-260-1333 |
www.letableaunyc.com

"Off the beaten path in the trendy East Village", this top-of-the-line French bistro is celebrated for its "imaginative" kitchen, "jolly" service and tabs that "don't break the bank"; no surprise, the "tiny dimensions" can "translate into long waits" and "crowds."

Levana *Mediterranean* | ▽ 20 | 16 | 18 | $65 |

W 60s | 141 W. 69th St. (bet. B'way & Columbus Ave.) | 212-877-8457 |
www.levana.com

To go "upscale" and "still have it kosher", try this "unusual" Mediterranean near Lincoln Center, where the "reliable" glatt menu features "less traditional" choices like venison; despite "looking and feeling its age", it's "well worth" the "pricey" outlay.

Le Veau d'Or Ⓢ *French* | ▽ 17 | 14 | 19 | $53 |

E 60s | 129 E. 60th St. (bet. Lexington & Park Aves.) | 212-838-8133
"Time-warp" aficionados say that visiting this 1937-vintage East Side bistro is "like coming home to grandma's" since it "keeps chugging along" with a "no-surprises" "French comfort food" menu; the dated decor is something that grandpa would have liked.

Lever House Ⓢ *American* | 22 | 22 | 21 | $73 |

E 50s | 390 Park Ave. (enter on 53rd St., bet. Madison & Park Aves.) |
212-888-2700 | www.leverhouse.com

An ever-"buzzing" magnet for the "corporate-card" crowd, this mod Midtowner owes its success to Dan Silverman's "enticing" New American menu; its "striking", "futuristic" setting can be "rather noisy", though it's still suitable for "business entertaining."

L'Express ❶ *French* | 17 | 14 | 14 | $30 |

Flatiron | 249 Park Ave. S. (20th St.) | 212-254-5858 | www.lexpressnyc.com
One of NYC's "few" all-nighters, this 24/7 Flatiron bistro can get "ridiculously busy" serving "simple" French fare for "reasonable" sums;

a few express doubts about the "tight" tables and "indifferent" staff, but "where else can clubbers get a decent meal at 4 AM?"

Le Zie 2000 ● *Italian*   21 | 14 | 19 | $39

Chelsea | 172 Seventh Ave. (bet. 20th & 21st Sts.) | 212-206-8686 | www.lezie.com

"Always buzzing", this "tightly packed" Chelsea trattoria does "unusual" Venetian-style food at "affordable" rates (though they "knock up the prices for the specials"); the rear dining room and bar are "quieter" if you "don't like to chew and shout at the same time."

Liebman's *Deli*   19 | 9 | 15 | $20

Bronx | 552 W. 235th St. (Johnson Ave.) | 718-548-4534 | www.liebmansdeli.com

A "real throwback", this easily affordable Bronx Jewish deli is an "old-time temple" to all the "traditional" kosher "standards", from "authentic" knishes to big fat sandwiches; noodges note there's "no ambiance", apparently not realizing that's the way delis are supposed to look.

Lil' Frankie's Pizza ●≠ *Pizza*   22 | 17 | 18 | $25

E Village | 19-21 First Ave. (bet. 1st & 2nd Sts.) | 212-420-4900 | www.lilfrankies.com

Frank's "funkier offshoot" is a "haven" for "young" East Villagers who make it a "go-to" for cheap, "casual" Italian eats, notably its thin-crust pizza and "homemade pastas"; it's a "cozy" lil' space with "piped-in tunes", but the "hip" hordes can be a "hassle."

Lili's Noodle Shop & Grill *Noodle Shop*   16 | 12 | 15 | $22

E 80s | 1500 Third Ave. (bet. 84th & 85th Sts.) | 212-639-1313
Financial District | Embassy Suites | 102 North End Ave. (Vesey St.) | 212-786-1300 | www.lilisnoodle.com
W 50s | 200 W. 57th St. (enter on 7th Ave., bet. 56th & 57th Sts.) | 212-586-5333 | www.lilis57.com

Comments range from "the best Chinese in the area" to "waste of a good space", but the majority feels this noodle-shop trio is a "good bet" if "you're expecting a cheap, fast meal" that's "well prepared and fresh."

Lima's Taste ● *Peruvian*   ▽ 21 | 14 | 15 | $34

W Village | 122 Christopher St. (Bedford St.) | 212-242-0010 | www.limastaste.com

You'll get a taste of the Andes at this "authentic" West Villager where the "real Peruvian" menu (led by "primo" ceviche) is a bona fide "winner"; given its "homey" looks, regulars focus on the "potent drinks" and "reasonable tabs" instead.

☑ L'Impero ⓢ *Italian*   26 | 23 | 24 | $74

E 40s | 45 Tudor City Pl. (42nd St.) | 212-599-5045 | www.limpero.com

New chef Michael White faces high expectations at this Tudor City "jewel" where "well-heeled" diners feel "cosseted" by the "superior" Italian fare, "calming" milieu and "polished" service; comparatively "reasonable prix fixe" deals help allay the "upper-echelon" cost.

Lisca *Italian*   20 | 16 | 20 | $42

W 90s | 660 Amsterdam Ave. (bet. 92nd & 93rd Sts.) | 212-799-3987

A "homey neighborhood spot" "without a scene or attitude", this "family-run" UWS Tuscan is "better than most" at providing "reliable"

	FOOD	DECOR	SERVICE	COST

good food along with "engaging service"; it's especially "welcome" given its "decent" prices and "quiet" acoustics.

Little D Eatery Ⓜ American/Eclectic — ▽ 20 | 15 | 18 | $39

Park Slope | 434 Seventh Ave. (bet. 14th & 15th Sts.) | Brooklyn | 718-369-3144 | www.littled-eatery.com

"Mix and match" is the philosophy at this Park Slope Eclectic–New American where the "seasonal selection" of small plates presents an "array of appealing choices" delivered by an "attentive staff"; the format's a little "unexpected", but it's a "solid local" that price-sensitive "Slopers swear by."

Little Giant American — 22 | 18 | 20 | $42

LES | 85 Orchard St. (Broome St.) | 212-226-5047 | www.littlegiantnyc.com

This Lower East Side "charmer" "works wonders" with New Americana thanks to the "creative flair" of its "tiny open kitchen"; the "unpretentious" style and "reasonable"-for-the-quality prices ensure that this "little place with a big heart" is "packed regularly."

Little Owl American/Mediterranean — 24 | 18 | 22 | $50

W Village | 90 Bedford St. (Grove St.) | 212-741-4695 | www.thelittleowlnyc.com

Despite "matchbox" dimensions, this "ambitious" West Villager "delivers big" with "flawless execution" of Med–New American dishes backed up by "smart" service; all agree it's "something special", in fact enough so that it's "nearly impossible to get a table."

Lobster Box ❶ Seafood — 17 | 15 | 16 | $41

Bronx | 34 City Island Ave. (bet. Belden & Rochelle Sts.) | 718-885-1952 | www.lobsterbox.com

Buoyed by "water views" of the Sound, this City Island seafood "perennial" is a "bountiful" endeavor famed for "lobster done every which way"; it's a no-brainer on "summer weekends", but given the "clichéd decor" and "indifferent service", some think it may be "coasting."

Locanda Vini & Olii Ⓜ Italian — ▽ 26 | 24 | 24 | $47

Clinton Hill | 129 Gates Ave. (bet. Cambridge Pl. & Garden Ave.) | Brooklyn | 718-622-9202 | www.locandany.com

A "lovely" former Clinton Hill pharmacy is the backdrop for this mid-priced Tuscan's "mouthwatering" "rustic" offerings and "hands-on" service; indeed, the "care and effort" on display have the locals so "pleased" that they "feel guilty telling" about it.

Lodge ❶ American — ▽ 16 | 20 | 17 | $29

Williamsburg | 318 Grand St. (Havemeyer St.) | Brooklyn | 718-486-9400 | www.lodgenyc.com

Whether "ironic" or "genuinely cool", the "hunting lodge" theme is the "big draw" at this Williamsburg American; "heavily tattooed" staffers serving "simple" eats and drinks in "Mason jars" keep the "local hipsters" content, especially at brunch time.

Loft ❶ French/Italian — 17 | 20 | 14 | $42

W 80s | 505 Columbus Ave. (bet. 84th & 85th Sts.) | 212-362-6440 | www.loftnyc.net

The Upper West Side tries for "trendy" at this "loungey" venue, offering "overdue" refuge for "well-kept" types who hail the "flavorful"

Franco-Italian menu and "lively bar scene"; "rude" service and "too much hype" are the downsides.

Lombardi's ⌲ Pizza   24 | 13 | 16 | $22

NoLita | 32 Spring St. (bet. Mott & Mulberry Sts.) | 212-941-7994 | www.firstpizza.com

For a "pie with few rivals", this NoLita "mainstay" lives up to its billing for "top-class" coal-fired pizza with a "distinct smoky taste", "ultrathin crust" and "zesty" toppings; given all this, be prepared for "crazy lines."

Londel's Supper Club Ⓜ Southern   ▽ 22 | 17 | 19 | $31

Harlem | 2620 Frederick Douglass Blvd. (bet. 139th & 140th Sts.) | 212-234-6114 | www.londelsrestaurant.com

Proprietor Londel Davis "makes you feel welcome" at his Harlem Southerner, home to "soulfully solid" spreads in "plentiful" portions; extras include live jazz on weekend evenings and a "wonderful" Sunday buffet for those ready to "brunch it up."

London Lennie's Seafood   21 | 17 | 18 | $41

Rego Park | 63-88 Woodhaven Blvd. (bet. Fleet Ct. & Penelope Ave.) | Queens | 718-894-8084 | www.londonlennies.com

Ever "dependable" for fish lovers, this "longtime favorite" in Rego Park serves the "freshest seafood" in roomy digs; though the setup's "a little stodgy" and the acoustics "loud", it remains "wildly popular", with "waits for seating" the norm.

Long Tan ● Thai   19 | 18 | 18 | $28

Park Slope | 196 Fifth Ave. (bet. Berkeley Pl. & Union St.) | Brooklyn | 718-622-8444 | www.long-tan.com

This "out-of-the-ordinary" Park Slope Thai earns "popularity" with its "inventive" cooking and "good value"; the "sleek" design and pleasant garden add points for "cool", while "excellent" drinks create "a bit of a scene" with the "loyal" bar crowd.

Loreley German   ▽ 18 | 15 | 16 | $26

LES | 7 Rivington St. (Bowery St.) | 212-253-7077 | www.loreleynyc.com

"Younger" folk gather on "bench seating" at this "boisterous", low-budget LES brauhaus to wash down "hearty" German "comfort" grub with an "outstanding" selection of brews; revelers report the "good times" get "even better" in the biergarten out back.

NEW Los Dados Mexican   - | - | - | M

Meatpacking | 73 Gansevoort St. (Washington St.) | 646-810-7290 | www.losdadosmexican.com

Mexican regional home cooking comes to the Meatpacking District via this new cantina that's the brainchild of chef Sue Torres (Sueños) and nightlife maven David Rabin (Lotus); the cozy space, fka Meet, features a communal table, kitschy religious shrines and a festive feel fueled by moderate tabs and free-flowing tequila.

Los Dos Molinos Ⓢ Ⓜ Southwestern   21 | 17 | 16 | $32

Gramercy | 119 E. 18th St. (bet. Irving Pl. & Park Ave. S.) | 212-505-1574

At this "upbeat" Gramercy Southwesterner, the "fairly priced" vittles deliver a fiery "kick" best quenched with "fishbowl margaritas"; "peak hours" typically draw "noisy" crowds undeterred by the "cheesy decor" and sometime service.

| | | FOOD | DECOR | SERVICE | COST |

Loulou *French* ▽ 22 | 20 | 20 | $35
Fort Greene | 222 DeKalb Ave. (bet. Adelphi St. & Clermont Ave.) | Brooklyn | 718-246-0633 | www.louloubrooklyn.com
The French countryside comes to Fort Greene via this budget-friendly bistro, serving "consistently top-notch" Gallic "standbys" in a "warm" milieu complete with a "lovely" garden; the "cozy" room can be a "squeeze", but flirts observe that's all the more *"romantique."*

Luca *Italian* 20 | 15 | 19 | $39
E 80s | 1712 First Ave. (bet. 88th & 89th Sts.) | 212-987-9260 | www.lucatogo.com
Known for chef-owner Luca Marcato's "personal touch", this "inviting" Yorkville Italian "hits the spot" with its "addictive" "rustic" cooking and "family atmosphere"; *certo,* the room's "not fancy", but "satisfying" eats at a "reasonable price" make it a local "staple."

NEW Lucali ⊘ *Pizza* ▽ 27 | 21 | 20 | $18
Carroll Gardens | 575 Henry St. (bet. Carroll St. & 1st Pl.) | Brooklyn | 718-858-4086
"Old-school styling" yields "pizza perfection" at this new Carroll Gardens "neighborhood joint", an "instant classic" for "transcendent" brick-oven pies served in "charming" digs that recall "Brooklyn gone by"; manned by a chef-owner who's "committed to the art", it attracts "long lines" "for a good reason."

Lucien ❷ *French* 21 | 18 | 19 | $41
E Village | 14 First Ave. (1st St.) | 212-260-6481 | www.luciennyc.com
"Oh-so-Gallic", this "intimate" East Village "hideaway" "transports you to Paris" with its French bistro "classics" and "convivial" setting overseen by "beloved" owner Lucien Bahaj; for "relaxed" regulars, the "tight" space and "slow service" are just part of the deal.

Lucky Strike ❷ *French* 17 | 15 | 16 | $33
SoHo | 59 Grand St. (bet. W. B'way & Wooster St.) | 212-941-0772 | www.luckystrikeny.com
You "don't dress up" for the "easygoing" "Left Bank experience" at this SoHo "stalwart" from Keith McNally; despite seeming "passé" to trendoids, it's a "standby" for "basic" French bistro fare and classic cocktails, loaded with locals in the mood to "unwind."

Lucy *Pan-Latin* 19 | 20 | 18 | $46
Flatiron | ABC Carpet & Home | 35 E. 18th St. (bet. B'way & Park Ave. S.) | 212-475-5829 | www.lucylatinkitchen.com
"Dark and hip", this Flatiron Pan-Latino in ABC Carpet & Home allows patrons the chance to nibble on "intriguing" vittles, then "do some shopping" afterward; though service skews toward "slow", at least they "don't rush you out."

Lumi ❷ *Italian* 19 | 18 | 19 | $52
E 70s | 963 Lexington Ave. (70th St.) | 212-570-2335 | www.lumirestaurant.com
"Steady" as they come, this "attractive" UES Italian supplies "satisfying" food and "old-world" service in fireplace-equipped quarters abetted by an "alfresco" cafe; most maintain it's a "solid" local alternative, though some surmise "you can do better for the money."

		FOOD	DECOR	SERVICE	COST

NEW Lunetta Ⓜ *Italian* — ▽ 20 | 17 | 18 | $35

Boerum Hill | 116 Smith St. (bet. Dean & Pacific Sts.) | Brooklyn |
718-488-6269 | www.lunetta-ny.com

Moonstruck admirers claim the Italian cooking "can be a revelation" at
this "cheerful" Smith Street newcomer where a "skilled" chef turns out
"innovative" seasonal fare; customers also reflect warmly on the "casual" interior, backyard garden and "reasonable" cost.

Ⓩ Lupa ● *Italian* — 25 | 18 | 21 | $50

G Village | 170 Thompson St. (bet. Bleecker & Houston Sts.) | 212-982-5089 |
www.luparestaurant.com

The Batali-Bastianich-Denton "magic" will "blow you away" at this
"down-to-earth" Village Italian with "dynamite" Roman cuisine served
by an "enthusiastic" staff at less than their usual prices; the "hectic"
atmosphere and "cheek-by-jowl" seating are "part of the charm", but
"eternal" waits remain a "hassle."

Lure Fishbar *Seafood* — 23 | 24 | 23 | $58

SoHo | 142 Mercer St., downstairs (Prince St.) | 212-431-7676 |
www.lurefishbar.com

Making a "shipshape" "comeback" following a fire, this SoHo seafooder wins kudos for its "super-fresh fish" and sushi, "first-rate" service and elegant, "yachtlike" space; despite the "high price tag", its
"attitude-less" allure keeps the "upscale" clientele "all on board."

Lusardi's *Italian* — 24 | 18 | 22 | $59

E 70s | 1494 Second Ave. (bet. 77th & 78th Sts.) | 212-249-2020 |
www.lusardis.com

A "longtime" UES "favorite", this "clublike" enclave "never loses its
touch" for "top-flight" Northern Italian food and "professional" service; sure, it's "pricey" and "a little stuffy", but "well-heeled" locals attest it's "worth every penny."

Luz *Nuevo Latino* — ▽ 24 | 20 | 20 | $31

Fort Greene | 177 Vanderbilt Ave. (bet. Myrtle Ave. & Willoughby St.) |
Brooklyn | 718-246-4000 | www.luzrestaurant.com

Enlightened diners make this "cool" Fort Greene Nuevo Latino a "destination" for an "inventive menu" supplemented by "fruity drinks"; it's
still "little known", but the "low-key" style and big "bang for your
buck" promise a bright future.

Macelleria ● *Italian/Steak* — 21 | 18 | 19 | $50

Meatpacking | 48 Gansevoort St. (bet. Greenwich & Washington Sts.) |
212-741-2555 | www.macelleriarestaurant.com

Honoring the Meatpacking District's roots, this "old-school" Italian
steakhouse offers "high quality" and "big portions" in "cozy" digs with
"meat-fridge" fixtures and a "top-notch" wine cellar; the "simple"
style is "refreshing" in this "bandwagon" neighborhood, though skeptics synopsize it as a "second-tier" experience.

Madison Bistro *French* — 18 | 15 | 17 | $45

Murray Hill | 238 Madison Ave. (bet. 37th & 38th Sts.) | 212-447-1919 |
www.madisonbistro.com

"Quaint" and "unpretentious", this "snug" Murray Hill bistro does a
"super" job accommodating its *réguliers* with "old-time" French com-

fort food and "obliging" service; notwithstanding "tightly placed tables" and "pricey" propensities, it's "popular and appropriately so."

Madison's Italian
| 20 | 17 | 19 | $40 |

Bronx | 5686 Riverdale Ave. (259th St.) | 718-543-3850

With a "quite decent" stab at "stylish" atmospherics, this midpriced "neighborhood" Italian ranks with "Riverdale's best" for "tasty food in comfortable surroundings"; its "upscale Manhattan" feel is a "treat" for the "core group of locals" who madly "love it."

Magnolia American
| 19 | 17 | 17 | $30 |

Park Slope | 486 Sixth Ave. (12th St.) | Brooklyn | 718-369-4814 | www.magnoliabrooklyn.com

Defining a "great local", this "cute" New American stirs up "neighborhood hype" in Park Slope with "damn good food", "tasteful" decor and "friendly service"; even those who deem it "ordinary" concede it's "convenient."

NEW Mai House ●🅢 Vietnamese
| 21 | 21 | 20 | $54 |

TriBeCa | 186 Franklin St. (bet. Greenwich & Hudson Sts.) | 212-431-0606 | www.myriadrestaurantgroup.com

"Pretty" people and power spice cadets make themselves at home at this TriBeCa newcomer that produces "spot-on" "nouveau Vietnamese" cooking and flaunts "exciting plays on the traditional" (as does the "spacious", minimally "chic" setting); paupers pout it's "expensive", but the "flair" will mai-ghtily "impress a date."

Maison ● French
| 17 | 16 | 16 | $35 |

W 50s | 1700 Broadway (enter on 7th Ave., bet. 53rd & 54th Sts.) | 212-757-2233 | www.maisonnyc.com

"Low-maintenance types" claim this "handy" Midtown brasserie delivers the goods, supplying "reasonably priced" "basic French" fare 24/7 in a "casual" milieu; it's best known for its vast outdoor seating, leading cynics to suggest "maybe the tourists are right about this one."

Malagueta Ⓜ Brazilian
| ▽ 26 | 12 | 22 | $30 |

Astoria | 25-35 36th Ave. (28th St.) | Queens | 718-937-4821

A "taste of Rio" in Astoria, this "tranquil" Brazilian "hideaway" is a "joy" for "incredible" "home-cooked food" and "warm service" at a pleasing price; too bad they "forgot about the decor", but its rep as a "diamond in the rough" is beginning to reach beyond the borough.

Malatesta Trattoria ●🍴 Italian
| 21 | 17 | 18 | $32 |

W Village | 649 Washington St. (Christopher St.) | 212-741-1207

For "all-authentic" Northern Italiana, this way West Villager passes the test with its "tasty", "no-nonsense" cooking and "hot Euro" staffers; the "chill" sidewalk tables and "great value" are similarly "worth the trek."

Maloney & Porcelli Steak
| 22 | 19 | 21 | $64 |

E 50s | 37 E. 50th St. (bet. Madison & Park Aves.) | 212-750-2233 | www.maloneyandporcelli.com

"Suits drinking brown liquor" wolf down "man-size" slabs of "prime meat" (including that "famous" crackling pork shank) at this handsome Midtown chop shop; it's a "formulaic" but "consistently solid"

| | FOOD | DECOR | SERVICE | COST |

spread, and they'll always "treat you right", even if it's best savored "on someone else's tab."

Mamá Mexico ● *Mexican* — 20 | 17 | 17 | $36
E 40s | 214 E. 49th St. (bet. 2nd & 3rd Aves.) | 212-935-1316
W 100s | 2672 Broadway (102nd St.) | 212-864-2323
www.mamamexico.com
There's always a "hopping" scene going on at this affordable Mexican duo where the "mariachi action", "flowing tequila" and "gaudy" backdrops can lead to "too much fun"; "fantastic" food (including "fresh guacamole made at your table") helps make the "really noisy" acoustics more bearable.

Mama's Food Shop ☒⊅ *American* — 20 | 11 | 15 | $15
E Village | 200 E. Third St. (bet. Aves. A & B) | 212-777-4425 |
www.mamasfoodshop.com
When "stomach and pocketbook are both close to empty", the "punky" cafeteria staff at this East Village "hole-in-the-wall" "piles your plate" with "classic" American "home cookin'" for "cheap"; regulars with a "serious addiction" shrug "simple is best."

Mamlouk ●Ⓜ *Mideastern* — ▽ 23 | 18 | 18 | $48
E Village | 211 E. Fourth St. (bet. Aves. A & B) | 212-529-3477
"Pace yourself" at this East Village Middle Easterner where the "wonderful" eats "keep coming and coming" via a $40 prix fixe "feast" that spans six courses; what with the "rich" food, "cool" Arabian interior and weekend "belly dancers", it's a "totally different experience."

Mancora ● *Peruvian* — ▽ 21 | 15 | 20 | $26
E Village | 99 First Ave. (6th St.) | 212-253-1011
"One of the best values" around, this "authentic" East Village Peruvian plies "hearty servings" of "delectable" rotisserie chicken and other "mouthwatering discoveries" at a cost comparable to "eating at home"; maybe the decor "could be better", but otherwise surveyors say they're "impressed."

Mandarin Court *Chinese* — 20 | 8 | 13 | $20
Chinatown | 61 Mott St. (bet. Bayard & Canal Sts.) | 212-608-3838
"Excellent dim sum" for just a "small sum" is the verdict on this Chinatown "old-timer" that rolls out a "wide variety" of "hot, fresh treats"; despite "zero ambiance", chow that's this "hard to resist" keeps business "bustling."

Mandoo Bar *Korean* — 20 | 12 | 16 | $20
Garment District | 2 W. 32nd St. (bet. B'way & 5th Ave.) | 212-279-3075
The "superlative dumplings" at this "no-fuss" Garment District Korean are just the ticket for a "quick bite"; don't mind the "spartan" setup – the can-do staffers and bargain prices will keep you "happy."

Manducatis *Italian* — 22 | 13 | 19 | $45
LIC | 13-27 Jackson Ave. (47th Ave.) | Queens | 718-729-4602 |
www.manducatis.com
As a "last redoubt for mama's cooking", this "true family" Italian in Long Island City seems "lost in time" with its "soulful" "homestyle" dishes, "wonderful wines" and "old-world" hospitality; the aging digs "may need a makeover", but otherwise it has an "amazing reputation."

	FOOD	DECOR	SERVICE	COST

Manetta's ⧄ *Italian* — ▽ 22 | 17 | 20 | $38

LIC | 10-76 Jackson Ave. (49th Ave.) | Queens | 718-786-6171
This "family-run" LIC Italian "neighborhood favorite" does wonders with its "wood-fired" pizzas and "homemade pastas"; the "accommodating" service and "affordable" cost translate into "lots of repeat business."

Mangia ⧄ *Mediterranean* — 20 | 12 | 13 | $21

E 40s | 16 E. 48th St. (bet. 5th & Madison Aves.) | 212-754-7600
Financial District | Trump Bldg. | 40 Wall St. (bet. Nassau & William Sts.) | 212-425-4040
Flatiron | 22 W. 23rd St. (bet. 5th & 6th Aves.) | 212-647-0200
W 50s | 50 W. 57th St. (bet. 5th & 6th Aves.) | 212-582-5554
www.mangiatogo.com
"Corporate" types count on this Med foursome for classy "take-out lunches" featuring "lots of choices" from a "fancy salad bar" to the "imaginative" sandwich board; ok, the "cost adds up" and service is "spotty", but it sure is "quick" and "easy."

NEW Mantra 986 *American/Pan-Asian* — - | - | - | M

E 50s | 986 Second Ave. (bet. 52nd & 53rd Sts.) | 212-813-1595 | www.mantra986.com
A nightclub-ish setting is the backdrop for this new split-level East Midtowner that appeals to a young crowd with a midpriced mix of New American and Pan-Asian dishes; an upstairs lounge (with a balcony overlooking Second Avenue) handles the overflow and can be reserved for private parties.

Mara's Homemade *Cajun/Creole* — 19 | 10 | 19 | $31

E Village | 342 E. Sixth St. (bet. 1st & 2nd Aves.) | 212-598-1110 | www.marashomemade.com
At this East Village "hole-in-the-wall", you'll find "awesome" Cajun-Creole cookin' and "authentic N'Awlins style"; true, it's on the "funky" side, but "festive drinks" and the chance to "eat crawfish like a pro" make for real "fun on the bayou."

Marco Polo Ristorante *Italian* — ▽ 20 | 17 | 20 | $46

Carroll Gardens | 345 Court St. (Union St.) | Brooklyn | 718-852-5015 | www.marcopoloristorante.com
"Old favorites" save the day at this Carroll Gardens Italian turning out *molto bene* standards in a kitschy but "comfortable" setting enhanced by "snappy" service; holdouts hedge it's a bit "pricey" and "stuffy", but "Tony and Carmela could eat here happily."

Maremma ◑ *Italian* — 21 | 19 | 20 | $51

W Village | 228 W. 10th St. (bet. Bleecker & Hudson Sts.) | 212-645-0200 | www.maremmanyc.com
Overseen by Cesare Casella and his "solicitous staff", this bi-level West Villager augments its "impressive" Tuscan menu with "inventive surprises" without losing "that comfort-food feeling"; an "inviting" haven of "eclectic" rusticana, it has finally "found its groove."

Maria Pia *Italian* — 19 | 15 | 18 | $36

W 50s | 319 W. 51st St. (bet. 8th & 9th Aves.) | 212-765-6463 | www.mariapianyc.com
The "genuine article", this "cordial" Theater District Italian serves "flavorful red-sauce" fare with "no noses" in the air and, better still, for

"moderate" sums (the $21.95 dinner "prix fixe is so worth it"); since the "nondescript" room can get "cramped" during the "pre-theater rush", the "garden is a must."

Marina Cafe Seafood

18	22	18	$42

Staten Island | 154 Mansion Ave. (Hillside Terr.) | 718-967-3077 | www.marinacafegrand.com

A "grand view" of Great Kills Harbor and "fine fresh seafood" are the main "attractions" at this Staten Island cafe, though the "updated decor" also helps justify the "Park Avenue prices"; merrymakers maintain "summer evenings" on the tiki bar deck are "not to be missed."

Marinella Italian

▽ 23	17	22	$40

G Village | 49 Carmine St. (Bedford St.) | 212-807-7472

Hailed as a "quintessential local joint", this Village "blackboard-menu" Italian is a "superior" source of "old-school" cuisine and service so "super-friendly" it's "like coming home"; the "peaceful" vibe and modest prices prove it's "not trendy at all."

Mario's ⓂⒾ Italian

22	16	21	$40

Bronx | 2342 Arthur Ave. (bet. 184th & 186th Sts.) | 718-584-1188

"Retro in the best of ways", this "family-run" 1919-vintage "charmer" remains an Arthur Avenue "favorite" for "generations of red-sauce lovers" who understand that the combo of classic Southern Italiana and great thin-crust pizza "refreshes the soul"; equally stirring is the "attentiveness" of its "staff of old-timers."

MarkJoseph Steakhouse Ⓢ Steak

24	18	21	$69

Financial District | 261 Water St. (off Peck Slip) | 212-277-0020 | www.markjosephsteakhouse.com

"They mean business" at this "manly" Financial District chop shop that "wows Wall Street types" with "big", "succulent steaks" "seared to perfection" and dispatched by "slick" servers; cash-endowed carnivores overlook the "stark" backdrop as well as the typically pricey steakhouse tabs.

Markt Belgian

19	18	16	$42

Flatiron | 676 Sixth Ave. (21st St.) | 212-727-3314 | www.marktrestaurant.com

Expect the "same look and feel" on a "smaller" scale at this "trendy Belgian brasserie" that's traded its Meatpacking District address for new Flatiron digs; it remains a "no-brainer" for those in the markt for "premier moules frites" blessed by Belgian brews.

Maroons Jamaican

22	15	18	$35

Chelsea | 244 W. 16th St. (bet. 7th & 8th Aves.) | 212-206-8640 | www.maroonsnyc.com

The "heavy-duty home cooking" and light-duty tabs leave 'em "fat and happy" at this Chelsea Jamaican-Southerner whose "soulful" specialties deliver a "spicy kick"; indeed, the grub's so "satisfying", it's easy to overlook being packed in "tight" and marooned by "hit-or-miss" service.

Marseille ❶ French/Mediterranean

20	19	19	$47

W 40s | 630 Ninth Ave. (44th St.) | 212-333-3410 | www.marseillenyc.com

Beaucoup "brasserie character" (including "upbeat din") marks this Hell's Kitchen French-Med where the "tempting" menu surprises with "refreshing twists"; add "congenial" servers who "get you out fast" and you have an "obvious pre-theater choice."

Maruzzella ● *Italian* | 22 | 16 | 22 | $40

E 70s | 1483 First Ave. (bet. 77th & 78th Sts.) | 212-988-8877 | www.maruzzellanyc.com

A "local favorite" that's even "more inviting since an expansion", this "reliable" UES Italian is a "go-to" for "delightful traditional" eats for fairly "favorable" fares; given the "super" service, locals "wish there were more like it."

Mary Ann's *Tex-Mex* | 15 | 11 | 14 | $25

Chelsea | 116 Eighth Ave. (16th St.) | 212-633-0877 ♥
E Village | 80 Second Ave. (5th St.) | 212-475-5939 ♥
TriBeCa | 107 W. Broadway (bet. Chambers & Reade Sts.) | 212-766-0911 | www.maryannsmexican.com
W 90s | 2452 Broadway (bet. 90th & 91st Sts.) | 212-877-0132

"Why go to Cabo" when there's this "high-volume" Tex-Mex mini-chain made for "gorging on staples" chased with "mean margaritas"; contras condemn the "predictable" chow, "tacky" looks and "sloppy" service, but admit they do the job while staying "totally affordable."

Mary's Fish Camp ⊠ *Seafood* | 25 | 13 | 18 | $41

W Village | 64 Charles St. (W. 4th St.) | 646-486-2185 | www.marysfishcamp.com

Camp followers dream of the "transcendent lobster roll" and other "fresher-than-fresh seafood" at this "upbeat little" Village "fish shack"; the "beachy", ultra-"informal" space is "always jammed", but drift by once and you'll be "hooked."

Mas ⊠ *American* | 25 | 24 | 25 | $74

G Village | 39 Downing St. (bet. Bedford & Varick Sts.) | 212-255-1790 | www.masfarmhouse.com

"Go with someone special" to this "intimate" Village New American, a paradigm of "relaxed sophistication" where chef Galen Zamarra's "exceptional", "market-fresh" menu wins mas-sive support; its "impressive wine list", "classic service" and "stylish rustic" setting are likewise "well worth" the "grown-up" cost.

⊠ Masa ⊠ *Japanese* | 27 | 24 | 26 | $485

W 60s | Time Warner Ctr. | 10 Columbus Circle, 4th fl. (60th St. at B'way)

⊠ Bar Masa ●⊠ *Japanese*

W 60s | Time Warner Ctr. | 10 Columbus Circle, 4th fl. (60th St. at B'way)
212-823-9800 | www.masanyc.com

At this Zen-like Time Warner Center Japanese, you can enjoy star chef Masayoshi Takayama's "exquisite" omakase – an "unforgettable" "parade of perfection" for an "astronomical" $400 prix fixe that some consider a deal when compared to the cost of floor seats for the Knicks; the more "unassuming" Bar Masa next door is "not cheap", but still a "bargain compared to its big brother."

⊠ Matsuri ● *Japanese* | 23 | 26 | 20 | $59

Chelsea | Maritime Hotel | 369 W. 16th St., downstairs (9th Ave.) | 212-243-6400 | www.themaritimehotel.com

This "top-of-the-line", bottom-of-the-building Chelsea Japanese earns "wows" for its spectacular subterranean setting, not to mention chef Tadashi Ono's "brilliant sushi", a "knockout sake list" and "hospitable" service; the "happening scene" is populated by "trendy" folk equipped with "deep pockets", while its adjacent nightclub/party space is a great venue to celebrate with your 175 dearest friends.

Maurizio Trattoria Italian — ▽ 21 | 17 | 21 | $50

G Village | 35 W. 13th St. (bet. 5th & 6th Aves.) | 212-206-6474 | www.mauriziotrattoria.com

It's something of a "neighborhood secret", but cognoscenti count on this "delightful little" Village Tuscan for "well-executed" "classic" dishes and "gracious personal service"; a location "across from the Quad Cinema" makes it a natural, if pricey, post-flick pick.

Max Italian — 23 | 15 | 17 | $27

E Village | 51 Ave. B (bet. 3rd & 4th Sts.) | 212-539-0111 ●♥
NEW TriBeCa | 181 Duane St. (bet. Greenwich & Hudson Sts.) | 212-966-5939
www.max-ny.com

Max SoHa ●♥ Italian

W 100s | 1274 Amsterdam Ave. (123rd St.) | 212-531-2221 | www.maxsoha.com

"Earthy" meals that "linger in your mind" make this "quaint" East Villager (with a "collegiate" outpost near Columbia and a new TriBeCa sibling) a "favorite" for "homestyle Italian" cooking; "shockingly low" prices keep them packed.

Max Brenner Dessert — 17 | 19 | 14 | $24

NEW E Village | 141 Second Ave. (9th St.) | 212-388-0030
Union Sq | 841 Broadway (bet. 13th & 14th Sts.) | 212-388-0030
www.maxbrenner.com

"Go right to dessert" at this "Wonka-esque" global chocolatier whose "sweet feasts" easily outperform its "average" French fare; apart from being off-limits for weight-watchers, the main problem here is "flighty" servers suffering from "sugar shock."

Maya Mexican — 23 | 19 | 19 | $51

E 60s | 1191 First Ave. (bet. 64th & 65th Sts.) | 212-585-1818 | www.modernmexican.com

"Haute Mexican" cooking gets an "imaginative spin" at this "stylish" Eastsider that "outshines" its rivals with "superior" cuisine and "prompt" service; "wickedly good" margaritas fuel the fiestalike fun, but bring *mucho dinero* to settle the bill.

NEW Maze French — 23 | 21 | 20 | $71

W 50s | The London NYC | 151 W. 54th St. (bet. 6th & 7th Aves.) | 212-468-8889 | www.thelondonnyc.com

"If you can't get in to Gordon Ramsay", this Midtown hotel's "more relaxed" bar/eatery offers the "same quality" from the same chef via an "exquisite" lineup of New French small plates; the "refined" feel and "spot-on" service score well too, but the cost of a meal here can "add up."

Maz Mezcal Mexican — 20 | 17 | 18 | $36

E 80s | 316 E. 86th St. (bet. 1st & 2nd Aves.) | 212-472-1599 | www.mazmezcal.com

Long a "best bet" for a "true Mexican fix", this "lively" UES eatery matches "top-notch" menu "classics" with "deadly" tequilas and simpatico service; it's "lotsa fun" for "reasonable" sums, but "go early" since it's often "jammed" with compadres.

McCormick & Schmick's *Seafood* | 20 | 18 | 20 | $50 |

W 50s | 1285 Sixth Ave. (enter on 52nd St., bet. 6th & 7th Aves.) | 212-459-1222 | www.mccormickandschmicks.com

Linkage to a "big fish" chain makes this Midtowner a "safe" harbor for a "mind-boggling selection" of "solid basic seafood"; aye, the eating and "Anywhere, USA" vibe show "little imagination", but overall the "mainstream" shtick is "better than you'd expect."

Mediterraneo ● *Italian/Pizza* | 19 | 15 | 15 | $39 |

E 60s | 1260 Second Ave. (66th St.) | 212-734-7407 | www.mediterraneonyc.com

Young "Euros" ensure this "causal", affordable East Side Italian is "always filled" as they sample a "tasty array of pastas" and "thin-crust pizzas" served by expats "right off the boat"; those parked on the "coveted" sidewalk seats suggest it's "more about the scene."

Mee Noodle Shop *Noodle Shop* | 18 | 4 | 12 | $15 |

E 40s | 922 Second Ave. (49th St.) | 212-888-0027
Murray Hill | 547 Second Ave. (bet. 30th & 31st Sts.) | 212-779-1596
W 50s | 795 Ninth Ave. (53rd St.) | 212-765-2929

Meting out "fresh", "stewlike soups" at "unbeatable" prices, this "no-fuss" Chinese noodle trio is hard to beat for a "satisfying quick feed"; "slapdash" service and "dumpy" digs cause many to opt for their "lightning"-fast delivery.

☑ Megu *Japanese* | 24 | 26 | 22 | $94 |

TriBeCa | 62 Thomas St. (bet. Church St. & W. B'way)

☑ Megu Midtown *Japanese*

E 40s | Trump World Tower | 845 United Nations Plaza (1st Ave. & 47th St.) | 212-964-7777 | www.megunyc.com

For a "dining event" that "makes a mega-impression", this "glitzy" Japanese duo flaunts "lavish surroundings" (built around an "ice Buddha"), "brilliant" "work-of-art" food and "bend-over-backwards service"; if the Eastsider is "less awe-inspiring" than the "soaring" TriBeCa original, they're equally "hyper-priced."

Meltemi *Greek/Seafood* | 18 | 13 | 18 | $46 |

E 50s | 905 First Ave. (51st St.) | 212-355-4040

"No froufrou" distracts from the "standard Greek fare" at this East Midtown "warhorse", a "hospitable" retreat for "nicely done" seafood; some sniff "unmemorable", but for "U.N. types" and area "ancients", it's like a "trip to the old country."

Menchanko-tei *Noodle Shop* | 20 | 10 | 15 | $22 |

E 40s | 131 E. 45th St. (bet. Lexington & 3rd Aves.) | 212-986-6805 ●
W 50s | 43-45 W. 55th St. (bet. 5th & 6th Aves.) | 212-247-1585 www.menchankotei.com

"Budget-minded salarymen" declare that these inexpensive Midtown ramen shops are the "real deal" for "heaping bowls" of "awesome Japanese soul food"; skeptics menchan the barely "utilitarian" setups, but note you'll be "in and out" in a flash.

	FOOD	DECOR	SERVICE	COST

Mercadito *Mexican* `22` `16` `16` `$38`
E Village | 179 Ave. B (bet. 11th & 12th Sts.) | 212-529-6490 ◗
W Village | 100 Seventh Ave. S. (bet. Bleecker & Grove Sts.) | 212-647-0830
www.mercaditony.com

You "can't get a better fish taco" than at these "creative" cross-Village Mexicans with "eminently shareable" small plates and "potent" potables; party-poopers protest "skimpy" portions that can "run up a tab."

NEW Mercat ◗🅕 *Spanish* `-` `-` `-` `E`
NoHo | 45 Bond St. (bet. Bowery & Lafayette St.) | 212-529-8600 | www.mercatnyc.com

Bustling from day one, this hip NoHo arrival is Barcelona native Jaime Reixach's attempt to re-create the tapas bars of his hometown; the white-tiled space, with open kitchen, separate jamon and cheese station and a downstairs lounge, can be echo-y, so brush up on your lip-reading.

Mercer Kitchen ◗ *American/French* `22` `23` `19` `$56`
SoHo | Mercer Hotel | 99 Prince St. (Mercer St.) | 212-966-5454 | www.jean-georges.com

The "cool factor" is intact at Jean-Georges Vongerichten's SoHo French–New American, whose subterranean "chicness" and "pricey", "well-crafted menu" make everyone from "glitterati" to "out-of-towners" feel "special"; the crowd sure "looks good" in the "dark" setting, though the "staff could use some attitude sprucing."

Mermaid Inn *Seafood* `23` `17` `20` `$43`
E Village | 96 Second Ave. (bet. 5th & 6th Sts.) | 212-674-5870 | www.themermaidnyc.com

Seemingly shipped from "somewhere in Maine", this "unpretentious" East Village seafooder "hits the mark" with "high-quality" cooking that appeals to "serious" afishionados; the "cheery staff", "quaint nautical decor" and "garden area" help make it an inn spot.

🅩 Mesa Grill *Southwestern* `24` `20` `21` `$55`
Flatiron | 102 Fifth Ave. (bet. 15th & 16th Sts.) | 212-807-7400 | www.mesagrill.com

Showcasing "Southwestern with snazz", this seriously tabbed Flatiron standby is home plate for TV super-chef Bobby Flay, whose "bold riffs" on regional cuisine "pack a big taste wallop" (brunch is sure to "wake you up"); "enthusiastic" service bolsters the "loud", "upbeat" vibe in a room that's lately been looking a little "long in the tooth."

Meskerem *Ethiopian* `20` `8` `13` `$23`
G Village | 124 MacDougal St. (bet. Bleecker & W. 3rd Sts.) | 212-777-8111
W 40s | 468 W. 47th St. (bet. 9th & 10th Aves.) | 212-664-0520 ◗

To "break out of your normal routine", try the "hands-on" experience at this Ethiopian duo where "hearty", "perfectly spiced" stews served "sans utensils" are scooped up with "tangy" injera bread; "amazing value" helps offset the "low-frills" feel and "haphazard service."

Métisse *French* `19` `16` `19` `$40`
W 100s | 239 W. 105th St. (bet. Amsterdam Ave. & B'way) | 212-666-8825 | www.metisserestaurant.com

A "tried-and-true respite" for "Columbia profs" and other clued-in locals, this "nifty" Upper Westsider supplies "well-executed", well-priced French classics in a "quiet", "cozy" milieu; if the "staff lacks finesse, it makes up for it in charm."

Metrazur 🗲 American
20 | 21 | 18 | $49

E 40s | Grand Central | East Balcony (42nd St. & Park Ave.) | 212-687-4600 | www.charliepalmer.com

"Exciting" views of Grand Central's Concourse and "solid" New American cuisine set Charlie Palmer's balcony "bastion" apart from the pack; it's "expensive" and the "commuters scurrying" around below may be "faster than the waiters", but there's more than enough incentive here to take another train.

NEW Metro Marché French
19 | 15 | 19 | $36

W 40s | Port Authority | 625 Eighth Ave. (41st St.) | 212-239-1010 | www.metromarche.com

Granted, it's the "last place you'd look" for a French brasserie, but this Port Authority newcomer is a "pleasant surprise" for "reasonably priced" Gallic grub and "quick" service; though "somewhat impersonal", it's a "convenient oasis" before a show or "hopping a Greyhound."

Mexicana Mama M⊅ Mexican
23 | 13 | 18 | $35

G Village | 47 E. 12th St. (bet. B'way & University Pl.) | 212-253-7594
W Village | 525 Hudson St. (bet. Charles & W. 10th Sts.) | 212-924-4119

At the "high end of Mexican", this taqueria twosome turns out "mouthwatering" dishes with "nuevo twists" that most "can't get enough of"; those opposed to "cramped seating and killer waits" should forgo the "teeny" West Village original for its "larger" eastern offshoot.

Mexican Radio ● Mexican
18 | 13 | 15 | $32

NoLita | 19 Cleveland Pl. (bet. Kenmare & Spring Sts.) | 212-343-0140 | www.mexrad.com

Twentysomethings "tune in" to this "casual", low-budget NoLita joint for its "yummy" if "unadventurous" Mexican eats and "kitschy-cool" setting; service may be "on siesta", but after a few "deadly" margaritas "not too much of the meal matters."

Mezzaluna ● Italian
19 | 15 | 17 | $44

E 70s | 1295 Third Ave. (bet. 74th & 75th Sts.) | 212-535-9600 | www.mezzalunany.com

Regulars who make this UES Italian vet their "local canteen" crowd in for "fine" "fresh" pastas and "wood-oven" pizzas; though the "close quarters" and upscale prices detract, it's "worth bumping elbows" for a meal that you "can always count on."

Mezzogiorno ● Italian
20 | 17 | 18 | $42

SoHo | 195 Spring St. (Sullivan St.) | 212-334-2112 | www.mezzogiorno.com

For a "SoHo shopping break" and a conversation without shouting, there's always this "comfortable" Tuscan "old reliable" with its "strong" renditions of pizza and pasta "staples"; "passable" service and spendy tabs are balanced by "sidewalk dining" that's perfect on a "summer day."

Mezzo Mezzo ● Greek
▽ 18 | 17 | 18 | $33

Astoria | 31-29 Ditmars Blvd. (bet. 32nd & 33rd Sts.) | Queens | 718-278-0444 | www.mezzomezzony.com

This "homey" Astorian is a "casually accommodating" place with "enjoyable" Greek grub, an "outdoor cafe" and Saturday night "belly dancing";

though "un-mythical" on the whole, it works as an affordable "alternative" to "waiting on line at Taverna Kyclades up the block."

Michael Jordan's
The Steak House NYC *Steak*

| 20 | 21 | 19 | $62 |

E 40s | Grand Central | West Balcony (42nd St. & Vanderbilt Ave.) | 212-655-2300 | www.theglaziergroup.com

To "eat like Mike", try this "competitive" mezzanine meatery "overlooking the rush" of Grand Central Concourse, scoring well for its "generous" cuts of "quality" beef; some blow the whistle on "expense-account" pricing and "delayed" service, but the $24 prix fixe lunch is a winner and overall it scores "more often than the Knicks."

Michael's ☒ *Californian*

| 21 | 21 | 21 | $66 |

W 50s | 24 W. 55th St. (bet. 5th & 6th Aves.) | 212-767-0555 | www.michaelsnewyork.com

You can eavesdrop on the "next big media merger" while enjoying "classy" Californian cuisine and "professional service" at this "attractive", airy Midtown "power spot"; the "unparalleled people-watching" and "contemporary art" displays help distract from the "Beverly Hills" pricing.

Mi Cocina *Mexican*

| 22 | 18 | 19 | $41 |

W Village | 57 Jane St. (Hudson St.) | 212-627-8273

They know "what Mexican cuisine is all about" at this "cozy" West Village stalwart that "avoids the typical" with its "consistently excellent" cooking; given the "sunny" service and "absolute treat" of a tequila selection, amigos ignore the "steep"-for-the-genre prices.

Mill Basin Kosher Deli *Deli*

| 21 | 15 | 17 | $22 |

Mill Basin | 5823 Ave. T (59th St.) | Brooklyn | 718-241-4910 | www.millbasindeli.com

At this kosher Jewish deli–cum–"art gallery", "all the classic dishes" (i.e. "pastrami supreme") are offered alongside classic Erté and Lichtenstein "eye candy" on the walls; service is "genial" if "maybe too fast", and some say the "overstuffed" sandwiches are "overpriced", but that probably comes from being in Mill Basin.

Mill Korean *Korean*

| 19 | 13 | 16 | $20 |

W 100s | 2895 Broadway (bet. 112th & 113th Sts.) | 212-666-7653

With its "magnum-size portions" of Seoul food, this "inexpensive" UWS "neighborhood staple" helps Columbia students "soothe a craving" "without heading to Koreatown"; too bad the "cramped digs" and "thinly spread" service can make the scene "a little chaotic."

☒ Milos, Estiatorio ● *Greek/Seafood*

| 26 | 23 | 22 | $73 |

W 50s | 125 W. 55th St. (bet. 6th & 7th Aves.) | 212-245-7400 | www.milos.ca

"Zeus couldn't eat better" than mere mortals do at this all-white, high-ceilinged Midtown Greek known for "pristine" seafood "grilled to perfection" (the "only way to get it fresher is to stick your head in the fish tank"); "smooth service" and "resortlike" decor add to the "quality" experience, but "bring the platinum card" to deal with the Olympic prices – or stick to its less expensive, but equally delicious, appetizers.

	FOOD	DECOR	SERVICE	COST

Minetta Tavern ● _Italian_
18 | 18 | 18 | $42

G Village | 113 MacDougal St. (bet. Bleecker & W. 3rd Sts.) | 212-475-3850
For a "trip down memory lane", visit this 1937-vintage Village "hide-away" where "old-fashioned" waiters bring out "huge portions" of Northern Italian fare; except for the prices, "they haven't changed the menu in decades", and if it's looking "a little worn", at least it's "reliable."

Mingala Burmese _Burmese_
20 | 10 | 17 | $23

E 70s | 1393B Second Ave. (bet. 72nd & 73rd Sts.) | 212-744-8008
E Village | 21-23 E. Seventh St. (bet. 2nd & 3rd Aves.) |
212-529-3656

"Good for vegetarians", these Burmese twins offer a "different" cuisine that's a "gentler" combination of Indian, Chinese and Thai tastes; the decor's either "folksy" or "drab", but there's no debating the "low prices."

Mint _Indian_
▽ 19 | 19 | 15 | $44

E 50s | San Carlos Hotel | 150 E. 50th St. (bet. Lexington & 3rd Aves.) |
212-644-8888 | www.mintny.com

"Solid" subcontinental specialties that "don't cost a mint" satisfy surveyors at this "upscale" East Midtown Indian; the "sleek" interior may seem "a bit unsettling" as does service that "leaves a lot to be desired."

Miracle Grill _Southwestern_
18 | 14 | 17 | $31

W Village | 415 Bleecker St. (bet. Bank & W. 11th Sts.) | 212-924-1900
Park Slope | 222 Seventh Ave. (4th St.) | Brooklyn | 718-369-4541

"Tasty" Southwestern vittles make for "worthy" brunches at this "laid-back", low-priced duo in the Village and Park Slope; the settings are "comfortable" – Brooklyn's "wonderful" deck actually "manages to feel private" – though some report "spotty service" from Miracle workers.

Miriam _Israeli/Mediterranean_
21 | 18 | 19 | $32

NEW Cobble Hill | 229 Court St. (bet. Baltic & Warren Sts.) | Brooklyn |
718-522-2220
Park Slope | 79 Fifth Ave. (Prospect Pl.) | Brooklyn | 718-622-2250
www.miriamrestaurant.com

With their "zesty", "inventive" Israeli/Med eats, this pleasingly priced Park Sloper and its new Cobble Hill spin-off are "keepers" with especially "busy" weekend brunches; "romantic" settings with mosaics and lanterns make them "feel exotic and homey at the same time."

Mishima _Japanese_
23 | 12 | 20 | $36

Murray Hill | 164 Lexington Ave. (bet. 30th & 31st Sts.) | 212-532-9596 |
www.mishimany.com

Murray Hillers bow to this split-level Japanese's "melt-on-your-tongue fresh" sushi as well as "perfectly executed" cooked items; "bargain" pricing and "accommodating" service add to the "peaceful", "pleasant" vibe; P.S. "definitely eat upstairs."

Miss Mamie's _Southern_
▽ 21 | 12 | 18 | $26

Harlem | 366 W. 110th St. (bet. Columbus & Manhattan Aves.) |
212-865-6744
Miss Maude's _Southern_
Harlem | 547 Lenox Ave. (bet. 137th & 138th Sts.) | 212-690-3100
www.spoonbreadinc.com

The "chicken's always crispy" at this "deeelicious" Harlem soul food duo where "happiness is short ribs, collards and beer"; ok, they're not much on looks, but when you're hankering for small-town North Carolina, this is the fastest way to get there.

Mizu Sushi ☒ *Japanese*   22 | 14 | 17 | $36

Flatiron | 29 E. 20th St. (bet. B'way & Park Ave. S.) | 212-505-6688

"Creative rolls with fresh ingredients" at "affordable" prices are the forte of this Flatiron Japanese where rustic, exposed-brick decor and a "loud" hip-hop soundtrack lure the young and "rambunctious"; it's "extremely popular" on weekends, so brace yourself for "intolerable lines."

Mo-Bay ● *Caribbean/Soul Food*   21 | 18 | 15 | $29

Harlem | 17 W. 125th St. (bet. 5th & Lenox Aves.) | 212-876-9300 | www.mobayrestaurant.com

"Caribbean-soul food fusion" is the thing at this "laid-back" Harlem joint where the food and the tabs are as "good" as the service is "slow"; there's also "great" live jazz for music aficionados, though the "sound of the band can be overwhelming."

Moda *Italian/Mediterranean*   – | – | – | E

W 50s | Flatotel | 135 W. 52nd St. (bet. 6th & 7th Aves.) | 212-887-9880 | www.flatotel.com

Rustic Mediterranean/Italian dishes are served in the sleek dining room of this Midtown hotel that's perhaps better known for its outdoor patio bar, a popular after-work destination set in an atrium breezeway; although the food's on the pricey side, it does offer a bargain $24.07 lunch.

☑ Modern, The ☒ *American/French*   26 | 26 | 24 | $110

W 50s | Museum of Modern Art | 9 W. 53rd St. (bet. 5th & 6th Aves.) | 212-333-1220 | www.themodernnyc.com

Set in a "coolly elegant" room overlooking MoMA's sculpture garden, Danny Meyer's "splendid" French-New American is helmed by chef Gabriel Kreuther who "balances tradition with innovation" for prix fixe meals that are "as sophisticated as any Picasso" (and almost as expensive); a "thoroughly professional" staff adds to the "formal" scene, though the "livelier" adjacent bar offers a "more flexible" small-plates menu at a "more reasonable" price; N.B. jackets required at dinner.

NEW Moim Ⓜ *Korean*   – | – | – | M

Park Slope | 206 Garfield Pl. (bet. 7th & 8th Aves.) | Brooklyn | 718-499-8092 | www.moimrestaurant.com

Park Slope goes Korean with the arrival of this slick newcomer just off Seventh Avenue featuring modern, moderately priced dishes served in sleek, black brick-lined environs; an appealing back patio is just the ticket for warm-weather dining.

Molyvos ● *Greek*   22 | 19 | 20 | $53

W 50s | 871 Seventh Ave. (bet. 55th & 56th Sts.) | 212-582-7500 | www.molyvos.com

A "reliable favorite" for "delectable" Greek eats, this warm, "welcoming" Midtown taverna is also admired for its "dedicated" servers and "spacious" setting; it works as both an "ideal lunch venue" or dinner destination "before Carnegie Hall", and though "pricey", the $36 pre-theater prix fixe is enough of "a steal" to keep the place packed.

	FOOD	DECOR	SERVICE	COST

NEW Momento *Italian* — — — | E

Astoria | 29-35 Newton Ave. (bet. 28th & 30th Sts.) | Queens | 718-267-2771 | www.momentobistro.com

Rustic French doors lining the facade of this new Astoria Italian suggest a sleepy little country bistro, but inside are several dining areas as well as two bars; a sizable wine list and occasional live entertainment keep the energy level high.

Momofuku Noodle Bar *Noodle Shop* — 24 | 13 | 16 | $27

E Village | 163 First Ave. (bet. 10th & 11th Sts.) | 212-475-7899 | www.eatmomofuku.com

David Chang's "addictive" noodle soups and pork buns keep the "hordes" coming to this "affordable" Japanese-inspired East Villager, a "necessary foodie experience" with waits "no matter when you go"; sure, it's "absurdly small" and service can be "harried", but "it couldn't be more delicious."

Momofuku Ssäm Bar ◕ *American/Korean* — 24 | 16 | 18 | $33

E Village | 207 Second Ave. (13th St.) | 212-254-3500 | www.eatmomofuku.com

Think "haute cuisine in blue jeans" to get the gist of David Chang's New American–Korean yearling, a "simple" East Villager with "more space" than his Noodle Bar but the same "amazing blend of flavors"; "real-deal" burritolike *ssäms* are offered for lunch and "gutsy" seasonal concoctions for dinner, but either way, you can expect "crushing crowds."

Momoya *Japanese* — 24 | 20 | 18 | $41

Chelsea | 185 Seventh Ave. (21st St.) | 212-989-4466

"Skillful" sushi chefs whip up "wonderfully inventive" maki paired with "great sake" at this "refined" Chelsea Japanese; while the "minimalist" decor lies somewhere between "cool" and "cold", the warm reaction from locals is translating into "increasing waits."

Monkey Bar ☒ *American* — — — | E

E 50s | Elysée Hotel | 60 E. 54th St. (bet. Madison & Park Aves.) | 212-838-2600 | www.theglaziergroup.com

Reinvented yet again, this longtime fixture in Midtown's Elysée Hotel is now helmed by chef Patricia Yeo, who's fashioned a New American menu inflected with subtle Asian touches; the stylish room, reminiscent of a plush 1940s supper club, oozes enough retro charm to distract from the very up-to-the-minute pricing, while the adjacent bar continues to host all kinds of youthful monkey business.

Mon Petit Cafe *French* — 18 | 14 | 18 | $36

E 60s | 801 Lexington Ave. (62nd St.) | 212-355-2233 | www.monpetitcafe.com

"Convenient to Bloomie's" and "perfect for ladies of a certain age", this "lace-curtain" UES bistro "serves the neighborhood well" with "tasty", "reasonably priced" French fare; popular for lunch, it's "calmer" at dinner.

Monster Sushi *Japanese* — 18 | 10 | 15 | $31

Chelsea | 158 W. 23rd St. (bet. 6th & 7th Aves.) | 212-620-9131 ◕

W 40s | 22 W. 46th St. (bet. 5th & 6th Aves.) | 212-398-7707

(continued)

Monster Sushi

W Village | 535 Hudson St. (Charles St.) | 646-336-1833
www.monstersushi.com

The "name says it all" at this Japanese threesome where the "ridiculously large" rolls and "mounds" of sashimi are "monstrous" enough to be "borderline silly"; "Morimoto it's not", but tabs are "moderate" enough to blunt the "so-so" service and "stark" settings.

Montparnasse ◐ *French*   19 | 18 | 18 | $45

E 50s | The Pod Hotel | 230 E. 51st St. (bet. 2nd & 3rd Aves.) | 212-758-6633 |
www.montparnasseny.com

A "steady standby", this "traditional" Midtown French gratifies with "excellent coq au vin" and a "well-priced" $22.95 pre-theater deal; its "mature" clientele appreciates the "deferential" service and tables spaced "far enough apart" to allow "intimate conversation."

NEW Morandi ◐ *Italian*   19 | 18 | 19 | $54

G Village | 211 Waverly Pl. (Charles St.) | 212-627-7575 |
www.morandiny.com

Über-restaurateur Keith McNally does Italian for the first time at this "buzzy" new Village trattoria featuring his usual transporting atmospherics – in this case, "Tuscan farmhouse" chic; behind the stoves, Jody Williams (ex Gusto) turns out an "inventive" seasonal menu that would be "secondary to the scene" only here.

Moran's Chelsea *American*   18 | 19 | 19 | $42

Chelsea | 146 10th Ave. (19th St.) | 212-627-3030 |
www.moranschelsea.com

"Old-fashioned in every way", this Chelsea "trip back in time" purveys "hearty" Americana in a "Waterford-and-wood-burning-fireplace" setting; add in "accommodating" staffers who "pour a great Guinness" and the "whole is definitely equal to more than the sum of its parts."

Morgan, The Ⓜ *American*   20 | 23 | 21 | $41

Murray Hill | The Morgan Library & Museum | 225 Madison Ave. (bet. 36th & 37th Sts.) | 212-683-2130

Murray Hill's revamped Morgan Library offers two lunchtime venues: a "charming" atrium cafe or J.P. Morgan's "clubbier" former dining room; both feature a moderately priced New American menu that "blends old NY and modern influences."

☑ Morimoto *Japanese*   24 | 26 | 22 | $82

Chelsea | 88 10th Ave. (bet. 15th & 16th Sts.) | 212-989-8883 |
www.morimotonyc.com

"It's showtime" at this "flashy" West Chelsea Japanese where Iron Chef Masaharu Morimoto's "mouthwatering delicacies" "vie for attention" with Tadao Ando's "spectacular", "ultramodern" interiors and the "futuristic loos"; even though it "costs a bundle", many urge you to "splurge for omakase."

Morrell Wine Bar & Cafe *American*   19 | 16 | 19 | $45

W 40s | 1 Rockefeller Plaza (49th St., bet. 5th & 6th Aves.) | 212-262-7700 |
www.morrellwinebar.com

Situated in the "heart of Rockefeller Plaza", this petite, "packed" cafe provides a full-on "view of the Christmas tree" during the holidays and "great people-watching" all year round, particularly from its sidewalk seats; look for an "incredible international wine list" paired with "dependable" albeit "pricey" Americana.

Morton's, The Steakhouse Steak

| 24 | 20 | 22 | $69 |

E 40s | 551 Fifth Ave. (45th St.) | 212-972-3315 | www.mortons.com

This costly Midtown chophouse caters to captains of commerce content to pay "primo prices for prime meat" in a dark wood–paneled, old-boy setting; though many "could do without" the "Saran-wrapped" show-and-tell presentation – "I know what steak looks like" – at least the waiters are "friendly" about it.

Moustache ●⊞ Mideastern

| 21 | 11 | 14 | $23 |

E Village | 265 E. 10th St. (bet. Ave. A & 1st Ave.) | 212-228-2022
W Village | 90 Bedford St. (bet. Barrow & Grove Sts.) | 212-229-2220

"Smooth-as-silk hummus" and other "deliciously seasoned" Middle Eastern eats are the draw at these crosstown Village siblings; "cheap" tabs make them always "crowded", and though both are "tiny", the East Side branch spreads out with a bonus "back garden."

Moutarde French

| 18 | 19 | 16 | $36 |

Park Slope | 239 Fifth Ave. (Carroll St.) | Brooklyn | 718-623-3600

"Young, carefree Park Slope" types say this "surprisingly durable" Gallic bistro offers a "well-executed" menu of *cuisine de maman* in a "French Disneyland" setting; "indifferent service" and "tight quarters" detract, though for most it's an easily affordable "Plan B."

Mr. Chow ● Chinese

| 20 | 19 | 18 | $74 |

E 50s | 324 E. 57th St. (bet. 1st & 2nd Aves.) | 212-751-9030

Mr. Chow Tribeca ● Chinese

TriBeCa | 121 Hudson St. (N. Moore St.) | 212-965-9500 | www.mrchow.com

Michael Chow's "perennial see-and-be-seen" Midtown Chinese continues after 29 years to feed "zingy" Sino specialties and "flowing lychee martinis" to a "dressy", often celeb-studded, crowd; trouble is, the waiters may insist on "ordering for you", resulting in "three times what you can eat at four times what you should pay"; N.B. the year-old TriBeCa spin-off has yet to win a following.

☑ Mr. K's Chinese

| 23 | 24 | 23 | $57 |

E 50s | 570 Lexington Ave. (51st St.) | 212-583-1668 | www.mrks.com

"Not Chinatown" by a long shot, this "glam" Midtown Chinese is known for "retro", "refined" dishes served by a "top-shelf" staff in a "Pepto-Bismol pink" deco setting; its "wannabe-emperor-and-empress" crowd shrugs off the "pricey"-for-the-genre tabs.

Mr. Tang Chinese

| 19 | 13 | 15 | $27 |

Chinatown | 50 Mott St. (Bayard St.) | 212-233-8898
Brighton Beach | 2650 Coney Island Ave. (Ave. X) | Brooklyn | 718-769-9444 ⊞

"Reliable sources" of "fresh seafood" and other "traditional" Chinese cookery, this Brighton Beach/C-town duo is "trying to be gourmet, but isn't quite there yet"; modest pricing makes the "rude" service and crude decor easier to overlook.

	FOOD	DECOR	SERVICE	COST

Mughlai ● *Indian* — 19 | 13 | 17 | $32

W 70s | 320 Columbus Ave. (75th St.) | 212-724-6363
Having "stood the test of time", this "solid" UWS Indian continues to serve "satisfying", "spiced-just-right" standards for "affordable" tabs; the staff may be "underseasoned" and decor "no-frills", but you "can't beat the location."

My Moon *Mediterranean* — ▽ 19 | 28 | 20 | $34

Williamsburg | 184 N. 10th St. (bet. Bedford & Driggs Aves.) | Brooklyn | 718-599-7007 | www.mymoonnyc.com
Perhaps Williamsburg's "best place for a first date", this "romantic" Mediterranean boasts an "amazing outdoor garden" as well as a "Gothic" "converted-warehouse" interior; while the modestly priced menu is quite "good", many wish it "matched the ambiance."

Nam *Vietnamese* — 22 | 18 | 20 | $39

TriBeCa | 110 Reade St. (W. B'way) | 212-267-1777 | www.namnyc.com
"Highly satisfying" food with "beguiling flavor combinations" draws "great-looking" folk to this "civilized" Vietnamese parked in an "out-of-the-way" TriBeCa address; "pleasant" servers and "chic" digs make it "feel a lot more expensive than it is."

Nana ⊘ *Asian Fusion* — 21 | 18 | 19 | $28

Park Slope | 155 Fifth Ave. (bet. Lincoln & St. Johns Pls.) | Brooklyn | 718-230-3749 | www.nana-parkslope.com
"You can make a meal of the appetizers alone" at this "consistent", cash-only Park Slope Asian fusion specialist where the extensive offerings are all "easy on the wallet"; it "would be even better without the DJ", but the "spectacular" garden is a respite from the "loud" interior.

Nanni ☒ *Italian* — 24 | 15 | 22 | $54

E 40s | 146 E. 46th St. (bet. Lexington & 3rd Aves.) | 212-697-4161 | www.nannirestaurant.com
"As delicious today as it was decades ago", this "old-world" vet just east of Grand Central vends rather "pricey" Northern Italiana via old-school waiters "full of personality"; it feels like "home away from home" to fans, in part due to the "elbow-to-elbow" seating and "land-that-time-forgot" decor.

Naples 45 ☒ *Italian* — 17 | 14 | 16 | $34

E 40s | MetLife Bldg. | 200 Park Ave. (45th St.) | 212-972-7001 | www.patinagroup.com
Brick-oven pizza is "the thing to order" at this "large", inexpensive Italian that's almost as "loud" as the adjacent Grand Central Terminal; it's "convenient" for commuters and "informal business lunches", so just ignore the "harried" staff and "Pottery Barn" decor; closed weekends.

Native *Eclectic* — ▽ 19 | 16 | 15 | $32

Harlem | 161 Lenox Ave. (118th St.) | 212-665-2525
Happy habitués hail this "hip" Harlem haunt for its "unusual" Eclectic menu that "stretches across the continents" yet still supplies some serious "soul-food flair"; fair pricing and "outdoor seating" (a rarity in this "gentrifying neighborhood") offset the "small" setting and any lack of service.

	FOOD	DECOR	SERVICE	COST

NEW Natsumi ● *Italian/Japanese* | – | – | – | E |

W 50s | Amsterdam Court Hotel | 226 W. 50th St. (bet. B'way & 8th Ave.) |
212-258-2988

From the team behind Haru comes this original new Theater District
Italo-Japanese fusion practitioner whose menu includes the likes of
green tea ravioli; the two-part setting features a sushi bar/dining room
separated by a hotel lobby from the lounge/raw bar.

Neary's ● *Pub Food* | 15 | 11 | 17 | $42 |

E 50s | 358 E. 57th St. (1st Ave.) | 212-751-1434

The nearest NYC comes to having a real leprechaun, host-owner
Jimmy Neary "seems to know everyone on the East Side" and feeds
them all at this "classic" Midtown pub where the "filling", "old-
fashioned" Irish grub comes with a side of "nostalgia"; its "crew of
characters – employees included" – is worth the price of admission.

Negril ● *Caribbean/Jamaican* | 20 | 17 | 16 | $34 |

Chelsea | 362 W. 23rd St. (bet. 8th & 9th Aves.) | 212-807-6411
G Village | 70 W. Third St. (bet. La Guardia Pl. & Thompson St.) |
212-477-2804 M

"Fiery jerk" and other "scrumptious" spicy specialties transport
Manhattanites to Jamaica at these "lively" tropical twins where "ur-
ban cool and Caribbean heat" collide; while the Village outpost is
larger and more upscale, both share "slow" island service.

Nello ● *Italian* | 19 | 17 | 16 | $79 |

E 60s | 696 Madison Ave. (bet. 62nd & 63rd Sts.) | 212-980-9099

It helps to "be a celebrity to be seated and served well" at this Madison
Avenue Northern Italian; while the food's "refined", the crowd "Euro"
and the mood "buzzy", mega-"attitude" and "wild overpricing" make
the experience a hell no to average Joes.

NEW Nelson Blue ● *New Zealand* | – | – | – | M |

Seaport | 233 Front St. (Peck Slip) | 212-346-9090 |
www.nelsonblue.com

Docked on burgeoning Front Street, this New Zealand gastropub is
adding to what may become the Seaport's new Restaurant Row; expect
Kiwi dishes at publike prices paired with antipodean suds served in
airy digs adorned with handcrafted tribal objects like a Maori war canoe.

Nëo Sushi ● *Japanese* | 22 | 17 | 19 | $54 |

W 80s | 2298 Broadway (83rd St.) | 212-769-1003 |
www.neosushi.com

"Creative, not-so-traditional" sushi graces the menu of this UWS
Japanese, a "Nobu wannabe" whose "adventurous" approach and
"pretty-to-look-at" plates amaze maki mavens; a few find it "overly nëo"
and "exorbitantly priced", but it's "wonderful for a special splurge."

Neptune Room *Seafood* | 22 | 19 | 21 | $49 |

W 80s | 511 Amsterdam Ave. (bet. 84th & 85th Sts.) | 212-496-4100 |
www.theneptuneroom.com

"Fresh-off-the-boat", "still-wriggling" seafood is the catch of the day
at this UWS seafooder also equipped with a "basic raw bar"; though
"a little expensive for the quality", compensations include "friendly
service", "cool loos" and a "great brunch – without a line."

Nero ◐ *Italian*

	FOOD	DECOR	SERVICE	COST
	20	18	17	$42

Meatpacking | 46 Gansevoort St. (Greenwich St.) | 212-675-5224 |
www.neronyc.com

"Something real" in the "overhyped Meatpacking District", this "underrated" Italian serves "solid" food for "decent" dough without the "attitude" or "glitz" of its nearby rivals; a high-ceilinged, brick-lined setting and "dim lighting" make it "romantic", despite "no-personality" service.

New Bo-Ky ⇄ *Noodle Shop*

	FOOD	DECOR	SERVICE	COST
	▽ 22	5	12	$12

Chinatown | 80 Bayard St. (bet. Mott & Mulberry Sts.) | 212-406-2292
"It doesn't get cheaper or more authentic" than this C-town noodle shop where Chinese and Vietnamese super soups make "jury duty" more palatable; though "decor and service are nonexistent", it's "always crowded" given its "best-value" tabs and tastes.

New Green Bo ◐⇄ *Chinese*

	FOOD	DECOR	SERVICE	COST
	22	5	12	$18

Chinatown | 66 Bayard St. (bet. Elizabeth & Mott Sts.) | 212-625-2359
"Sublime" soup dumplings and other "heavenly" Shanghainese specialties spur the "lines" at this Chinatown "hole-in-the-wall"; "shockingly low" tabs make up for "no atmosphere whatsoever", "indifferent service" and "sharing tables with strangers."

New Leaf Cafe Ⓜ *American*

	FOOD	DECOR	SERVICE	COST
	20	23	17	$40

Washington Heights | Fort Tryon Park | 1 Margaret Corbin Dr. (190th St.) |
212-568-5323 | www.nyrp.org
"You won't believe you're in Manhattan" at this "picturesque" New American in Fort Tryon Park, a "little vacation from the city" with "surprisingly good" food and a "magical terrace"; having the talented Scott Campbell (@SQC) signed on as executive chef is a good omen.

New York Burger Co. *Hamburgers* •

	FOOD	DECOR	SERVICE	COST
	18	8	11	$13

Flatiron | 303 Park Ave. S. (bet. 23rd & 24th Sts.) | 212-254-2727
Flatiron | 678 Sixth Ave. (bet. 21st & 22nd Sts.) | 212-229-1404
www.newyorkburgerco.com
"Freshly prepared" patties that "don't skimp" on the meat backed up by "hand-cut fries" and "thick shakes" make these Flatiron "burger factories" a "not-bad backup" when Shake Shack is backed up; too bad the decor and service "don't match the food quality."

Nha Trang *Vietnamese*

	FOOD	DECOR	SERVICE	COST
	21	7	15	$16

Chinatown | 148 Centre St. (bet. Walker & White Sts.) | 212-941-9292
Chinatown | 87 Baxter St. (bet. Bayard & Canal Sts.) | 212-233-5948
These "no-nonsense" Chinatown Vietnamese offer "delectable" specialties "sautéed with just the right amount of piquancy" and sold for "rock-bottom" dough; even though the decor's "questionable", "hustling" servers "will have you in and out so quickly it won't matter."

Nice Matin ◐ *French/Mediterranean*

	FOOD	DECOR	SERVICE	COST
	20	18	17	$45

W 70s | 201 W. 79th St. (Amsterdam Ave.) | 212-873-6423 |
www.nicematinnyc.com
A "touch of the Riviera on 79th Street", this "breezy" French-Med bistro is a "popular" stop for "*très* UWS" types seeking "satisfying", midpriced repasts; the "cheery" vibe and "faux brasserie gestalt" overcome a staff with "turnover higher than *The Apprentice*."

	FOOD	DECOR	SERVICE	COST

Nick & Stef's Steakhouse ⊠ Steak
22 | 18 | 21 | $60

Garment District | 9 Penn Plaza (enter on 33rd St., bet. 7th & 8th Aves.) | 212-563-4444 | www.patinagroup.com

"Convenient" to both Penn Station and MSG (with a "private entrance" to the arena no less), this Midtown carnivorium serves "juicy" steaks to a "mostly male" audience; maybe it "could use more spark", but it's "better than you'd expect" with "fast service" to get you to the game on time.

Nick and Toni's Cafe Mediterranean
18 | 14 | 17 | $49

W 60s | 100 W. 67th St. (bet. B'way & Columbus Ave.) | 212-496-4000 | www.nickandtoniscafe.com

East Hampton meets the UWS at this "dependable" yet "pricey" Med, a "cozy" spin-off that's "not as glitzy or trendy" as the Long Island original; a "wood-burning oven" lends flavor to "everything from pizza to fish", though the service could stand some fire under it.

Nick's Pizza
24 | 13 | 17 | $23

E 90s | 1814 Second Ave. (94th St.) | 212-987-5700 ●
Forest Hills | 108-26 Ascan Ave. (bet. Austin & Burns Sts.) | Queens | 718-263-1126 ⊄

"Superlative" thin-crust pizzas with "charred, crispy crusts" and "primo" toppings "make the world a better place" at this pizzeria pair; sure, the ambiance is "very basic" and staffers "seem trained to avoid smiling", but "who cares" with pies and prices this "heavenly"?

Nicky's
Vietnamese Sandwiches ⊄ Sandwiches
21 | 5 | 15 | $9

E Village | 150 E. Second St. (Ave. A) | 212-388-1088
Boerum Hill | 311 Atlantic Ave. (bet. Hoyt & Smith Sts.) | Brooklyn | 718-855-8838 Ⓜ

"Tiny" is putting it mildly at these "no-frills" Vietnamese storefronts cranking out "exceptional" banh mi sandwiches and "homemade lemonade" to a "mostly take-out" crowd; granted, they're "nothing fancy" but the "dirt-cheap" tabs make them just right for a "quick bite."

Nicola's ● Italian
22 | 16 | 21 | $58

E 80s | 146 E. 84th St. (bet. Lexington & 3rd Aves.) | 212-249-9850

A "neighborhood joint" in the "richest zip code in the country", this UES Italian draws "Dalton and Spence parents" with its "elevated" cooking and "skilled" service; still, it's "on the expensive side", and "best if they know you" – otherwise you may be "ignored."

99 Miles to Philly ●⊄ Cheese Steaks
18 | 6 | 14 | $11

E Village | 94 Third Ave. (bet. 12th & 13th Sts.) | 212-253-2700 | www.99milestophilly.net

South Philly "seems closer than 99 miles" away at this East Villager where "decent replicas" of the city's trademark gooey, "drippy" cheese steak sandwich keep the "faithful" coming; given its "cheap prices", no one cares about the "slow" service and authentically absent decor.

Ninja Japanese
▽ 19 | 25 | 21 | $68

TriBeCa | 25 Hudson St. (bet. Duane & Reade Sts.) | 212-274-8500 | www.ninjanewyork.com

"More theme park than restaurant", this "entertaining" TriBeCa Japanese looks like a mountainside "Ninja village" where "better than expected" food is served by a "funny" staff performing "bonus" magic tricks; it's "delightfully tacky" if "unbelievably pricey", and works best with "kids" in tow.

Nino's ● *Italian* | 21 | 18 | 21 | $55 |

E 70s | 1354 First Ave. (bet. 72nd & 73rd Sts.) | 212-988-0002 | www.ninosnyc.com

NEW Nino's Bellissima Pizza *Italian*

E 40s | 890 Second Ave. (bet. 47th & 48th Sts.) | 212-355-5540

Nino's Positano *Italian*

E 40s | 890 Second Ave. (bet. 47th & 48th Sts.) | 212-355-5540 | www.ninospositano.com

Nino's Tuscany *Italian*

W 50s | 117 W. 58th St. (bet. 6th & 7th Aves.) | 212-757-8630 | www.ninostuscany.com

Fans of this Italian mini-chain single out the UES original for "celebrity sightings" and "snazzy jazz", "cozy" Tuscany for "beautiful murals" and "excellent piano", and the "comfortable" Positano for "quiet conversation" (plus brick-oven pizza from new offshoot Bellissima); all locations share "classic" cooking, "seamless service" and serious tabs.

Nippon 🄢 *Japanese* | ▽ 22 | 17 | 20 | $49 |

E 50s | 155 E. 52nd St. (bet. Lexington & 3rd Aves.) | 212-758-0226 | www.restaurantnippon.com

One of NYC's first sushi restaurants, this "old-style" East Midtowner has been serving "traditional" Japanese fare since 1963; it's just as "reliable" (and "pricey") today, though the "classic", cypress-lined digs are either "dated" or "aging gracefully", depending on who's talking.

NEW Noble Food & Wine 🄢 *American* | - | - | - | M |

NoLita | 7 Spring St. (bet. Bowery & Elizabeth St.) | 212-777-0877

At this new NoLita wine bar/eatery you'll find locally sourced New Americana either at a granite-topped bar or in a low-lit, wood-paneled back room; a state-of-the-art wine preservation system allows oenophiles to enjoy by-the-glass samplings of high-end vintages.

🖿 Nobu *Japanese* | 27 | 23 | 23 | $82 |

TriBeCa | 105 Hudson St. (Franklin St.) | 212-219-0500

🖿 Nobu, Next Door ● *Japanese*

TriBeCa | 105 Hudson St. (bet. Franklin & N. Moore Sts.) | 212-334-4445
www.myriadrestaurantgroup.com

"Exquisite", "palate-awakening" Japanese-Peruvian delicacies gratify gourmets at this ever-"buzzing" TriBeCan that hosts a "who's who" crowd right out of an "episode of *Entourage*"; constants include "informative" service and "one big bill" at meal's end, but "getting a table is a problem – unless you're Cameron Diaz"; its more "casual" Next Door sibling is "less expensive" and "every bit as delicious", "without the reservation fuss" since it only takes walk-ins.

🖿 Nobu 57 ● *Japanese* | 26 | 24 | 22 | $82 |

W 50s | 40 W. 57th St. (bet. 5th & 6th Aves.) | 212-757-3000 | www.myriadrestaurantgroup.com

Differentiated from its Downtown sire by its "bigger" dimensions, David Rockwell's "stunning" design and somewhat "easier" reservations, this "glam" Midtowner serves the same "provocative" Japanese-Peruvian fusion fare for the same "spendy" tabs; but even if this "hedge-fund cafeteria" lacks the original's "intimacy", the "hip" folk, "tourists" and "movie stars" in attendance don't seem to mind.

Nocello *Italian*
21 | 16 | 21 | $49

W 50s | 257 W. 55th St. (bet. B'way & 8th Ave.) | 212-713-0224 | www.nocello.net

"Carnegie Hall convenience" is the main selling point of this Midtown Tuscan where the midpriced food is "well prepared" and the "genial" service "fast paced"; maybe the "old-world" decor could stand a re-furb, but it's still plenty "popular."

Noche Mexicana *Mexican*
▽ 22 | 9 | 16 | $18

W 100s | 852 Amsterdam Ave. (bet. 101st & 102nd Sts.) | 212-662-6900 | www.noche-mexicana.com

For "addictive", "real-deal" Mexicana, the "college crowd" joins Columbia-area locals at this "tiny hole-in-the-wall" where prices are such a "bargain" that nobody minds the strictly "no-frills" digs and oftentimes "slow" service.

NoHo Star ● *American*
18 | 15 | 16 | $31

NoHo | 330 Lafayette St. (Bleecker St.) | 212-925-0070 | www.nohostar.com

Still twinkling "after all these years", this low-cost NoHo "stalwart" dishes up "solid", "dependable" New American grub "morning, noon and night" while adding a "Chinese slant" come suppertime; locals like its "homey" feel and overlook the "din" and "below-average" service.

Nomad *African*
▽ 22 | 19 | 21 | $33

E Village | 78 Second Ave. (4th St.) | 212-253-5410 | www.nomadny.com

Wanderers seeking "authentic" North African fare report that this East Village yearling turns out "savory" tagines and other "aromatic" dishes in "cramped but stylish" digs; better yet, it's "value priced" and staffed by a "well-intentioned" crew.

NEW NoNO Kitchen *Cajun/Creole*
▽ 19 | 16 | 19 | $31

Park Slope | 293 Seventh Ave. (bet. 7th & 8th Sts.) | Brooklyn | 718-369-8348

Bringing "Bourbon Street to Brooklyn", this "change-of-pace" Park Slope newcomer dispenses "satisfying" Cajun-Creole eats way north of New Orleans; though it's still "ironing out some kinks", "helpful" service and "down-home value" suggest it's "a comer."

Noodle Pudding ⓜ⇪ *Italian*
24 | 17 | 21 | $36

Brooklyn Heights | 38 Henry St. (bet. Cranberry & Middagh Sts.) | Brooklyn | 718-625-3737

A "cast of regulars" forms "lines out the door" for the "delectable", "affordable" home cooking at this "loud" and "crowded" Brooklyn Heights Italian; "above-and-beyond service" embellishes its glow, tarnished only by the "bummer" no-reservations policy.

Nook ●⇪ *Eclectic*
22 | 12 | 17 | $30

W 50s | 746 Ninth Ave. (bet. 50th & 51st Sts.) | 212-247-5500 | www.nynook.com

Though "just as tiny as the name suggests", this Hell's Kitchen Eclectic delivers "big tastes" with a "short but fabulous menu"; the BYO policy compensates for the "cramped" quarters and staff "attitude."

	FOOD	DECOR	SERVICE	COST

Norma's *American*

25 | 19 | 21 | $36

W 50s | Le Parker Meridien | 118 W. 57th St. (bet. 6th & 7th Aves.) |
212-708-7460 | www.parkermeridien.com

Hey, wake up! – "astounding" breakfasts and brunches are served at
this "swanky" Midtown New American where the "good-humored
staff" keeps its "power-player" crowd happy; sure, it "costs" and can
get "crowded as the dickens", but "where else can you get oatmeal
brûlée" – or a $1,000 caviar omelet?

North Square *American*

22 | 18 | 21 | $45

G Village | Washington Square Hotel | 103 Waverly Pl. (MacDougal St.) |
212-254-1200 | www.northsquareny.com

An "under-the-radar" subterranean "surprise", this "grown-up" New
American may be the "best unhip place in the Village"; given the "stylish" cooking, "courteous" service and "gentle prices", it's no wonder
fans plead "don't tell anyone."

Notaro *Italian*

20 | 16 | 21 | $36

Murray Hill | 635 Second Ave. (bet. 34th & 35th Sts.) | 212-686-3400 |
www.notaroristorante.com

When it comes to "reliable finds", this Murray Hill Tuscan "sleeper" is
appreciated for its "well-prepared standards", "solicitous service" and
"bargain" tabs (especially that $19.95 early-bird); regulars say the
"family atmosphere" is perfect for "relaxing and lingering."

Novecento ● *Argentinean/Steak*

∇ 22 | 17 | 17 | $41

SoHo | 343 W. Broadway (bet. Broome & Grand Sts.) | 212-925-4706 |
www.novecentogroup.com

Save for its "fantastic" Argentine steaks, this SoHo "standby" is the
"opposite of a standard steakhouse" – "no suits, no porterhouse and
no big bills", just "flavorful" fare, "laid-back service" and a "very
downtown scene" that only "gets loud when there's soccer on TV."

Novitá *Italian*

24 | 19 | 22 | $53

Gramercy | 102 E. 22nd St. (bet. Lexington Ave. & Park Ave. S.) |
212-677-2222 | www.novitanyc.com

"Gramercy's secret winner", this "elegant-casual" Northern Italian
"just keeps getting better" with "high-quality" cooking, "gracious service" and an "intimate" air; since it's "across from a major modeling
agency", keep your eye out for random mannequins drifting in.

Nurnberger Bierhaus *German*

∇ 21 | 16 | 20 | $35

Staten Island | 817 Castleton Ave. (Davis Ave.) | 718-816-7461 |
www.nurnbergerbierhaus.com

Folks with "Teutonic appetites" say this "old-world" German pub on
Staten Island's North Shore doles out "tremendous portions" of "authentic" grub washed down with "great" beer; though on the "small"
side, it's home to a "boisterous" bar scene.

Nyonya ●🚫 *Malaysian*

22 | 12 | 13 | $21

Little Italy | 194 Grand St. (bet. Mott & Mulberry Sts.) | 212-334-3669
Sunset Park | 5323 Eighth Ave. (54th St.) | Brooklyn | 718-633-0808
www.penangusa.com

"Unusual spices" make for "fantastic" Malaysian meals at this "deservedly popular" Little Italy/Sunset Park pair that's "not for the timid

palate" ("be brave and enjoy"); fans ignore the "spotty service" and "no-credit-card" policy since the price point is "almost too cheap to believe."

Oceana ☒ *American/Seafood* | 26 | 23 | 24 | $93

E 50s | 55 E. 54th St. (bet. Madison & Park Aves.) | 212-759-5941 | www.oceanarestaurant.com

Dining's "still shipshape" at this pricey Midtown New American, the "kingfish" of seafood with "delectable" fresh fare heading the "superb", $78 prix fixe-only menu; "doting service" and a "soothing nautical setting" ("portholes and all") make for an experience that's so transporting you can almost feel the salt spray.

Ocean Grill ♦ *Seafood* | 23 | 20 | 20 | $51

W 70s | 384 Columbus Ave. (bet. 78th & 79th Sts.) | 212-579-2300 | www.brguestrestaurants.com

"Fail-safe seafood" so fresh it's "still flapping" is the signature of Steve Hanson's "ocean-liner"–like UWS poisson palace where a "happy vibe" and an "accommodating" crew have fans angling for reservations; it can be "noisy", but the "bargain" $24.07 lunch prix fixe and "lovely brunch" are a "catch."

Odeon ♦ *American/French* | 19 | 18 | 18 | $44

TriBeCa | 145 W. Broadway (bet. Duane & Thomas Sts.) | 212-233-0507 | www.theodeonrestaurant.com

Ever the "late-night" dining "landmark", this TriBeCa "trailblazer" presents "well-prepared" Franco-American bistro fare "without pretension"; it's still "a bit of a scene" with a smattering of "celebs" posed against an "art deco" backdrop, though regulars say the "later you go, the better it is."

O.G. ♦ *Pan-Asian* | ▽ 23 | 15 | 23 | $35

E Village | 507 E. Sixth St. (bet. Aves. A & B) | 212-477-4649

"Throw away your old ideas" about Pan-Asian fare: the "innovative" menu at this "creative little" East Village "gem" trumps the "tight" seating and "simple" decor; "terrific service" and "good value" have made it a "solid neighborhood favorite."

Old Homestead *Steak* | 23 | 17 | 20 | $67

Meatpacking | 56 Ninth Ave. (bet. 14th & 15th Sts.) | 212-242-9040 | www.theoldhomesteadsteakhouse.com

This circa-1868 Meatpacking District chop shop earned its spurs tendering "flawless", "William Howard Taft-size" portions of beef that are "worth the weighty price"; its "old-school character" extends to both decor and service, but there's modernization afoot via a new sidewalk cafe dubbed Prime Burger, vending gourmet patties.

Olea *Mediterranean* | ▽ 20 | 20 | 19 | $33

Fort Greene | 171 Lafayette Ave. (Adelphi St.) | Brooklyn | 718-643-7003 | www.oleabrooklyn.com

It's "hard to go wrong" ordering from the "ambitious" menu of "classic" Mediterranean tapas and main courses at this "friendly" Fort Greene spot; abetted by a "well-chosen" wine list, the "low-key, low-lit" room can turn "surprisingly romantic" after dark – fortunately the bill won't disrupt that mood.

	FOOD	DECOR	SERVICE	COST

Oliva ◐ *Spanish*
▽ 20 | 14 | 17 | $34

LES | 161 E. Houston St. (Allen St.) | 212-228-4143 | www.olivanyc.com
For "tapas galore" tempered with some "good sangria", try this LES Basque where the modest pricing, "great bartenders" and overall "fun atmosphere" make for "lively" dining; more sedate types caution the "food is good if you can take the noise."

Olives *.Mediterranean*
22 | 21 | 20 | $57

Union Sq | W Union Sq. | 201 Park Ave. S. (17th St.) | 212-353-8345 | www.toddenglish.com
A "champion" at putting together "well-crafted" meals, chef Todd English "knows how to do it right" at his "modern" Med in the W Union Square Hotel; though a few find it "not as fantastic as the prices would suggest", the "busy bar scene" puts plenty of "electricity in the air."

Ollie's *Chinese*
16 | 9 | 13 | $21

NEW **W 40s** | Manhattan Plaza | 411 W. 42nd St. (bet. 9th & 10th Aves.) | 212-868-6588
W 60s | 1991 Broadway (bet. 67th & 68th Sts.) | 212-595-8181 ◐
W 80s | 2315 Broadway (84th St.) | 212-362-3111 ◐
W 100s | 2957 Broadway (116th St.) | 212-932-3300 ◐
"Frenetic and crowded", this "cheap 'n' cheerful" West Side foursome is famed for "decent" Chinese food served so fast "you arrive at 7 and are out by 6:45"; those opposed to "dingy" digs, "wham-bam" vibes and "grumpy" service advise "order in."

Omai *Vietnamese*
23 | 17 | 18 | $39

Chelsea | 158 Ninth Ave. (bet. 19th & 20th Sts.) | 212-633-0550 | www.omainyc.com
"Hidden" behind a "nondescript" Chelsea storefront, this "tiny" Vietnamese offers "upscale" fare that's "so good they don't need a sign on the door"; the "simple" setting may be "cramped", but a "nice" staff and tabs that "won't break the bank" supply the "oh-my" factor.

Omen ◐ *Japanese*
▽ 25 | 19 | 20 | $54

SoHo | 113 Thompson St. (bet. Prince & Spring Sts.) | 212-925-8923
"Delicate", Kyoto-style dishes that "reflect the nuances of Japanese cuisine" are the hallmark of this sushi-free SoHo "retreat"; yes, it's "a bit pricey", but where else are patrons so "in awe of the food" they may be "sitting next to Richard Gere and not even realize it"?

NEW Omido ◐ *Japanese*
- | - | - | E

W 50s | 1695 Broadway (bet. 53rd & 54th Sts.) | 212-247-8110 | www.omidonyc.com
Letterman groupies now have an upscale option in this small Midtown Japanese next to the Ed Sullivan Theater that's been stylishly designed by the AvroKO team; the standard offerings include sushi, sashimi and cooked staples that can be paired with a selection of beer and sake.

Omonia Cafe ◐ *Greek*
19 | 14 | 15 | $20

Bay Ridge | 7612-14 Third Ave. (bet. 76th & 77th Sts.) | Brooklyn | 718-491-1435
Astoria | 32-20 Broadway (33rd St.) | Queens | 718-274-6650
Sweet tooths "forget counting calories" and "indulge" in "scrumptious" Greek desserts at this Hellenic coffeehouse twosome; the

"relaxing European atmosphere" comes by way of "open-air seating", "good strong coffee" and "unrushed" service that will make you feel you're in Athens.

Once Upon a Tart . . . *Coffeehouse* 22 | 13 | 14 | $15
SoHo | 135 Sullivan St. (bet. Houston & Prince Sts.) | 212-387-8869 | www.onceuponatart.com

"Aromatic tarts" are the specialty at this "quaint" SoHo cafe also offering "wholesome salads", "tasty sandwiches" and other "delicious goodies"; "mishmash decor", a "cramped" setting and "sourpuss" service suggest it may be better to "sit outside."

One *American* 18 | 21 | 17 | $52
Meatpacking | 1 Little W. 12th St. (9th Ave.) | 212-255-9717 | www.onelw12.com

It's "all about the scene" at this "dark" Meatpacking District resto/lounge where "pretty people party", pausing to put away "pretty good", pretty pricey New American small plates washed down with "interesting cocktails"; since it's "more club than restaurant", sit outside to "hear and be heard."

O'Neals' ● *American* 17 | 16 | 19 | $45
W 60s | 49 W. 64th St. (bet. B'way & CPW) | 212-787-4663 | www.onealsny.com

Located "in the shadow of Lincoln Center", this warm, atmospheric "neighborhood tavern" with "tons of tables" and a "hopping bar" turns out "down-to-earth" American "square meals" for fairly "reasonable" sums; the staff "gets you out fast for your concert", though word is it's best "after the theater crowd leaves."

One 83 *Italian* 21 | 22 | 23 | $48
E 80s | 1608 First Ave. (bet. 83rd & 84th Sts.) | 212-327-4700 | www.one83restaurant.com

"Adults" seeking "quiet", "civilized" dining head for this midpriced UES Northern Italian "sleeper", an "all-around fine" place with "consistently good food", well-spaced tables and an "eager-to-please" staff; another plus: a "covered garden that's a treat" in warm weather.

☒ One if by Land, Two if by Sea *American* 23 | 26 | 24 | $89
G Village | 17 Barrow St. (bet. 7th Ave. S. & W. 4th St.) | 212-228-0822 | www.oneifbyland.com

"As romantic as they say", this "genteel" Village New American set in "Aaron Burr's old carriage house" is made for "proposing in style", blending a "beautiful", flower-filled room and "soft piano-playing" with an "elegant" $75 prix fixe menu and "superior service"; "so what if it costs a bundle", you'll reap the rewards when you get home.

101 *American/Italian* 19 | 19 | 18 | $41
Bay Ridge | 10018 Fourth Ave. (bet. 100th & 101st Sts.) | Brooklyn | 718-833-1313 ●
Staten Island | 3900 Richmond Ave. (Amboy Rd.) | 718-227-3286 ☒

Known best for its "boisterous" "bar scene", this Bay Ridge Italian-New American (with a SI offshoot) still delivers "consistently decent" fare; there's "people-watching" aplenty via a crowd that ranges from "yuppies" to *Saturday Night Fever* wannabes.

	FOOD	DECOR	SERVICE	COST

107 West *Cajun/Tex-Mex*
| 18 | 13 | 17 | $28 |

Washington Heights | 811 W. 187th St. (bet. Ft. Washington &
Pinehurst Aves.) | 212-923-3311

W 100s | 2787 Broadway (bet. 107th & 108th Sts.) | 212-864-1555
www.107west.com

Two West Side Cajun–Tex-Mex "standbys" that can be counted on for
"large portions" of "tasty" "comfort" fare at "fair prices"; no surprise,
they attract lots of "families" and other locals who consider them a
"solid" bet despite "tired" decor and "slow" (if "congenial") service.

Ono *Japanese*
| 21 | 24 | 19 | $63 |

Meatpacking | Gansevoort Hotel | 18 Ninth Ave. (enter on 13th St.,
bet. Hudson St. & 9th Ave.) | 212-660-6766 | www.chinagrillmgt.com

Jeffrey Chodorow's "cool" Meatpacking District Japanese is the "gorgeous" backdrop for "super" sushi and robata grill items served either
in the "sleek" interior or "tented garden"; it can be "expensive" and a
"tad too trendy", but the crowd's "great-looking" and the drinks "stiff."

NEW Open the Sesame ⊅ *Thai*
| - | - | - | I |

LES | 198A Orchard St. (bet. Houston & Stanton Sts.) | 212-777-7009

Exotic SE Asian street food is the focus at this unassuming LES Thai
whose menu also includes more standard noodle and rice dishes; a nondescript facade and a meditative mood within make it a low-budget
alternative to the neighborhood's typically trendy scenes.

Orchard, The ⊠ *American*
| 24 | 22 | 21 | $51 |

LES | 162 Orchard St. (bet. Rivington & Stanton Sts.) | 212-353-3570 |
www.theorchardny.com

"Proving how far the LES has come", this "sophisticated" New
American "winner" ("ápizz's sister restaurant") serves "delicious",
"Mediterranean-inspired" cuisine in a "calm", "minimalist" room
"bathed in an amber glow"; strong points include the "phenomenal
flatbreads", "thoughtful service" and "well-spaced tables."

Oriental Garden *Chinese/Seafood*
| 24 | 12 | 16 | $30 |

Chinatown | 14 Elizabeth St. (bet. Bayard & Canal Sts.) | 212-619-0085

Setting the "standard for fresh-from-the-tank" seafood, this "dynamite" Chinatown Cantonese also rolls out "limitless dim sum varieties"; the "right price" makes the perpetual "noise", "inattention to
decor" and "hurried but hilarious" service more palatable.

Orsay ◗ *French*
| 18 | 20 | 17 | $54 |

E 70s | 1057 Lexington Ave. (75th St.) | 212-517-6400 |
www.orsayrestaurant.com

"Snob appeal" makes the "straightforward" bistro fare all the tastier at
this "very UES" French brasserie with an "elegant art nouveau" ambiance; though some are put off by the "high prices" and "attitude
français", the "ladies who lunch" trill it "hits just the right note."

Orso ◗ *Italian*
| 23 | 17 | 20 | $54 |

W 40s | 322 W. 46th St. (bet. 8th & 9th Aves.) | 212-489-7212 |
www.orsorestaurant.com

There's a "showbiz feeling" in the air at this Restaurant Row Northern
Italian where the "wonderful" cooking and "welcoming atmosphere"
make it a pre-show "favorite" and an "après-theater" "hangout for the

stars"; to get in, go at "off hours" (i.e. lunch), otherwise this can be one of the "toughest tickets" on Broadway.

Osaka *Japanese*

∇ 21 | 16 | 18 | $32

Cobble Hill | 272 Court St. (bet. Degraw & Kane Sts.) | Brooklyn | 718-643-0044 | www.osakany.com

If you like your sushi "huge" and your rolls "monster-size", this "reasonably priced" Cobble Hill Japanese sets the standard for "hip Brooklyn dining"; maybe the decor "needs updating", but the "peaceful" back garden is "wonderful for eating under the stars."

Osso Buco *Italian*

17 | 14 | 17 | $34

E 90s | 1662 Third Ave. (93rd St.) | 212-426-5422
G Village | 88 University Pl. (bet. 11th & 12th Sts.) | 212-645-4525
www.ossobuco2go.com

"Solid, hearty" and "huge" sum up the "reliable" repasts at these "ebullient", "family-style" Italians (think "Carmine's without the fanfare") where "large groups" have "fun sharing"; "cheap enough" tabs defuse the "no-frills" settings and any service deficits.

Osteria al Doge ● *Italian*

20 | 17 | 19 | $48

W 40s | 142 W. 44th St. (bet. B'way & 6th Ave.) | 212-944-3643 | www.osteria-doge.com

The "well-managed" staff is "mindful of curtain times" at this "charming" if "high-decibel" "pre-theater standby" off Times Square; its audience applauds the "upscale" Italian cuisine with a "Venetian disposition" and the "balcony seating option" when the "close quarters" get "too lively."

Osteria del Circo ● *Italian*

22 | 23 | 21 | $60

W 50s | 120 W. 55th St. (bet. 6th & 7th Aves.) | 212-265-3636 | www.osteriadelcirco.com

"Deluxe" dishes served by a "pro staff" in a "colorful", "circuslike setting" make for "showy" dining at the Maccioni family's "festive" Northern Italian "near Carnegie Hall and City Center"; though a "high price tag" is part of the package, the $25 "prix fixe lunch is a bargain."

Osteria del Sole ● *Italian*

21 | 17 | 17 | $43

W Village | 267 W. Fourth St. (Perry St.) | 212-620-6840

"*Authentico*" Sardinian cuisine paired with a winning wine list makes this moderately priced Village Italian a "local treasure"; granted, one man's "cozy" is another's "cramped", but there's agreement on the "pleasant" vibe and "accommodating service" by "real Italians."

Osteria Gelsi ● *Italian*

24 | 17 | 19 | $45

Garment District | 507 Ninth Ave. (38th St.) | 212-244-0088 | www.gelsiny.com

Despite an "iffy" Garment District location behind Port Authority, this "real-deal" Italian is "worth the journey" for "novel Puglian food" that's "cooked with loving care"; "family-run" and "reasonably priced", it's a "delightful change in a changing neighborhood."

Osteria Laguna ● *Italian*

21 | 18 | 19 | $43

E 40s | 209 E. 42nd St. (bet. 2nd & 3rd Aves.) | 212-557-0001 | www.osteria-laguna.com

"Above-average" Italian cooking draws "business-lunchers" to this "sunny" Midtowner near the U.N., an "airy" retreat with French doors that open to the street; a "reasonably priced" wine list plus "courteous" service add to the all-around "pleasant" experience, even when the "noise level" rises.

Ota-Ya *Japanese*
20 | 15 | 19 | $32

E 80s | 1572 Second Ave. (bet. 81st & 82nd Sts.) | 212-988-1188 | www.ota-ya.com

"Everything's fresh and delicious" at this "surprisingly quiet" UES Japanese "sleeper", a "local sushi joint" that's developing a "loyal following" with its "creative rolls", "inexpensive pricing" and "spot-on service"; too bad the "bland atmosphere" has some yawning "boring."

Otto ● *Pizza*
22 | 19 | 19 | $38

G Village | 1 Fifth Ave. (enter on 8th St., bet. 5th Ave. & University Pl.) | 212-995-9559 | www.ottopizzeria.com

"Top-notch gourmet" pizzas, "lick-the-plate" pastas and a "powerhouse Italian wine list" arrive in a faux "train station" setting at this "bustling" Batali-Bastianich Village enoteca/pizzeria that's "as good as Lupa – at half the price and twice the noise"; no surprise, it draws lots of "kids", "parties" and "rambunctious" types.

Z Ouest *American*
25 | 21 | 22 | $61

W 80s | 2315 Broadway (bet. 83rd & 84th Sts.) | 212-580-8700 | www.ouestny.com

Upper Westsiders rave about this "polished" New American destination where Tom Valenti's "exceptional" "comfort food with a spark" is served by a crew of "polite" staffers in a "smart", "1940s-inspired" setting; it's "not cheap" but "reservations are hard to come by", because once you settle into one of those "commodious banquettes", you'll feel "celebratory."

Our Place *Chinese*
20 | 15 | 19 | $34

E 50s | 141 E. 55th St. (bet. Lexington & 3rd Aves.) | 212-753-3900 | www.ourplace-teagarden.com
E 80s | 1444 Third Ave. (82nd St.) | 212-288-4888 | www.ourplaceuptown.com

The "always delish", "high-end" Shanghai cuisine at these "white-tablecloth" Eastsiders may cost "a bit more" but is worth a bit more; "relaxed" settings and "efficient" service make the "super-fast delivery" beside the point.

Outback Steakhouse *Steak*
14 | 12 | 15 | $32

E 50s | 919 Third Ave. (enter on 56th St., bet. 2nd & 3rd Aves.) | 212-935-6400
Flatiron | 60 W. 23rd St. (bet. 5th & 6th Aves.) | 212-989-3122
Dyker Heights | 1475 86th St. (15th Ave.) | Brooklyn | 718-837-7200
Bayside | Bay Terrace | 23-48 Bell Blvd. (26th Ave.) | Queens | 718-819-0908
Elmhurst | Queens Pl. | 88-01 Queens Blvd. (56th Ave.) | Queens | 718-760-7200
www.outback.com

You'll get a "cookie-cutter" "fill up" at this "faux Australian" steakhouse chain where the "average" chow suffers from "sodium overload"; sure, "you might as well be in Toledo", but "kids love it" so long as you "order what they do best" – that bloomin' onion.

	FOOD	DECOR	SERVICE	COST

NEW Ovelia *Greek* — ▽ 21 | 21 | 16 | $32

Astoria | 34-01 30th Ave. (bet. 34th & 35th Sts.) | Queens | 718-721-7217 | www.ovelia-ny.com

Expect "simple, traditional" food at this "palatable" new Astoria Greek where the vibe's decidedly more "trendy" than the status quo, with "modern" decor, club music and a fiber optic–embedded bartop; "sausages ground on the premises" bump up the "authenticity" factor as do those low outer-borough prices.

Oyster Bar Ⓢ *Seafood* — 21 | 17 | 16 | $46

E 40s | Grand Central | lower level (42nd St. & Vanderbilt Ave.) | 212-490-6650 | www.oysterbarny.com

Though Grand Central's "classic" seafooder has "been there forever", it's still "required eating" for anyone hooked on "marvelous, unadulterated fish", "legendary pan roasts", "unsurpassed oysters" and a spectacular white wine list; the "cavernous" underground space and "vaulted tile ceiling" make for a "louder-than-a-train-whistle" experience that's "totally Manhattan."

NEW Pacificana *Chinese* — ▽ 24 | 21 | 22 | $29

Sunset Park | 813 55th St., 2nd fl. (8th Ave.) | Brooklyn | 718-871-2880

More "high class" now than during its last life as Ocean Palace, this Sunset Park address now houses a new Cantonese rolling out some of "NY's best dim sum" in a "lovely", "high-ceilinged" space; "unusual variety" and fair pricing blot out any "minor language problems."

Paladar ❶ *Nuevo Latino* — ▽ 18 | 14 | 17 | $34

LES | 161 Ludlow St. (bet. Houston & Stanton Sts.) | 212-473-3535 | www.paladarrestaurant.com

There's "lots of spice for the buck" at this "hip" LES Nuevo Latino, a "festive" venue for chef Aarón Sanchez's "inventive" eats washed down with *"muy bonito"* mojitos; "crazy wait times" on weekends pass quickly enough at the "fun" bar.

Ⓩ Palm *Steak* — 24 | 17 | 21 | $66

E 40s | 837 Second Ave. (bet. 44th & 45th Sts.) | 212-687-2953 Ⓢ
E 40s | 840 Second Ave. (bet. 44th & 45th Sts.) | 212-697-5198
W 50s | 250 W. 50th St. (bet. B'way & 8th Ave.) | 212-333-7256 ❶
www.thepalm.com

"Masculine eating" is alive and well at these "boisterous" crosstown chophouses where a "gruff" crew dishes out "gargantuan steaks" and "colossal lobsters" in "macho" surroundings; purists prefer the original, circa-1926 west-side-of-Second-Avenue location, but wherever you wind up, you'd better "have plenty of money in your palm."

Paloma ❶Ⓜ *American* — ▽ 19 | 18 | 19 | $27

Greenpoint | 60 Greenpoint Ave. (bet. Franklin & West Sts.) | Brooklyn | 718-349-2400 | www.palomanyc.com

A *Top Chef* contestant crafts an "original" New American menu at this Greenpoint "hipster" joint where the "video projections on the wall" – everything from "Bollywood to Bardot" – are either "brilliant" or "distracting"; many wonder "is it a club or a restaurant?", but all agree it's a great value.

subscribe to zagat.com

	FOOD	DECOR	SERVICE	COST

NEW Palo Santo *Pan-Latin* ▽ 25 | 23 | 20 | $39

Park Slope | 652 Union St. (bet. 4th & 5th Aves.) | Brooklyn | 718-636-6311 | www.palosanto.us

Adventurous types are "well rewarded" at this "welcome" Park Slope newcomer purveying a "tapas-style" array of "superb" Pan-Latin vittles; "friendly" service, "reasonable rates" and a "gorgeous brownstone" setting complete with a "tropical garden" make this one a "must go."

Pampano *Mexican/Seafood* 25 | 22 | 21 | $54

E 40s | 209 E. 49th St. (bet. 2nd & 3rd Aves.) | 212-751-4545 | www.modernmexican.com

Taking a "quantum leap above your everyday Mexican", this "lus-cious" Midtowner from chef Richard Sandoval and tenor Plácido Domingo specializes in "complex", "original" seafood that's "beautiful to behold"; add a "bright", split-level setting and "prompt, helpful" staff, and most patrons just "want to sing."

NEW Pamplona ● *Spanish* - | - | - | M

Gramercy | 37 E. 28th St. (bet. Madison Ave. & Park Ave. S.) | 212-213-2328

A reworking of the former fine-dining room Ureña, this new Gramercy Spaniard from chef Alex Ureña is a casual take on its predecessor offering a foam-free, tapas-heavy Basque bistro menu in all-beige, cozy-chic environs; enhancing the pleasant vibe is the decidedly relaxed price point.

Pam Real Thai Food ⊅ *Thai* 22 | 8 | 15 | $22

W 40s | 402 W. 47th St. (bet. 9th & 10th Aves.) | 212-315-4441 ●Ⓜ
W 40s | 404 W. 49th St. (bet. 9th & 10th Aves.) | 212-333-7500
www.pamrealthai.com

At this Hell's Kitchen duo, the "authentically seasoned", truly "tasty" Thai and tempting tabs easily trump the "no-credit-cards" policy, "'80s airline terminal" look and service that's "a tad abrupt"; order takeout, and pam!, it's there.

Panino'teca 275 Ⓜ *Italian* ▽ 18 | 16 | 17 | $23

Carroll Gardens | 275 Smith St. (bet. Degraw & Sackett Sts.) | Brooklyn | 718-237-2728 | www.paninoteca275.com

Carroll Gardens locals looking to "lounge with some wine and anti-pasti" like this "family-friendly" Italian dispensing "inventive panini" as well as "flavorful" entrees; "totally affordable" tabs and a "relaxing" back garden cancel out the "cramped" interior and "spotty" service.

Paola's *Italian* 23 | 19 | 22 | $52

E 80s | 245 E. 84th St. (bet. 2nd & 3rd Aves.) | 212-794-1890 | www.paolasrestaurant.com

Paola Bottero's "warm" greeting sets the tone at this "homey" UES Italian standby known for its "good all-around menu" of traditional "classics"; the flower-bedecked room exudes "charm", while sidewalk seating on a "leafy block" is a big bonus.

Papaya King *Hot Dogs* 20 | 4 | 12 | $7

E 80s | 179 E. 86th St. (3rd Ave.) | 212-369-0648 ●⊅
Harlem | 121 W. 125th St. (bet. Lenox & 7th Aves.) | 212-678-4268 ⊅

(continued)

(continued)

Papaya King

W Village | 200 W. 14th St. (7th Ave. S.) | 212-367-8090 ⊘
www.papayaking.com

"Tube steak" connoisseurs commend the "juicy" grilled franks paired with "frothy" potables at these "stand-up", low-down "snack shacks"; forget the "yelling" staff and "gross" decor – it's "hard to say no" when you're paying "almost nothing" for an "only-in-NY experience."

Pappardella ⊘ *Italian*

19 | 16 | 18 | $36

W 70s | 316 Columbus Ave. (75th St.) | 212-595-7996

Upper Westsiders in need of "comforting Italian" food head to this perennially "pleasing" pasta palace where the "hearty" portions are "ample enough for leftovers"; prices are "affordable", the staff "cordial" and there's "bonus" sidewalk seating when it gets too "loud" and "close" inside.

Paradou ⊘ *French*

19 | 17 | 18 | $44

Meatpacking | 8 Little W. 12th St. (bet. Greenwich & Washington Sts.) | 212-463-8345 | www.paradounyc.com

Approximating "Marseille in Manhattan", this "intimate" French "oasis" in the Meatpacking District offers well-priced Provençal fare in an "unpretentious" setting; occasionally "rude" service is forgotten once you're seated in its "delightful" if "unfancy" all-seasons garden.

Paris Commune *French*

18 | 18 | 17 | $41

W Village | 99 Bank St. (Greenwich St.) | 212-929-0509 |
www.pariscommune.net

"Everyone looks pretty" at this "charming" Village bistro offering "affordable", "down-to-earth" French food and a "perfect brunch"; some say it's "gone downhill" after moving from its "old space", yet it's usually "packed" – go figure; P.S. there's a "sexy, secluded wine bar" downstairs.

Park, The ⊘ *Mediterranean*

15 | 23 | 14 | $41

Chelsea | 118 10th Ave. (bet. 17th & 18th Sts.) | 212-352-3313 |
www.theparknyc.com

Folks flaunting "sunglasses at night" like this "sexy" West Chelsea "scene" for its "stone fireplaces", hot tubs and a "lovely garden" (the "main draw"); critics say it's "losing its steam", citing a "mundane" Med menu and a staff apparently off "auditioning for something" else.

NEW Park Avenue . . . *American*

- | - | - | E

E 60s | 100 E. 63rd St. (bet. Lexington & Park Aves.) | 212-644-1900 |
www.parkavenyc.com

The former Park Avenue Cafe space has morphed into this homage to the four seasons, where the hip AvroKO-designed decor totally changes quarterly; the inventive New American cooking is similarly seasonal, and priced to match its tony East Side address.

Park Place *Continental*

∇ 20 | 15 | 19 | $37

Bronx | 5816 Mosholu Ave. (B'way) | 718-548-0977

"One of Riverdale's better neighborhood restaurants", this "excellent value" Continental "churns out great specials" that are big enough to be "shareable"; "pleasant" service keeps longtimers repeating, but even they concede the "need for a face-lift."

	FOOD	DECOR	SERVICE	COST

Park Side ◐ *Italian* | 24 | 19 | 21 | $44

Corona | 107-01 Corona Ave. (51st Ave.) | Queens | 718-271-9321
"Tuxedo-clad" waiters present "excellent" Italian "classics" at this "old-world" Corona "institution" that's always "mobbed" with a "dolled-up", "pinky-ringed" crowd; "long waits" are the norm, but you can pass the time watching "old men play bocce" across the street.

Park Terrace Bistro *French/Moroccan* | ▽ 22 | 20 | 20 | $34

Inwood | 4959 Broadway (bet. Isham & 207th Sts.) | 212-567-2828 | www.parkterracebistro.com
"Flavorful", "aromatic" fare and a "shadowy", "romantic" ambiance combine to make this "breath-of-fresh-air" French-Moroccan a "great date" place in underserved Inwood; "enthusiastic" staffers, "reasonable" prices and a "downtown ambiance" ice the cake.

Parma ◐ *Italian* | 22 | 14 | 20 | $55

E 70s | 1404 Third Ave. (bet. 79th & 80th Sts.) | 212-535-3520
"If you're a regular, you're family" at this "old-fashioned" Northern Italian turning out "pricey", "high-quality" food ferried by "kind waiters"; although the storefront setting "could use some updating", its well-heeled UES crowd likes it as is.

Pars Grill House & Bar *Persian* | ▽ 21 | 14 | 18 | $32

Chelsea | 249 W. 26th St. (bet. 7th & 8th Aves.) | 212-929-9860
A "good addition to the Chelsea dining scene", this "sweet little" Persian proffers "surprisingly good" kebabs and such for "affordable" tabs in a "cafe"-style space; it's "never crowded, but it deserves to be."

Pascalou *French* | 22 | 14 | 18 | $42

E 90s | 1308 Madison Ave. (bet. 92nd & 93rd Sts.) | 212-534-7522
"Stretch your legs" before squeezing into this Carnegie Hill boîte, a "miniature" setting for "terrific French fare" at "fair prices"; service reflects the "congenial" vibe within, though diners bigger than a "size two" may want to "snag an outside table."

Pasha *Turkish* | 21 | 18 | 19 | $40

W 70s | 70 W. 71st St. (bet. Columbus Ave. & CPW) | 212-579-8751 | www.pashanewyork.com
"Istanbul, here we come": this Lincoln Center–area Turk purveys "well-priced" meals in an "exotic" setting so "dark" you'll need "night vision goggles to read the menu"; "gracious service" seals the deal.

Pasquale's Rigoletto *Italian* | 23 | 17 | 20 | $41

Bronx | 2311 Arthur Ave. (Crescent Ave.) | 718-365-6644
Locals "have a blast" at this "popular" Arthur Avenue "throwback" known for its "generous helpings" of "no-fuss, no-muss" Italian standards; "plenty of hospitality" and pleasing pricing make this "festive" "barn of a place" ideal for "family gatherings."

Pasticcio *Italian* | 19 | 18 | 19 | $38

Murray Hill | 447 Third Ave. (bet. 30th & 31st Sts.) | 212-679-2551
NEW Glendale | Shops at Atlas Park | 80-00 Cooper Ave. (80th St.) | Queens | 718-417-1544 Ⓜ
www.pasticcionyc.com
"Una favorita" in Murray Hill, this longtime Italian is "full of friendly people" noshing on "traditional" eats or sampling sparkling vino at

	FOOD	DECOR	SERVICE	COST

Proseccheria, its wine bar; early visitors to the new Glendale offshoot in the Shops at Atlas Park say it's a "nice choice in the mall."

☒ Pastis ● French
21 | 20 | 17 | $46

Meatpacking | 9 Ninth Ave. (Little W. 12th St.) | 212-929-4844 | www.pastisny.com

Keith McNally produces "French bistro to perfection" at this very "cosmopolitan" Meatpacking District "pioneer", a "baby" Balthazar that's "packed to the gills" with "fashionistas", "tourists" and the "am-I-famous-yet?" set; although the staff is more "preoccupied with crowd control", it serves "genuinely worthwhile food" here; P.S. "it's tamer at breakfast" – and just as "glam."

Pastrami Queen Deli
19 | 5 | 13 | $22

E 70s | 1125 Lexington Ave. (bet. 78th & 79th Sts.) | 212-734-1500 | www.pastramiqueen.com

"Kosher's last frontier" on the UES, this relocated (and "newly shrunken") deli supplies "incredible cholesterol" via its "fabulous" overstuffed sandwiches; drawbacks include "no ambiance" and the fact that "you'll leave larger than when you entered"; N.B. don't forget to bring your Lipitor.

Patois Ⓜ French
21 | 19 | 19 | $37

Carroll Gardens | 255 Smith St. (bet. Degraw & Douglass Sts.) | Brooklyn | 718-855-1535

The "first of the chic Smith Street" destinations, this Carroll Gardens "labor of love" features "never-fail" French bistro eats served in a "well-tailored" interior or rear "garden getaway"; oddly enough, what was once a "special-occasion place" is now "one of the more reasonable spots on the strip."

Patricia's ● Italian
22 | 12 | 19 | $26

Bronx | 1080 Morris Park Ave. (bet. Haight & Lurting Aves.) | 718-409-9069
Bronx | 3764 E. Tremont Ave. (bet. Randall & Roosevelt Aves.) | 718-918-1800

"Inexpensive", "family-oriented" Bronx Italians serving "flavorful" pizzas and pastas in "loud, crowded" digs with "not much room to relax"; if "storefront" decor complete with "TV sets" doesn't appeal, "get it to go."

Patroon ☒ American/Steak
21 | 20 | 21 | $63

E 40s | 160 E. 46th St. (bet. Lexington & 3rd Aves.) | 212-883-7373 | www.patroonrestaurant.com

"Masters of the universe" dig the smooth 1930s-NY vibe at Ken Aretsky's "clubby" Midtown New American, where "excellent" steaks, "pro" service and "expense-account" pricing make it a prime player for "power dining"; bonuses include a swinging rooftop bar and a variety of "handsome" private rooms; open weekdays only.

Patsy's Italian
21 | 16 | 20 | $51

W 50s | 236 W. 56th St. (bet. B'way & 8th Ave.) | 212-247-3491 | www.patsys.com

"Sinatra's ghost still haunts" this "retro" Southern Italian near Carnegie Hall that's a "throwback" in many ways other than its pricing; "crusty waiters", "celebrity pix on the walls" and a crowd that looks like a "casting call for the *Sopranos*" add up to a "so NY" experience or a so-so experience depending whom you ask.

	FOOD	DECOR	SERVICE	COST

Patsy's Pizzeria *Pizza* — 20 | 12 | 15 | $24

Chelsea | 318 W. 23rd St. (bet. 8th & 9th Aves.) | 646-486-7400
E 60s | 1312 Second Ave. (69th St.) | 212-639-1000
E 60s | 206 E. 60th St. (bet. 2nd & 3rd Aves.) | 212-688-9707
G Village | 67 University Pl. (bet. 10th & 11th Sts.) | 212-533-3500
Harlem | 2287-91 First Ave. (bet. 117th & 118th Sts.) | 212-534-9783 ⊟
Murray Hill | 509 Third Ave. (bet. 34th & 35th Sts.) | 212-689-7500
W 70s | 61 W. 74th St. (bet. Columbus Ave. & CPW) | 212-579-3000
www.patsyspizzeriany.com

"Perfectly charred" brick-oven pizzas with "zesty sauce" and "delicious thin crusts" overcome the "lackluster service" and "nonexistent" decor at this all-over-town chainlet; piezanos praise East Harlem's "venerable" independent original as "still the best", and "worth the trek."

Paul & Jimmy's *Italian* — 19 | 16 | 20 | $44

Gramercy | 123 E. 18th St. (bet. Irving Pl. & Park Ave. S.) | 212-475-9540 |
www.paulandjimmys.com

"Always quiet" and "comfortable", this "reliable" third-generation Gramercy Italian is "growing old gracefully" (if "not adventurously"); the midpriced, "traditional red-sauce" menu holds "no surprises", but "loyal" adherents stick by its "old-time" ways.

Payard Bistro 🗷 *Dessert/French* — 24 | 21 | 20 | $53

E 70s | 1032 Lexington Ave. (bet. 73rd & 74th Sts.) | 212-717-5252 |
www.payard.com

"Sinful desserts" are "virtually mandatory" at François Payard's stylish UES patisserie/French bistro that also works for breakfast, "fancy" lunches, "elegant afternoon tea" or "*magnifique*" dinners; somewhat "snooty" staffers set back the "civilized" if "pricey" experience.

Peanut Butter & Co. *Sandwiches* — 20 | 12 | 16 | $13

G Village | 240 Sullivan St. (bet. Bleecker & W. 3rd Sts.) | 212-677-3995 |
www.ilovepeanutbutter.com

"If peanut butter's your idea of heaven", then this Village cafe is the "pearly gates", serving "lip-smacking" sandwiches including the infamous 'Elvis' (PB&J, banana and bacon – "yum"); "overpricing" is overlooked for the "novelty" of "eating like a kid" again.

🗷 Pearl Oyster Bar 🗷 *Seafood* — 26 | 15 | 19 | $43

G Village | 18 Cornelia St. (bet. Bleecker & W. 4th Sts.) | 212-691-8211 |
www.pearloysterbar.com

"Neptune would be proud" of the "legendary" lobster rolls and "sublime" New England–style fish served at Rebecca Charles' "no-frills" Village seafood shack; it's "cheaper than driving to Maine", though it may take as long given the "endless waits" to get in.

Pearl Room *Seafood* — 23 | 21 | 22 | $47

Bay Ridge | 8201 Third Ave. (82nd St.) | Brooklyn | 718-833-6666 |
www.thepearlroom.com

"Excellent" cooking, "personable service" and a "cool", "modern" atmosphere make this "upscale" Bay Ridge seafooder a "classy" destination, though a few carp at the "Manhattan prices"; the "top-shelf" bar does a "brisk business" too, sometimes "three deep" with amenable "young singles."

	FOOD	DECOR	SERVICE	COST

Peasant Ⓜ *Italian* | 24 | 23 | 20 | $54

NoLita | 194 Elizabeth St. (bet. Prince & Spring Sts.) | 212-965-9511 | www.peasantnyc.com

"Unconventional" cuisine served from an "opera set of an open kitchen" is the draw at this "candlelit" NoLita Italian that's "fit for a king" – and priced accordingly – though needing a "waiter to decipher" the foreign-language menu strikes some as "a bit much"; romeos rhapsodize over its more "casual" subterranean wine bar.

Peep ◐ *Thai* | 19 | 20 | 17 | $31

SoHo | 177 Prince St. (bet. Sullivan & Thompson Sts.) | 212-254-7337 | www.peepsoho.net

"Crazy crowds" of the "young" and "trendy" meet cute at this "affordable" SoHo Thai where the "pink neon", "Hello Kitty" decor matches the "zingy" chow; the real "peep show" comes via "novelty bathrooms" whose one-way mirrors allow you to contemplate the scene "from your throne" – and pray that they're really one-way.

Peking Duck House *Chinese* | 22 | 15 | 18 | $36

Chinatown | 28 Mott St. (bet. Mosco & Pell Sts.) | 212-227-1810
E 50s | 236 E. 53rd St. (bet. 2nd & 3rd Aves.) | 212-759-8260
www.pekingduckhousenyc.com

"Carved tableside", the "luscious" namesake specialty is "as good as it gets" at this Chinese pair, though some say the rest of the menu isn't "all it's quacked up to be"; decor varies from the "spare-as-a-bone" Midtown location to the "fancy-for-Chinatown" Downtown sibling.

Pellegrino's *Italian* | 22 | 18 | 21 | $40

Little Italy | 138 Mulberry St. (bet. Grand & Hester Sts.) | 212-226-3177

Just the way "out-of-towners picture Little Italy", this "bustling", modestly priced trattoria offers *delizioso* basics served by "bantering waiters" "straight out of the old country"; dining options include the "comfy" if "plain" interior or alfresco "curbside tables" with "people-watching" on the side.

Penelope ⊄ *American* | 21 | 17 | 18 | $23

Murray Hill | 159 Lexington Ave. (30th St.) | 212-481-3800 | www.penelopenyc.com

"Tantalizing" "down-home cooking" and "country cottage" decor make this "girlie" Murray Hill American feel like "grandma's kitchen"; downsides include "long waits for brunch" and a "cash-only policy", but you "can't complain with such reasonable prices."

Pepe Giallo To Go *Italian* | 21 | 10 | 15 | $24

Chelsea | 253 10th Ave. (bet. 24th & 25th Sts.) | 212-242-6055
Pepe Rosso *Italian*
E Village | 127 Ave. C (8th St.) | 212-529-7747
Pepe Rosso Caffe *Italian*
E 40s | Grand Central | lower level (42nd St. & Vanderbilt Ave.) | 212-867-6054
🆕 **Pepe Rosso Osteria** Ⓢ *Italian*
W 50s | 346 W. 52nd St. (bet. 8th & 9th Aves.) | 212-245-4585
Pepe Rosso To Go *Italian*
SoHo | 149 Sullivan St. (bet. Houston & Prince Sts.) | 212-677-4555

(continued)

Pepe Verde To Go ⊟ *Italian*

W Village | 559 Hudson St. (bet. Perry & W. 11th Sts.) | 212-255-2221
www.peperossotogo.com

"Simple pastas" "in a hurry" sum up the scene at these "Italian pit stops" where the "cheap" chow is served in "food-court" settings; they're fine "for the eat-and-run crowd", though best for "takeout."

Pepolino *Italian* | 24 | 17 | 22 | $50 |

TriBeCa | 281 W. Broadway (bet. Canal & Lispenard Sts.) | 212-966-9983 | www.pepolino.com

For "upscale Northern Italian with downtown coolness", it's "worth the schlep" to this TriBeCa "diamond in the rough" where "original" dishes and "amiable service" distract from the "expensive" tabs and "cramped" digs; for more breathing room, "ask for an upstairs table."

NEW Pera ⊠ *Mediterranean/Turkish* | 22 | 23 | 19 | $54 |

E 40s | 303 Madison Ave. (bet. 41st & 42nd Sts.) | 212-878-6301 | www.peranyc.com

A "breath of fresh air" near Grand Central, this "upscale" Med newcomer provides "delicious" offerings with a Turkish bent in "elegant yet not stuffy" digs; the high "suit ratio" reflects the immoderate prices, so "make sure you're able to expense" this one.

Perbacco ●⊟ *Italian* | 24 | 16 | 20 | $40 |

E Village | 234 E. Fourth St. (bet. Aves. A & B) | 212-253-2038

"Mouthwatering" Italian "small bites" paired with "sensational wines" keep regulars "enthralled" at this "cute little East Villager; ok, it's "crowded", a bit "rushed" and "cash only", but a staff that was apparently "in Rome until yesterday" lays on the "charm."

NEW Peri Ela ⊟ *Turkish* | ∇ 19 | 17 | 20 | $40 |

E 90s | 1361 Lexington Ave. (bet. 90th & 91st Sts.) | 212-410-4300 | www.periela.com

Already a "popular" choice in "barren" Carnegie Hill, this young Turk is "refreshingly different", offering "authentic" eats served by a staff that's "shyly friendly if a tad unskilled"; the space is "small" yet "pleasant", the BYO policy a definite "plus" and the "cash-only" rule a drag.

NEW Perilla *American* | - | - | - | E |

G Village | 9 Jones St. (bet. Bleecker & W. 4th Sts.) | 212-929-6868 | www.perillanyc.com

Last year's *Top Chef* winner, Harold Dieterle, strikes out on his own at this slim Village newcomer (fka Inside) offering New Americana with an Eastern bent that's been drawing crowds from day one; the understated verging on spare interior is in sharp contrast to the emphatic pricing.

Periyali *Greek* | 23 | 20 | 22 | $55 |

Flatiron | 35 W. 20th St. (bet. 5th & 6th Aves.) | 212-463-7890 | www.periyali.com

"Lovely renovated decor" is receiving almost as many kudos as the "inspired" "haute Greek" cooking at this perennial Flatiron "grande dame"; while the "subdued" atmosphere and "truly gracious" staff please longtime regulars, younger types say "unexciting" – at least until they see the check.

	FOOD	DECOR	SERVICE	COST

Per Lei ● Italian
| | 20 | 17 | 17 | $50 |

E 70s | 1347 Second Ave. (71st St.) | 212-439-9200 | www.perleinyc.com
Spun off from nearby Baraonda, this similarly "Euro-trendy" Upper
Eastsider delivers "surprisingly good" Italian food in a "striking" room
or at sidewalk seats perfect for "people-watching"; on the downside,
critics claim it's "not a place to have a conversation" and has "more
style than substance."

Perry Street ● American
| | 24 | 24 | 23 | $71 |

W Village | 176 Perry St. (West St.) | 212-352-1900 | www.jean-georges.com
Jean-Georges Vongerichten's "sophisticated" Way West Village New
American is the "restaurant equivalent of haute couture", with a
"sleek minimalist" room setting the stage for "exquisite" cookery; add
"subtle" service, a "sexy", "Gucci-sunglasses" crowd and a "bargain"
$24 prix fixe lunch to offset the otherwise "steep prices", and you've
got a "must-try" destination.

Z Per Se American/French
| | 28 | 28 | 28 | $301 |

W 60s | Time Warner Ctr. | 10 Columbus Circle, 4th fl. (60th St. at B'way) |
212-823-9335 | www.perseny.com
Like a "four-hour stroll through culinary paradise", Thomas Keller's
French–New American offers "epic dining" in a "Zen-like space" featuring "drop-dead views" of Central Park and Columbus Circle; "tele-
pathic service" (voted No. 1 in this Survey) adds to the overall "magic",
so even if the reservations process can be "grueling" and the prix fixe-
only tariffs "stratospheric", this "once-in-a-blue-moon treat" is "everything it's cracked up to be" – "Per-Fect!"; N.B. jackets required.

Persepolis Persian
| | 19 | 15 | 18 | $37 |

E 70s | 1407 Second Ave. (bet. 73th & 74th Sts.) | 212-535-1100 |
www.persepolisnyc.com
There's no visa required to "visit Persia on the UES" at this "exotic"
spot offering "fragrant", "savory" food (especially the "unique" signature dish, sour cherry rice); its new digs are "peppered with Iranian expats" who relish the "relaxed" pace and "modest" tabs.

Pershing Square American/French
| | 15 | 16 | 16 | $37 |

E 40s | 90 E. 42nd St. (Park Ave.) | 212-286-9600 | www.pershingsquare.com
Just south of Grand Central, this "expansive" Franco-American brasserie
is a good place to meet for breakfast, lunch or a drink before heading
back to Stamford; despite its "great pancakes" and Midtown convenience, critics consider it "chainlike" and "way too noisy" at prime times.

Pescatore ● Italian/Seafood
| | 18 | 15 | 18 | $39 |

E 50s | 955 Second Ave. (bet. 50th & 51st Sts.) | 212-752-7151 |
www.pescatorerestaurant.com
Ever the "crowd-pleaser", this "mid-tier" Midtown "neighborhood"
trattoria delivers "well-executed" Italian seafood and pasta; perhaps
"service could be better", but it's a real "price performer" with a striking "second-floor balcony" overlooking Second Avenue.

Petaluma Italian
| | 18 | 16 | 18 | $44 |

E 70s | 1356 First Ave. (73rd St.) | 212-772-8800 | www.petalumanyc.com
"Solid as a rock", this longtime Yorkville Italian dispenses "pleasant",
"no-fuss" food for "reasonable" costs in a "spacious", "white-linen"

setting; its client base ranges from the "stroller set" to "business-lunchers" to "Sotheby's dealers" who would auction off anything other than their table here.

❷ Peter Luger Steak House ⊅ *Steak* — 28 | 14 | 20 | $71

Williamsburg | 178 Broadway (Driggs Ave.) | Brooklyn | 718-387-7400 | www.peterluger.com

The "holy grail of steakhouses", this Williamsburg "landmark" (NYC's No. 1 chop shop for the 24th year running) makes carnivores "salivate just hearing the name" that's synonymous with the "ultimate" in "succulent" beef, particularly those "buttery, perfectly marbled porterhouses"; "don't look for coddling" from the "brutally efficient" staff – just "consider them an amusement", like the "old-world" *brauhaus* atmospherics and that "outdated cash-only" policy.

Pete's Downtown Ⓜ *Italian* — ▽ 18 | 16 | 19 | $35

Dumbo | 2 Water St. (Old Fulton St.) | Brooklyn | 718-858-3510 | www.petesdowntown.com

Perhaps the "greatest view in the entire world" – Manhattan's Financial District across the river – is the draw at this Dumbo Italian where "an appetite and a camera" are the only requisites for entry; maybe the "old-style" grub is only "adequate", but living up to its nickname – the "poor man's River Café" – it's "reasonably priced."

Pete's Tavern ❶ *Pub Food* — 14 | 16 | 16 | $30

Gramercy | 129 E. 18th St. (Irving Pl.) | 212-473-7676 | www.petestavern.com

It's "all about the ambiance" at this "boisterous" 1864-vintage Gramercy pub that "reeks of old NY", from the "warped wooden floors" to the "O.-Henry-ate-here memorabilia"; regulars stick to the "decent burgers" and try to avoid the "drunken frat boys" on game days.

Petite Abeille *Belgian* — 19 | 14 | 16 | $28

Flatiron | 44 W. 17th St. (bet. 5th & 6th Aves.) | 212-604-9350
Gramercy | 401 E. 20th St. (1st Ave.) | 212-727-1505
TriBeCa | 134 W. Broadway (Duane St.) | 212-791-1360
W Village | 466 Hudson St. (Barrow St.) | 212-741-6479 ⊅
www.petiteabeille.com

"Easy dining" with "European flair" draws "all age groups" to these "bright" Belgian bistros for a moules frites fix washed down with imported brews; service may be "wonky", but "the price is right" and they sure "perk up the neighborhood."

NEW Petite Crevette ⧉⊅ *Seafood* — ▽ 24 | 14 | 17 | $28

Carroll Gardens | 144 Union St. (enter on Hicks St.) | Brooklyn | 718-855-2632

"Delicious", "just-reeled-in fish" is the hook at this "sorta French" Carroll Gardens seafooder where "BYO" keeps prices low; "spotty service" and "hole-in-the-wall" looks are the catches, and "they're not kidding when they say petite."

Petrossian ❶ *Continental/French* — 24 | 24 | 23 | $73

W 50s | 182 W. 58th St. (7th Ave.) | 212-245-2214 | www.petrossian.com

"Life is good" at this "sedate" French-Continental near Carnegie Hall, where the "first-class" fare, "gorgeous deco-inspired room" and "pitch-perfect service" make for a "czar's experience" (it also does the job for a "champagne and caviar fix"); if the "fancy prices" tend to "spoil the celebration", opt for a prix fixe menu or the "equally good cafe."

	FOOD	DECOR	SERVICE	COST

Philip Marie ●Ⓜ American
20 | **18** | **21** | **$40**

W Village | 569 Hudson St. (W. 11th St.) | 212-242-6200 |
www.philipmarie.com

New Americana with "updated twists" lies in store at this "delightful
little" boîte with "reasonable" pricing, "wonderful" service and sidewalk
seating that's ideal for "Village people–watching"; the "private room
for two in the wine cellar" is just the ticket for "secretive romantics."

Philippe ● Chinese
23 | **20** | **20** | **$65**

E 60s | 33 E. 60th St. (bet. Madison & Park Aves.) | 212-644-8885 |
www.philippechow.com

The "scene" is the thing at this Midtown Chinese yearling that strikes
some as a "Mr. Chow's clone" given its "adventurous chef", "sleek"
setting, dim lighting and "pounding music"; similarly, the "extraordinary" pricing doesn't faze "all the beautiful people" in attendance.

Pho Bang ⊅ Vietnamese
21 | **6** | **13** | **$13**

Chinatown | 3 Pike St. (bet. Division St. & E. B'way) | 212-233-3947
Little Italy | 157 Mott St. (bet. Broome & Grand Sts.) | 212-966-3797
Elmhurst | 82-90 Broadway (Elmhurst Ave.) | Queens | 718-205-1500
Flushing | 41-07 Kissena Blvd. (Main St.) | Queens | 718-939-5520

Phans of "fab pho" report these "plain" Vietnamese noodle shops dish
up "surprisingly tasty" eats for excellent "bang pho the buck"; thus,
the "run-down" digs and "what-service?" service aren't so troubling
since "they're practically giving it away."

Phoenix Garden ⊅ Chinese
24 | **8** | **13** | **$27**

E 40s | 242 E. 40th St. (bet. 2nd & 3rd Aves.) | 212-983-6666

"Chinatown comes Uptown" via this Tudor City–area Cantonese
where the "magnificent cooking" struggles against "ungracious service", "not-much-to-look-at" decor and a "cash-only" rule; redeeming
factors include "budget" pricing and a "BYO policy."

Pho Pasteur Vietnamese
∇ **21** | **6** | **14** | **$17**

Chinatown | 85 Baxter St. (bet. Bayard & Canal Sts.) |
212-608-3656

"You can't go wrong with a bowl of pho" or other "filling" Vietnamese
"comfort food" served at this "refuge" from bustling C-town; "casual"
puts it politely, but "best-deal" tabs and a location "right behind the
courthouses" draw in-the-know jurors.

Pho Viet Huong Vietnamese
∇ **23** | **10** | **14** | **$17**

Chinatown | 73 Mulberry St. (bet. Bayard & Canal Sts.) |
212-233-8988

"Pho-nominal" "homestyle Vietnamese" cooking makes for "happy
campers" at this Chinatown "cheapskates' paradise"; despite "sparse
decor" and "no service", this "real deal" helps "take the sting out
of jury duty."

Piadina ●⊅ Italian
∇ **20** | **17** | **17** | **$34**

G Village | 57 W. 10th St. (bet. 5th & 6th Aves.) | 212-460-8017

Whether it's the "first date or the 10th", this "grottolike" Village
Italian is a "romantic" lair luring young "collegiate" types with "delicious" dishes, a "welcoming" vibe and, naturally, "good prices"; the
sole drawback is its "cash-only" status.

	FOOD	DECOR	SERVICE	COST

Piano Due ☒ *Italian*   `25` `25` `24` `$73`

W 50s | Equitable Center Arcade | 151 W. 51st St., 2nd fl. (bet. 6th & 7th Aves.) | 212-399-9400 | www.pianoduenyc.net

"Still a secret", Michael Cetrulo's "tucked-away" Midtown Italian is "fabulous from soup to nuts", with a "flavorful, beautifully presented" menu served by an "exceptional" crew in a "plush", second-floor setting; downstairs, the "colorful" Palio bar is a suitable warm-up decorated with that "stunning" fresco of the "Siena horse race."

Piccola Venezia *Italian*   `25` `17` `23` `$52`

Astoria | 42-01 28th Ave. (42nd St.) | Queens | 718-721-8470 | www.piccola-venezia.com

"Don't let the neighborhood look deceive you": this "old-fashioned, red-velvet" Astoria Italian has long been a "destination" for "outstanding" red-sauce fare with "continental flair"; an "extensive wine cellar" and "terrific" service are additional pluses, so even though "expensive" for Queens, it's "cheaper" than what it would cost in Manhattan.

Piccolo Angolo ⓜ *Italian*   `25` `13` `21` `$38`

W Village | 621 Hudson St. (Jane St.) | 212-229-9177 | www.piccoloangolo.com

"Colorful" owner Renato Migliorini makes you "feel like family" at his ultra-"cozy" Village Italian serving "gutsy", "homestyle cooking" for "moderate" sums; an "effusive" staff doles out portions big enough for "leftovers for a week" – no wonder there's "never an empty seat."

☒ Picholine *French/Mediterranean*   `27` `24` `25` `$87`

W 60s | 35 W. 64th St. (bet. B'way & CPW) | 212-724-8585 | www.picholinenyc.com

"Celebrate", "pamper yourself" or just "swoon" at Terry Brennan's "better-than-ever" UWS French-Med where the "revamped" $65 prix fixe menu is "always excellent" and the "siren call of the cheese trolley" can be heard above the "raves" resounding through the "understatedly elegant" room; "dignified" service enhances the "formal atmosphere", while "top-notch" private party rooms seal the deal.

PicNic Market & Café *Deli/French*   `20` `14` `18` `$38`

W 100s | 2665 Broadway (101st St.) | 212-222-8222 | www.picnicmarket.com

Doing double duty as deli and cafe, this "gentrification personified" Upper Westsider purveys "no-pretensions" French fare "made with care" and served by an "earnest" staff; though a few feel it's a bit "pricey for the modest setting", that doesn't seem to be deterring anyone.

Pietrasanta *Italian*   `19` `13` `17` `$36`

W 40s | 683 Ninth Ave. (47th St.) | 212-265-9471

"Stick to the pasta" to savor the "simple", "homemade" victuals that this "popular" Hell's Kitchen Italian does best; the "cramped" space may be a tad "tattered" and service occasionally "chaotic", yet pretheater-goers endure both in exchange for inexpensive tabs.

Pietro's ☒ *Italian/Steak*   `23` `14` `21` `$60`

E 40s | 232 E. 43rd St. (bet. 2nd & 3rd Aves.) | 212-682-9760

For "civilized" dining near Grand Central, check out this "step-back-in-time" Italian steakhouse that may "lack buzz" but still furnishes "first-

| | FOOD | DECOR | SERVICE | COST |

rate" meals and an "old-school" staff (including an "amazing coat check woman"); like many of its "dedicated older followers", it "could use a face-lift", though pricing is distinctly up to date.

Pigalle ● French
18 | 17 | 17 | $36

W 40s | Hilton Garden Inn Times Sq. | 790 Eighth Ave. (48th St.) | 212-489-2233 | www.pigallenyc.com
Sure, it's "usually mobbed", since this "convenient" Hell's Kitchen "way station en route to the theater" churns out "reliable" French brasserie eats at "survival prices"; even though the staff can be "overwhelmed", it still works well for a "quickie" before the show.

Pig Heaven ● Chinese
19 | 14 | 18 | $34

E 80s | 1540 Second Ave. (bet. 80th & 81st Sts.) | 212-744-4333
No surprise, "pork abounds" on the menu of this UES Chinese where the "above-average" cooking is "so naughty but so good"; "gracious hostess" Nancy Lee "remembers your favorites" and distracts from the "kitschy", "porcine"-themed decor and that "turn-off" of a name.

Ping's Seafood ● Chinese/Seafood
22 | 12 | 13 | $26

Chinatown | 22 Mott St. (bet. Bayard & Pell Sts.) | 212-602-9988
Elmhurst | 83-02 Queens Blvd. (Goldsmith St.) | Queens | 718-396-1238
"Tasty morsels" of "classic Hong Kong seafood" and an "extensive selection" of "delicious dim sum" are dispensed by this "bustling" Chinatown-Elmhurst pair where tabs are "reasonable" enough to overcome the "shabby" setups and "annoyed" staff.

Pink Tea Cup ●≠ Soul Food/Southern
20 | 10 | 16 | $23

W Village | 42 Grove St. (bet. Bedford & Bleecker Sts.) | 212-807-6755 | www.thepinkteacup.com
Despite the name, there's "nothing dainty" about this venerable Villager specializing in "stick-to-your-hips" Southern cooking; both the decor and service need "sprucing up", but those seeking a wallet-friendly "cholesterol splurge" are willing to brave the "lines" out the door.

Pinocchio Ⓜ Italian
21 | 16 | 23 | $45

E 90s | 1748 First Ave. (bet. 90th & 91st Sts.) | 212-828-5810
"Everyone knows everyone" at this "obscure" Yorkville "hideaway" that's a neighborhood "asset" for locals; "wonderful" Italian classics and a "couldn't-be-friendlier" owner are further advantages, though it would be nice to have "a bit more space" in the "tight", "narrow" room.

Pintaile's Pizza Pizza
20 | 6 | 12 | $15

E 80s | 1573 York Ave. (bet. 83rd & 84th Sts.) | 212-396-3479
E 90s | 26 E. 91st St. (bet. 5th & Madison Aves.) | 212-722-1967
"Super-thin" whole-wheat crusts and "brilliant" toppings in "crazy combinations" distinguish these "yuppie" Yorkville pizzerias that draw everyone from the "lactose intolerant" to "vegans and full-fledged carnivores"; since decor is "limited", they're best for "takeout" or delivery.

Pio Pio Peruvian
23 | 13 | 16 | $22

E 90s | 1746 First Ave. (bet. 90th & 91st Sts.) | 212-426-5800
NEW **W 90s** | 702 Amsterdam Ave. (94th St.) | 212-665-3000
Bronx | 264 Cypress Ave. (bet. 138th & 139th Sts.) | 718-401-3300
Jackson Heights | 84-13 Northern Blvd. (bet. 84th & 85th Sts.) | Queens | 718-426-1010

(continued)

Pio Pio

Rego Park | 62-30 Woodhaven Blvd. (63rd Ave.) | Queens | 718-458-0606 ▭

"So much food for so little money" could be the motto of this Peruvian mini-chain famed for "fabulous rotisserie chickens" slathered with "addictive" sauces; "sardine" seating, "so-so service" and "raucous" atmospherics come with the territory.

Pipa *Spanish*   21 | 23 | 17 | $42

Flatiron | ABC Carpet & Home | 38 E. 19th St. (bet. B'way & Park Ave. S.) | 212-677-2233 | www.abchome.com

"Young hotties" and "tinkling chandeliers" collide at this "shabby-chic" Flatiron Spaniard that's "full of beautiful things to look at" while you consume "tasty" tapas and "psychedelic sangria"; too bad the staff "couldn't care less" and tabs may be "pricier than you'd like."

Pisticci *Italian*   23 | 19 | 20 | $32

W 100s | 125 La Salle St. (B'way) | 212-932-3500 | www.pisticcinyc.com

Now that "word's out", this "charming" Columbia-area "hideaway" is packed with "college students" tucking into "terrific" Italian repasts and grooving to weekly "live jazz"; service is "friendly", the decor a take on "nouveau-SoHo" rusticity and the price "just right."

Pizza 33 ❶ *Pizza*   21 | 7 | 12 | $11

Chelsea | 171 W. 23rd St. (bet. 6th & 7th Aves.) | 212-337-3661
Chelsea | 268 W. 23rd St. (8th Ave.) | 212-206-0999
🆕 **G Village** | 527 Sixth Ave. (14th St.) | 212-255-6333
Murray Hill | 489 Third Ave. (33rd St.) | 212-545-9191
www.pizza33.net

"Godsends when the bars close", these brick-oven pizzerias are celebrated for both their "late-night" hours and "crispy, chewy crusts"; what with the "cramped" settings, they're best enjoyed "on the run."

P.J. Clarke's ❶ *Pub Food*   17 | 16 | 16 | $33

E 50s | 915 Third Ave. (55th St.) | 212-317-1616
🆕 **P.J. Clarke's at Lincoln Square** ❶ *Pub Food*
W 60s | 44 W. 63rd St. (Columbus Ave.) | 212-957-9700
P.J. Clarke's on the Hudson *Pub Food*
Financial District | 4 World Financial Ctr. (Vesey St.) | 212-285-1500
www.pjclarkes.com

"Amazing burgers", "properly poured" brews and vintage decor are the draws at this "pub-grub paradise" set in a circa-1884 Midtown saloon; the newer satellites in the Financial District and opposite Lincoln Center may be "Disney versions", but are popular nonetheless.

Place, The *American/Mediterranean*   21 | 21 | 22 | $46

W Village | 310 W. Fourth St. (bet. Bank & 12th Sts.) | 212-924-2711 | www.theplaceny.com

"Dark" surroundings and a "delicious" Med–New American menu make for a highly "romantic rendezvous" at this "candlelit" West Villager; a "warm" staff and acoustics that allow you to "carry on a conversation" add to the seductive feel; N.B. the short-lived 10th Street satellite has shuttered.

| | FOOD | DECOR | SERVICE | COST |

Planet Thailand ● *Japanese/Thai* | 19 | 19 | 15 | $26 |
Williamsburg | 133 N. Seventh St. (bet. Bedford Ave. & Berry St.) | Brooklyn | 718-599-5758

Planethailand 212 ● *Thai*
Flatiron | 30 W. 24th St. (bet. 5th & 6th Aves.) | 212-727-7026 | www.pt212.com

"Cheap and cheery", the "hip" Williamsburg branch of this Thai-Japanese duo churns out "tasty" chow in a "cavernous", "dance club"-like setting, while its smaller Flatiron sibling offers a more limited menu and "Thai theme park" decor; "hit-or-miss" service is available at both.

Pó *Italian* | 25 | 16 | 21 | $49 |
G Village | 31 Cornelia St. (bet. Bleecker & W. 4th Sts.) | 212-645-2189
NEW **Carroll Gardens** | 276 Smith St. (bet. Degraw & Sackett Sts.) | Brooklyn | 718-875-1980
www.porestaurant.com

"True foodies" say this "still-going-strong" Village Italian turns out "perfectly prepared" fare backed up by "smooth" service and a "no-problem" price point; now if they could only do something about the "tight" setting that makes "sitting on your neighbor's lap" part of the package; N.B. the Carroll Gardens outPóst opened post-Survey.

Z Poke 🅩🚭 *Japanese* | 26 | 15 | 18 | $38 |
E 80s | 343 E. 85th St. (bet. 1st & 2nd Aves.) | 212-249-0569

"Super-fresh fish" meets "creative cutters" to become "sublime sushi" at this "no-reservations" UES Japanese where the "BYO bonus" keeps "prices cheap"; despite an "echo chamber" of a setting and "kind of snarly" service, there are "long waits if you don't get there early."

Pomodoro Rosso *Italian* | 21 | 15 | 20 | $40 |
W 70s | 229 Columbus Ave. (bet. 70th & 71st Sts.) | 212-721-3009

An "easy walk from Lincoln Center", this "quintessential neighborhood Italian" packs 'em in with "dependable" "traditional" cooking at "value" tabs; an "efficient" staff abets the "pleasant" vibe, even though it's famed as the "Seinfeld break-up restaurant."

NEW **p*ong** ●Ⓜ *Dessert* | ▽ 21 | 20 | 23 | $49 |
G Village | 150 W. 10th St. (bet. Greenwich Ave. & Waverly Pl.) | 212-929-0898 | www.p-ong.com

The latest of NY's high-concept dessert bars, this "heavenly" haute Villager from sweets master Pichet Ong offers Asian-influenced sweet-and-savory American small plates from a menu that includes expansive (and "expensive") tasting options; the "modern" design is well-suited to its adventurous approach, including those "sublime handcrafted cocktails."

Pongal *Indian/Vegetarian* | 21 | 13 | 15 | $24 |
E 60s | 1154 First Ave. (bet. 63rd & 64th Sts.) | 212-355-4600
Gramercy | 110 Lexington Ave. (bet. 27th & 28th Sts.) | 212-696-9458

"Dosas are the real winners" on the "flavorful" Southern Indian menu of this kosher vegetarian duo where the food's "not too spicy, nor too bland"; "devoted regulars" say the "bargain" rates trump the "nonexistent decor" and "clueless" service.

	FOOD	DECOR	SERVICE	COST

Pongsri Thai *Thai* | 20 | 11 | 17 | $24

Chelsea | 165 W. 23rd St. (bet. 6th & 7th Aves.) | 212-645-8808
Chinatown | 106 Bayard St. (Baxter St.) | 212-349-3132
Gramercy | 311 Second Ave. (18th St.) | 212-477-2727
W 40s | 244 W. 48th St. (bet. B'way & 8th Ave.) | 212-582-3392 ◗

"Quality" Thai "done right" with "subtle flavorings" keeps the "crowds" coming to this "popular" chainlet; "gentle prices" make up for the "advanced thrift shop" decor and "polite" but "conveyor belt"-style service.

Ponticello *Italian* | ▽ 23 | 18 | 21 | $48

Astoria | 46-11 Broadway (bet. 46th & 47th Sts.) | Queens | 718-278-4514 | www.ponticelloristorante.com

A "stroll down memory lane", this "old-school" Astoria Italian offers "first-rate" fare from a kitchen that's "willing to cook anything you want", "even if it's not on the menu"; service is "friendly", tabs are "pricey for Queens" and the crowd is right off of the *Godfather* set."

Pop Burger ◗ *American* | 19 | 14 | 12 | $19

Meatpacking | 58-60 Ninth Ave. (bet. 14th & 15th Sts.) | 212-414-8686 | www.popburger.com

"Addictive" mini-burgers channeling "White Castle" are the bait at this low-budget Meatpacking District New American, though it's the "awesome lounge scene" in back that keeps the crowd "buzzing late into the night"; many wonder "is the service supposed to be that bad?"

Popover Cafe *American* | 18 | 14 | 16 | $26

W 80s | 551 Amsterdam Ave. (bet. 86th & 87th Sts.) | 212-595-8555 | www.popovercafe.com

It's "all about the popovers" at this "favorite" UWS American whose well-priced, "tasty comfort food" plays second fiddle to its "warm, flaky" namesake; expect weekend "waits", "sweet but inefficient" service and a "cute", "gingham-tablecloth-and-teddy-bear"-laden setting.

Porcão Churrascaria *Brazilian/Steak* | 21 | 20 | 21 | $66

Gramercy | 360 Park Ave. S. (26th St.) | 212-252-7080 | www.porcaous.com

"Avoid the decoy food" at the "salad bar utopia" and save yourself for the "onslaught" of "exceptional" rodizio-style meats at this Gramercy Brazilian steakhouse; though the "price tag is a bit hefty", you do get an "astonishing amount of food" from a staff that "pays attention."

Porter House New York *Steak* | 22 | 25 | 22 | $76

W 60s | Time Warner Ctr. | 10 Columbus Circle, 4th fl. (60th St. at B'way) | 212-823-9500 | www.porterhousenewyork.com

A "stylish", wood-paneled room with Central Park views sets the stage for Michael Lomonaco's "21st-century steakhouse" on the fourth floor of the Time Warner Center, where the meat's "perfectly prepared" and the "sides live up to the main event"; factor in "attentive" service "without airs" for a "great experience" that "justifies the cost."

Portofino Grille *Italian* | 19 | 20 | 20 | $45

E 60s | 1162 First Ave. (bet. 63rd & 64th Sts.) | 212-832-4141 | www.portofinogrille.com

"Famous for its twinkling stars on the ceiling", this "reliable", up-market East Side "charmer" offers "tasty" Italian cuisine delivered by a "caring" staff; though a few find the "over-the-top" setting more "cheesy" than "cozy", the operative word here is "grown-up."

Portofino's *Italian/Seafood* ▽ 19 | 19 | 20 | $45

Bronx | 555 City Island Ave. (Cross St.) | 718-885-1220 | www.portofinocityisland.com

"Manhattan-style" dining comes to City Island at this "upscale" Italian known for its "surprisingly good" seafood and "old-fashioned service"; despite the "romantic" appeal (a fireplace in winter, an outdoor deck in summer), critics say it's "a bit pricey" and getting "tired."

Positano ● *Italian* ▽ 21 | 16 | 19 | $41

Little Italy | 122 Mulberry St. (bet. Canal & Hester Sts.) | 212-334-9808 | www.positanolittleitaly.com

"Quaint" and "relaxed", this "friendly" Little Italy standby turns out "home-cooked" Southern Italian food for moderate sums; regulars recommend a sidewalk table for its view of the "best show in town."

Post House *Steak* 23 | 20 | 22 | $72

E 60s | Lowell Hotel | 28 E. 63rd St. (bet. Madison & Park Aves.) | 212-935-2888 | www.theposthouse.com

A "gentleman's steakhouse" that "even women like", this "solid" Eastsider is "less cramped" and "more serene" than the competition; "top-flight" beef, "to-die-for" sides and "classy" service draw "upscale" eaters willing to pay – or "expense" – those "expected high prices."

Posto *Pizza* 23 | 15 | 18 | $24

Gramercy | 310 Second Ave. (18th St.) | 212-716-1200

"Crispy", "gossamer-thin" crusts accessorized with a "tremendous assortment of toppings" make for "heaven on a plate" at this "hip" Gramercy pizza purveyor; sure, the quarters are "tight" and the sidewalk seats overlook "blah Second Avenue", but at least the pricing is "kind."

Prem-on Thai ● *Thai* ▽ 21 | 20 | 18 | $33

G Village | 138 W. Houston St. (bet. MacDougal & Sullivan Sts.) | 212-353-2338 | www.prem-on.com

"Not your typical Thai", this "high-end", "high-fashion" Siamese on the Village/SoHo border offers "clever", "well-presented" dishes prepared just as "spicy as you want"; "stylish" modern decor, modest tabs and an overall cool vibe draw a "young-ish NYU crowd."

Press 195 *Sandwiches* 20 | 12 | 15 | $18

Park Slope | 195 Fifth Ave. (bet. Sackett & Union Sts.) | Brooklyn | 718-857-1950 ⊞

Bayside | 40-11 Bell Blvd. (bet. 40th & 41st Aves.) | Queens | 718-281-1950 www.press195.com

"Superb ingredients" in "creative combinations" done "your way" make for "perfectly pressed" panini at this "casual" Brooklyn/Queens pair; "hip" ambiance and "delightful" backyard gardens im-press fans, but "be prepared to wait" since the "sandwiches take forever" to be made.

Primavera ● *Italian* 22 | 22 | 23 | $71

E 80s | 1578 First Ave. (82nd St.) | 212-861-8608 | www.primaveranyc.com

That "old-world elegance" "never fails to impress" at this UES standby where "well-heeled", well-coiffed regulars savor "outstanding" Northern Italian cuisine served by a "first-class" crew (chef-owner

Nicola Civetta is as "smooth as a vintage Amarone"); P.S. it's "expensive", "not that anyone here cares."

Prime Grill *Steak*

FOOD	DECOR	SERVICE	COST
22	19	18	$65

E 40s | 60 E. 49th St. (bet. Madison & Park Aves.) | 212-692-9292 | www.theprimegrill.com

"You'd never know it's kosher", but this Midtown steakhouse "holds the dairy" while dishing out "high-quality" meats and "tasty sushi" in "traditional" digs; despite subprime service, "ambitious pricing" and "chaotic" decibel levels, the observant still "line up to get in."

Primola *Italian*

23	15	20	$60

E 60s | 1226 Second Ave. (bet. 64th & 65th Sts.) | 212-758-1775

"It pays to be a regular" at this "clubby" East Side Italian where "the better they know you, the better it is"; expect "delicious" cooking, "steep prices", "not much decor" and "every head turning to see who you are when you walk in the door."

NEW Provence ● *French*

▽ 21	20	20	$57

SoHo | 38 MacDougal St. (Prince St.) | 212-475-7500 | www.provencenyc.com

SoHo Francophiles "feel the Mistral blowing" at this "charming" bistro "newly reopened" by the team behind Cookshop and Five Points; the "fine food", "attractive" setting and all-weather garden room seem "better the second time around", even if it's a "little pricier" now too.

Provence en Boite *Bakery/French*

▽ 20	15	19	$34

Carroll Gardens | 263 Smith St. (Degraw St.) | Brooklyn | 718-797-0707 | www.provenceenboite.com

A "pleasant addition" to Carroll Gardens, this "mom-and-pop" French bistro supplies "basic fare" and *superbe* baked goods as well as "cheerful" owners; if the setting is too "casual", at least the "gorgeous" desserts and croissants count as "art."

Prune *American*

24	16	21	$48

E Village | 54 E. First St. (bet. 1st & 2nd Aves.) | 212-677-6221 | www.prunerestaurant.com

"Stretch your palate" at this "tiny" East Village "treasure" where chef Gabrielle Hamilton serves "hearty, heartfelt" and "never dull" New Americana; "everyone knows" about the "innovative" brunch, so "expect to wait" for a table and plan to be "crunched."

NEW PT ●≠ *Italian*

▽ 24	18	21	$37

Williamsburg | 331 Bedford Ave. (bet. S. 2nd & 3rd Sts.) | Brooklyn | 718-388-7438

Just a few steps below street level, this "interesting" new Williamsburg enoteca (an offshoot of nearby D.O.C. Wine Bar) exudes "rusticity" with exposed-brick walls and diffused candlelight; the "reasonably priced" seasonal Italian menu is matched by "fabulous" wines from around The Boot.

Public *Eclectic*

23	26	21	$53

NoLita | 210 Elizabeth St. (bet. Prince & Spring Sts.) | 212-343-7011 | www.public-nyc.com

This "high-concept", high-noise-level NoLita Eclectic looks like a cross between a "library" and a "nightclub", and the "exotic" menu with "nouvelle Australian" accents is equally "adventurous"; though "not as insanely trendy as it used to be", it's still "hip", "hopping" and "not for the masses."

	FOOD	DECOR	SERVICE	COST

NEW Public House *Pub Food* — | — | — | M

E 40s | 140 E. 41st St. (bet. Lexington & 3rd Aves.) | 212-682-3710 | www.publichousenyc.com

NYC gets its own link of the national franchise with the arrival of this new modestly priced Midtown megapub that's one block south of Grand Central; since the atmosphere could be Anywhere U.S.A., it's appropriately convenient for commuters.

Pump Energy Food *Health Food* 19 | 5 | 13 | $14

E 50s | Crystal Pavilion | 805 Third Ave. (50th St.) | 212-421-3055 ⊠
Flatiron | 31 E. 21st St. (bet. B'way & Park Ave. S.) | 212-253-7676
Garment District | 112 W. 38th St. (bet. B'way & 6th Ave.) | 212-764-2100
Murray Hill | 113 E. 31st St. (bet. Lexington Ave. & Park Ave. S.) | 212-213-5733
W 50s | 40 W. 55th St. (bet. 5th & 6th Aves.) | 212-246-6844
www.thepumpenergyfood.com

The "low-fat", "high-protein" offerings at this "dependable" health food mini-chain make its "gym-obsessed crowd" feel "virtuous", as does the "reasonable" pricing; what with the "eyesore" decor and servers tougher than your trainer, aesthetes advise "have it delivered."

Punch *Eclectic* 19 | 16 | 18 | $38

Flatiron | 913 Broadway (bet. 20th & 21st Sts.) | 212-673-6333 | www.punchrestaurant.com

Although this "unpretentious" Flatiron Eclectic boasts an "updated look", a new chef and a "tweaked" menu, it still remains "off the radar" for many; fans praise the "delightful" cooking, "unrushed" service and "value" pricing – adding that Wined Up, the upstairs lounge, may be "even better."

Pure Food and Wine *Vegan/Vegetarian* 22 | 22 | 21 | $55

Gramercy | 54 Irving Pl. (bet. 17th & 18th Sts.) | 212-477-1010 | www.purefoodandwine.com

"Stove-free" cooking is the hook at this "ingenious" Gramercy purveyor of "mind-changing" vegan fare that makes for "invigorating" raw dining; while a "lovely" garden adds to the "sensual" experience, some find it "a bit pricey" considering how "tough it is to get full" here.

Puttanesca *Italian* 18 | 16 | 17 | $37

W 50s | 859 Ninth Ave. (56th St.) | 212-581-4177 | www.puttanesca.com

"Good bang for the buck" keeps this "reliable" Hell's Kitchen Italian packed "before showtime", given its proximity to the Theater District and Lincoln Center; the food's "decent if generic", the service "hit-or-miss" and the acoustics reminiscent of an "airport runway."

Pylos ● *Greek* 25 | 22 | 21 | $42

E Village | 128 E. Seventh St. (bet. Ave. A & 1st Ave.) | 212-473-0220 | www.pylosrestaurant.com

At this "sexy" Greek "gem" in "funky Alphabet City", the "heavenly" offerings "taste like home cooking but better" and are enhanced by a "first-rate", all-Hellenic wine list; add in "attentive" service and "fantastic" decor and it's "worthy of a place on Mount Olympus."

	FOOD	DECOR	SERVICE	COST

Q Thai Bistro *Thai*
| 21 | 19 | 20 | $35 |

Forest Hills | 108-25 Ascan Ave. (bet. Austin & Burns Sts.) | Queens | 718-261-6599 | www.qbistrony.com

This Thai "neighborhood favorite" brings some "sophistication" to Forest Hills with its "French-influenced" "nouvelle" menu; in keeping with its "upscale" aspirations, the ambiance is "chic", the service "friendly" and the tabs tolerable, this being Queens.

Quaint *American*
| ▽ 20 | 19 | 19 | $30 |

Sunnyside | 46-10 Skillman Ave. (bet. 46th & 47th Sts.) | Queens | 917-779-9220 | www.quaintnyc.com

A "small, seasonal" New American menu brings Sunnysiders to this "charming" bistro with a "sweet little back garden"; despite the name, it's "far from old-fashioned" with the "open kitchen" producing "ambitious" comfort food that's aiming to be "SoHo" hip, but "not quite there" yet.

Quality Meats ● *American/Steak*
| 24 | 24 | 23 | $71 |

W 50s | 57 W. 58th St. (bet. 5th & 6th Aves.) | 212-371-7777 | www.qualitymeatsnyc.com

Midtowners who "feel like steak but want a hipper scene" than normal head for this New American chophouse set in a "butcher shop-chic" space, where a "dead-on" staff, "delectable" meats and "prime prices" are also part of the package; make sure not to miss the "tableside steak sauces" and "homemade ice cream."

Quatorze Bis *French*
| 21 | 18 | 20 | $56 |

E 70s | 323 E. 79th St. (bet. 1st & 2nd Aves.) | 212-535-1414

"When you can't get to Paris", there's always this *"charmant"* French bistro in the UES' "79th *arrondissement*" offering "above-average" "Gallic comfort cuisine" for rather "pricey" tabs; the "buzzy", "vibrant" scene keeps its "air-kissing" crowd content.

Quattro Gatti *Italian*
| 20 | 16 | 19 | $45 |

E 80s | 205 E. 81st St. (bet. 2nd & 3rd Aves.) | 212-570-1073

For "traditional red-sauce" cooking and "great service" ("if you can understand the waiters' accents"), try this UES Italian "standby"; while the "old-school" atmosphere is "soothing", some say it's "time to update the interior" or backdate the prices.

Queen *Italian*
| 24 | 14 | 19 | $41 |

Brooklyn Heights | 84 Court St. (bet. Livingston & Schermerhorn Sts.) | Brooklyn | 718-596-5955 | www.queenrestaurant.com

"Keepin' it real" in Brooklyn Heights, this 50-year-old "neighborhood secret" serves "totally delicious" Italian fare highlighted by the "best bread basket" and "amazing fresh mozzarella"; there's "nothing cutting-edge about it, and it's all the better for it", so just ignore the "chintzy" decor and "slow service."

Queen's Hideaway *American*
| ▽ 20 | 12 | 14 | $34 |

Greenpoint | 222 Franklin St. (bet. Green & Huron Sts.) | Brooklyn | 718-383-2355 | www.thequeenshideaway.com

A "hideaway indeed", this "tiny", low-budget Greenpoint "hole-in-the-wall" with "soul" features a "quirky" New American menu strong on "local, seasonal" ingredients; a back garden compensates for the "disorganized service" and decor that "won't be in *Architectural Digest*" anytime soon.

	FOOD	DECOR	SERVICE	COST

Quercy *French*   ▽ 20 | 14 | 18 | $37

Cobble Hill | 242 Court St. (bet. Baltic & Kane Sts.) | Brooklyn | 718-243-2151
Like its sibling, La Lunchonette, this Cobble Hill bistro dispenses "simple French fare" that's "authentic" and "dependable", "not ooh-la-la", in a "sweet neighborhood" setting; given the "friendly staff", affordable tabs and occasional live jazz, boosters feel it "should do better business."

Rachel's American Bistro ◐ *American*   17 | 13 | 17 | $36

W 40s | 608 Ninth Ave. (bet. 43rd & 44th Sts.) | 212-957-9050 | www.rachelsnyc.com
"Flavorful", modestly priced New Americana is yours at this "busy" Hell's Kitchen bistro that's particularly "convenient to the 42nd Street theater district"; it's "nothing fancy" – some say "nothing special" – but don't forget to "bring a shoehorn" to squeeze into the "tight quarters."

Rack & Soul *BBQ/Southern*   20 | 9 | 15 | $25

W 100s | 2818 Broadway (109th St.) | 212-222-4800 | www.rackandsoul.com
This "real-deal" UWS chicken 'n' ribs purveyor "goes whole hog" bringing "messy" BBQ and "down-home" Southern eats to the cost-conscious "Columbia crowd"; service may be only "adequate" and the decor a "step above a school cafeteria", but fans flock in for "finger-licking" rather than "frills."

Rain *Pan-Asian*   21 | 21 | 19 | $42

W 80s | 100 W. 82nd St. (bet. Amsterdam & Columbus Aves.) | 212-501-0776 | www.rainrestaurant.com
An "Upper West Side treasure", this "winning" Pan-Asian pioneer stays "crowded" thanks to "interestingly spiced" fusion fare that's "not too harmful on the wallet"; "noisy" conditions distract from the otherwise "transporting" "rain forest–like setting."

☑ Rainbow Room Ⓜ *Italian*   19 | 27 | 21 | VE

W 40s | GE Bldg. | 30 Rockefeller Plaza, 65th fl. (enter on 49th St., bet. 5th & 6th Aves.)

Rainbow Grill *Italian*

W 40s | GE Bldg. | 30 Rockefeller Plaza, 65th fl. (enter on 49th St., bet. 5th & 6th Aves.)
212-632-5100 | www.rainbowroom.com
"There's no place like" this 65th-floor Rock Center "destination" where the views are "worth a million bucks" and reflected in the "skyscraper prices"; the Northern Italian cuisine is "decent", but "you don't go for the food" – it's the "art deco splendor" and "revolving dance floor" that make for "enchanted evenings" here; it's open to the public select Fridays and Saturdays for prix fixe-only dinner ($200) and Sundays for brunch ($80); the adjacent Rainbow Grill offers a less pricey à la carte menu.

Rai Rai Ken ◐⊟ *Noodle Shop*   ▽ 22 | 12 | 17 | $13

E Village | 214 E. 10th St. (bet. 1st & 2nd Aves.) | 212-477-7030
"As authentic as it comes", this "tiny", "counter-seating-only" East Village ramen shop has the requisite "long wooden bar" and "crowded Tokyo conditions"; the noodles are "seriously delicious", "incredibly satisfying" and "very affordable" – so start "praying for a seat."

	FOOD	DECOR	SERVICE	COST

NEW Ramen Setagaya ⊅ *Noodle Shop* — — — I

E Village | 141 First Ave. (bet. 9th St. & St. Marks Pl.) | 212-529-2740
This East Village outpost of the Tokyo-based noodle chain is a ramen-only specialist where the inexpensive offerings are made from 90 percent Japanese ingredients; already challenging Momofuku Noodle Bar for authenticity, it claims that its secret weapon lies in the broth.

Z Rao's 🔒⊅ *Italian* 22 16 21 $61

Harlem | 455 E. 114th St. (Pleasant Ave.) | 212-722-6709 | www.raos.com
"Still the toughest reservation in town", Frank Pellegrino's "mystique"-laden East Harlem Southern Italian requires knowing a "friend with a table" for the chance to dine on "amazing" "old-world" dishes while rubbing elbows with the famous and the infamous; alternatives include doing it yourself with a jar of their "supermarket sauce" or "flying to Vegas to try the new one in Caesars Palace."

Raoul's ● *French* 24 20 21 $55

SoHo | 180 Prince St. (bet. Sullivan & Thompson Sts.) | 212-966-3518 | www.raouls.com
Expect "ambiance à la Paris" at this "long-standing" (since 1975) dark French bistro that "never goes out of style"; it was "cool before SoHo was cool" thanks to its "excellent" steak au poivre, "charming" service and "romantic back garden", and if it's a little "expensive", "what a scene" you get in return.

Rare Bar & Grill *Hamburgers* 21 15 16 $30

G Village | 228 Bleecker St. (bet. Carmine St. & 6th Ave.) | 212-691-7273
Murray Hill | Shelburne Murray Hill Hotel | 303 Lexington Ave. (37th St.) | 212-481-1999
www.rarebarandgrill.com
A "noisy" "young" crowd slips into "heavenly food comas" at these "high-end" burger joints where the "brilliant" beef can be customized "with all the fixin's"; maybe the decor and service are "nothing special", but neither is the tab and the "french fry sampler is unforgettable."

NEW Rayuela *Pan-Latin* — — — M

LES | 165 Allen St. (bet. Rivington & Stanton Sts.) | 212-253-8840 | www.rayuelanyc.com
The name of this big new Lower Eastsider translates as 'hopscotch' and its Pan-Latin menu jumps around Latin America and Spain; built around a live olive tree, the stylish, split-level space exudes big-city rusticity.

Real Madrid *Spanish* ▽ 21 14 20 $38

Staten Island | 2075 Forest Ave. (Union Ave.) | 718-447-7885 | www.realmadrid-restaurant.com
Serving "dependable" Spanish cuisine for over 20 years, this "authentic" Staten Island standby sure knows its seafood and sangria; its "reasonable" prices and "gracious" service work equally well for everyday dining or "special occasions."

Red Cat *American/Mediterranean* 24 20 22 $53

Chelsea | 227 10th Ave. (bet. 23rd & 24th Sts.) | 212-242-1122 | www.theredcat.com
Chef-owner Jimmy Bradley's "Chelsea charmer" is "still purring along", luring "avid" regulars and other "adult diners" with its "smartly

chosen" New American–Med offerings, "smiling waiters" and "buzzing atmosphere"; the only catch is, it's "so damn popular" that it can be "hard to snag a table."

Redeye Grill ● *American/Seafood* ` 20 | 19 | 19 | $53 `

W 50s | 890 Seventh Ave. (56th St.) | 212-541-9000 | www.redeyegrill.com

Shelly Fireman's "big", bustling New American attracts business-lunchers, show-goers and "tourists" with its across-the-street-from-"Carnegie-Hall convenience"; as befits the self-proclaimed "home of the dancing shrimp", you can expect "delish fish" and an "invigorating" atmosphere, though it's a bit "on the pricey side."

NEW Régate *French* ` – | – | – | M `

LES | 198 Orchard St. (bet. Houston & Stanton Sts.) | 212-228-8555 | www.regate-bistro.com

Young, easygoing Euros helm this new LES Gallic bistro, a tiny spot specializing in the casual cooking found at the French resort of Ile de Ré; affordable prices, amiable service and soccer broadcasts on the TV behind the bar reflect its modest intentions.

Regency *American* ` ▽ 18 | 22 | 20 | $61 `

E 60s | Regency Hotel | 540 Park Ave. (61st St.) | 212-339-4050 | www.loewshotels.com

NY's "elite" types rise and shine with the "consummate power breakfast" at this East Side New American where big deals go down with the bacon and eggs and it's easy to play who's who; after dark, the space moonlights as Feinstein's, a "favorite" cabaret for top-line talent.

Regional *Italian* ` 17 | 15 | 15 | $35 `

W 90s | 2607 Broadway (bet. 98th & 99th Sts.) | 212-666-1915

This "undiscovered" Upper Westsider's "unusual" menu covers 20 "different regions of Italy", but despite "great potential", the cooking falls somewhere between "fairly good" and "average"; "spotty" service and a "sterile" setting don't help, though "at this price, who cares?"

Regional Thai *Thai* ` 18 | 12 | 15 | $28 `

Chelsea | 208 Seventh Ave. (22nd St.) | 212-807-9872
E 70s | 1479 First Ave. (77th St.) | 212-744-6374

Bringing "Thailand's greatest hits" to Chelsea and the UES, this "decent" duo draws "constant crowds" with its "reliable" kitchen and "value" pricing; regarding the "tired" decor and "spaced-out service", regulars have "two words" of advice: "take out."

Relish ● *American* ` ▽ 22 | 21 | 19 | $28 `

Williamsburg | 225 Wythe Ave. (bet. Metropolitan Ave. & N. 3rd St.) | Brooklyn | 718-963-4546 | www.relish.com

A restored "stainless-steel dining car" is the setting for this Williamsburg New American serving a "satisfying" array of affordable comfort chow; "tragically hip" types stand in for the usual truck drivers, and instead of a parking lot, there's a "super-duper" garden.

Remi *Italian* ` 22 | 21 | 20 | $58 `

W 50s | 145 W. 53rd St. (bet. 6th & 7th Aves.) | 212-581-4242 | www.remi-ny.com

"Quality dining" is alive and well at this "memorable" Midtown Italian whose "well-balanced" menu skews Venetian; "graceful" service and

| | FOOD | DECOR | SERVICE | COST |

a "huge fresco" of the Grand Canal add to its allure, and though the pricing's decidedly "upscale", prix fixe deals are available.

René Pujol ⓜ *French* | 22 | 19 | 22 | $55 |
W 50s | 321 W. 51st St. (bet. 8th & 9th Aves.) | 212-246-3023 | www.renepujol.com

There's "nothing nouveau" going on at this "tried-and-true" Theater District "grande dame" serving "solid" French fare and a "quality" dinner prix fixe; the decor "could use some freshening", but "efficient" "pro" service means you'll make the curtain on time.

Republic *Pan-Asian* | 18 | 13 | 15 | $21 |
Union Sq | 37 Union Sq. W. (bet. 16th & 17th Sts.) | 212-627-7172 | www.thinknoodles.com

For "cheap eats", it's hard to beat this Union Square noodle shop where the Pan-Asian food's "delicious" and the service "militant" but "super-quick"; downsides include "wood bench" "picnic table"–style seating and "ear-clanging" acoustics – so "don't go to discuss life with a friend."

Re Sette *Italian* | ▽ 23 | 19 | 21 | $53 |
W 40s | 7 W. 45th St. (bet. 5th & 6th Aves.) | 212-221-7530 | www.resette.com

Regional Barese dishes are "beautifully prepared" at this "relaxed" Midtown Italian that's "away from the crowds" yet "close to the theaters"; book a private party at the King's Table upstairs for "extra-special" service and "eat like", well, you know . . .

NEW Resto ⓞⓜ *Belgian* | - | - | - | M |
Gramercy | 111 E. 29th St. (bet. Lexington Ave. & Park Ave. S.) | 212-685-5585 | www.restonyc.com

An instant scene, this casual new Gramercy Belgian is drawing young folks with a pleasing menu washed down with a long list of brews; prices are moderate, reservations aren't taken and the noise level is thunderous given its tile floor, tin ceiling, marble-topped bar and enthusiastic crowd.

NEW Revel ⓞ *Eclectic* | - | - | - | E |
Meatpacking | 10 Little W. 12th St. (bet. 9th Ave. & Washington St.) | 212-741-5369

The funky bar/eatery that's operated without a name for several years now has one, along with an expanded Eclectic menu that includes dishes cooked on volcanic stones; still, the big draw is its spectacular back garden that's a sanctuary from the Meatpacking District revelry.

Revival *American/French* | ▽ 19 | 16 | 15 | $31 |
Harlem | 2367 Frederick Douglass Blvd. (127th St.) | 212-222-8338 | www.harlemrevival.com

Still rather "unknown", this Harlem spot "tries interesting things" "with varying degrees of success" by adding Caribbean, Creole and soul touches to its Franco-American menu; verdicts range from "amazing" to "disappointing", but it's still a "value" and certainly "welcome" in an underserved area.

Ribot ⓩ *Mediterranean* | ▽ 19 | 20 | 18 | $49 |
E 40s | 780 Third Ave. (48th St.) | 212-355-3700 | www.ribotnyc.com

Named for an Italian racehorse, this "elegant", "high-ceilinged" Midtowner trots out a Mediterranean menu that's "more than decent" and "getting better"; naysayers whinny over "hovering" service and regret being the "only ones there without implants."

Rice ⊋ Eclectic
19 | 14 | 17 | $20

Gramercy | 115 Lexington Ave. (28th St.) | 212-686-5400
NoHo | 292 Elizabeth St. (bet. Bleecker & Houston Sts.) | 212-226-5775 ●
Dumbo | 81 Washington St. (bet. Front & York Sts.) | Brooklyn |
718-222-9880
Fort Greene | 166 DeKalb Ave. (Cumberland St.) | Brooklyn | 718-858-2700
www.riceny.com
It's "rice every which way" at this "modest" Eclectic quartet where a "cornucopia" of "exotic" starch options lets you "have it your way" (especially if you're "vegetarian friendly"); maybe the end result is "uneven", but at least "very little money" is involved.

Rice 'n' Beans Brazilian
▽ 19 | 8 | 16 | $25

W 50s | 744 Ninth Ave. (bet. 50th & 51st Sts.) | 212-265-4444 |
www.ricenbeansrestaurant.com
"Straight off a Rio side street", this Hell's Kitchen "sleeper" serves "transporting", "stick-to-your ribs" Brazilian grub for "dirt-cheap" tabs; the trade-offs are "nonattentive" (albeit "good-natured") service and digs the dimensions of a "coat closet."

Rickshaw Dumpling Bar Chinese
18 | 9 | 13 | $13

Flatiron | 61 W. 23rd St. (bet. 5th & 6th Aves.) | 212-924-9220
NEW **G Village** | 53 E. Eighth St. (bet. B'way & University Pl.) | 212-461-1750
www.rickshawdumplings.com
At this "fast food"-style Flatiron Chinese, exec chef Anita Lo vends "addictive dumplings" that can be "cleverly mixed and matched" with soup or salad for a "filling meal"; "confusing" menus and a "sterile", "cramped" setting are ultimately trumped by the super-"cheap" pricing; N.B. the Village branch opened post-Survey.

Riingo American/Japanese
19 | 19 | 19 | $57

E 40s | Alex Hotel | 205 E. 45th St. (bet. 2nd & 3rd Aves.) | 212-867-4200 |
www.riingo.com
For "stylish" Midtown dining, Marcus Samuelsson's New American-Japanese fusionfest provides "tasty" dishes that are "pricey" but "less expensive" than his better-known Aquavit; the "skinny" setting and sometimes somnolent service are redeemed by "amazing" cocktails and "all-day-long" hours.

Risotteria Italian
21 | 10 | 16 | $23

G Village | 270 Bleecker St. (Morton St.) | 212-924-6664 | www.risotteria.com
Thanks to a "clever menu" in which "everything is gluten-free", this Village Italian "fulfills an important function" for folks with "dietary restrictions" (vegetarians included); its specialty risottos are "cheap and gratifying", even if the "phone booth-size" space is "not much to look at."

⊠ River Café American
26 | 28 | 26 | $111

Dumbo | 1 Water St. (bet. Furman & Old Fulton Sts.) | Brooklyn |
718-522-5200 | www.rivercafe.com
"Sheer bliss from start to finish", Dumbo's "classic stunner" under the Brooklyn Bridge "wows visitors" with "top-notch" New American fare, a "flower-laden" interior and "glorious" river/skyline views (it's *the* place to propose – no matter what the proposition"); just remember to

	FOOD	DECOR	SERVICE	COST

"dress sharp" (jackets required) and prepare for a "wallet busting" ($95 prix fixe–only dinner); N.B. they do spectacular parties.

Riverdale Garden *American* — 24 | 19 | 18 | $46

Bronx | 4576 Manhattan College Pkwy. (242nd St.) | 718-884-5232 | www.riverdalegarden.com

The "Bronx is blessed" to have this "Manhattan-caliber" New American, whose "unassuming" setting belies its "consistently classy", "farm-fresh" preparations; though it's a bit "pricey" and service can be "idiosyncratic", a "beautiful" back garden and "valet parking" more than compensate.

River Room ᴹ *Southern* — ▽ 19 | 24 | 15 | $42

Harlem | Riverbank State Park | W. 145th St. (Riverside Dr.) | 212-491-1500 | www.theriverroomofharlem.com

Set in Harlem's "secret" Riverbank State Park, this "upscale" yet mid-priced Southerner claims "priceless" views of the Hudson, Palisades and GW Bridge through its plate-glass windows; "pleasant" live weekend jazz jives with the "sophisticated" mood, not the "disappearing" staff.

🄩 Roberto 🄱 *Italian* — 27 | 18 | 21 | $49

Bronx | 603 Crescent Ave. (Hughes Ave.) | 718-733-9503 | www.robertobronx.com

At this "neighborhood treasure" in the Bronx's version of Little Italy, Roberto Paciullo sends diners on "life-changing" tours of his native Salerno ("forget the menu", he'll "take good care of you"); still, that no-reservations policy makes for "looong" waits.

Roberto Passon ● *Italian* — 22 | 16 | 20 | $44

W 50s | 741 Ninth Ave. (50th St.) | 212-582-5599 | www.robertopasson.com

"More than just a neighborhood trattoria", this "popular" Hell's Kitchen Italian draws both locals and the Broadway-bound with "straightforward" cooking plus "interesting flourishes"; though prices are generally "reasonable", "beware the cost of the specials."

Roc ● *Italian* — 21 | 20 | 21 | $52

TriBeCa | 190A Duane St. (Greenwich St.) | 212-625-3333 | www.rocrestaurant.com

This "consistent performer" in TriBeCa has the "quality" thing down pat, with "delicious" Italian food, "chic" digs and "charming" service; sure, you'll pay "above-average prices", but that doesn't faze its "rich and beautiful" following.

Rocco ᴹ *Italian* — ▽ 20 | 13 | 19 | $38

G Village | 181 Thompson St. (bet. Bleecker & Houston Sts.) | 212-677-0590 | www.roccorestaurant.com

Serving "affordable", "well-prepared" Southern Italiana in the same Village spot since 1922, this "old-line", "elbows-on-the-table kind of place" is "like going home for a visit"; the decor is straight out of a "1940s movie version of what an Italian restaurant should be."

Rock Center Café *American* — 19 | 22 | 19 | $45

W 50s | Rockefeller Ctr. | 20 W. 50th St. (bet. 5th & 6th Aves.) | 212-332-7620 | www.patinarestaurantgroup.com

An all-seasons "people-watching" paradise, this midpriced Rock Center "tourist favorite" features an American menu that's "better than you'd expect"; still, it's the "skating rink" views in the winter and "alfresco summer dining" that make it a bona fide "NYC experience."

Rocking Horse Cafe *Mexican* 20 | 16 | 17 | $36

Chelsea | 182 Eighth Ave. (bet. 19th & 20th Sts.) | 212-463-9511 | www.rockinghorsecafe.com

"Festive" Chelsea "haute Mex" that draws "young", "cacophonous" crowds with "nouveau" cuisine washed down with "devastating margaritas"; despite some "inconsistent" moments (i.e. "slow service"), it's still a "scene" after 20 years in business.

Roebling Tea Room ⏺ *American* ▽ 21 | 20 | 16 | $22

Williamsburg | 143 Roebling St. (Metropolitan Ave.) | Brooklyn | 718-963-0760 | www.roeblingtearoom.com

The "eclectic" array of affordable "small plates and sandwiches" at this Williamsburg tearoom is accompanied by a "huge selection" of leaves, plus "ample couches" and "high funk" decor; it draws a "cool crowd", which may explain the "glacial" service.

Rolf's *German* 17 | 20 | 16 | $39

Gramercy | 281 Third Ave. (22nd St.) | 212-477-4750

"Oof" goes the schnitzel at this long-running Gramercy Park German where the "authentic" fare comes with a side of "storybook" "spectacle" during the holidays via a "dizzying" display of Christmas lights; it's "from another world and time", starting with those "enormous portions."

Roll-n-Roaster ⏺ *Sandwiches* 19 | 8 | 11 | $14

Sheepshead Bay | 2901 Emmons Ave. (bet. E. 29th St. & Nostrand Ave.) | Brooklyn | 718-769-5831 | www.rollnroaster.com

You can "have cheez on anything you pleez" at this Sheepshead Bay "institution" that's been rolling out "excellent roast beef sandwiches" and fries since 1970; regulars know it's a "quick bite" at a "good price", but when it comes to "decor, fuhgeddaboudit."

Room Service *Thai* 19 | 19 | 17 | $27

Chelsea | 166 Eighth Ave. (bet. 18th & 19th Sts.) | 212-691-0299

"Trendy to a fault", this Chelsea Thai looks like a chic hotel lobby with "techno-hallucinatory" decor, a "skinny" client base and an "energetic", "club music" soundtrack; "gimmicky" though it may be, the "imaginative" fusion fare comes at "unbelievably affordable" rates.

Roppongi *Japanese* 19 | 14 | 17 | $36

W 80s | 434 Amsterdam Ave. (81st St.) | 212-362-8182 | www.ropponginyc.net

"In the shadow of Haru" (its across-the-street rival), this UWS Japanese "secret" delivers "pleasant" repasts in "minimalist", "not as crowded" surroundings; the sushi is "fresh", the cooked dishes "creative" and, best of all, tabs are "reasonable for the neighborhood."

⊠ Rosa Mexicano ⏺ *Mexican* 22 | 21 | 20 | $47

E 50s | 1063 First Ave. (58th St.) | 212-753-7407
Flatiron | 9 E. 18th St. (bet. B'way & 5th Ave.) | 212-533-3350
W 60s | 61 Columbus Ave. (62nd St.) | 212-977-7700
www.rosamexicano.com

"Lively" folks in "celebratory" mode pack this "hip 'n' hopping" threesome for their "designer Mexican" settings and menus, led by "world-class" guacamole made tableside ("to kill for") and washed down with "deliciously deadly" pomegranate margaritas; though everything's "*muy bien*", they're "best experienced on someone else's dime."

	FOOD	DECOR	SERVICE	COST

🆕 Rosanjin 🅂 *Japanese*   ▽ 25 | 21 | 23 | $155

TriBeCa | 141 Duane St. (bet. Church St. & W. B'way) | 212-346-7991 | www.rosanjintribeca.com

"Beautiful in every way", this pocket-size new TriBeCa Japanese with a museumlike hush is set in subtly sleek digs and purveys "authentic" "Kyoto-style" kaiseki dinners at "Per Se prices" ($150 prix fixe only); expect a traditional parade of "precious", artfully presented morsels.

Rose Water *American*   25 | 18 | 22 | $42

Park Slope | 787 Union St. (6th Ave.) | Brooklyn | 718-783-3800 | www.rosewaterrestaurant.com

"Green" is the watchword at this Park Slope New American whose "fresh-from-the-farmer's-market" menu "constantly evolves" with the chef's choice of both "lowly and lofty ingredients"; the "big flavors" may contrast with the "tiny room", but not with the overall "attention to detail" and "outstanding service."

Rossini's *Italian*   23 | 19 | 25 | $59

Murray Hill | 108 E. 38th St. (bet. Lexington & Park Aves.) | 212-683-0135 | www.rossinisrestaurant.com

Think "very old world" to get the gist of this Murray Hill Northern Italian vet known for its "delicious" food, "professional service" and live opera Saturday night; if the "decor's getting a little tired", the prices will keep you "wide awake."

Rothmann's *Steak*   22 | 20 | 22 | $65

E 50s | 3 E. 54th St. (bet. 5th & Madison Aves.) | 212-319-5500 | www.rothmannssteakhouse.com

This East Midtowner "may not get its due" among the city's steak-house stars, but fans say it's a "serious contender" citing "fantastic" chops, "attentive" service and handsome "wood-and-linen" digs; given the strong "business" following, "corporate credit cards" absorb the "excessive" tabs.

Roth's Westside Steakhouse *Steak*   19 | 16 | 18 | $49

W 90s | 680 Columbus Ave. (93rd St.) | 212-280-4103 | www.rothswestsidesteakhouse.com

"Much needed on the UWS", this "dependable" chop shop embellishes its "solid" menu and "friendly" service with nightly "light jazz"; tabs are "not bad" for the genre, so most agree "you have to give it credit."

Rouge *French*   20 | 17 | 18 | $39

Forest Hills | 107-02 70th Rd. (Austin St.) | Queens | 718-793-5514

"Raising the bar in Forest Hills", this "inviting" bistro "fills a niche", dishing out "classic" French fare in a Left Bank setting; maybe it's "not exciting", but things pick up in the summer when "you can dine alfresco."

Royal Siam *Thai*   19 | 12 | 17 | $27

Chelsea | 240 Eighth Ave. (bet. 22nd & 23rd Sts.) | 212-741-1732

Typical "Thai value" keeps locals loyal to this "never-too-crowded" Chelsea "mainstay"; sure, the setting's "so-so" and there's "nothing unusual" on the plate, but what's there is "always good."

	FOOD	DECOR	SERVICE	COST

Roy's New York *Hawaiian* — 25 | 19 | 22 | $54

Financial District | Marriott Financial Ctr. | 130 Washington St.
(bet. Albany & Carlisle Sts.) | 212-266-6262 | www.roysnewyork.com
Fans of Roy Yamaguchi say "*mahalo*" to this Financial District outpost
of the chef's Hawaiian empire, where "delicate, delicious" fusion fare
can be savored "without the sunburn"; despite "high prices" and decor
that "transports you to a mall in the Midwest", many say it "doesn't
get the recognition it deserves."

RUB BBQ *BBQ* — 20 | 9 | 15 | $28

Chelsea | 208 W. 23rd St. (bet. 7th & 8th Aves.) | 212-524-4300 |
www.rubbbq.net
"No-nonsense" "Kansas City"–style barbecue is yours at this "rowdy"
Chelsea pit stop that will "cure any urges" for "messy", hickory-
smoked meat; ok, the setting and service are "not so special" and they
seem to "run out of some good stuff every night", but overall it's a
"solid contender in NYC's BBQ wars."

Ruby Foo's ◕ *Pan-Asian* — 19 | 21 | 17 | $42

W 40s | 1626 Broadway (49th St.) | 212-489-5600
W 70s | 2182 Broadway (77th St.) | 212-724-6700
www.brguestrestaurants.com
"Definitely not Chinatown", these "big, brash", party-centric Pan-Asians
serve a variety of "tasty" dishes in "flashy", "kitschy", "lacquered" settings that seem "turned up to 11"; they're "frenzied" "fun for the kids"
and "tourists", so regulars advise "go at off times – if there are any."

Rue 57 ◕ *French* — 19 | 18 | 17 | $45

W 50s | 60 W. 57th St. (6th Ave.) | 212-307-5656 | www.rue57.com
"Everyone gets what they like" at this "bustling" Midtowner that min-
gles midpriced French brasserie plates with sushi – a "strange" but
"convenient" combo; "on-and-off service" and "acoustic trauma" detract, but it is "strategically located" for lunch or "after Carnegie Hall."

Rughetta ⊠ *Italian* — 22 | 16 | 21 | $44

E 80s | 347 E. 85th St. (bet. 1st & 2nd Aves.) | 212-517-3118 |
www.rughetta.com
"Known only to locals", this versatile UES Italian works well for either
a "romantic evening" or a "casual night out"; the "authentic Roman"
cuisine is "excellent" and quite "reasonable", but the "narrow space"
can get "crowded" – "pity it's not bigger."

Russian Samovar ◕ *Continental* — 19 | 18 | 18 | $49

W 50s | 256 W. 52nd St. (bet. B'way & 8th Ave.) | 212-757-0168 |
www.russiansamovar.com
Caviar and "habit-forming flavored vodkas" collide at this Theater
District Continental that's straight out of "Mother Russia" with "soviet
service" and "KGB agent" look-alikes in attendance; the live piano music evokes "Moscow nights", albeit at "New York prices."

NEW Russian Tea Room *Continental/Russian* — 19 | 25 | 19 | $69

W 50s | 150 W. 57th St. (bet. 6th & 7th Aves.) | 212-581-7100 |
www.russiantearoomnyc.com
Back after a four-year hiatus, this Midtown "icon" just "slightly to the
left of Carnegie Hall" offers modern takes on Continental and Russian

classics at prices "fit for a czar"; even though it's "not what it once was", the "cheerfully gaudy" decor is little changed from Warner LeRoy's 1999 renovation, and if some sense an "identity crisis", it's "still an experience."

Ruth's Chris Steak House Steak

23	19	22	$66

W 50s | 148 W. 51st St. (bet. 6th & 7th Aves.) | 212-245-9600 | www.ruthschris.com

Yes, this Theater District link of the New Orleans–based steakhouse chain is ever "dependable" for "succulent" slabs of beef "dripping with butter" that are "just as delicious as they are expensive"; while service is "gracious", some find the ambiance more "Omaha" than "New York."

Sabor ● Nuevo Latino

∇ 19	16	16	$34

E 80s | 1725 Second Ave. (89th St.) | 212-369-9373

Back with an "eclectic" Nuevo Latino menu (and under nuevo ownership), this "welcoming", low-budget Yorkville "neighborhood" spot mixes "tasty", "ample-portioned tapas" with "strong sangria"; too bad the "crowded space" and "inattentive" service are "nothing special."

Sachiko's on Clinton ● Ⓜ Japanese

∇ 25	17	21	$56

LES | 25 Clinton St. (bet. Houston & Stanton Sts.) | 212-253-2900 | www.sachikosonclinton.com

Sushi and sashimi are "artfully presented" and "impeccably fresh" at this "low-profile" LES Japanese; "knowledgeable" staffers help navigate the "subtly inventive" plates and "comprehensive sake menu", though to some eyes the "calm" interior reads as "bland."

Sacred Chow Vegan/Vegetarian

∇ 23	13	21	$20

G Village | 227 Sullivan St. (bet. Bleecker & W. 3rd Sts.) | 212-337-0863 | www.sacredchow.com

For inexpensive kosher health food, try this Greenwich Village "secret" with its vegan "food from the gods" (there are "gluten-free" options too); adding to the authenticity, the "incredibly edible" offerings are dished out by servers "who look the part."

Sac's Place Pizza

∇ 21	13	17	$24

Astoria | 25-41 Broadway (29th St.) | Queens | 718-204-5002

"Worth-the-trip" coal-fired pizza comes out of the brick oven of this "unassuming", "family-run" Astoria Italian where "they sell it by the slice" too; maybe the other offerings fall short, but the "addictive" pies are "neighborhood favorites."

NEW Safran French/Vietnamese

∇ 20	20	18	$37

Chelsea | 88 Seventh Ave. (bet. 15th & 16th Sts.) | 212-929-1778 | www.safran88.com

"Unique" French-Vietnamese fusion fare lands on an "otherwise drab strip" of Chelsea at this coolly "fashionable", yet eminently affordable, spot; locals agree it's a "great addition to the neighborhood."

S'Agapo ● Greek

∇ 20	11	18	$35

Astoria | 34-21 34th Ave. (35th St.) | Queens | 718-626-0303

It's "easy to become a regular" at this "sweet", modestly priced Astoria Greek where service is "friendly" and the "no-frills" classics come "mom approved"; given that there's "nothing on the decor side" going on, the "outdoor seating" is a "saving grace."

	FOOD	DECOR	SERVICE	COST

Sahara ● *Turkish* | 20 | 15 | 16 | $27

Gravesend | 2337 Coney Island Ave. (bet. Aves. T & U) | Brooklyn | 718-376-8594 | www.saharapalace.com

Setting the "standard for Turkish" in Gravesend, this "vast bazaar" purveys "authentic" dishes "by the truckload" at "fabulous" prices; despite "erratic" service and "not breathtaking" decor ("dim the lights, please"), it's "hard to stop eating" here.

Saigon Grill ● *Vietnamese* | 22 | 12 | 15 | $24

G Village | 91-93 University Pl. (bet. 11th & 12th Sts.) | 212-982-3691
W 90s | 620 Amsterdam Ave. (90th St.) | 212-875-9072
www.saigongrill.com

"Phenomenal" eats, "budget" pricing and "chaotic" conditions say it all about these Vietnamese "mainstays"; despite "recent labor conflicts" that have suspended delivery, on-site your "food arrives immediately."

Sakagura *Japanese* | 24 | 21 | 22 | $47

E 40s | 211 E. 43rd St., downstairs (bet. 2nd & 3rd Aves.) | 212-953-7253 | www.sakagura.com

Hidden in the "basement of a random office building" near Grand Central, this "eccentric" Japanese *izakaya* is praised for its "wide sake selection" as well as its "deft" small plates; perhaps dinnertime tabs can "add up", but "it's a bargain for lunch."

Sala *Spanish* | 22 | 19 | 18 | $38

Flatiron | 35 W. 19th St. (bet. 5th & 6th Aves.) | 212-229-2300
NoHo | 344 Bowery (Great Jones St.) | 212-979-6606
www.salanyc.com

Full of "twentysomething tapas lovers", these "noisy", "date-worthy" Spaniards boast "on-point sangria" and "tempting" plates for "decent" dough; despite "long waits" to get in and "slow service", the "intimate" ambiance appeals to "romantic" types.

Salaam Bombay *Indian* | 20 | 16 | 18 | $34

TriBeCa | 317 Greenwich St. (bet. Duane & Reade Sts.) | 212-226-9400 | www.salaambombay.com

An "extensive" lunch buffet at the "bargain" price of $13.95 lures "office gangs" to this TriBeCa Indian that's "several cuts above the rest"; too bad the à la carte dinner menu is a bit more "hit-or-miss" and the interior "has seen better days."

Sal Anthony's Lanza *Italian* | 19 | 17 | 18 | $41

E Village | 168 First Ave. (bet. 10th & 11th Sts.) | 212-674-7014
Sal Anthony's S.P.Q.R. *Italian*
Little Italy | 133 Mulberry St. (bet. Grand & Hester Sts.) | 212-925-3120
www.salanthonys.com

This East Village–Little Italy pair is "fine" for "consistent" if "generic" Southern Italian dining; "generous portions" plus a "great prix fixe" draw an "older" following, and even if the decor is a bit "faded", sometimes "old school" is "what you want."

Sala Thai ● *Thai* | 21 | 13 | 17 | $27

E 80s | 1718 Second Ave. (bet. 89th & 90th Sts.) | 212-410-5557

There's "tasty" Thai at this "grown-up" UES neighborhood "sleeper" that's "been there forever"; "pleasant", "well-presented" standards and low prices compensate for "shabby surroundings" and service that's just "adequate"; P.S. "delivery arrives in a flash."

Salt 🛡 American
21	18	20	$41

SoHo | 58 MacDougal St. (bet. Houston & Prince Sts.) | 212-674-4968

Salt Bar ●🛡Ⓜ⇦ American
LES | 29A Clinton St. (bet. Houston & Stanton Sts.) | 212-979-8471
www.saltnyc.com

Known for its "homey", "robust" cooking, this SoHo New American is staffed by a "gracious" crew who manages to make the "tight", "communal table"-strewn space feel "cozy"; its LES offshoot is more of a "classy" drinks-and-nibbles joint, without a full-blown menu.

Salute! Italian/Mediterranean
19	20	18	$47

Murray Hill | 270 Madison Ave. (39th St.) | 212-213-3440 |
www.salutenyc.com

Murray Hill "suits" tuck into "savory power lunches" and eavesdrop on "great stock tips" at this "chic", midpriced Med-Italian; an "extensive" menu and "decent" wine list suggest they're "trying hard to please", "erratic" service and "expense-account prices" to the contrary.

Samba-Lé ●⇦ Brazilian
▽ 19	21	19	$42

E Village | 23 Ave. A (bet. Houston & 2nd Sts.) | 212-529-2919

Brazilian tapas washed down with cool caipirinhas keep this "original" East Villager full; given the "live samba music" on weekends and "noisy" ambiance, some see more scene than cuisine here.

Sambuca Italian
18	16	18	$38

W 70s | 20 W. 72nd St. (bet. Columbus Ave. & CPW) | 212-787-5656 |
www.sambucanyc.com

"Come hungry" to this "budget" UWS Italian that dishes out family-size platters so "ginormous" that you can "bring six people and order for one"; the nondescript setting is "less chaotic than Carmine's", while a separate sans-gluten menu lets everyone "eat freely."

Sammy's Roumanian Jewish
19	9	17	$49

LES | 157 Chrystie St. (Delancey St.) | 212-673-0330

"Oy gevalt", this Lower East Side "cardiologist's nightmare" may be the "last of its breed", what with its "heartburn"-inducing menu of Jewish standards that are "to die for (and from)"; expect a "meshuggah" scene out of a "'50s bar mitzvah" complete with a pianist providing another kind of "schmaltz."

San Domenico Italian
23	21	22	$75

W 50s | 240 Central Park S. (bet. B'way & 7th Ave.) | 212-265-5959 |
www.sandomeniconewyork.com

So "civilized" that "jackets are still required", this "timeless" CPS Italian now in its 20th year is the "calm", "elegant" home to chef Odette Fada's "refined" cuisine and a "caring staff" overseen by owner Tony May; granted, the "bill is as sophisticated as the food", but what else would you expect from such a "special-occasion treat"?

NEW Sandro's ●🛡 Italian
-	-	-	M

E 80s | 306 E. 81st St. (bet. 1st & 2nd Aves.) | 212-288-7374

On a quiet UES block, chef Sandro Fioriti has revived his 1980s trattoria in a modern, white brick–walled space; it serves as an attractive backdrop for midpriced Roman-style meals that go down nicely with a house-infused grappa.

San Luigi *Italian* | 16 | 13 | 14 | $34 |

W 70s | 311 Amsterdam Ave. (bet. 74th & 75th Sts.) | 212-362-8828
This UWS Italian "new kid on the block" provides "hefty portions" but rather "average" flavors in a setting that's a bit too "suburban" for many ("TVs everywhere are a turnoff"); "affordable" tabs and "low wine markups" help explain the "overwhelmed" service.

San Pietro ⑤ *Italian* | 24 | 19 | 23 | $73 |

E 50s | 18 E. 54th St. (bet. 5th & Madison Aves.) | 212-753-9015 | www.sanpietro.net
"Business titans" rule at this "traditional" Midtown Italian that's home to an "elite" crowd of lunchtime "regulars" (after dark, theatergoers supplant the "power hungry"); living up to its "high-end" standards, the cooking is "fabulous", the service "polished" and the pricing "in the hedge fund manager's realm."

Sant Ambroeus *Italian* | 22 | 19 | 19 | $57 |

E 70s | 1000 Madison Ave. (bet. 77th & 78th Sts.) | 212-570-2211
W Village | 259 W. Fourth St. (Perry St.) | 212-604-9254
www.santambroeus.com
"Fashionistas pretend to eat" their salads at this "super-soigné" duo where the "excellent" Milanese fare lures in everyone from "art dealers" to "society" dames to matinee idols; no kidding, the "people-watching" is primo, ditto the "expensive-but-you're-worth-it-darling" prices.

Sapa *French/Vietnamese* | 22 | 25 | 20 | $55 |

Flatiron | 43 W. 24th St. (bet. B'way & 6th Ave.) | 212-929-1800 | www.sapanyc.com
Maybe the "oh-so-cool" setting (and "theatrical" loo) is the "most impressive aspect" of this Flatiron "experience", however, the "adventurous" French-Vietnamese fusion fare more than holds its own; just beware, "when the bar is in full holler", it can be a tad too "sceney"; N.B. the departure of chef Patricia Yeo puts its Food rating in question.

Sapori D'Ischia Ⓜ *Italian* | 25 | 17 | 21 | $46 |

Woodside | 55-15 37th Ave. (56th St.) | Queens | 718-446-1500
Obscured "amid Woodside warehouses", this daytime specialty food shop morphs into a "gourmet restaurant" at night serving some pretty "fabulous" Italian food – so long as you don't mind "salami hanging over your head"; P.S. on Thursdays, live opera singers are the "big draw."

Sapphire Indian *Indian* | 20 | 18 | 19 | $41 |

W 60s | 1845 Broadway (bet. 60th & 61st Sts.) | 212-245-4444 | www.sapphireny.com
For "convenience to Lincoln Center", this Indian gem off Columbus Circle is geographically desirable with "better-than-average" fare that packs more "flavor" than the "bland" room; it may be "a little pricey" for the genre, but the $12.95 lunch buffet is a bona fide "bargain."

Sapporo East ◑ *Japanese* | ∇ 21 | 9 | 16 | $26 |

E Village | 164 First Ave. (10th St.) | 212-260-1330
"So-fresh" sushi and other "belly-filling" Japanese dishes prompt "long lines" at this "no-frills" East Village "greasy spoon"; luckily, "ef-

	FOOD	DECOR	SERVICE	COST

"ficient" servers keep things "quick", and the "bargain" prices compensate for being "packed in like the 4 train at rush hour."

Sarabeth's *American* `20` `17` `17` `$33`

Chelsea | Chelsea Mkt. | 75 Ninth Ave. (bet. 15th & 16th Sts.) | 212-989-2424 | www.sarabeth.com
E 70s | Whitney Museum | 945 Madison Ave. (75th St.) | 212-570-3670 | www.sarabeth.com Ⓜ
E 90s | 1295 Madison Ave. (bet. 92nd & 93rd Sts.) | 212-410-7335 | www.sarabeth.com
W 50s | 40 Central Park S. (bet. 5th & 6th Aves.) | 212-826-5959 | www.sarabethscps.com
W 80s | 423 Amsterdam Ave. (bet. 80th & 81st Sts.) | 212-496-6280 | www.sarabeth.com

These "genteel", "preppy" Americans boast "loyal followings" of ladies thanks to their "brunch for the ages" served in settings that lie somewhere between "Laura Ashley" and "Martha Stewart"; "crazy lines" and "inattentive service" can be avoided by showing up during "off hours."

Saravanaas *Indian* `▽ 23` `11` `14` `$21`

Gramercy | 81 Lexington Ave. (26th St.) | 212-679-0204 | www.saravanaas.com

The "excellent" meatless menu at this "authentic" Gramercy South Indian opens the gates to "dosa heaven"; though service is "not too helpful" and the sari decor is "nothing to speak of", the "ridiculously cheap" tabs at this "veggie paradise" "make up for everything."

Sardi's Ⓜ *Continental* `16` `21` `19` `$52`

W 40s | 234 W. 44th St. (bet. B'way & 8th Ave.) | 212-221-8440 | www.sardis.com

"It is what it is" – a "Theaterland tradition" since 1921 with "prosaic" Continental cuisine that's eclipsed by the "caricatures of celebrities" on the walls; though the "glory days" may be long gone, it's still a "timeless" piece of "old NY" with waiters to match.

Sarge's Deli ● *Deli* `19` `7` `14` `$23`

Murray Hill | 548 Third Ave. (bet. 36th & 37th Sts.) | 212-679-0442 | www.sargesdeli.com

"Matzo ball soup at midnight" is "no problem" at this "real-deal" 24/7 Murray Hill deli, a "been-there-forever" "time machine" serving "humongous" sandwiches made with meats pickled in-house; "depressing" decor and "crusty" service are part of the shtick.

🆕 Sasabune Ⓢ *Japanese* `▽ 26` `10` `20` `$83`

E 70s | 401 E. 73rd St. (bet. 1st & York Aves.) | 212-249-8583

It's "omakase or the highway" at this UES "sushi boot camp" where chef Kenji Takahashi will "direct what and how you should eat"; there are "no rolls" and "no menus", just the "freshest fish money can buy" at correspondingly "high prices."

🆕 Saucy ● *Eclectic* `-` `-` `-` `M`

E 70s | 1409 York Ave. (75th St.) | 212-249-3700 | www.saucyny.com

The gimmick at this midpriced Yorkville Eclectic is a menu that lets diners choose from 50 different sauces to be paired with chicken, beef or pasta; the decor is equally quirky, featuring large spice-filled burlap bags hung from a mirrored ceiling.

	FOOD	DECOR	SERVICE	COST

☒ Saul *American* — 27 | 19 | 24 | $57

Boerum Hill | 140 Smith St. (bet. Bergen & Dean Sts.) | Brooklyn | 718-935-9844 | www.saulrestaurant.com

Helmed by chef-owner Saul Bolton, this Boerum Hill New American "deserves all the raves" for its "sophisticated" yet "unpretentious" seasonal menu; a "remarkably helpful" staff, "civilized" setting and fair pricing add up to a "top-flight" experience.

Savann *French/Mediterranean* — 19 | 14 | 18 | $40

W 70s | 414 Amsterdam Ave. (bet. 79th & 80th Sts.) | 212-580-0202 | www.savann.com

This UWS "neighborhood standby" is a "pleasant" stop for "competent", "low-priced" French-Med dishes and also offers a "calm" atmosphere for conversation "without screaming"; its "underrated" status may explain why it's "not more crowded."

Savoia *Pizza* — 21 | 16 | 18 | $29

Carroll Gardens | 277 Smith St. (bet. Degraw & Sackett Sts.) | Brooklyn | 718-797-2727

"Fabulous" Neapolitan-style pizza from a wood-fired oven is the forte of this "casual" Carroll Gardens Italian, but there's also a "short list" of "hearty", equally "flavorful" main dishes; the "warm" albeit "unsophisticated" setting is particularly "good for families with kids."

NEW savorNY *Eclectic* — - | - | - | M

LES | 63 Clinton St. (bet. Rivington & Stanton Sts.) | 212-358-7125 | www.savornyrestaurant.com

Snug is the word for this tiny LES newcomer serving affordable, globetrotting small plates off a menu split into three playful categories – 'forks, fingers and finales'; the wine list is sorted by tasting notes, rather than the usual red/white divide.

Savoy *American/Mediterranean* — 24 | 20 | 22 | $54

SoHo | 70 Prince St. (Crosby St.) | 212-219-8570 | www.savoynyc.com

Peter Hoffman's SoHo "treasure" uses the "products of area farmers" in "imaginative" ways as part of his Med–New American cooking; upstairs is more formal than the "convivial" first floor, but despite "romantic" fireplaces on both levels, some say a renovation several years back "killed the charm."

Scaletta *Italian* — 21 | 18 | 22 | $51

W 70s | 50 W. 77th St. (bet. Columbus Ave. & CPW) | 212-769-9191 | www.scalettaristorante.com

A "welcome respite" for the UWS, this "sedate" Northern Italian draws "mature" types with "refined" cooking and "accommodating" service; the "civilized" setting is conducive to "lingering conversations", even if younger folks feel out of place and outpriced.

Scalinatella ◐ *Italian* — 25 | 16 | 21 | $74

E 60s | 201 E. 61st St. (3rd Ave.) | 212-207-8280

"Sensational" "*molto Italiano*" classics come "from Capri with love" at this UES rock-walled cellar; the genial mood and "courteous" staff help blunt the considerable "sticker shock" – particularly the "prices of the specials", which are "conveniently not mentioned."

	FOOD	DECOR	SERVICE	COST

Z Scalini Fedeli 🅂 *Italian*   26 | 25 | 25 | $83

TriBeCa | 165 Duane St. (bet. Greenwich & Hudson Sts.) | 212-528-0400 |
www.scalinifedeli.com

From the "secluded cobblestone street" out front to the "serene"
mood inside, this TriBeCa "delight" (the original Bouley) has got "special occasion" written all over it; chef Michael Cetrulo's "superb"
Northern Italian cuisine and the staff's "impeccable" service justify
costs that are definitely worth the $65 per head dinner prix fixe.

Scarlatto ● *Italian*   21 | 18 | 19 | $43

W 40s | 250 W. 47th St. (bet. B'way & 8th Ave.) | 212-730-4535 |
www.scarlattonyc.com

"Blowups from *Roman Holiday*" serve as decor at this Theater District
Northern Italian set in the former digs of the much "missed" Pierre au
Tunnel (the "show must go on"); it's already "very popular" due to its
simple formula: "big portions" at "extremely reasonable prices."

Schiller's ● *Eclectic*   18 | 19 | 16 | $36

LES | 131 Rivington St. (Norfolk St.) | 212-260-4555 | www.schillersny.com
Think "Balthazar for emerging adults" to get the gist of this "high-
volume" LES Eclectic from Keith McNally that lures the "youthful" with
quirky cocktails and "straightforward" bistro grub; though it may be
"too sceney" for oldsters (i.e. anyone over 40), the "unisex bathrooms" have universal appeal.

Scottadito Osteria Toscana *Italian*   ▽ 19 | 20 | 19 | $37

Park Slope | 788A Union St. (bet. 6th & 7th Aves.) | Brooklyn |
718-636-4800 | www.scottadito.com

"Robust" Tuscan cuisine based on "fresh, organic" ingredients is yours at
this Park Slope Italian that looks like a "rustic farmhouse"; the amorous
adore the "fireplace" and "romantic wine cellar", while pragmatists
are glad that they don't charge too much and "now take credit cards."

SEA *Thai*   20 | 21 | 16 | $25

E Village | 75 Second Ave. (bet. 4th & 5th Sts.) | 212-228-5505
Williamsburg | 114 N. Sixth St. (Berry St.) | Brooklyn | 718-384-8850 ●
www.spicenyc.net

The Williamsburg branch of this "trendy" Thai twosome is an "eye-
popping" thing with a "party central" vibe, "boom-box" acoustics and
its own "pond and Buddha", while its plain-Jane East Village sibling
"takes tight seating to new levels"; either way, the vittles are tasty,
"cheap and filling."

Sea Grill 🅂 *Seafood*   24 | 24 | 22 | $65

W 40s | Rockefeller Ctr. | 19 W. 49th St. (bet. 5th & 6th Aves.) |
212-332-7610 | www.theseagrillnyc.com

"So what if it's touristy", the "sublime seafood" still shines at this
"Rock Center favorite" where "window seats are a must" in the winter
to catch the "views of the Christmas tree" and ice skating rink; sure,
prices are "prime", but worth it for "stylish", "special-occasion" dining.

NEW Sea Salt ●🅂 *Seafood*   - | - | - | M

E Village | 99 Second Ave. (bet. 5th & 6th Sts.) | 212-979-5400
A display of seafood on ice anchors this East Village Med where chef
Orhan Yegen grills the day's catch, serving it either priced by the

| | FOOD | DECOR | SERVICE | COST |

pound or as part of an à la carte menu; the airy, tile-lined space has a fresh modern feel that's unusual for lower Second Avenue.

NEW Sense ●Ⓜ Japanese
| | – | – | – | M |

Williamsburg | 106 N. Sixth St. (bet. Berry St. & Wythe Ave.) | Brooklyn | 718-218-8666

Hyper-stylized but approachable, this new Williamsburg sensation welcomes diners with tricky lighting and a red-and-black color scheme that recalls a nightclub; the Japanese offerings – heavy on the sushi – seem almost incidental to the scene.

Serafina ● Italian
| | 18 | 15 | 15 | $41 |

E 50s | 38 E. 58th St. (bet. Madison & Park Aves.) | 212-832-8888 🚱
E 60s | 29 E. 61st St. (bet. Madison & Park Aves.) | 212-702-9898
E 70s | 1022 Madison Ave., 2nd fl. (79th St.) | 212-734-2676
NoHo | 393 Lafayette St. (4th St.) | 212-995-9595
W 50s | Dream Hotel | 210 W. 55th St. (B'way) | 212-315-1700
www.serafinarestaurant.com

Though each location of this "chic" Italian quintet "has a different feel", they all share "delicious thin-crust pizzas and salads" that attract an "energized", "Euro" following; critics note that "service could be improved – if there was any."

Serendipity 3 ● Dessert
| | 18 | 19 | 14 | $29 |

E 60s | 225 E. 60th St. (bet. 2nd & 3rd Aves.) | 212-838-3531 | www.serendipity3.com

"Whimsy" is on the menu at this "kitschy" East Side dessert parlor-cum-toy shop that looks like a "cross between grandma's attic and Alice's tea party"; while it's renowned for its "unforgettable" frozen hot chocolate that draws kids of all ages, less sweet are the "rude" staff and "tiresome", "touristy" lines.

Sette ● Italian
| | 18 | 15 | 17 | $38 |

Chelsea | 191 Seventh Ave. (bet. 21st & 22nd Sts.) | 212-675-5935 | www.settenyc.com

Maybe it "won't knock your socks off", but this "basic" Chelsea Italian is still a "good fallback" for "consistent", "midpriced" dining; a "neighborhood crowd" mixes with "see-and-be-seen types" and tries to forget the "loud" acoustics and "absentminded service."

Sette Enoteca e Cucina Italian
| | 19 | 15 | 17 | $38 |

Park Slope | 207 Seventh Ave. (3rd St.) | Brooklyn | 718-499-7767 | www.setteparkslope.com

"Creative variations on Italian staples" abetted by an "affordable" wine list ("20 bottles for $20" apiece) are highlights of this Park Sloper; service veers from "helpful" to "amateurish", while the former patio, now an enclosed "year-round" atrium, draws only middling responses.

Sette Mezzo ●≠ Italian
| | 23 | 14 | 18 | $65 |

E 70s | 969 Lexington Ave. (bet. 70th & 71st Sts.) | 212-472-0400

Some dub it a "private club passing as a restaurant", and it certainly "helps if they know your face" at this UES "CEO" Italian serving *bellissimo* food "prepared with love"; "service can be rushed" and the "cash-only" pricing is as "uppity" as the scene, but the "rich and famous like it" and that's all that counts.

	FOOD	DECOR	SERVICE	COST

Seven ●☑ *American* | 18 | 18 | 17 | $41 |

Chelsea | 350 Seventh Ave. (bet. 29th & 30th Sts.) | 212-967-1919 |
www.sevenbarandgrill.com

A "nice surprise" near MSG and Penn Station, this New American
"oasis" works for pre- or post-event dining as well as "business
lunches"; it's more a "white tablecloth" place than a pub, yet the bar is
always "bustling" here.

718 *French* | 21 | 21 | 20 | $39 |

Astoria | 35-01 Ditmars Blvd. (35th St.) | Queens | 718-204-5553 |
www.718restaurant.com

"Inventive" French cooking with a slight "Spanish flair" and "chic"
loungelike quarters manned by a "sexy staff" ensure this Astorian
shines as one of the neighborhood's "bright spots"; even those put
off by the "limited menu" gravitate to the "sidewalk seating" for a
"cocktail or two."

Sevilla ● *Spanish* | 23 | 14 | 20 | $38 |

W Village | 62 Charles St. (W. 4th St.) | 212-929-3189 |
www.sevillarestaurantandbar.com

After 67 years, "only the prices have changed" at this "garlicky"
Village Spaniard that's a "sentimental favorite" for "addictive" paella
and sangria "on the cheap"; the "well-seasoned waiters" and "run-
down" decor provide "plenty of character."

Sezz Medi' *Mediterranean/Pizza* | 21 | 16 | 18 | $32 |

W 100s | 1260 Amsterdam Ave. (123rd St.) | 212-932-2901 |
www.sezzmedi.com

"Superb brick-oven pizza" backed up by "consistently tasty" Med
mains mark this UWS "oasis" that lends some "sophistication to a
strip of generic restaurants" in Morningside Heights; "uneven service"
and undistinguished decor seem to be its only shortcomings.

Sfoglia ☑ *Italian* | 23 | 19 | 20 | $56 |

E 90s | 1402 Lexington Ave. (92nd St.) | 212-831-1402 |
www.sfogliarestaurant.com

Carnegie Hill dwellers are delighted to have a "destination restaurant in the neighborhood", this "seriously good", seriously "tiny"
Northern Italian that's "all the rage" and thus "impossible to get
into" ("if it were any smaller, it would be a phone booth"); thus,
"reserve ahead" – way ahead.

Shabu-Shabu 70 *Japanese* | 20 | 13 | 22 | $37 |

E 70s | 314 E. 70th St. (bet. 1st & 2nd Aves.) | 212-861-5635

"Super-super" say fans of the cook-it-yourself "signature dish" at this
affordable UES Japanese that also vends "expertly prepared sushi";
"friendly" service that "feels like home" makes up for decor in need of
an "extreme makeover."

Shabu-Tatsu *Japanese* | ▽ 20 | 11 | 16 | $34 |

E Village | 216 E. 10th St. (bet. 1st & 2nd Aves.) | 212-477-2972

"Attentive" staffers are ready to "explain the ins and outs" of cooking
your meal at this low-budget East Village Japanese that specializes in
shabu-shabu and sukiyaki; "drab" surroundings to the contrary, it's
"great for a group" in the mood for something "tasty and different."

	FOOD	DECOR	SERVICE	COST

Shaffer City Oyster Bar & Grill 🗷 *Seafood* — 21 | 15 | 20 | $48

Flatiron | 5 W. 21st St. (bet. 5th & 6th Aves.) | 212-255-9827 |
www.shaffercity.com

"Fresh is the word" for this "unpretentious" Flatiron seafooder run by
the "entertaining" Jay Shaffer; the "huge assortment" of "first-class"
oysters and fish may not be cheap, but the "suburban mall" decor is.

Shake Shack *Hamburgers* — 23 | 13 | 12 | $14

Flatiron | Madison Square Park | 23rd St. | 212-889-6600 |
www.shakeshack.com

Danny Meyer's alfresco "destination" in Madison Square Park vends
"craveable" burgers, hot dogs and "mind-freezingly thick" shakes; given
the high quality and modest prices, expect "legendary" lines, but at
least it's now open year-round, with hours varying seasonally.

Shanghai Cuisine ⇄ *Chinese* — ▽ 21 | 12 | 14 | $22

Chinatown | 89 Bayard St. (Mulberry St.) | 212-732-8988

"Perfectly cooked, very affordable" soup dumplings are the signature
dish at this Chinatown "definition of a hole-in-the-wall" that also offers "tasty" Shanghainese "staples"; downsides include a "cash-only"
policy and chop-chop "fast" service.

Shanghai Pavilion *Chinese* — 21 | 19 | 20 | $36

E 70s | 1378 Third Ave. (bet. 78th & 79th Sts.) | 212-585-3388

"Impressively authentic" Shanghai dishes and a "polished staff" make
this atypically "fancy" UES Chinese a "clear favorite in the neighborhood"; even better, it "feels like it should be expensive", but isn't.

Sharz Cafe & Wine Bar *Mediterranean* — 21 | 15 | 21 | $38

E 80s | 435 E. 86th St. (bet. 1st & York Aves.) | 212-876-7282

"Much needed on the far East Side", this Med bistro "mainstay" supplies "fresh, satisfying" food for "bargain" tabs; the "intimate" digs
can get "crowded", but "knowledgeable" servers and a "wonderful"
wine selection make for a "good night out."

NEW Sheep Station ●⇄ *Australian* — ▽ 19 | 17 | 18 | $24

Park Slope | 149 Fourth Ave. (Douglass St.) | Brooklyn | 718-857-4337 |
www.sheepstation.net

"Aussie comfort food" lands in Park Slope at this "laid-back" newcomer where expats, "singles" and "artist types" dig the "Down Under
vibe" and prices; although the "pioneering" eats "fall flat" for a few, an
"interesting selection of beer and wine" draws universal huzzahs.

Shelly's Trattoria *Italian* — 20 | 17 | 19 | $57

W 50s | 41 W. 57th St. (bet. 5th & 6th Aves.) | 212-245-2422 |
www.shellysnewyork.com

Shelly Fireman's ever-evolving Midtowner has now added Italian
items to its former chops–and–raw bar lineup to mixed response (a
"winner" vs. a "step down"); fortunately, it still boasts "City Center"
convenience, "prompt" service and solid value.

Shula's Steak House *Steak* — 20 | 19 | 19 | $65

W 40s | Westin NY Times Sq. | 270 W. 43rd St. (bet. B'way & 8th Ave.) |
212-201-2776 | www.donshula.com

Coach Don Shula's Times Square chophouse is a shrine to "all things
football", starting with its "pigskin menus"; while the Angus beef is

| | FOOD | DECOR | SERVICE | COST |

"reliable" enough, it's not in the same league as NYC's top steak-houses, so critics blow the whistle on the "formulaic" digs and "prices that'll send you to a heart doctor before the cholesterol does."

Shun Lee Cafe ● *Chinese* | 21 | 16 | 17 | $40 |

W 60s | 43 W. 65th St. (bet. Columbus Ave. & CPW) | 212-769-3888 |
www.shunleewest.com

Dim sum carts "in constant motion" are the draw at this Lincoln Center-area Chinese that's "more casual" than its "big sister next door" (and more "reasonably priced"); though the "black-and-white checkerboard" decor may "need a face-lift", the new sushi options are a "plus."

Shun Lee Palace ● *Chinese* | 24 | 20 | 22 | $55 |

E 50s | 155 E. 55th St. (bet. Lexington & 3rd Aves.) | 212-371-8844 |
www.shunleepalace.com

The "emperor would be proud" of Michael Tong's "opulent" Midtown Chinese that makes a "lavish impression" with its "fusion-free", "museum-quality meals" and "second-to-none" service; if you "like to dress up" and are prepared to pay "premium prices", this "oldie but goodie" is certainly "worth the splurge."

Shun Lee West ● *Chinese* | 23 | 21 | 21 | $53 |

W 60s | 43 W. 65th St. (bet. Columbus Ave. & CPW) | 212-595-8895 |
www.shunleewest.com

"Deservedly an institution", this "gourmet" Chinese near Lincoln Center offers "interesting", "refined" dishes delivered by a "swift" staff in a "wow"-inducing black-and-white room; though diners like the dragons on the lacquered walls, they're ambivalent about the "high prices."

Siam Square Ⓜ *Thai* | ∇ 24 | 19 | 21 | $28 |

Bronx | 564 Kappock St. (Henry Hudson Pkwy.) | 718-432-8200 |
www.siamsq.com

A "real find in Riverdale", this "quiet" Thai offers modestly priced, "fusion-style" specials and "solid" standards "made with ingredients you can clearly identify"; "courteous" servers add to the "warm" vibe.

NEW Silent H *Vietnamese* | - | - | - | I |

Williamsburg | 79 Berry St. (N. 9th St.) | Brooklyn | 718-218-7063 |
www.silenthbrooklyn.com

Filling a Vietnamese niche in Williamsburg, this long, airy cafe is a natural fit for its funky neighborhood with wooden benches and tall windows overlooking the street; the menu is similarly area-appropriate given its low prices and BYO policy.

Sip Sak *Turkish* | 20 | 13 | 15 | $28 |

E 40s | 928 Second Ave. (bet. 49th & 50th Sts.) | 212-583-1900 |
www.sip-sak.com

"Flavor abounds" at this "boisterous" U.N.-area Turk that's best known for its "eccentric" chef-owner who provides "lots of drama"; the list of "inexpensive", "freshly prepared" dishes "goes on forever", but regulars suggest making a meal from a "sampler of meze."

Sistina ● *Italian* | 24 | 18 | 20 | $67 |

E 80s | 1555 Second Ave. (bet. 80th & 81st Sts.) | 212-861-7660
First-rate, "sophisticated" Italian cooking comes with a "big dollop of ingenuity" at this "civilized" UES vet that draws a smart neighbor-

	FOOD	DECOR	SERVICE	COST

hood crowd; "attentive" service and a "terrific wine list" trump the "expensive" tab.

NEW 67 Burger M *Hamburgers*
∇ 21 | 14 | 16 | $14

Fort Greene | 67 Lafayette Ave. (Fulton St.) | Brooklyn | 718-797-7150 | www.67burger.com

"Tasty burgers" meet "quirky atmosphere" at this "relaxed" BAM-convenient Fort Greener where one "big", "tasty" patty and some "scrumptious fries" are nearly "enough to feed a family"; thanks to the "special brews" on tap, the "slow" service is easier to overlook.

S'mac *American*
19 | 9 | 14 | $13

E Village | 345 E. 12th St. (bet. 1st & 2nd Aves.) | 212-358-7912 | www.smacnyc.com

"Blow your low-carb diet" at this "funky" East Village American, a "one-trick pony" serving only mac 'n' cheese in "sizzling skillets" (either "pre-designed concoctions" or "make-your-own combos"); the portions are "large", the space "tiny" and the prices a "bargain."

Smith & Wollensky *Steak*
23 | 18 | 20 | $66

E 40s | 797 Third Ave. (49th St.) | 212-753-1530 | www.smithandwollensky.com

This "macho" Midtown steakhouse is a "classic", "clubby" spot where "the boys go" to exercise their "expense accounts" on "big slabs of beef" and fine wines; those seeking to "tone it down a little" hit Wollensky's Grill next door, with super burgers, lower prices and later hours.

NEW Smoke Joint *BBQ*
23 | 13 | 18 | $17

Fort Greene | 87 S. Elliot Pl. (Lafayette Ave.) | Brooklyn | 718-797-1011 | www.thesmokejoint.com

Small on space but big on flavor, this "no-frills" Fort Greene newcomer near BAM "hits the spot" for "darn good BBQ" smoked on-site over a variety of woods; a "kooky" but "friendly" staff and "reasonable prices" make it all the more "addictive."

Smorgas Chef *Scandinavian*
19 | 14 | 18 | $33

E 40s | 924 Second Ave. (49th St.) | 212-486-1411 ●
Financial District | 53 Stone St. (William St.) | 212-422-3500
W Village | 283 W. 12th St. (4th St.) | 212-243-7073 ●
www.smorgaschef.com

A "welcome change from the usual", these "inexpensive", "almost authentic" Scandinavians specialize in traditional items like meatballs, gravlax and lingonberries; decor skews "shabby", except for the "charming" Financial District satellite.

Snack *Greek*
∇ 24 | 11 | 17 | $26

SoHo | 105 Thompson St. (bet. Prince & Spring Sts.) | 212-925-1040

Appropriately "snack-size", this SoHo Greek "matchbox" is a "haven" for "high-class" Hellenica at "unbeatable prices" ("best food I've ever had in a closet"); plan on "getting to know your neighbors intimately" – "if you can get a table", that is.

Snack Taverna *Greek*
22 | 16 | 18 | $41

W Village | 63 Bedford St. (Morton St.) | 212-929-3499

Hellenic dishes arrive with a "serious gourmet twist" at Snack's bigger, pricier Village sibling that recruits regulars with an "upscale yet down-

	FOOD	DECOR	SERVICE	COST

town" vibe; the wine list is "well chosen", service "informal but informative" and the Greek coffee "stronger than Hercules."

Soba Nippon Japanese ▽ 22 16 19 $34

W 50s | 19 W. 52nd St. (bet. 5th & 6th Aves.) | 212-489-2525

"Lunchtime is busy", but this affordable Japanese soba shop still supplies a semblance of "serenity" in the "frenzy of Midtown" with its "bamboo walls" and "attentive" staff; "soba connoisseurs" report that the "delicious namesake noodles" are made "fresh from their own buckwheat farm."

Soba-ya Japanese 24 17 20 $29

E Village | 229 E. Ninth St. (bet. 2nd & 3rd Aves.) | 212-533-6966 | www.sobaya-nyc.com

For a "perfect slurp", check out this "buzzy" East Village Japanese where a "rich variety of soba" are "handmade on-site"; since the staff is as "sweet" as the tabs, it's naturally "very popular", so "just ignore the packs of NYU students – they're harmless."

NEW Socialista Cuban - - - E

W Village | 505 West St. (bet. Horatio & Jane Sts.) | 212-929-4303 | www.socialista.us

The latest challenger for the 'it' restaurant crown is this new Cuban in the far West Village, set in a faux-distressed space channeling Hemingway's Havana; in contrast to the name, getting in is strictly capitalista thanks to a secret reservations phone number.

Soda Shop ⊕ American/Dessert ▽ 19 23 17 $19

TriBeCa | Cosmopolitan Hotel | 125 Chambers St. (bet. Church St. & W. B'way) | 212-571-1100 | www.sodashopnewyork.com

"Kids of all ages" dig the "old-fashioned" American comfort chow at this "mom-and-pop shop" in TriBeCa outfitted in "retro" soda fountain style; serving "mostly desserts" (plus "candy you haven't seen since childhood"), it's a "super-nostalgic" trip that's particularly "good for families" with kids.

Sofrito ● Puerto Rican 22 20 18 $39

E 50s | 400 E. 57th St. (bet. 1st Ave. & Sutton Pl.) | 212-754-5999 | www.sofritony.com

Jimmy Rodriguez's latest "hot, hot, hot" spot supplies "upscale" Puerto Rican specialties that are "surprisingly inexpensive" given the "ritzy" Sutton Place address; too bad about the "spotty" service, but few notice, distracted by the "loud acoustics" and "big-time singles scene."

NEW Solace American - - - M

E 60s | 406 E. 64th St. (bet. 1st & York Aves.) | 212-750-0434

Situated in a converted UES townhouse, this inviting new arrival headed by chef-owner David Regueiro (ex Aureole) serves seasonal New Americana in a white-tablecloth setting; while its polished interior is welcomingly warm, the spacious back patio may be the real star here.

Solera ⊠ Spanish 22 19 21 $55

E 50s | 216 E. 53rd St. (bet. 2nd & 3rd Aves.) | 212-644-1166 | www.soleranyc.com

There's "superb Spanish food" and "fine takes on classic tapas" at this East Midtown brownstone duplex; "attentive service" and "quiet", "pleasant" environs make it especially appealing even if it's on the pricey side.

Solo *Mediterranean* ▽ 22 | 23 | 19 | $71
E 50s | Sony Plaza Atrium | 550 Madison Ave. (bet. 55th & 56th Sts.) | 212-833-7800 | www.solonyc.com
"Kosher chic" is alive and well at this "high-class" Midtown Med that's a "serious power scene for the Jewish community" – credit its "elegant" ambiance and "wonderful" glatt cuisine, not the fluctuating service and "overly expensive" pricing.

Sol y Sombra ◐ *Spanish* ▽ 19 | 15 | 18 | $37
W 80s | 462 Amsterdam Ave. (bet. 82nd & 83rd Sts.) | 212-400-4036
"Relaxed" and "underappreciated", this UWS Spaniard is a "perfect light-bite" locus for "quality" tapas washed down with "*excelente*" sangria; still, both decor and service "need polishing" and "it can get expensive if you order enough to get really full."

Son Cubano ☒ *Cuban* 21 | 21 | 19 | $47
Meatpacking | 405 W. 14th St. (bet. 9th Ave. & Washington St.) | 212-366-1640 | www.soncubanonyc.com
"Meaningful conversation is unlikely" at this "clubbish" Meatpacking District Cuban where "thunderous" live music and "*fantastico*" drinks fuel the "celebratory mood"; though the midpriced "food is better than it has to be", it's beside the point once the "sangria starts flowing."

Song ⊄ *Thai* 24 | 17 | 19 | $21
Park Slope | 295 Fifth Ave. (bet. 1st & 2nd Sts.) | Brooklyn | 718-965-1108
"Cheaper than eating at home", this "McDonald's priced" Park Slope Thai puts out "delicious" dishes that are "served quick"; but like its sibling, Joya, the "deafeningly loud" acoustics and industrial "concrete bunker" design "drown out any chance at conversation."

Sorrel ℳ⊄ *American* ▽ 23 | 18 | 20 | $39
Prospect Heights | 605 Carlton Ave. (St. Marks Ave.) | Brooklyn | 718-622-1190
Hidden "on a quiet residential block" in Prospect Heights, this "little known", "cash-only" New American purveys an "excellent" seasonal menu that "changes daily"; despite the high "quality-to-cost ratio", it remains undiscovered.

Sosa Borella ◐ *Argentinean/Italian* 21 | 16 | 19 | $38
W 50s | 832 Eighth Ave. (50th St.) | 212-262-7774 | www.sosaborella.com
The Italian-Argentinean fusion at this Theater District "find" is "not so crazy", yielding an "interesting" menu that covers both countries' cuisines; thanks to its "casual vibe", "efficient" service and moderate tabs, it's winning a strong local following.

NEW Soto ◐☒ *Japanese* - | - | - | E
G Village | 357 Sixth Ave. (bet. Washington Pl. & W. 4th St.) | 212-414-3088
Atlanta sushi master Sotohiro Kosugi makes his NYC debut with this new high-end entry set in an unassuming Village storefront; look for unusual sushi and sashimi airlifted from Japan and Alaska, but remember such quality can't come cheap.

	FOOD	DECOR	SERVICE	COST

NEW Southern Hospitality ◐ *Southern* — | — | — | I

E 70s | 1460 Second Ave. (bet. 76th & 77th Sts.) | 212-249-1001 |
www.southernhospitalitybbq.com

Celeb ownership is the hook at the new UES Southerner from pop star
Justin Timberlake; bearing more than a casual resemblance to Brother
Jimmy's across the street, it's done up in faux honky-tonk style and
priced with frat boys' limited budgets in mind.

South Fin Grill *Seafood/Steak* 20 | 24 | 17 | $51

Staten Island | 300 Father Capodanno Blvd. (Sand Ln.) | 718-447-7679 |
www.southfingrill.com

"Sensational" views of the Verrazano Bridge grace this Staten Island
surf 'n' turfer perched "right on the boardwalk"; despite "inconsistent"
food and "forgetful" service, the outdoor deck is "as good as it gets."

☑ Sparks Steak House Ⓢ *Steak* 25 | 19 | 22 | $72

E 40s | 210 E. 46th St. (bet. 2nd & 3rd Aves.) | 212-687-4855 |
www.sparkssteakhouse.com

"Still the capital of carnivorous consumption", this "old-school"
Midtown chop shop is mobbed with "masculine" types seeking "to-die-
for" steaks and "phenomenal wines"; just be prepared to wait "till the
cows come home" for a table and to "mortgage the house" to pay the bill.

Spice *Thai* 20 | 15 | 16 | $27

Chelsea | 199 Eighth Ave. (bet. 20th & 21st Sts.) | 212-989-1116
E 70s | 1411 Second Ave. (bet. 73rd & 74th Sts.) | 212-988-5348
G Village | 60 University Pl. (10th St.) | 212-982-3758
www.spicenyc.net

This "trendy" Thai trio offers "great Bangkok for your buck" with "delicious" (if "not truly authentic") eats that are more than "gently
priced"; its epic "popularity" translates into "long waits" and "rushed"
service, but its "young hipster" following doesn't seem to mind.

NEW Spice Fusion *Indian* — | — | — | M

W 40s | 777 Eighth Ave. (bet. 47th & 48th Sts.) | 212-757-8100 |
www.myspicefusion.com

A quiet little enclave in the touristy Theater District, this new Indian
offers a bargain $9.95 lunch buffet and a $20 pre-theater dinner prix
fixe supplementing its à la carte menu; the basement setting features
earth-tone walls, hardwood floors and muted lighting.

☑ Spice Market ◐ *SE Asian* 22 | 26 | 20 | $58

Meatpacking | 403 W. 13th St. (9th Ave.) | 212-675-2322 |
www.jean-georges.com

Brace yourself for "visual overload" at Jean-Georges Vongerichten's
"theatrical" SE Asian in the Meatpacking District, where "exotic" decor
is matched by "intriguing" Thai-Malay-Vietnamese street food; the
"maddening crowd" is also drawn by reasonable-for-the-quality prices
and servers wearing "sexy" uniforms; P.S. the "basement catacombs"
are a "great place to throw an intimate party."

Spicy & Tasty ⊅ *Chinese* 23 | 10 | 14 | $22

Flushing | 39-07 Prince St. (39th Ave.) | Queens | 718-359-1601
"Perfectly named", this "fiery" Szechuan offers "unique", "dizzyingly
delicious" dishes "worth going to China for, let alone Flushing"; "re-

	FOOD	DECOR	SERVICE	COST

markably low costs" trump the "rough-and-tumble" decor and the staff's "limited English."

Spiga *Italian* 21 | 17 | 17 | $48

W 80s | 200 W. 84th St. (bet. Amsterdam Ave. & B'way) | 212-362-5506 | www.spiganyc.com

Featuring midpriced, "creative" Italian cooking, this "intimate" Upper Westsider "hits the mark most of the time"; the "approachable wine list" and "dark", "romantic" setting distract from the "indifferent" service.

Spigolo *Italian* 25 | 16 | 22 | $57

E 80s | 1561 Second Ave. (81st St.) | 212-744-1100

"Grand food" in a "miniature space" sums up this UES "gem" that's "much more than a neighborhood Italian"; owners Scott and Heather Fratangelo "really care about their customers" and their "hard work shows" – no wonder this "success story" has turned into such a "tough reservation", "even for regulars", high prices notwithstanding.

NEW Spirito Ⓜ *Italian* - | - | - | M

Park Slope | 287 Ninth St. (bet. 4th & 5th Aves.) | Brooklyn | 718-832-0085

The Vespa scooter hanging above the door signals that this new Park Slope arrival isn't your typical local trattoria, and the menu follows through with both modern and classic takes on Italian dishes; a sizable bar area and roof deck are inducements to linger here.

NEW Spitzer's Corner ❶ *American* - | - | - | M

LES | 101 Rivington St. (Ludlow St.) | 212-228-0027

Creative New Americana accompanied by a vast list of craft beers is drawing hordes of hipsters to this new LES gastropub parked on a prime Rivington Street corner; communal picnic tables and walls lined with reclaimed wood add to its casually rustic vibe.

NEW Spoon ❶ *Japanese/Pan-Asian* - | - | - | M

E Village | 141 First Ave. (bet. 9th St. & St. Marks Pl.) | 212-529-2746

Tucked behind the East Village's Ramen Setagaya noodle bar is this new Pan-Asian with a loungelike vibe; the midpriced menu features Japanese small plates and sushi as well as Malaysian and Thai dishes, and there's a nifty back garden to boot.

NEW Spotlight Live ❶ *American* - | - | - | E

W 40s | 1604 Broadway (bet. 48th & 49th Sts.) | 212-246-2693 | www.spotlightlive.com

Think karaoke den meets *American Idol* to get the gist of this new Times Square dinner theater where wannabe warblers perform with pro backup singers (an outside JumboTron allows sidewalk critics a look too); needless to say, the glitzy, nightclubbish decor and American menu take a back seat to the action onstage.

Spotted Pig ❶ *British* 22 | 17 | 16 | $43

W Village | 314 W. 11th St. (Greenwich St.) | 212-620-0393 | www.thespottedpig.com

It's perpetually "SRO" at this "overly hip" British gastropub in the West Village, where both "celebs" and the "teeming masses" turn up to "pig out" on chef April Bloomfield's "amazing" "un-pub grub"; while her gnudi may "send you to heaven", the "staff attitude" and "epic waits" for entry are not as celestial.

	FOOD	DECOR	SERVICE	COST

☑ Sripraphai ⊘ *Thai*
26 | 13 | 17 | $23

Woodside | 64-13 39th Ave. (bet. 64th & 65th Sts.) | Queens | 718-899-9599

"Spicy really means spicy" at this Woodside Thai ranked "head, shoulders and waist" above the competition (and voted No. 1 for the genre); success has led to a "remodeling" and "long lines", but it still "lives up to its reputation" for "cheap", "thrilling" eating.

Stage Deli ❶ *Deli*
20 | 10 | 14 | $27

W 50s | 834 Seventh Ave. (bet. 53rd & 54th Sts.) | 212-245-7850 | www.stagedeli.com

"Stretch your jaw before you go" to this circa-1938 Midtown deli as the "crazy large" portions and "architectural miracle" sandwiches provide plenty to chew on; teams of tourists, "cattle car" ambiance and "crusty" service from a staff right out of "American Gothic" come with the territory.

Stamatis ❶ *Greek/Seafood*
22 | 11 | 17 | $31

Astoria | 29-12 23rd Ave. (bet. 29th & 31st Sts.) | Queens | 718-932-8596
Astoria | 31-14 Broadway (bet. 31st & 32nd Sts.) | Queens | 718-204-8964

Separately owned but similarly "homey", these "old-school" Astoria Greeks "know how to deal with fish" as well as other "delicious" Hellenic "favorites"; the decor may be "just above diner", but mini-tabs and "mega-portions" keep 'em coming back.

NEW Stand ❶ *Hamburgers*
19 | 15 | 16 | $22

G Village | 24 E. 12th St. (bet. 5th Ave. & University Pl.) | 212-488-5900

"Better-than-average" patties are flipped at this "fancy" Village burger joint, but the "excellent" shakes made with Il Laboratorio gelato (and laced with alcohol) are the true "standouts"; "slick" looks, modest tariffs and "poky" service all signify that it's definitely "not fast food."

Stanton Social ❶ *Eclectic*
23 | 23 | 19 | $50

LES | 99 Stanton St. (bet. Ludlow & Orchard Sts.) | 212-995-0099 | www.thestantonsocial.com

"Trendoids abound" at this "buzzy", slightly pricey LES Eclectic that lures "under-30" types and is especially "popular with the ladies"; despite its "inspired" menu of globe-trotting small plates, the "crushingly loud" scene is the real draw here.

Steak Frites ❶ *French*
18 | 16 | 16 | $42

Union Sq | 9 E. 16th St. (bet. 5th Ave. & Union Sq. W.) | 212-463-7101 | www.steakfritesnyc.com

The "eponymous dish" is the way to go at this "approachable" Union Square French bistro; while the "Americanized" "midpriced" menu is more than adequate, "worn" decor and "inconsistent" service suggest the place is "past its prime."

NEW Stella Maris *European*
- | - | - | M

Seaport | 213 Front St. (bet. Beekman St. & Peck Slip) | 212-233-2417

Its name means 'star of the sea', and not surprisingly, fresh-caught fish and a first-rate raw bar headline the moderately priced modern European menu of this new Seaport bistro; a bakery/sandwich shop adjacent to its sleek dining room is open all day.

	FOOD	DECOR	SERVICE	COST

NEW Sticky Rice *Thai* ▽ 19 | 18 | 17 | $22

LES | 85 Orchard St. (bet. Broome & Grand Sts.) | 212-274-8208

For "interesting takes" on traditional Thai dishes and barbecue, this "little" LES newcomer is fast becoming a "favorite"; the "relaxed" mood makes it feel "undiscovered", but some say they need to work on improving service and fixing a few "bland" offerings.

NEW STK ● *Steak* 20 | 23 | 19 | $67

Meatpacking | 26 Little W. 12th St. (bet. 9th Ave. & Washington St.) | 646-624-2444 | www.stkhouse.com

Appropriately set in the Meatpacking District, this "sceney", seriously priced new steakhouse tweaks the genre with a "chic", "lady"-friendly vibe; the "sleek" digs mirror its "trendy" location, replete with a "nightclub"-like setting and a "young" crowd, "bouncing from table to table between courses."

Stone Park Café *American* 24 | 20 | 21 | $45

Park Slope | 324 Fifth Ave. (3rd St.) | Brooklyn | 718-369-0082 | www.stoneparkcafe.com

"Taking a good local place to the next level", this Park Slope New American draws "food-smart" folks with a "thoughtful" menu, "handsome" setting and "attractive" staff; in sum, it's a less expensive Brooklyn version of "Manhattan sophistication" and "always packed."

Strip House ● *Steak* 25 | 22 | 21 | $70

G Village | 13 E. 12th St. (bet. 5th Ave. & University Pl.) | 212-328-0000 | www.theglaziergroup.com

"Gypsy Rose Lee" would appreciate this "burlesque-themed" Village steakhouse for its "dimly lit" red interior festooned with vintage "pin-up photos" (think "Smith & Wollensky meets Scores"); in addition to double entendres, it also grinds out some of the city's best beef backed up with "amazing" sides at "thank-God-for-expense-accounts" prices.

Suba ● *Spanish* 21 | 26 | 19 | $51

LES | 109 Ludlow St. (bet. Delancey & Rivington Sts.) | 212-982-5714 | www.subanyc.com

An "incredible redesign" has made this "super-sexy", high-end LES Spaniard even more "alluring" with its ever-"romantic" grotto room and moat; the food is "much improved" thanks to a new chef and the cocktails are "fantastic", but the "wow"-worthy scene "surpasses" the rest.

Sueños Ⓜ *Mexican* 23 | 19 | 20 | $45

Chelsea | 311 W. 17th St. (bet. 8th & 9th Aves.) | 212-243-1333 | www.suenosnyc.com

"Way beyond the usual", Sue Torres' "upscale" Chelsea Mexican is known for its "authentic" eats jazzed up with "creative" flourishes and "congenial" service; it's "hidden in an alley" and "a little pricey" for the genre, but well "worth it."

Ⓩ Sugiyama ●ⓍⓂ *Japanese* 27 | 20 | 26 | $94

W 50s | 251 W. 55th St. (bet. B'way & 8th Ave.) | 212-956-0670 | www.sugiyama-nyc.com

It's all about "attention to detail" at Nao Sugiyama's "outstanding" Midtown Japanese known for its marvelous "modern kaiseki" meals that are "as much about presentation as taste"; just "let them take

| | FOOD | DECOR | SERVICE | COST |

care of you", and the "soothing" "ceremonial" atmosphere will help blunt the "heart attack"–inducing bill.

Superfine 🅼 *Mediterranean*
▽ 18 | 19 | 18 | $29

Dumbo | 126 Front St. (bet. Jay & Pearl Sts.) | Brooklyn | 718-243-9005
Dumbo's "hipster paradise", this "funky", low-budget Med is set in a cavernous former warehouse where "tasty" food, "vintage cocktails" and a "pool table" turn up the volume; service "needs to be quicker", but Sunday's "bluegrass brunch" is not to be missed.

Supper 🚫 *Italian*
24 | 19 | 19 | $35

E Village | 156 E. Second St. (bet. Aves. A & B) | 212-477-7600 | www.supperrestaurant.com
"Delicious", well-priced Northern Italian cuisine, especially "amazing pastas", are dished out in "rustic", candlelit digs at this "truly unique" East Villager; "they don't take reservations" (or plastic), but the "long waits" are made bearable by the "wine bar next door."

Surya *Indian*
▽ 24 | 18 | 21 | $34

W Village | 302 Bleecker St. (bet. Grove St. & 7th Ave. S.) | 212-807-7770 | www.suryany.com
"Nice and spicy" food from "different regions of India" arrives in a "stark" setting at this Village "jewel in the crown"; service is "efficient" and the prices modest, but what's "really special" is the "cute garden."

Sushi Ann 🅂 *Japanese*
▽ 23 | 16 | 20 | $60

E 50s | 38 E. 51st St. (bet. Madison & Park Aves.) | 212-755-1780 | www.sushiann.com
More "steady" than "trendy", this "traditional" Midtown Japanese is "busy for lunch but more accessible at dinner", with "attentive" service and a "somewhat formal" (verging on "sterile") setting; though the sushi is sublimely "delicate", the prices aren't.

Sushiden *Japanese*
25 | 16 | 21 | $59

E 40s | 19 E. 49th St. (bet. 5th & Madison Aves.) | 212-758-2700
W 40s | 123 W. 49th St. (bet. 6th & 7th Aves.) | 212-398-2800 🅂
www.sushiden.com
These crosstown Midtown Japanese are popular with expats and "business" types thanks to their "extraordinarily fresh fish" and "polite", "kimono-clad" servers; despite "austere decor", they are worth flexing the "expense account" for sushi that's the "genuine article."

Sushi Hana ◗ *Japanese*
21 | 17 | 18 | $37

E 70s | 1501 Second Ave. (78th St.) | 212-327-0582
W 80s | 466 Amsterdam Ave. (bet. 82nd & 83rd Sts.) | 212-874-0369
For "civilized sushi", try these "above-average" crosstown Japanese neighborhood places where the fish is "fresh, tasty" and "not overly expensive"; the UES outpost has the edge over its sibling thanks to "renovated" decor and a sake bar adjunct around the corner.

SushiSamba ◗ *Brazilian/Japanese*
22 | 20 | 17 | $48

Flatiron | 245 Park Ave. S. (bet. 19th & 20th Sts.) | 212-475-9377
W Village | 87 Seventh Ave. S. (Barrow St.) | 212-691-7885
www.sushisamba.com
Solid sushi gets a "Latin spin" at these midpriced fusion specialists where the "main attraction" is the "party-while-eating" vibe and

	FOOD	DECOR	SERVICE	COST

where you "don't expect to see your waiter that often"; the "night-clubbish" scene crests at the Village outlet's "amazing" refurbished roof deck and the Flatiron's "banging" adjacent lounge.

☑ Sushi Seki ●⑤ *Japanese*   `27` `13` `21` `$66`

E 60s | 1143 First Ave. (bet. 62nd & 63rd Sts.) | 212-371-0238

"Put your trust in chef Seki" and he'll lead the way to "omakase heaven" at this "cult-ish" UES Japanese where the "faultless" sushi easily out-"sparkles" the dull decor; even better, you can "keep it coming" (while "spending a small fortune") until 3 AM.

Sushi Sen-nin *Japanese*   `25` `17` `21` `$54`

E 80s | 1420 Third Ave. (bet. 80th & 81st Sts.) | 212-249-4992 ⑤
Murray Hill | 30 E. 33rd St. (bet. Madison Ave. & Park Ave. S.) |
212-889-2208
www.sushisennin.com

The "fish is as fresh as ever" at this Japanese twosome where sushi-seekers swear the "special rolls" look like "works of art" and are appropriately priced; Murray Hill's "dramatic" new decor ratchets up the "wow" factor.

Sushiya *Japanese*   ▽ `20` `13` `18` `$34`

W 50s | 28 W. 56th St. (bet. 5th & 6th Aves.) | 212-247-5760 |
www.sushiya56.com

"Good if unspectacular sushi" is sliced for "moderate" sums at this Midtown Japanese with a "loyal following" at lunchtime; the "plain", "unremarkable" setting is counterbalanced by "generally good service" and "not too crowded" conditions.

☑ Sushi Yasuda ⑤ *Japanese*   `28` `22` `24` `$78`

E 40s | 204 E. 43rd St. (bet. 2nd & 3rd Aves.) | 212-972-1001 |
www.sushiyasuda.com

Sushi verges on the "spiritual" at this Grand Central-area "pinnacle" once again voted NYC's No. 1 Japanese, where chef Naomichi Yasuda provides raw fish "bliss" via "celestial" morsels that "span the seven seas" ("bring a snorkel if you want it fresher"); service is "knowledge-able", the decor "simple" but elegant and the overall vibe "calm" – at least until the bill arrives.

Sushi Zen ⑤ *Japanese*   `25` `20` `22` `$58`

W 40s | 108 W. 44th St. (bet. B'way & 6th Ave.) | 212-302-0707 |
www.sushizen-ny.com

This "refined" Japanese, a "standard-bearer" for "high-quality" sushi in the Theater District, gets "inventive" with "interesting combinations" as well as more traditional items; everything is fine here, except perhaps for that "ka-ching" sound you hear when paying the bill.

NEW Suteishi *Japanese*   ▽ `25` `20` `23` `$44`

Seaport | 24 Peck Slip (Front St.) | 212-766-2344 |
www.suteishi.com

A "pearl hidden in the Seaport" area, this new Japanese is a refuge for "delightful", moderately priced sushi sliced by one of the "friendliest chefs" around; the industrial-chic setting (think retractable garage doors) on burgeoning Front Street features bonus views of the Brooklyn Bridge.

	FOOD	DECOR	SERVICE	COST

Swagat Indian Cuisine *Indian* 　　　　　　　| 19 | 11 | 18 | $27 |

W 70s | 411A Amsterdam Ave. (bet. 79th & 80th Sts.) | 212-362-1400
"Affordable" and "tasty" are the watchwords at this UWS Indian where the "vest-pocket" dimensions can result in "bumping elbows with your neighbor"; since the decor is strictly "hole-in-the-wall" and service "just ok", insiders tout "takeout" as the way to go; N.B. the Swagats and the Zagats are not related.

Sweet Melissa *Dessert/Sandwiches* 　　　| 21 | 16 | 15 | $16 |

Cobble Hill | 276 Court St. (bet. Butler & Douglass Sts.) | Brooklyn | 718-855-3410
Park Slope | 175 Seventh Ave. (bet. 1st & 2nd Sts.) | Brooklyn | 718-502-9153
www.sweetmelissapatisserie.com
These "calorie rich" Brooklyn patisserie/sandwich shops (aka "Mommy & Me Central") offer "delicate" desserts that sate "sweet tooth cravings"; despite the "afternoon tea" and "wonderful" gardens, the "pricey" tabs and "disorganized" service may leave a sour taste.

Sweet-n-Tart Cafe ●◐⇗ *Chinese* 　　　　| 20 | 11 | 15 | $17 |

Flushing | 136-11 38th Ave. (Main St.) | Queens | 718-661-3380 | www.sweetntart.com
"Bring an adventurous spirit" to this cash-only Flushing Chinese featuring a "snack-heavy" menu of dim sum and "authentic Cantonese" items; despite "dated" decor, it's "quick, tasty" and, best of all, "cheap."

Sweetwater ●⇗ *American/French* 　　　| ▽ 21 | 20 | 18 | $31 |

Williamsburg | 105 N. Sixth St. (bet. Berry St. & Wythe Ave.) | Brooklyn | 718-963-0608 | www.sweetwaterny.com
What started out as a Williamsburg "working class bar" is now a "trendy bistro" that has kept its cash-only, pre-gentrified prices; regulars report "surprisingly good" Franco-American food served by a "hipster" crew in an "inviting", "publike" space, plus a "beautiful garden."

Swifty's ● *American* 　　　　　　　　　| 18 | 18 | 18 | $59 |

E 70s | 1007 Lexington Ave. (bet. 72nd & 73rd Sts.) | 212-535-6000 | www.swiftysny.com
"Blue bloods and blue hairs" populate this "Waspy" UES "club" where the "above-average" American grub plays second fiddle to "who sits where"; while it's not true that there's a "two-face-lift minimum" for entry, it does sport "more strands of pearls per square foot than any place in town."

Sylvia's *Soul Food* 　　　　　　　　　| 19 | 13 | 16 | $29 |

Harlem | 328 Lenox Ave. (bet. 126th & 127th Sts.) | 212-996-0660 | www.sylviassoulfood.com
Whether it's "soul food heaven" or just "living on its reputation", this venerable Harlem "legend" still draws everyone from "Al Sharpton" to "Asian tour groups" with its "piping hot, stick-to-your-ribs" eats; "hit-or-miss" service and "not-so-nice" decor are beside the point during its entertaining jazz and gospel brunches.

Symposium *Greek* 　　　　　　　　　　| 20 | 15 | 20 | $25 |

W 100s | 544 W. 113th St. (bet. Amsterdam Ave. & B'way) | 212-865-1011
"Around since the days of Socrates" (actually 1969), this Columbia-area "godsend" offers "hearty" Greek dishes in "interesting" digs fes-

tooned "floor-to-ceiling" with "surreal murals"; "modest" prices and "warm" hospitality make it a "college student" perennial.

☑ Tabla *American*

	25	25	25	$79

Gramercy | 11 Madison Ave. (25th St.) | 212-889-0667 | www.tablany.com

"Exotic and exquisite", this Madison Square Park "original" showcases chef Floyd Cardoz's New American dishes, inflected with "sensitive" Indian spicing and as "beautiful to look at as they are to eat"; "top-of-the-line" service and decor add to the overall "luscious" package, and though it "doesn't come cheap" ($64 and up prix fixe-only dinner), the Bread Bar downstairs offers equally "fantastic food for a fraction of the price."

Table d'Hôte *French*

	21	16	19	$46

E 90s | 44 E. 92nd St. (bet. Madison & Park Aves.) | 212-348-8125

"Delicious", midpriced French fare turns up at this "longtime favorite" UES bistro that also boasts "excellent prix fixes" and "convenience to the 92nd Street Y"; maybe it's "too small" for comfort, but at least you have the chance to "overhear a good conversation."

Taboon *Mediterranean/Mideastern*

	24	20	20	$50

W 50s | 773 10th Ave. (52nd St.) | 212-713-0271

Forget the "desolate location": this Med–Middle Eastern "treasure" parked "way out west on 10th Avenue" is "worth the trek" for "to-die-for bread" fresh from its taboon oven; "pleasant" service and a "relaxed" setting ice the cake.

NEW Tailor ◑Ⓜ *Dessert*

	–	–	–	E

SoHo | 525 Broome St. (bet. Sullivan & Thompson Sts.) | 212-334-5182 | www.tailornyc.com

Young, tattooed wd-50 disciple Sam Mason weaves the avant-garde techniques of molecular gastronomy with the vintage apothecary aesthetic peculiar to Downtown at this sepia-toned SoHo newcomer showcasing small plates of sweet and salty creations (half desserts, half savories – all pricey); a sizable downstairs bar/lounge shakes things up with similarly unconventional cocktails.

Takahachi *Japanese*

	24	16	21	$38

E Village | 85 Ave. A (bet. 5th & 6th Sts.) | 212-505-6524 ◑
TriBeCa | 145 Duane St. (bet. Church St. & W. B'way) | 212-571-1830
www.takahachi.net

Though it "flies under the radar", this "modest" Japanese duo offers "first-rate" sushi and "creative" hot dishes that are much "easier on the wallet" than its "flashier Downtown rivals"; all right, the atmosphere ain't about to achieve any awards, but the "superior service" just may.

Taksim *Turkish*

	20	11	17	$25

E 50s | 1030 Second Ave. (bet. 54th & 55th Sts.) | 212-421-3004 | www.taksim.us

The "cult following" of this East Midtown Turk thinks it's "all about the appetizers" and touts making a meal of the "tasty little snacks" ("if I knew it was this good, I wouldn't have redone my kitchen"); "dirt-cheap" tabs and a "cheerful" staff help distract from the "cramped" setup.

	FOOD	DECOR	SERVICE	COST

Tamarind ● *Indian*
25 | 22 | 23 | $51

Flatiron | 41-43 E. 22nd St. (bet. B'way & Park Ave. S.) | 212-674-7400 | www.tamarinde22.com

It "keeps getting better" say fans of this Flatiron "haute Indian" where food "seasoned to perfection" is served by a "gracious" staff in a "chic", "modern" setting; it's "not cheap, but you get what you pay for", and there's a $24 prix fixe lunch as well as an adjacent tearoom offering "lighter, less pricey" options.

Tang Pavilion *Chinese*
23 | 17 | 21 | $36

W 50s | 65 W. 55th St. (bet. 5th & 6th Aves.) | 212-956-6888

"Not your typical" Chinese, this Midtown "surprise" supplies "subtle", Shanghai-style specialties served "fast and hot"; the "upscale" quarters are "roomier than most", the prices "reasonable" and the staff "efficient" – no wonder it's a "pre-City Center favorite."

⊠ Tanoreen Ⓜ *Mediterranean/Mideastern*
27 | 12 | 22 | $26

Bay Ridge | 7704 Third Ave. (bet. 77th & 78th Sts.) | Brooklyn | 718-748-5600 | www.tanoreen.com

It's "hard to stop eating" at this "extraordinary" Med–Middle Eastern in Bay Ridge that's a "destination" just to see chef-owner Rawia Bishara in action; maybe the "tiny" space "could use a good decorator", but otherwise "everything's fantastic" at this "great value" BYO.

⊠ Tao ● *Pan-Asian*
23 | 27 | 19 | $55

E 50s | 42 E. 58th St. (bet. Madison & Park Aves.) | 212-888-2288 | www.taorestaurant.com

Brace yourself for "Zensory overload" at this "showy" Midtown Pan-Asian, a "noisy", perennially "packed" place with "larger-than-life" "nightclubby" decor arranged around a great "big Buddha"; although it's "way tao trendy" and pricey for some, the food's "tastier" than you'd expect and the people-watching "inspirational."

Taormina *Italian*
▽ 24 | 20 | 22 | $46

Little Italy | 147 Mulberry St. (bet. Grand & Hester Sts.) | 212-219-1007

"Real-deal" Italian cooking is yours at this 25-year-old Little Italy vet (rumored to have been "John Gotti's favorite") that's staffed by "old-time waiters" who "know the score"; it's "better if you're a regular" and best if you can snag a sidewalk seat to "watch the street show."

Tarallucci e Vino *Italian*
19 | 19 | 17 | $37

E Village | 163 First Ave. (10th St.) | 212-388-1190 ●
Flatiron | 15 E. 18th St. (bet. B'way & 5th Ave.) | 212-228-5400

"Simple" grazing is the focus at this Flatiron Italian (and its more "bohemian" East Village sibling) where "great coffee" and pastries in the AM yield to an affordable small-plates menu at night; it's just right for a "casual" light meal in a "comfortable" setting.

Tartine ⊅ *French*
22 | 14 | 17 | $30

W Village | 253 W. 11th St. (4th St.) | 212-229-2611

On a "charming" West Village corner, this "unpretentious", "tight fit" French bistro serves "straightforward" classics; no reservations, "cheap prices" and a BYO policy with "free corkage" inevitably result in "long lines."

	FOOD	DECOR	SERVICE	COST

NEW Tasca ● *Spanish*   ▽ 20 | 18 | 18 | $41

W Village | 130 Seventh Ave. S. (W. 10th St.) | 212-620-6815
Supporters say it's "easy to make a meal" from the "delectable", "reasonably priced" tapas at this "sexy" new Village Spaniard that also offers "dangerously good" sangria; despite "insane crowds" at the bar, some say it "needs more time."

Taste *American*   ▽ 20 | 16 | 19 | $49

E 80s | 1413 Third Ave. (80th St.) | 212-717-9798 | www.elizabar.com
Eli Zabar "knows what he's doing" at this UES cafe-by-day/restaurant-by-night where the perfect "seasonal" New Americana is always "well prepared"; despite its high quality, it's "not that well known", so "table availability" is rarely an issue.

Tasting Room *American*   22 | 18 | 22 | $62

E Village | 72 E. First St. (bet. 1st & 2nd Aves.) | 212-358-7831 ●
NoLita | 264 Elizabeth St. (bet. Houston & Prince Sts.) | 212-358-7831 Ⓜ
www.thetastingroomnyc.com
While Colin Alevras' "farmer's market fresh" cuisine is as "inventive" as ever, there's "now room to breathe" since this New American moved to larger digs in NoLita (the East Village original is now a wine bar/cafe); still, some say it's "lost its magic" citing "overpricing", "impersonal" decor and even "uneven cooking" at times.

Taverna Kyclades *Greek/Seafood*   25 | 12 | 18 | $32

Astoria | 33-07 Ditmars Blvd. (bet. 33rd & 35th Sts.) | Queens | 718-545-8666 | www.tavernakyclades.com
"Off-the-boat fresh" seafood comes at "bargain" tabs at this "casual" Astoria Greek; the "cafeteria" vibe, "small" dimensions and "no-reservations" policy are beside the point: the "lines to get in speak for themselves" – to get it "more authentic, go to Athens."

Ⓩ Tavern on the Green *American*   15 | 24 | 17 | $64

W 60s | Central Park W. (bet. 66th & 67th Sts.) | 212-873-3200 | www.tavernonthegreen.com
"More spectacle than restaurant", this "over-the-top wonderland" in Central Park is best celebrated for its gorgeous garden and "kitschy", "fairy-tale" ambiance by way of "Liberace", not the only "adequate" American eats, "gaping tourists" and "rushed" service; nonetheless, it's capable of doing great parties, and on the right "spring evening", it still may render you "starry-eyed."

Tea & Sympathy *British*   19 | 16 | 16 | $26

W Village | 108 Greenwich Ave. (bet. 12th & 13th Sts.) | 212-807-8329 | www.teaandsympathynewyork.com
"Homesick Brits" tout this West Village "hang-your-hatter" for its "fantasy English food" like bangers and mash plus "daily high tea"; the "tiny", "cramped" digs and slack service may be "sore points", but, no question, this one's an "original."

Tea Box Ⓢ *Japanese*   ▽ 20 | 18 | 19 | $33

E 50s | Takashimaya | 693 Fifth Ave. (bet. 54th & 55th Sts.) | 212-350-0180
After a Midtown "shopping spree", this "oasis" in the Takashimaya basement purveys "delicate", "exquisitely presented" Japanese fare; add "oodles" of tea and "understated" decor, and it's easy to appreciate it.

	FOOD	DECOR	SERVICE	COST

teany ⌷ *Vegan/Vegetarian* | 18 | 15 | 17 | $17 |

LES | 90 Rivington St. (bet. Ludlow & Orchard Sts.) | 212-475-9190 | www.teany.com

A "near endless tea selection" is the draw at this inexpensive, "iPod"-size LES vegan/vegetarian where the "animal-free" menu is "limited" but "not too oppressive"; owned by pop star Moby, it's "worth a shot" provided that you don't mind "weak service" and "plain" decor.

NEW Ted's Montana Grill *American* | 15 | 15 | 16 | $39 |

W 50s | 110 W. 51st St. (bet. 6th & 7th Aves.) | 212-245-5220 | www.tedsmontanagrill.com

Ted Turner's national franchise famed for its "humongous, fall-off-the-bun" bison burgers comes to Rock Center; despite "lunchtime crowds", many say the "novelty wears thin" quickly, citing "mediocre" American eats, "brusque" staffers and a "chain restaurant" look.

Z Telepan *American* | 25 | 20 | 23 | $69 |

W 60s | 72 W. 69th St. (bet. Columbus Ave. & CPW) | 212-580-4300 | www.telepan-ny.com

Bill Telepan – one "heck of a chef" – is the mastermind behind this "brilliant" New American near Lincoln Center, where they "hit the ground running and have just kept going" thanks to an "exceptional", "market-driven menu", "pro" service and a "grown-up, non-sceney" setting; more debatable are the "pasture"-colored walls and unneighborly tabs, but many feel this "triumph" verges on the "transcendent."

Telly's Taverna ● *Greek/Seafood* | 22 | 14 | 18 | $35 |

Astoria | 28-13 23rd Ave. (bet. 28th & 29th Sts.) | Queens | 718-728-9056 | www.tellystaverna.com

"Fresh fish is the specialty" of this Astoria taverna where the "grilled, well-seasoned" seafood (at "can't-be-beat" prices) feels like a flight-free "trip to Greece"; the "pleasant" back garden is a calming refuge when the "spacious" dining room gets too "noisy."

Temple Canteen *Indian* | - | - | - | I |

Flushing | Hindu Temple Society of North America | 45-57 Bowne St., downstairs (Holly Ave.) | Queens | 718-460-8493 | www.nyganeshtemple.org

Authentic South Indian staples draw dosa devotees to this brightly lit cafeteria in the basement of a Hindu temple in Flushing; decor's at an absolute minimum and you'll bus your own tray, but real-deal eats and cheap tabs have inspired a cultlike following here.

Tempo *Mediterranean* | 25 | 23 | 24 | $50 |

Park Slope | 256 Fifth Ave. (bet. Carroll St. & Garfield Pl.) | Brooklyn | 718-636-2020 | www.tempobrooklyn.com

Devotees feel this "highly accomplished" Park Slope Med "should be better known" given its "innovative" kitchen, "gracious" staff and "tranquil", "bring-the-parents-for-dinner" vibe; it's now prix fixe only, though the same quality "would cost a lot more in Manhattan."

Tenzan *Japanese* | 23 | 15 | 19 | $32 |

W 70s | 285 Columbus Ave. (73rd St.) | 212-580-7300 ●
Bensonhurst | 7116 18th Ave. (71st St.) | Brooklyn | 718-621-3238

"No one comes for the ambiance" – it's the "high quality", "extremely fresh" sushi sliced in "huge slabs" for modest tabs that keeps these cross-borough Japanese perpetually "mobbed"; "rush-you-in-rush-you-out" service leads lingerers to opt for "takeout."

Teodora Italian   22 | 16 | 20 | $48

E 50s | 141 E. 57th St. (bet. Lexington & 3rd Aves.) | 212-826-7101
The "atmosphere's relaxed" at this "low-key" Midtown "hideaway" where the Northern Italian food is "delicious" and "upstairs is more comfortable" than down; all right, it's "nothing too exciting" and may be "a little expensive", but at least you're "never rushed."

Terrace in the Sky M French/Mediterranean   22 | 25 | 22 | $67

W 100s | 400 W. 119th St. (bet. Amsterdam Ave. & Morningside Dr.) | 212-666-9490 | www.terraceinthesky.com
"Panoramas of Upper Manhattan" are just one of the highlights of this Morningside Heights rooftop French-Med; others are the "excellent" food, "romantic" mood and smooth service, so despite the "old-fashioned" air, it's a natural for "special occasions" and private parties.

Tevere Italian   ▽ 22 | 19 | 21 | $53

E 80s | 155 E. 84th St. (bet. Lexington & 3rd Aves.) | 212-744-0210 | www.teverenyc.com
"If it's romantic and it has to be kosher", amorous observant types are all over this "fine-dining" UES Italian with "tasty" cooking and an ambiance subdued enough to "hear yourself think"; yes, it's "costly" – particularly the wines – "but that's to be expected."

Thai Pavilion Thai   ▽ 22 | 13 | 22 | $23

Astoria | 37-10 30th Ave. (37th St.) | Queens | 718-777-5546 | www.thaipavilionny.com
"Seriously good food" trumps the "bland" decor at this Astoria Thai where the "authentic", "big portions" come at "cheap" tabs; an "amazingly attentive" staff blunts the need for takeout or delivery (although both are available).

Thalassa Greek/Seafood   22 | 25 | 22 | $63

TriBeCa | 179 Franklin St. (bet. Greenwich & Hudson Sts.) | 212-941-7661 | www.thalassanyc.com
For "chic Greek" grazing in TriBeCa, this "stylish" seafooder sells fish "so fresh you'd think they caught it after you ordered it"; service is as "crisp" as the "loftlike", "white-napkin" setting, but by-the-pound entree pricing means it's most economical to stick to the appetizers.

Thalia ● American   21 | 20 | 19 | $47

W 50s | 828 Eighth Ave. (50th St.) | 212-399-4444 | www.restaurantthalia.com
A pioneer of the new, "spiffy" Hell's Kitchen, this "spacious", "high-ceilinged" spot decorated with vintage theater posters draws "lively" show-goers with its "quality" New Americana; since it's "well-located" and "won't break the bank", it can get a bit "hectic."

Thomas Beisl ● Austrian   19 | 16 | 19 | $37

Fort Greene | 25 Lafayette Ave. (Ashland Pl.) | Brooklyn | 718-222-5800
"Proximity to BAM" may be the "main advantage" of this Fort Greene Austrian "mainstay", but fans say its "real McCoy" cooking and "value" make it "worth a visit" even if you're not theater-bound; a "delightful outdoor garden" seals the deal.

	FOOD	DECOR	SERVICE	COST

Thor ● *American*
18 | 19 | 16 | $59

LES | The Hotel on Rivington | 107 Rivington St. (bet. Essex & Ludlow Sts.) | 212-796-8040 | www.hotelonrivington.com

Right off a "trendy" hotel lobby, this "hip" LES New American serves food "on the better side of ok" that plays second fiddle to its "edgy" decor and "loud", party-hearty crowd; "overpricing", "incompetent" service and "way too much scene" are common complaints.

Tía Pol *Spanish*
24 | 15 | 18 | $38

Chelsea | 205 10th Ave. (bet. 22nd & 23rd Sts.) | 212-675-8805 | www.tiapol.com

You'll think you've "died and gone to Barcelona" at this Chelsea Spaniard featuring "adventurous" tapas in a "tiny hallway" of a space; it gets *muy cramped* muy fast, so prepare to "wait for an eternity for a table" – it's worth it.

Tides Ⓜⴕ *Seafood*
∇ 24 | 23 | 23 | $42

LES | 102 Norfolk St. (bet. Delancey & Rivington Sts.) | 212-254-8855 | www.tidesseafood.com

"One of the most unique ceilings in town" – made of bamboo stalks masquerading as sea grass – turns up at this "modern" LES seafooder also known for one of the "best lobster rolls south of Maine"; tabs are "reasonable", and "despite its small footprint, it doesn't seem cramped."

Tierras Colombianas ⴕ *Colombian*
22 | 12 | 18 | $23

Astoria | 33-01 Broadway (33rd St.) | Queens | 718-956-3012
Jackson Heights | 82-18 Roosevelt Ave. (82nd St.) | Queens | 718-426-8868

A "doggy bag" is a given at these Queens Colombians where the "huge platters" and "heaping" portions at "unbeatable" prices induce many to "eat till they can't walk"; they're a "good change of pace" provided you "bring a Spanish phrase book" and don't mind "diner"-esque digs.

Tintol ● *Portuguese*
∇ 21 | 16 | 19 | $41

W 40s | 155 W. 46th St. (bet. 6th & 7th Aves.) | 212-354-3838 | www.tintol.net

Something different for the Theater District, this "sophisticated" Portuguese provides "interesting" tapas and a "good selection" of wine in "dark" digs; prices can "add up quickly", but for a "chic" bite pre- or post-theater, it's "one of the few acceptable places" around.

Tiramisu ● *Italian*
20 | 15 | 17 | $35

E 80s | 1410 Third Ave. (80th St.) | 212-988-9780

"Quick and easy when you don't feel like cooking", this longtime UES Italian is always a "safe bet" for "families with kids" with its good "basic" grub and "loud" din; "awesome" pizza from the wood-burning oven makes up for "not a lot of warmth from the management."

☒ Tocqueville *American/French*
26 | 24 | 25 | $73

Union Sq | 1 E. 15th St. (bet. 5th Ave. & Union Sq. W.) | 212-647-1515 | www.tocquevillerestaurant.com

"Civilized dining for adults" is on the docket at this "oasis of calm" off Union Square where chef Marco Moreira demonstrates his "dexterity" with "serious" French-American cooking yielding "sublime" results; granted, the "minuscule portions" arrive at "major prices", but in return the place "purrs like a luxury automobile."

	FOOD	DECOR	SERVICE	COST

Todai *Japanese/Seafood* — ▽ 18 | 13 | 15 | $31

Murray Hill | 6 E. 32nd St. (bet. 5th & Madison Aves.) | 212-725-1333 | www.todainyc.com

"Eat till you drop, then go back for more" at this Murray Hill "gorgefest" where a "football field–length buffet table" offers hot and cold Japanese seafood for an "affordable flat price"; ok, "Nobu it isn't" (it's "more Wal-Mart"), but it's just the ticket if "quantity is your priority."

Tokyo Pop *Japanese* — 20 | 16 | 15 | $31

W 100s | 2728 Broadway (bet. 104th & 105th Sts.) | 212-932-1000

"Above-average" sushi is sliced at this Columbia-area Japanese that's a sibling of French bistro Café du Soleil across the street ("go figure"); "real care" is taken with the food prep and the milieu's "hip", though service careens from "ok" to "lousy."

NEW Toloache *Mexican* — - | - | - | M

W 50s | 251 W. 50th St. (bet. B'way & 8th Ave.) | 212-581-1818 | www.toloachenyc.com

Hell's Kitchen's gentrification continues with the arrival of this spiffy Nuevo Mexicano offering contemporary takes on traditional fare paired with a wide tequila selection; centered around a ceviche/guacamole bar, the split-level setup is decorated with a light touch that conveys a south-of-the-border mood without resorting to kitsch.

Tommaso *Italian* — ▽ 23 | 18 | 21 | $45

Dyker Heights | 1464 86th St. (bet. 14th & 15th Aves.) | Brooklyn | 718-236-9883 | www.tommasoinbrooklyn.com

Recalling "dinner at nona's on Sunday", this Dyker Heights "perennial" offers "traditional red-sauce" Italian fare in a "family restaurant" setting; bonus points go to its owner, Thomas Verdillo, who's known to "sporadically break out" into operatic arias.

Z Tomoe Sushi *Japanese* — 26 | 8 | 17 | $41

G Village | 172 Thompson St. (bet. Bleecker & Houston Sts.) | 212-777-9346

"Early or late, you still might wait" at this "flavor"-filled, decor-free Village Japanese where the "no-reservations" policy makes for "ridiculously long lines" at the door; the payoff is "delicious", "just-off-the-boat" sushi sliced in "gigantic" portions for "bargain" bucks – so "get your sleeping bags ready."

Tomo Sushi & Sake Bar ● *Japanese* — 20 | 15 | 17 | $26

W 100s | 2850 Broadway (bet. 110th & 111th Sts.) | 212-665-2916

UWS students tout this "reliable", Columbia-convenient Japanese for its "high-quality" sushi and "inexpensive" pricing; all agree it "could use a bit of a face-lift" and probably a service lift as well.

Tom's Z⊞ *Diner* — 19 | 16 | 24 | $14

Prospect Heights | 782 Washington Ave. (Sterling Pl.) | Brooklyn | 718-636-9738

The "food is good but the love is priceless" at this circa-1936 Prospect Heights diner where "kitsch-explosion" decor, "speed-demon service" and "cheap" checks make for a bona fide Brooklyn "experience"; real egg creams and lime rickeys distract from the fact that it's "closed on Sundays."

	FOOD	DECOR	SERVICE	COST

Tony's Di Napoli *Italian*   18 | 14 | 18 | $35

E 80s | 1606 Second Ave. (83rd St.) | 212-861-8686
W 40s | 147 W. 43rd St. (bet. B'way & 6th Ave.) | 212-221-0100 ◗
www.tonysnyc.com

"Hulk Hogan-size portions" of "hearty" Italian chow arrive "family-style" at this "mobbed", "Carmine's"-esque twosome; "holy cow, they're loud", but they're just the ticket "for the right crowd – like relatives you don't really want to hear."

Topaz Thai *Thai*   20 | 11 | 15 | $28

W 50s | 127 W. 56th St. (bet. 6th & 7th Aves.) | 212-957-8020

"Short stays and high turnover are encouraged" at this Midtown Thai near City Center that's good for a "quickie" though some "can't eat as fast as they serve"; "tasty" dishes for "cheap" sums make the "boring decor" and "tight" quarters tolerable.

Tosca Café ◗ *Italian*   ▽ 21 | 23 | 19 | $32

Bronx | 4038 E. Tremont Ave. (bet. Miles & Sampson Aves.) | 718-239-3300 | www.toscanyc.com

Up in Throgs Neck (i.e. the Bronx) lies this "upscale" Italian serving "traditional favorites" in "dance club"-like digs; "lovely waitresses" and "legendary nightlife at the bar" draw "young" types for "hottie cruising."

Tossed *American*   18 | 7 | 11 | $14

Flatiron | 295 Park Ave. S. (bet. 22nd & 23rd Sts.) | 212-674-6700
W 40s | 30 Rockefeller Plaza, concourse (bet. 49th & 50th Sts.) | 212-218-2525 🔁
www.tossed.com

Aka "rabbit heaven", this low-budget, "custom-salad" twosome is a fine "create-your-own"-lunch choice offering "unusual ingredient pairings"; despite "sketchy service" and nearly no decor, it's a "healthy option in a sea of temptation."

Totonno's Pizzeria Napolitano *Pizza*   22 | 9 | 14 | $22

E 80s | 1544 Second Ave. (bet. 80th & 81st Sts.) | 212-327-2800
Gramercy | 462 Second Ave. (26th St.) | 212-213-8800
Coney Island | 1524 Neptune Ave. (bet. W. 15th & 16th Sts.) | Brooklyn | 718-372-8606 Ⓜ⇄
www.totonnos.com

"Heaven-sent" crusts "burnt just right" and sprinkled with "quality" toppings are the formula for the "old-school" pies plied by this pizzeria trio; they all share "sports bar decor" and "feisty" staffers, but purists insist the real "Xanadu is in Coney", home of the circa-1924 flagship.

Tournesol *French*   24 | 16 | 20 | $39

LIC | 50-12 Vernon Blvd. (bet. 50th & 51st Aves.) | Queens | 718-472-4355

"French food in Queens is not a punch line" at this LIC bistro that serves "outstanding" Gallic classics and ups the "authenticity" with "English-challenged" staffers; while the "tiny" setup may induce "claustrophobia", at these prices nobody minds.

Town *American*   24 | 24 | 23 | $76

W 50s | Chambers Hotel | 15 W. 56th St. (bet. 5th & 6th Aves.) | 212-582-4445 | www.townnyc.com

"Cool and sophisticated", Geoffrey Zakarian's Midtown New American draws a "beautiful", "business-oriented" crowd with its "perfect contemporary" cooking; the "swank" subterranean digs are equally "enchanting", though the upmarket tariffs cause some to reserve it as a "special-occasion" place.

Trata Estiatorio *Greek/Seafood*
| 21 | 16 | 18 | $54 |

E 70s | 1331 Second Ave. (bet. 70th & 71st Sts.) | 212-535-3800 | www.trata.com

"Just caught" fish "served simply" is the hallmark of this UES "neighborhood" Greek seafooder whose whitewashed setting (and alfresco sidewalk seating) exudes a "taverna feel"; "by-the-pound pricing" can make for "expensive" eating, but fans feel it's "worth it."

Trattoria Alba ✪ *Italian*
| 20 | 17 | 22 | $40 |

Murray Hill | 233 E. 34th St. (bet. 2nd & 3rd Aves.) | 212-689-3200 | www.trattoriaalba.com

A "neighborhood restaurant in the best sense", this "longtime" Murray Hill Italian draws "older" folk with a "traditional" menu and a "staff that really cares"; sure, it's "old-fashioned" with "dated" decor, but the modest pricing is fine as is.

Trattoria Dell'Arte ✪ *Italian*
| 22 | 20 | 21 | $55 |

W 50s | 900 Seventh Ave. (bet. 56th & 57th Sts.) | 212-245-9800 | www.trattoriadellarte.com

Still "happening" after 20 years, this "high-energy" Midtown Italian is famed for its "affluent" following, super antipasto bar and "surrealist" body parts artwork (there's "always something interesting to look at"); it's "noisy, but a lot of fun" with "proximity to Carnegie Hall a plus."

Trattoria Dopo Teatro ✪ *Italian*
| 16 | 15 | 17 | $41 |

W 40s | 125 W. 44th St. (bet. B'way & 6th Ave.) | 212-869-2849 | www.dopoteatro.com

"Surprisingly big", this Theater District Italian draws "madhouse" crowds despite an "incredibly average" menu, "lowbrow" decor and "rushed" service; still, it's "convenient" to Broadway and the "secret" garden room supplies some charm.

ⓩ Trattoria L'incontro Ⓜ *Italian*
| 26 | 19 | 24 | $49 |

Astoria | 21-76 31st St. (Ditmars Blvd.) | Queens | 718-721-3532 | www.trattorialincontro.com

Astoria's "glorious, glorified neighborhood restaurant" boasts "outstanding" Italian cooking from chef Rocco Sacramone and first-rate service, though it's best known for its "overwhelmingly long list" of daily specials; a new wine bar adjunct dubbed Vino di Vino helps absorb the overflow crowds.

Trattoria Pesce & Pasta *Italian/Seafood*
| 18 | 14 | 17 | $32 |

E 50s | 1079 First Ave. (59th St.) | 212-888-7884 ✪
E 80s | 1562 Third Ave. (bet. 87th & 88th Sts.) | 212-987-4696 ✪
NEW **Garment District** | 536 Ninth Ave. (bet. 39th & 40th Sts.) | 212-594-5408
G Village | 262 Bleecker St. (bet. 6th Ave. & 7th Ave. S.) | 212-645-2993 ✪
W 90s | 625 Columbus Ave. (bet. 90th & 91st Sts.) | 212-579-7970 www.pescepasta.com

"Reliable but uninspiring", this "informal" Italian quintet puts out "consistent" seafood and pastas at "good value"; "casual" settings and "laid-back service" please those who "don't expect too much."

	FOOD	DECOR	SERVICE	COST

Trattoria Romana *Italian*
24 | 17 | 22 | $41

Staten Island | 1476 Hylan Blvd. (Benton Ave.) | 718-980-3113 | www.trattoriaromana.com

Staten Island may have "more Italian restaurants than citizens", but fans say this "authentic" trattoria is particularly "outstanding"; "tight" tables make it "too up close and personal" for some, but "face time with the chef" is "worth the boat trip."

tre dici 🗷 *Italian*
22 | 18 | 19 | $44

Chelsea | 128 W. 26th St. (bet. 6th & 7th Aves.) | 212-243-8183

Parked on an "off-the-beaten-path" stretch of the "Chelsea fur district", this "intimate", modestly priced Italian provides "better than expected" food in modern digs; "far better than the usual neighborhood" spot, it's still "undiscovered" – go figure.

NEW Tree ● *French*
▽ 24 | 16 | 19 | $40

E Village | 190 First Ave. (bet. 11th & 12th Sts.) | 212-358-7171 | www.treenyc.com

Instantly "popular", this new East Village bistro is drawing "boisterous" crowds with its "inspired", midpriced takes on "traditional" Gallic grub; the "little" storefront setting makes a vague attempt at "faux French atmosphere", but it plays second fiddle to the "great" back garden.

Trestle on Tenth *American*
19 | 18 | 19 | $49

Chelsea | 242 10th Ave. (24th St.) | 212-645-5659 | www.trestleontenth.com

"Charmingly informal", this Chelsea yearling offers a "meat-centric" array of "Swiss-influenced" New Americana (plus an "original, affordable" wine list) in a "brick-walled", art-lined interior or "lovely" back garden; although its performance can be "spotty", adherents insist it "has potential."

Triangolo ● *Italian*
21 | 16 | 22 | $39

E 80s | 345 E. 83rd St. (bet. 1st & 2nd Aves.) | 212-472-4488 | www.triangolorestaurant.com

"Flirtatious waiters" and reasonable prices make for "pleasant" dining at this venerable UES Italian that could be a "model for a neighborhood restaurant"; "solid basics" on the plate and a "no-rush" pace distract from the "elbow-to-elbow" layout.

Tribeca Grill *American*
22 | 21 | 21 | $57

TriBeCa | 375 Greenwich St. (Franklin St.) | 212-941-3900 | www.tribecagrill.com

"Like fine wine", this "original" New American via Drew Nieporent and Robert De Niro just "gets better with time" serving "reliable", albeit pricey, New American food with a side of "celebrity hipness" in "casual" environs; most feel it hasn't lost a beat over the years.

Trinity Place *Eclectic*
▽ 18 | 23 | 19 | $39

Financial District | 115 Broadway (enter on Cedar St., bet. B'way & Trinity Pl.) | 212-964-0939 | www.trinityplacenyc.com

The pub grub may be "fancied up" at this Financial District "hideaway", but it still takes a backseat to the "former bank vault" setting, complete with "huge", 35-ton doors; a very "noisy" weeknight "bar scene" makes it "better for lunch", when you don't have to deposit as much for a meal.

	FOOD	DECOR	SERVICE	COST

Trio ⏺🔲 Mediterranean
▽ 21 | 17 | 22 | $44

Murray Hill | 167 E. 33rd St. (bet. Lexington & 3rd Aves.) | 212-685-1001 | www.trionyc.com

Although it no longer features Croatian specialties, this "quiet" Murray Hill Med is as "delightful" as ever, ditto the "friendly" staff; while the decor (and clientele) may be "a bit dated", no one minds once the "piano player starts."

Triomphe French
24 | 22 | 23 | $63

W 40s | Iroquois Hotel | 49 W. 44th St. (bet. 5th & 6th Aves.) | 212-453-4233 | www.triomphe-newyork.com

"Largely undiscovered", this "secret little" Theater District rendez-vous "deserves to be more crowded" owing to its "fantastic" New French menu and overall "luxurious" air; "quiet in an area where quiet is unusual", it's best when "someone else pays."

Tsampa ⏺ Tibetan
▽ 20 | 20 | 19 | $25

E Village | 212 E. Ninth St. (bet. 2nd & 3rd Aves.) | 212-614-3226

To "get away from it all", try this East Village Tibetan "Zen den" serving a "hard-to-find" cuisine that's both "unusual" and "healthful"; there's "next to no lighting" and the staff can be "a little too relaxed", but no one cares when prices are this low.

Tse Yang Chinese
25 | 23 | 24 | $61

E 50s | 34 E. 51st St. (bet. Madison & Park Aves.) | 212-688-5447

"Extraordinary Peking duck" is the centerpiece of the "gourmet" menu at this "haute" East Midtown Chinese, a longtime supplier of "expertly prepared" cuisine; "upscale" quarters and "attentive but not obtrusive service" help rationalize the "could-it-get-more-expensive?" pricing.

Tupelo Grill 🔲 American
▽ 18 | 16 | 17 | $48

Garment District | 1 Penn Plaza, 33rd St. (bet. 7th & 8th Aves.) | 212-760-2700

When you "don't want a sports bar", this Penn Station–convenient American is an "acceptable" bet before an MSG event; "sparse decor", "expense-account" pricing and just "ok food" don't seem to matter since it's one of the "only games" around.

Turkish Cuisine ⏺ Turkish
20 | 15 | 19 | $31

W 40s | 631 Ninth Ave. (bet. 44th & 45th Sts.) | 212-397-9650 | www.turkishcuisinenyc.com

"Well-prepared", "no-nonsense" cooking is on the docket at this "homey" Hell's Kitchen Turk that's "recently been discovered" and thus can get particularly "crowded" pre-theater; "tired" decor and "slightly pushy" service are trumped by "bargain" tabs and that "funky garden."

Turkish Kitchen Turkish
22 | 19 | 19 | $39

Gramercy | 386 Third Ave. (bet. 27th & 28th Sts.) | 212-679-6633 | www.turkishkitchen.com

"No one goes home hungry" from this "mouthwatering" Gramercy Turk known for its "terrific appetizers" and a "steal" of a Sunday brunch; given the "value" pricing and "cocktail lounge atmosphere", it's "deservedly popular."

	FOOD	DECOR	SERVICE	COST

Turks & Frogs *Turkish*
20 | 18 | 19 | $40

TriBeCa | 458 Greenwich St. (bet. Desbrosses & Watts Sts.) | 212-966-4774 | www.turksandfrogs.com

Forget the "middle-of-nowhere" address – this TriBeCa Turk is still handier than "going to Istanbul" and serves appropriately "exotic" fare for "affordable" dough; the "cozy" setting and "hardworking" staff make for "unpretentious", "highly enjoyable" dining.

Turkuaz ● *Turkish*
19 | 20 | 18 | $33

W 100s | 2637 Broadway (100th St.) | 212-665-9541 | www.turkuazrestaurant.com

For Turkish cooking "without the jet lag", try this "enormous" Upper Westsider done up in a "deliriously kitschy" "sultan" style, with "tented ceilings" and "hammered tin tables"; the "no-surprises" menu is "tasty" enough, but the "belly dancing" is just plain "delicious" and the service "so friendly you'd think they owed you money."

Turquoise *Seafood*
22 | 18 | 20 | $55

E 80s | 240 E. 81st St. (bet. 2nd & 3rd Aves.) | 212-988-4892 | www.turquoiseseafood.com

"Tasty Mediterranean-style" seafood is the hook at this UES fishmonger, a "lively, familial" spot thanks to a "hoot" of an owner who will personally "customize" your order; it's "still pretty secret", but a "must-go" despite "not cheap" pricing.

Tuscan Square ⑤ *Italian*
16 | 18 | 16 | $44

W 50s | 16 W. 51st St. (bet. 5th & 6th Aves.) | 212-977-7777 | www.tuscansquare.ypguides.net

"Fine for tourists" and business-lunchers, this moderately priced Rock Center Italian vends "solid" if "average" food in a "formulaic", "Disney-like" setting; it's "largely overlooked at dinnertime", but a hit during the holidays due to its proximity to the "ice skating rink."

Tuscany Grill *Italian*
24 | 19 | 20 | $44

Bay Ridge | 8620 Third Ave. (bet. 86th & 87th Sts.) | Brooklyn | 718-921-5633

Those who "know good Italian when they taste it" tout this Bay Ridge standby for when you're in a "romantic" frame of mind; it's "small" but the mood's "intimate", the cooking's "authentic", the prices reasonable and the staff "couldn't be more welcoming."

12th St. Bar & Grill *American*
21 | 19 | 19 | $35

Park Slope | 1123 Eighth Ave. (12th St.) | Brooklyn | 718-965-9526

A "true neighborhood eatery" "nestled amid brownstones", this Park Slope "favorite" endears itself to locals with "dependable", "reasonable" New American fare, prix fixe deals and a solid Sunday brunch; better still, a recent redo spruced up its space.

12 Chairs *American/Mideastern*
▽ 19 | 12 | 15 | $25

SoHo | 56 MacDougal St. (bet. Houston & Prince Sts.) | 212-254-8640

An eminently "affordable" choice in a neighborhood short on bargains, this "sparse" "little" SoHo cafe specializes in "homey" Middle Eastern–accented American comfort food; if "service lacks" and it can get "crowded", it's "friendly" enough that most don't seem to mind.

	FOOD	DECOR	SERVICE	COST

Z 21 Club *American*   22 | 23 | 24 | $71

W 50s | 21 W. 52nd St. (bet. 5th & 6th Aves.) | 212-582-7200 | www.21club.com

This "venerable" onetime speakeasy, a "formidable fixture" in Midtown, delivers "satisfying" Traditional American fare to a "virtual who's who" of "high rollers" in "clubby", jackets-required quarters manned by a "solicitous yet unobtrusive" "formal" crew; to avoid a "shocker" of a tab, "check out the $40 pre-theater prix fixe"; N.B. party-throwers should note there are 10 "lovely" private rooms.

26 Seats **M** *French*   22 | 17 | 20 | $36

E Village | 168 Ave. B (bet. 10th & 11th Sts.) | 212-677-4787 | www.26seats.com

"They're not kidding" about the number of seats at this "popular", "tiny" East Village French where it's easy to feel like you're "dining at the home of a gourmet chef"; "inexpensive" prices seal the deal – so "make a reservation."

Two Boots *Pizza*   18 | 10 | 14 | $15

E 40s | Grand Central | lower level (42nd St. & Vanderbilt Ave.) | 212-557-7992 | www.twoboots.com

E Village | 42 Ave. A (3rd St.) | 212-254-1919 | www.twoboots.com ◐

NEW **LES** | 384 Grand St. (bet. Norfolk & Suffolk Sts.) | 212-228-8685 | www.twoboots.com

NoHo | 74 Bleecker St. (B'way) | 212-777-1033 | www.twoboots.com ◐

W 40s | 30 Rockefeller Plaza, downstairs (bet. 49th & 50th Sts.) | 212-332-8800 | www.twoboots.com

W Village | 201 W. 11th St. (7th Ave. S.) | 212-633-9096 | www.twoboots.com ◐

Park Slope | 514 Second St. (bet. 7th & 8th Aves.) | Brooklyn | 718-499-3253 | www.twobootsbrooklyn.com

There's a "great marketing scheme" at work at this "nontraditional" pizza chain where the pies come with "cornmeal crusts", "original" toppings and "obscure celeb" names; they are all "extremely child-friendly", especially the separately managed Park Slope branch.

212 ◐ *American*   16 | 16 | 15 | $46

E 60s | 133 E. 65th St. (bet. Lexington & Park Aves.) | 212-249-6565 | www.212restaurant.com

"Euro-fabulous" "twentysomethings" shriek "at each other" and "into their phones" at this Bloomie's-area New American eatery/vodka bar that's best when you "want to be seen but not heard"; "so-so" food, "distracted" service and "pricey" tabs don't dampen the "scene."

202 Cafe *Mediterranean*   21 | 20 | 18 | $33

Chelsea | Chelsea Mkt. | 75 Ninth Ave. (bet. 15th & 16th Sts.) | 646-638-1173

Made for "multitasking", this "comfortable" cafe in Nicole Farhi's Chelsea Market boutique allows diners to "shop for hip clothes in-between courses" of "tasty" Med fare; it's popular for a Brit-accented brunch that's happily much more "affordable" than the "designer duds."

2 West *Steak*   ▽ 21 | 23 | 24 | $63

Financial District | Ritz-Carlton Battery Park | 2 West St. (Battery Pl.) | 917-790-2525 | www.ritzcarlton.com

When "seeing clients in the Financial District", it's hard to beat this "hidden gem" of a hotel steakhouse in Battery Park that's a "perfect

	FOOD	DECOR	SERVICE	COST

retreat from the hustle and bustle"; "exemplary service" and "elegant, contemporary" environs offset expense account–worthy tabs.

Umberto's Clam House *Italian/Seafood* | 18 | 13 | 17 | $37 |

Little Italy | 386 Broome St. (Mulberry St.) | 212-343-2053 | www.umbertosclamhouse.com ●
Bronx | 2356 Arthur Ave. (186th St.) | 718-220-2526 | www.umbertosclamhousebronx.com

"Taking you back to the heyday of Little Italy", this "infamous" red-sauce "landmark" serves "classic" pasta and fish in a *"Godfather"*-esque milieu; those not "blown away" (as Joey Gallo was) say "leave it to the tourists" and decamp for the "better" Bronx outpost.

Una Pizza Napoletana Ⓜ⌦ *Pizza* | 23 | 10 | 13 | $28 |

E Village | 349 E. 12th St. (bet. 1st & 2nd Aves.) | 212-477-9950 | www.unapizza.com

"Pizza purists" praise this East Villager for its "simply prepared" Neapolitan pies made with "quality" imported ingredients, even if they're "criminally priced" at $21 per 12-inch model; "abysmal" service, no slices and a "limited selection" (four, to be exact) make some wonder if it's "worth the hassle."

Uncle Jack's Steakhouse *Steak* | 23 | 19 | 21 | $67 |

Garment District | 440 Ninth Ave. (bet. 34th & 35th Sts.) | 212-244-0005
Bayside | 39-40 Bell Blvd. (40th Ave.) | Queens | 718-229-1100
www.unclejacks.com

That "old-time steakhouse feel" thrives at this Bayside/Garment District duo where "giant chops" are presented in "boys' club" settings for "high price tags"; maybe they're "not Luger's", but "if steak is a religion, they're good parish churches."

Uncle Nick's *Greek* | 19 | 11 | 15 | $32 |

W 50s | 747 Ninth Ave. (bet. 50th & 51st Sts.) | 212-245-7992
"Rollicking good times" await at this "busy" Hell's Kitchen Hellenic specializing in "delicious" meze and grilled whole fish; it's "nothing fancy" with "rough-and-ready" service, plus an adjoining Ouzaria with much the "same menu" for "leftover laundry money."

ⓩ Union Square Cafe *American* | 26 | 22 | 26 | $65 |

Union Sq | 21 E. 16th St. (bet. 5th Ave. & Union Sq. W.) | 212-243-4020 | www.unionsquarecafe.com

Voted Most Popular in this Survey, Danny Meyer's New American off Union Square "proves its reputation every time", thanks to Michael Romano's "artfully executed" cuisine, a choice of "well-appointed" spaces and "friendly" service that "never wavers"; true, a reservation can be "problematic", but the walk-in bar area is always available to experience this "definition of comfortable NY dining."

Uno Chicago Grill *Pizza* | 14 | 12 | 14 | $23 |

E 80s | 220 E. 86th St. (bet. 2nd & 3rd Aves.) | 212-472-5656 ●
G Village | 391 Sixth Ave. (bet. 8th St. & Waverly Pl.) | 212-242-5230 ●
Seaport | Pier 17 | 89 South St. (Fulton St.) | 212-791-7999
W 80s | 432 Columbus Ave. (81st St.) | 212-595-4700 ●
Bay Ridge | 9201 Fourth Ave. (92nd St.) | Brooklyn | 718-748-8667 ●
Astoria | 37-11 35th Ave. (38th St.) | Queens | 718-706-8800 ●

(continued)

(continued)

Uno Chicago Grill

Bayside | 39-02 Bell Blvd. (39th Ave.) | Queens | 718-279-4900 ◗

Forest Hills | 107-16 70th Rd. (bet. Austin St. & Queens Blvd.) | Queens | 718-793-6700 ◗

www.unos.com

"Safe but not exciting" deep-dish pizza is served at this "typical chain" whose "expanded" menus also include "ordinary" American chow; service is "slow" and decor "bland", but "kids like it" and so will your wallet.

Uskudar *Turkish*   19 | 9 | 17 | $35

E 70s | 1405 Second Ave. (bet. 73rd & 74th Sts.) | 212-988-2641

"Shoebox"-size, this UES Turk tenders "standard" grub that's "reliable" but may "lack subtlety"; still, "cheerful hospitality" and decent value keep it "crowded all the time" with nonclaustrophobic locals.

Utsav *Indian*   21 | 18 | 19 | $37

W 40s | 1185 Sixth Ave., 2nd fl. (enter on 46th St., bet. 6th & 7th Aves.) | 212-575-2525 | www.utsavny.com

It may be "hard to find", but this "dressy" Theater District Indian is worth seeking out for its "not-too-spicy, beginner-friendly" food and "spacious" setting bedecked with "fabric canopies"; any meal here is a good bet, but the "copious" $15.95 lunch buffet is an especially appealing introduction for first-timers.

Uva ◗ *Italian*   21 | 21 | 20 | $37

E 70s | 1486 Second Ave. (bet. 77th & 78th Sts.) | 212-472-4552 | www.uvawinebarnewyork.com

This UES Italian "hot spot" attracts the "younger set" with "chic" digs, an "extensive wine list" and "good-looking sommeliers" (the "affordable" food is almost incidental here); the vibe's "bustling bordering on loud", so insiders head for the quieter "year-round" garden.

Valbella 🛇 *Italian*   24 | 24 | 23 | $78

Meatpacking | 421 W. 13th St. (bet. 9th Ave. & Washington St.) | 212-645-7777 | www.valbellany.com

Something "very adult" for the Meatpacking District, this "flawless" Northern Italian spin-off of the "Greenwich, CT, original" is a "posh" opportunity to savor "impeccable" food and service in a modern bi-level setting; maybe the prices soar, but its well-heeled crowd can easily afford it.

🆕 Vamos! *Mexican*   ▽ 16 | 17 | 17 | $32

Gramercy | 348 First Ave. (20th St.) | 212-358-7800 | www.vamosnyc.com

"Underserviced" Stuytown gets a lift with the arrival of this new, low-budget Mexican brought to you by the "owners of Petite Abeille"; too bad the food's just "middle of the road", but the "delicious margaritas" and all that "noise" suggest it "caters more to the bar crowd."

V&T ◗ *Italian/Pizza*   18 | 9 | 13 | $21

W 100s | 1024 Amsterdam Ave. (bet. 110th & 111th Sts.) | 212-666-8051

Since 1945, this Morningside Heights Italian "that time forgot" has been a "Columbia student favorite", dishing out "gooey" pizza in "dingy" digs for "cheap as hell" dough; "snail's pace service" and "bottled salad dressing" are "part of the charm."

	FOOD	DECOR	SERVICE	COST

Vatan Ⓜ *Indian*   **23** | **23** | **22** | **$34**

Gramercy | 409 Third Ave. (29th St.) | 212-689-5666 | www.vatanny.com

For $23.95, "endless plates" keep on coming at this "unique", all-you-can-eat Gramercy Indian vegetarian; the "over-the-top" faux village decor affords one of those transporting experiences that you can't put a price on.

Veniero's ❶ *Dessert*   **23** | **14** | **13** | **$15**

E Village | 342 E. 11th St. (bet. 1st & 2nd Aves.) | 212-674-7070 | www.venierospastry.com

Since 1894, this "beloved" East Village Italian pastry palace has been a destination for its "creamy cannoli" and other "naughty" desserts; there's "always a line" and the staff could use some "customer service lessons", but ultimately it's "justly celebrated."

Vento ❶ *Italian*   **19** | **19** | **18** | **$46**

Meatpacking | 675 Hudson St. (14th St.) | 212-699-2400 | www.brguestrestaurants.com

A "great location" in the "happening" Meatpacking District is the bait at Steve Hanson's "lively" Italian featuring an "affordable", small plates–centric menu; though service may need help, it's fun to "sit outside and drool" at the passing "hottie" parade.

Ⓩ Veritas *American*   **26** | **22** | **25** | **$98**

Flatiron | 43 E. 20th St. (bet. B'way & Park Ave. S.) | 212-353-3700 | www.veritas-nyc.com

Bolstered by an award-winning wine list, this "outstanding" Flatiron New American continues to impress those seeking "sophisticated", "delicious" dining in "handsome" environs; it's "luxurious from start to finish" with appropriately "first-class" service, though "costly" given the $76 prix fixe–only menu.

Vermicelli *Vietnamese*   **19** | **16** | **18** | **$29**

E 70s | 1492 Second Ave. (bet. 77th & 78th Sts.) | 212-288-8868 | www.vermicellirestaurant.com

Nope, "it isn't Italian" – despite the "odd name", this UES "neighborhood sleeper" offers "flavorful" Vietnamese eats that are "well spiced" and priced; though the ambiance is "unusually calm", many take out the "excellent box lunches" at midday.

Veselka *Ukrainian*   **18** | **12** | **14** | **$20**

E Village | 144 Second Ave. (9th St.) | 212-228-9682 ❶
E Village | First Park | 75 E. First St. (1st Ave.) | 347-907-3317 ⊟
www.veselka.com

"Go hungry and then go nap" after a meal at this bargain East Village Ukrainian where the "rib-sticking" "Eastern European soul food" is served "round the clock" by a "perfunctory" staff; the kiosk satellite features an abbreviated menu and a handful of alfresco tables.

Vespa *Italian*   **21** | **20** | **20** | **$39**

E 80s | 1625 Second Ave. (bet. 84th & 85th Sts.) | 212-472-2050 | www.barvespa.com

"La dolce vita" is alive and well at this "low-key" UES Italian where a "chic" "Euro vibe" enhances the "delicious", midpriced cooking; the "beautiful" patio is a "wonderful escape" as well as a "romantic refuge."

	FOOD	DECOR	SERVICE	COST

Vezzo *Pizza*
▽ 21 | 16 | 15 | $22

Murray Hill | 178 Lexington Ave. (31st St.) | 212-839-8300
"Fabulous thin-crust" pizza in an underserved part of Murray Hill has made it "hard to get a table" at this Italian yearling; an airy setting and a choice of "any topping you could possibly want" help blunt the "slow service" and "relatively pricey" tabs.

Via Brasil *Brazilian/Steak*
18 | 15 | 18 | $40

W 40s | 34 W. 46th St. (bet. 5th & 6th Aves.) | 212-997-1158 | www.viabrasilrestaurant.com
When "flying to Rio is a little much", there's always this "easygoing" Theater District Brazilian that puts "Ipanema on a platter" via "perfectly marinated" steaks and other "tasty" dishes; though a "recent remodel" gets "low marks", it "comes alive" on "live music nights."

Via Emilia ⑤🚭 *Italian*
21 | 16 | 19 | $36

Flatiron | 47 E. 21st St. (bet. B'way & Park Ave. S.) | 212-505-3072 | www.viaemilia.us
Relocation to "more spacious" digs has some longtime patrons of this Flatiron Italian claiming that it's now "devoid of charm"; but thankfully the "excellent value" and "same great" Emilia-Romagna food remains, along with that "makes-life-difficult" no-plastic policy.

Viand *Coffee Shop*
16 | 8 | 17 | $20

E 60s | 673 Madison Ave. (bet. 61st & 62nd Sts.) | 212-751-6622 🚭
E 70s | 1011 Madison Ave. (78th St.) | 212-249-8250
E 80s | 300 E. 86th St. (2nd Ave.) | 212-879-9425 ☽
W 70s | 2130 Broadway (75th St.) | 212-877-2888 ☯
www.viandnyc.com ☽
There's "no ambiance" at these "quick-in, quick-out" coffee shops, but they remain "NY classics" for their "old-fashioned" vibe, "lightning-fast" service and famous turkey sandwiches "carved right off the bone"; indeed, on many mornings you'll find Mayor Mike breakfasting at the 78th Street branch.

Via Oreto *Italian*
19 | 15 | 18 | $46

E 60s | 1121-23 First Ave. (bet. 61st & 62nd Sts.) | 212-308-0828
"Like dinner at the in-laws' without the stress", this "family-owned" UES Italian exudes a "comfortable", "right-out-of-the-*Sopranos*" vibe with a "caring" staff serving a "solid", midpriced menu of "basics"; "mama's special meatballs" are a revered Sunday/Monday tradition.

Via Quadronno *Italian*
21 | 15 | 16 | $38

E 70s | 25 E. 73rd St. (bet. 5th & Madison Aves.) | 212-650-9880 | www.viaquadronno.com
"Chic" Madison Avenue "art dealers" and "gorgeous Euro moms" patronize this all-day UES Italian for "quick pick-me-ups", particularly the "fab" panini and cappuccinos; "prices are high" for what you get, and the "tiny digs ensure you won't stay too long."

ViceVersa ⑤ *Italian*
23 | 21 | 22 | $53

W 50s | 325 W. 51st St. (bet. 8th & 9th Aves.) | 212-399-9291 | www.viceversarestaurant.com
One "reason to go to the Theater District even if you're not seeing a show", this "consistently fine" Italian serves a "first-rate" menu in a

sunny "modern" setting; service is "friendly" but "professional", and somehow it's "not too touristy in a touristy area."

Vico ●⇆ *Italian* | 21 | 15 | 19 | $59 |

E 90s | 1302 Madison Ave. (bet. 92nd & 93rd Sts.) | 212-876-2222

It helps "to be known" at this "clubby" Carnegie Hill Italian where "UES Wasps get excited" about the "surprisingly good" menu that really "looks great on the plate"; not as thrilling are the "expensive-for-what-it-is" tabs and "annoying" cash-only policy.

Victor's Cafe ● *Cuban* | 21 | 18 | 20 | $46 |

W 50s | 236 W. 52nd St. (bet. B'way & 8th Ave.) | 212-586-7714 | www.victorscafe.com

A "touch of Havana" in the Theater District, this palm-decorated "old reliable" has been dishing out "enticing" Cuban food since the early '60s; sure, it's a little "pricey" (maybe "outdated"), but the "ebullient" ambiance and "warm" service keep regulars regular.

Vida ⓜ⇆ *Eclectic* | ▽ 20 | 16 | 20 | $34 |

Staten Island | 381 Van Duzer St. (bet. Beach & Wright Sts.) | 718-720-1501

Featuring an "unusually creative", unusually affordable menu, this Staten Island Eclectic makes locals "feel very much at home – without having to do the dishes"; the only drawback is a "too cozy" setting that's so tiny there's "no privacy at all."

VietCafé ⓧ *Vietnamese* | ▽ 21 | 18 | 19 | $33 |

TriBeCa | 345 Greenwich St. (bet. Harrison & Jay Sts.) | 212-431-5888 | www.viet-cafe.com

"Haute Vietnamese" food comes to TriBeCa via this "tantalizing" Asian offering "light, delicate" dishes; still, the "small portions" and "high-tech" setting lead some to report there's "no sparkle" here.

View, The *Continental* | 18 | 24 | 19 | $80 |

W 40s | Marriott Marquis Hotel | 1535 Broadway, 47th fl. (bet. 45th & 46th Sts.) | 212-704-8900 | www.nymarriottmarquis.com

"Still twirlin' after all these years", this hotel Continental is NYC's only "rotating restaurant", with a literally "moving view" of Times Square and beyond; the food's just "so-so" and the prix fixe–only tabs are "pricey", but at least it's "aptly named."

Villa Berulia *Italian* | ▽ 23 | 19 | 24 | $49 |

Murray Hill | 107 E. 34th St. (bet. Lexington & Park Aves.) | 212-689-1970 | www.villaberulia.com

"Comfortable fine dining" is in store at this venerable Murray Hill Northern Italian known for its "top-quality" cooking and "absolutely delightful" staff; it mostly draws "time travelers" (i.e. "mostly older" types) who don't mind "pricey" tabs and "dated" decor.

Village *American/French* | 20 | 18 | 19 | $45 |

G Village | 62 W. Ninth St. (bet. 5th & 6th Aves.) | 212-505-3355 | www.villagerestaurant.com

The mood's "lively" at this "better-than-average" Village bistro where the Franco-American offerings are "consistently good", "especially for the price"; though the "barnlike" back dining room has a "skylight and high ceilings", it could also use a "sound absorber."

	FOOD	DECOR	SERVICE	COST

Villa Mosconi ⑤ Italian
`20` `15` `22` `$43`

G Village | 69 MacDougal St. (bet. Bleecker & Houston Sts.) | 212-673-0390 | www.villamosconi.com

There's a "dedicated neighborhood following" at this circa-1976 Village Italian, an "old-fashioned" affair with "solid" red sauce on the menu and "paint-by-numbers paintings" on the walls; "caring" staffers and modest prices "make you feel like a regular even if you're not."

Vincent's ● Italian
`21` `14` `18` `$34`

Little Italy | 119 Mott St. (Hester St.) | 212-226-8133 | www.originalvincents.com

For "real Italian, not New Age", try this circa-1904 Little Italy vet famed for its "secret-formula sauce" served in a "variety of levels of spiciness"; it's staffed by a crew of "interesting characters" and decorated with the "requisite pictures of the *Sopranos* cast members on the wall."

Virgil's Real Barbecue ● BBQ
`20` `13` `17` `$33`

W 40s | 152 W. 44th St. (bet. B'way & 6th Ave.) | 212-921-9494 | www.virgilsbbq.com

"Monstrous portions" of "lip-smacking", "stick-to-your-ribs ribs" grace the menu of this "stuff-your-face" BBQ "factory"; the Times Square location translates into "droves of tourists", "hurried service" and a general air of "pandemonium"; P.S. "don't forgo the bib."

Vivolo ⑤ Italian
`20` `17` `20` `$49`

E 70s | 140 E. 74th St. (bet. Lexington & Park Aves.) | 212-737-3533 | www.vivolonyc.com

Set in a "cozy", "wood-paneled" townhouse, this "old-school" UES duplex serves "reliable" Italiana that tastes even better "when the fireplace is lit" in the "inviting" upstairs parlor; it draws "well-dressed couples of a certain age" with an "outstanding" $26 early-bird.

Vong French/Thai
`22` `23` `21` `$61`

E 50s | 200 E. 54th St. (3rd Ave.) | 212-486-9592 | www.jean-georges.com

The "tableware is as entertaining as the food" at Jean-Georges Vongerichten's "exotic" Midtown French-Thai where the "artfully prepared" offerings match the "polished" staff and "Asian fantasy" setting; sure, the "tiny portions" come at "splurge"-worthy tabs, but a $20 "bargain" lunch and $35 pre-theater prix fixes are available.

Vynl American/Thai
`17` `20` `16` `$25`

NEW **E 70s** | 1491 Second Ave. (78th St.) | 212-249-6080
W 50s | 754 Ninth Ave. (51st St.) | 212-974-2003 ●
NEW **W 80s** | 507 Columbus Ave. (bet. 84th & 85th Sts.) | 212-362-1107
www.vynl-nyc.com

"Something for everyone" sums up the menu of this trio of "pretend diners" known for their "affordable" New American–Thai chow and "random service"; "tragically kitschy" "music-themed" loos are conversation starters, that is if you can be heard above the "cranking stereo."

Z NEW Wakiya ● Chinese
`–` `–` `–` `E`

Gramercy | Gramercy Park Hotel | 2 Lexington Ave. (21st St.) | 212-995-1330 | www.gramercyparkhotel.com

Ian Schrager's trendy rehabbed Gramercy Park Hotel is the setting for this nouveau Chinese named after star chef Yuji Wakiya, who offers an exciting 'sharing menu' of hot and cold items as well as dim sum; the long, slender space, done up in red and black, exudes a James Bond vibe (i.e. *Diamonds are Forever*), though pricing is far more modern.

Waldy's Wood Fired Pizza *Pizza*

FOOD	DECOR	SERVICE	COST
21	11	15	$16

Chelsea | 800 Sixth Ave. (bet. 27th & 28th Sts.) | 212-213-5042 | www.waldyspizza.com

"Highbrow pizza" by way of the "highly inventive" chef Waldy Malouf (Beacon) is yours at this "tiny" Chelsea storefront where "minimal" seating and "fast-food" decor make "delivery a better option"; bonus points go to the "gourmet toppings", especially the fresh herbs.

Walker's ● *Pub Food*

17	13	16	$28

TriBeCa | 16 N. Moore St. (Varick St.) | 212-941-0142

Serving "reliable pub grub" long "before TriBeCa was *TriBeCa*", this "neighborhood fixture" has the staples "down pat" with the "most affordable" dining around; expect plenty of "old NY" ambiance and a crowd of "regulars" who tout the burgers and brews.

Wallsé ● *Austrian*

26	22	23	$66

W Village | 344 W. 11th St. (Washington St.) | 212-352-2300 | www.wallse.com

A "small restaurant with big aspirations", this West Village "charmer" lets you skip the "schlep to Vienna" thanks to chef Kurt Gutenbrunner's "seriously delicious" Austrian cuisine; add "outstanding wines", "gracious service" and "great Julian Schnabel paintings on the wall", and the "high-end" pricing is what you'd expect.

Water Club *American*

20	24	21	$62

Murray Hill | East River at 30th St. (enter on 23rd St.) | 212-683-3333 | www.thewaterclub.com

For a "romantic getaway without leaving the city", this "special-occasion" Murray Hill American set on an East River barge "reminds us we're on an island" with its "spectacular views"; maybe it's "expensive" and "out of the way", but the food's "delicious" and the decor appropriately "nautical" at this "unique dining experience"; it's also a great place for a party.

WaterFalls Ⓜ *Italian*

▽ 20	19	19	$37

Staten Island | 2012 Victory Blvd. (bet. Bradley & Jewett Aves.) | 718-815-7200 | www.waterfalls-restaurant.com

Offering a "large variety of dishes" at modest prices, this Staten Island Italian is also "pretty" and "tranquil"; though a few find things a bit "cookie-cutter", at least the "consistent" kitchen assures that "you'll get a good meal" here.

Water's Edge Ⓩ *American/Seafood*

23	26	23	$60

LIC | East River & 44th Dr. (Vernon Blvd.) | Queens | 718-482-0033 | www.watersedgenyc.com

"Priceless" riverside views of Manhattan are the raisons d'être of this Long Island City New American seafooder that follows through with "tasty" cooking and "prompt" service; despite "free water taxi" service from Midtown, serious tabs make it "not your every-Saturday kind of place."

			FOOD	DECOR	SERVICE	COST

Z NEW Waverly Inn and Garden 🅾 *American* 18 | 21 | 17 | $57
W Village | 16 Bank St. (Waverly Pl.) | 212-243-7900
The hit of the year, this remake of a circa-1920 West Village tavern
produces "reliable", tasty Americana in a lovely, intimate setting that
plays to a "celeb-centric" crowd that is mostly friends of owner/*Vanity
Fair* editor Grayson Carter; it's virtually "impossible to get a table"
without connections, but walk-ins are allowed in the charming front
bar; sidewalk tables and the back 'garden room' are bonuses.

wd-50 🅾 *American/Eclectic* 23 | 19 | 23 | $82
LES | 50 Clinton St. (bet. Rivington & Stanton Sts.) | 212-477-2900 |
www.wd-50.com
"If you're up for an adventure", "go outside the box" at this
"unorthodox" Lower East Side American-Eclectic – aka "Molecular
Gastronomy Central" – where chef Wylie Dufresne's "envelope-
pushing" cuisine induces "love-it-or-hate-it" responses ("outstanding" vs. "outlandish"); there's no debate, however, that it's
"expensive" – and "never, ever boring."

West Bank Cafe 🅾 *American* 20 | 17 | 19 | $44
W 40s | Manhattan Plaza | 407 W. 42nd St. (bet. 9th & 10th Aves.) |
212-695-6909 | www.westbankcafe.com
"Pleasant" is the word on this "off-the-beaten-path" Hell's Kitchen
"keeper" with "dependable" New American cooking, a "good price
point" and a "quality bar-and-grill atmosphere"; proximity to 42nd
Street's Theater Row makes it a natural "hangout for working actors."

Westville *American* 23 | 12 | 18 | $23
W Village | 210 W. 10th St. (bet. Bleecker & W. 4th Sts.) | 212-741-7971
NEW Westville East *American*
E Village | 173 Ave. A (11th St.) | 212-677-2033
"Cheap eats and long lines" sum up this West Village American, a
"cult classic" specializing in "fresh greenmarket comfort foods"; the
"tight" setup is a bit "less cramped" at the new East Village offspring,
featuring twice as many seats.

Whole Foods Café *Eclectic/Health Food* 19 | 9 | 10 | $16
NEW LES | 95 E. Houston St., 2nd fl. (Bowery) | 212-420-1320
Union Sq | 4 Union Square S. (bet. B'way & University Pl.) | 212-673-5388
W 60s | Time Warner Ctr. | 10 Columbus Circle, downstairs (60th St.
at B'way) | 212-823-9600
www.wholefoods.com
There's "variety aplenty" at these "self-serve" cafeteria adjuncts to
the "foodie grocery stores", where the Eclectic offerings include a
plethora of "multicultural" items as well as "huge salad bars"; despite
"long check-out lines", "not enough seating" and an "every-man-for-
himself" ambiance, fans "never tire of it."

Whym *American* 21 | 18 | 19 | $41
W 50s | 889 Ninth Ave. (bet. 57th & 58th Sts.) | 212-315-0088 |
www.whymnyc.com
"Trendy people too lazy to go Downtown" like this "stylish" Hell's
Kitchen New American for its "industrial", "nightclublike" look and
"positive energy"; its "upscale aspirations" are reflected in the
"jazzed-up comfort-food" menu, not the "middle-class prices."

	FOOD	DECOR	SERVICE	COST

'wichcraft *Sandwiches* | 20 | 11 | 15 | $17 |

Chelsea | Terminal Warehouse | 224 12th Ave. (bet. 27th & 28th Sts.) | 212-780-0577
E 40s | 555 Fifth Ave. (46th St.) | 212-780-0577 🌀
NEW Flatiron | 11 E. 20th St. (bet. B'way & 5th Ave.) | 212-780-0577
G Village | 60 E. Eighth St. (Mercer St.) | 212-780-0577
NEW Murray Hill | Equinox | 1 Park Ave. S. (33rd St.) | 212-780-0577
SoHo | Equinox | 106 Crosby St. (Prince St.) | 212-780-0577
TriBeCa | 397 Greenwich St. (Beach St.) | 212-780-0577
W 40s | Bryant Park | Sixth Ave. (bet. 40th & 42nd Sts.) | 212-780-0577
www.wichcraftnyc.com
The "sandwich as art" is the philosophy of this breakfast-and-lunch chainlet from Craft's Tom Colicchio that creates "ambitious combos" via "high-quality ingredients"; though service can be "slow" and it costs "a lot of dough for not much bread", most admit to being under its "spell."

Wild Ginger *Thai* | 19 | 18 | 17 | $25 |

W Village | 51 Grove St. (bet. Bleecker St. & 7th Ave. S.) | 212-367-7200 | www.wildginger-ny.com
"Amazingly affordable" for such a "prime Village location", this "pleasant" Thai serves a "well-prepared" menu that's "not too fusiony"; it's also invitingly "atmospheric", with a "dimly lit", bamboo-heavy setting and "friendly" service.

NEW Wild Salmon *Seafood* | ▽ 21 | 20 | 18 | $59 |

E 40s | 622 Third Ave. (40th St.) | 212-404-1700 | www.chinagrillmgt.com
Like the name says, this new Midtown seafooder from restaurateur Jeffrey Chodorow focuses on salmon with "nearly everything on the menu flown in from the Pacific Northwest" – hence the "pricey" tabs; the "soaring" setting is now festooned with a copper mobile of flying fish.

Willie's Steak House 🕐 *Steak* | ▽ 23 | 16 | 19 | $26 |

Bronx | 1832 Westchester Ave. (bet. Taylor & Thieriot Aves.) | 718-822-9697 | www.williessteakhouse.com
An "extensive menu" of steaks and Latin dishes makes for "authentic", Spanish-style dining at this longtime Bronx chop shop that's well priced and well served for the genre; live jazz performances on Wednesdays and Saturdays are equally appealing.

Wo Hop 🕐🍴 *Chinese* | 21 | 6 | 14 | $17 |

Chinatown | 17 Mott St. (Canal St.) | 212-267-2536
Right "out of a Woody Allen movie", this 70-year-old Chinatown vet serves "old-fashioned" Cantonese chow at "ridiculously low prices" in a "basement-from-hell" setting; though formerly open 'round the clock, it's now 21/7, closed daily from 7-10 AM.

Wolfgang's Steakhouse *Steak* | 25 | 20 | 20 | $71 |

Murray Hill | 4 Park Ave. (33rd St.) | 212-889-3369
TriBeCa | 409 Greenwich St. (bet. Beach & Hubert Sts.) | 212-925-0350
www.wolfgangssteakhouse.com
"Masters of the universe" who "don't want to make the trip to Brooklyn" vow that these "Luger copy" steakhouses are "as good" as the original, and at least "take credit cards"; while the "mobbed" Murray Hill outpost is more atmospheric with its "vaulted ceilings",

it's much "noisier" than the "roomier" TriBeCa branch, but either way, "if the cholesterol doesn't stop your heart, the prices will."

Wollensky's Grill ● *Steak* — 23 | 17 | 20 | $51
E 40s | 201 E. 49th St. (3rd Ave.) | 212-753-0444 |
www.smithandwollensky.com

"Less formal" (and "more fun") than its next-door "big sister", Smith & Wollensky, this handsome East Midtown grill serves the same "great steaks and burgers" at "better prices"; night owls say the biggest draw is its "late hours" – "where else can you eat this good after midnight?"

NEW Wombat ●♉ *Australian* — ▽ 21 | 14 | 22 | $25
Williamsburg | 613 Grand St. (bet. Leonard & Lorimer Sts.) | Brooklyn |
718-218-7077 | www.thewombatbar.com

"Tiny" and "funky", this "surprisingly good" Williamsburg newcomer features a low-priced variety of hearty Australian dishes served till 2 AM; if the late-night carousing gets to you, there's also a hair-of-the-dingo brunch, available daily.

Wondee Siam *Thai* — 22 | 7 | 16 | $21
NEW E 80s | 1429 Third Ave. (bet. 80th & 81st Sts.) | 212-772-1494
W 50s | 792 Ninth Ave. (bet. 52nd & 53rd Sts.) | 212-459-9057 ♉
W 50s | 813 Ninth Ave. (bet. 53rd & 54th Sts.) | 917-286-1726

"Authentic Thai" at prices that will "make you think you're in Minneapolis, not Manhattan", keep the customers coming to this "simple" Hell's Kitchen trio; forget the "total lack of decor" and "spotty" service: "what's really special here is the taste"; N.B. the UES satellite opened post-Survey.

WonJo ● *Korean* — ▽ 20 | 12 | 14 | $32
Garment District | 23 W. 32nd St. (bet. B'way & 5th Ave.) | 212-695-5815

Do-it-yourself types like cooking their Korean BBQ over "real charcoal" at this "bustling" Garment District spot where the "not-so-good" service is trumped by gentle pricing and a 24/7 open-door policy; those sensitive to "smoke" say the "downstairs seating is better."

Woo Lae Oak *Korean* — 23 | 21 | 18 | $51
SoHo | 148 Mercer St. (bet. Houston & Prince Sts.) | 212-925-8200 |
www.woolaeoaksoho.com

One of NYC's "hippest Koreans", this "fashionable" SoHo grill is set in "sleek" digs, tended by an "eye-candy staff" and priced "on the expensive side"; more typical of the genre, it features "cook-it-yourself" dining.

Wu Liang Ye *Chinese* — 21 | 12 | 16 | $29
E 80s | 215 E. 86th St. (bet. 2nd & 3rd Aves.) | 212-534-8899
Murray Hill | 338 Lexington Ave. (bet. 39th & 40th Sts.) | 212-370-9648
W 40s | 36 W. 48th St. (bet. 5th & 6th Aves.) | 212-398-2308 ·

"Not for the faint of stomach", this Szechuan trio purveys "adventurous" eats made from "zesty" ingredients – "very spicy means *very spicy*" here – so for best results, go with "someone who knows how to order"; "aging" decor and "impersonal" service are offset by "moderate prices."

Xing ● *Asian Fusion* — 21 | 21 | 19 | $41
W 50s | 785 Ninth Ave. (52nd St.) | 646-289-3010 | www.xingrestaurant.com

Something "different" for Hell's Kitchen, this "contempo" Asian fusion practitioner features a "novel" menu that works well with the "sleek",

	FOOD	DECOR	SERVICE	COST

"upscale" design built around a "huge" aquarium; "killer cocktails" fuel the place's "high energy" and distract from its "pricey" tabs.

X.O. ⊅ *Chinese* — 18 | 9 | 12 | $17

Chinatown | 148 Hester St. (bet. Bowery & Elizabeth St.) | 212-965-8645
Chinatown | 96 Walker St. (bet. Centre & Lafayette Sts.) | 212-343-8339

If you like it "quick" and "cheap", these Hong Kong–style Chinatown cafes are just the ticket, featuring all-day dim sum and menus almost "too long to read" ("what *don't* they have?"); "indifferent" service and "dumpy" digs are the downsides.

Xunta ● *Spanish* — 19 | 12 | 13 | $29

E Village | 174 First Ave. (bet. 10th & 11th Sts.) | 212-614-0620 | www.xuntatapas.com

"Crowds of college students" cram into this "rowdy", low-budget East Village Spaniard where the "sangria flows" so freely that the "night is a blur" for most; still, a few remember "*qué bueno*" tapas, "uncomfortable" barrel seating and "absurdly loud" acoustics.

☑ Yakitori Totto ● *Japanese* — 26 | 18 | 20 | $43

W 50s | 251 W. 55th St., 2nd fl. (bet. B'way & 8th Ave.) | 212-245-4555

Bringing an "authentic yakitori experience to the Big Apple", this "unique" Midtowner's grilled skewers are a particular "favorite of Japanese expats"; some menu items may be a "bit much" for Westerners – "chicken knees, anyone?" – but that's not stopping it from being "always full."

Yama *Japanese* — 24 | 13 | 17 | $39

E 40s | 308 E. 49th St. (bet. 1st & 2nd Aves.) | 212-355-3370 ⑤
Gramercy | 122 E. 17th St. (Irving Pl.) | 212-475-0969 ⑤
G Village | 38-40 Carmine St. (bet. Bedford & Bleecker Sts.) | 212-989-9330 ⑤
G Village | 92 W. Houston St. (bet. La Guardia Pl. & Thompson St.) | 212-674-0935 ● Ⓜ
www.yamarestaurant.com

Ok, the "obscenely big" pieces of sushi served at this Japanese chainlet "ain't subtle", but they are "fresher than fresh" and extremely "well priced"; if the "absurd" waits and "lame decor" are off-putting, insiders say the 49th Street branch is the most "serene" with the "shortest lines."

York Grill *American* — 23 | 20 | 22 | $48

E 80s | 1690 York Ave. (bet. 88th & 89th Sts.) | 212-772-0261

"Traditional" is the word for this Yorkville "neighborhood" spot where a "civilized" "older crowd" savors "old-fashioned" Americana in "quiet", "clubby" environs; trendy types wish it were "more inventive", but still feel it's "consistently excellent" and not that expensive.

Yuca Bar ● *Pan-Latin* — 21 | 14 | 16 | $30

E Village | 111 Ave. A (7th St.) | 212-982-9533 | www.yucabarnyc.com

"Divine sangria" and "kick-ass mojitos" keep the mood "festive" at this East Village Pan-Latin that attracts the young with "great value"; it's most memorable, however, as a "primo people-watching location", directly opposite Tompkins Square Park.

	FOOD	DECOR	SERVICE	COST

Yuka *Japanese* — 21 | 11 | 19 | $26

E 80s | 1557 Second Ave. (bet. 80th & 81st Sts.) | 212-772-9675
"Bargain sushi hunters" are all over the $19 all-you-can-eat deal at this longtime UES Japanese; sure, the seating's "tight", the service "rushed" and the setting "informal" (verging on "worn"), but they "slice a generous piece of fish" and "for the price, you can't complain."

Yuki Sushi ● *Japanese* — 21 | 14 | 20 | $31

W 90s | 656 Amsterdam Ave. (92nd St.) | 212-787-8200
"Unassuming" yet "pleasant", this UWS Japanese is a "good neighborhood option" for "casual" dining if "not a life-changing experience"; the fish is "prepared with care" for an "affordable" price, while "sweet service" compensates for the "not-much-to-look-at" decor.

NEW Yushi *Japanese* — - | - | - | I

E 40s | 245 Park Ave. (enter on E. 47th St., bet. Park & Lex. Aves.) | 212-687-1900 ⓩ
Financial District | 4 World Financial Ctr. | 250 Vesey St. (West St.) | 212-945-3096
www.yushi.com
Be prepared to wait in line at these Japanese siblings in Midtown and the Financial District thanks to their fresh, affordable array of grab-and-go sushi and sashimi; cool design touches like steel tabletops and mod pod chairs help working stiffs overlook the canteen-style setting.

Yuva *Indian* — ▽ 24 | 19 | 23 | $38

E 50s | 230 E. 58th St. (bet. 2nd & 3rd Aves.) | 212-339-0090 | www.yuvanyc.com
"Delicious" dining is the deal at this East Midtown Indian where the dishes display "creative finesse" and the decor sports modern-rustic touches; the latest arrival on 58th Street's "high-end Indian Row", this "worthwhile" venue "ain't your average curry mill."

Zabar's Cafe ⊄ *Deli* — 20 | 6 | 11 | $16

W 80s | 2245 Broadway (80th St.) | 212-787-2000 | www.zabars.com
Backers brave bizarre service, white Formica digs and plenty of "pushy NYers" just for the bagels, lox and other "great" noshables at this UWS deli/cafe hitched to the famed gourmet market; what's more, even kvetchers concede prices here "can't be beat" for what you get.

Zarela *Mexican* — 21 | 15 | 17 | $42

E 50s | 953 Second Ave. (bet. 50th & 51st Sts.) | 212-644-6740 | www.zarela.com
Still "buzzing" on the East Side, Zarela Martinez's split-level "winner" shows what "true" Mexican cooking should be; "powerful" margaritas and modest prices are catalysts for the fiesta scene downstairs (upstairs is "more tranquil").

Zaytoons *Mideastern* — 22 | 13 | 17 | $18

Carroll Gardens | 283 Smith St. (Sackett St.) | Brooklyn | 718-875-1880
Fort Greene | 472 Myrtle Ave. (bet. Hall St. & Washington Ave.) | Brooklyn | 718-623-5522
www.zaytoonsrestaurant.com
"Nothing fancy", just "generous" helpings of "dependably delicious" dishes are the stock in trade of these "ever-reliable" Middle Eastern

BYOs in Carroll Gardens and Fort Greene; "quick" service and "super-competitive" pricing easily override the modest settings.

Za Za ● Italian
20 | 15 | 19 | $37

E 60s | 1207 First Ave. (bet. 65th & 66th Sts.) | 212-772-9997 | www.zazanyc.com

Filling Italiana that "doesn't taste generic" is the calling card of this Eastsider that also comes across with "friendly" service and "reasonable" tabs; perhaps there's "no decor" on the inside, but the "amazing" garden out back certainly "increases the enjoyment."

Zebú Grill Brazilian
21 | 16 | 20 | $38

E 90s | 305 E. 92nd St. (bet. 1st & 2nd Aves.) | 212-426-7500 | www.zebugrill.com

Marrying "homestyle cooking" with a "comforting" ambiance and "gracious" service, this "charming" UES Brazilian lures a "loyal crowd" with "basic" but reliably "wonderful" fare; regulars attest "you really get your money's worth" here.

NEW Zenkichi Ⓜ Japanese
▽ 23 | 26 | 24 | $48

Williamsburg | 77 N. Sixth St. (Wythe Ave.) | Brooklyn | 718-388-8985 | www.zenkichi.com

A single orange light marks the entrance to this "elaborately designed" Williamsburg *izakaya*, a "dark", "mazelike" space "out of a David Lynch movie"; the "delicious" Japanese small plates on offer may be "not very filling", but the wide variety of sakes will take care of that.

Zen Palate Vegetarian
19 | 16 | 17 | $27

NEW Financial District | 104 John St. (Cliff St.) | 212-962-4208
Union Sq | 34 Union Sq. E. (16th St.) | 212-614-9291
W 40s | 663 Ninth Ave. (46th St.) | 212-582-1669
www.zenpalate.com

"Meatless isn't so scary" at this vegetarian trio that does "amazing things" with "dressed-up" tofu- and soy-based dishes served in "meditative" digs; still, "hard-core carnivores" balk at the "mock meat" eats, saying "how about a bit of flavor?"

Zerza ● Moroccan
▽ 22 | 20 | 18 | $38

E Village | 304 E. Sixth St. (bet. 1st & 2nd Aves.) | 212-529-8250 | www.zerza.com

"Terrific" tagines and other "standout" Moroccan specialties fill out the modestly priced menu of this "cozy", split-level East Villager oddly parked on Sixth Street's Curry Row; the "staff tries very hard", ditto the Saturday night belly dancer.

NEW Zest Ⓜ American
▽ 26 | 23 | 20 | $47

Staten Island | 977 Bay St. (Willow Ave.) | 718-390-8477

The ambiance is more "212" than Staten Island at this new "fine-dining" arrival serving "excellent" French-accented New Americana "in the sticks" of Rosebank; indeed, the garden is so "lovely" that some "feel like they're in Brooklyn."

Zeytin Turkish
19 | 17 | 17 | $38

W 80s | 519 Columbus Ave. (85th St.) | 212-579-1145 | www.zeytinny.com

Upper Westsiders seeking "novel flavors" and "decent" prices find their way to this "pleasant", "no-frills" Turk; true, the food is more "solid" than spectacular and the "appetizers better than the entrees", but for a "change of pace", it's "just what the neighborhood needed."

Zip Burger ● Hamburgers
18 | 9 | 12 | $13

E 50s | 300½ E. 52nd St. (bet. 1st & 2nd Aves.) | 212-308-1308 | www.zipburger.com

You can build your own "quality" burger at this Eastsider that also doles out "fab" Belgian fries along with "delish" shakes in "not-much-to-look-at" digs; there's also a "great" array of toppings for those who don't mind "packing on the calories."

Zócalo Mexican
20 | 15 | 17 | $38

E 40s | Grand Central | lower level (42nd St. & Vanderbilt Ave.) | 212-687-5666
E 80s | 174 E. 82nd St. (bet. Lexington & 3rd Aves.) | 212-717-7772
www.zocalonyc.com

"Killer" margaritas help fuel the "daunting" din at this Upper East Side "designer Mexican" where the food is as "contemporary" as the "under-30" crowd; the Midtown spin-off can be as "busy as Grand Central at rush hour- wait, it *is* Grand Central at rush hour."

Zoë American
20 | 18 | 19 | $47

SoHo | 90 Prince St. (bet. B'way & Mercer St.) | 212-966-6722 | www.zoerestaurant.com

SoHo-cialites still drop into this area "fixture" that's as "zestful" as ever, supplying "throngs" of shoppers with "consistently good" New American cooking bolstered by "attentive" service; it's not cheap, but devotees don't seem to mind.

NEW Zoë Townhouse American
- | - | - | E

E 60s | 135 E. 62nd St. (bet. Lexington & Park Aves.) | 212-752-6000 | www.zoerestaurant.com

The owners of the erstwhile Jovia have brightened up this bi-level UES townhouse and turned it into a satellite of Zoë, their SoHo New American; while the prices won't faze affluent locals, bargain-seekers gravitate to its all-day 'pizza bar' menu.

NEW Zoma Ethiopian
▽ 23 | 22 | 23 | $27

Harlem | 2084 Frederick Douglass Blvd. (113th St.) | 212-662-0620 | www.zomanyc.com

Standing apart from other Ethiopians, this "classy" Harlem newcomer is "blessedly unkitschy" featuring "candlelight" and "spare", stylishly sleek appointments; menuwise, look for "well-spiced", well-priced renditions of classic savory stews eaten with spongy injera flatbread.

Zona Rosa ⊠ Mexican
18 | 16 | 17 | $46

W 50s | 40 W. 56th St. (bet. 5th & 6th Aves.) | 212-247-2800 | www.zonarosarestaurant.com

Favored for the "great" guacamole leading off its south-of-the-border lineup, this "upscale" Midtown Mexican attracts *amigos* with "attentive" service and "tasty" preparations; the less impressed tag it "over-priced" and opt for their "powerful" drinks.

Zucco Le French Diner ● French
▽ 22 | 17 | 20 | $29

LES | 188 Orchard St. (bet. Houston & Stanton Sts.) | 212-677-5200
A "hidden gem" on Orchard Street, this "quirky" LES French cafe in a "pint-sized" setting turns out totally "legit", sometimes "excellent"

	FOOD	DECOR	SERVICE	COST

Gallic fare for an attractive price; owner Zucco's accent is almost as "priceless" as watching those "beautiful people not eating what they've ordered."

Zum Schneider ⊄ *German*

	18	17	16	$27

E Village | 107 Ave. C (7th St.) | 212-598-1098 | www.zumschneider.com
"Hearty" German chow provides stomach lining for the crowds "pounding brews" from "humongous" steins at this East Village Bavarian, a "magnet" for those who want "Oktoberfest" every day; zum say the scene's too "rowdy", but others say "that's the point."

Zum Stammtisch *German*

	22	17	19	$34

Glendale | 69-46 Myrtle Ave. (bet. 69th Pl. & 70th St.) | Queens | 718-386-3014 | www.zumstammtisch.com
Even if the "trek to Glendale makes Germany seem closer", this inexpensive, "old-school" Bavarian werkhorse remains the "gold standard" for "terrific", "heavy" meals paired with "refreshing" brews; fans say the faux "alpine" setting is similarly *wunderbar.*

Zutto *Japanese*

	21	17	20	$39

TriBeCa | 77 Hudson St. (Harrison St.) | 212-233-3287 | www.sushizutto.com
"When you can't get a table at Nobu", consider this TriBeCa Japanese "staple" for its "fresh" sushi and "soothing" setting; that it's still a "secret" after 28 years in business is a mystery, especially considering its "best-buy" prices and "interesting" specials.

INDEXES

LOCATION MAPS

Cuisines

Includes restaurant names, locations and Food ratings. ☑ indicates places with the highest ratings, popularity and importance.

AFGHAN

Afghan Kebab | multi. 19

AFRICAN

Bouillabaisse 126 | Carroll Gdns 22
Les Enfants | LES 19

AMERICAN (NEW)

Aesop's Tables | SI 21
NEW Alchemy | Park Slope 18
Alice's Tea Cup | multi. 19
NEW Almond Flower | L Italy 23
☑ Annisa | G Vill 27
applewood | Park Slope 25
Arabelle | E 60s 21
Aspen | Flatiron 20
☑ Aureole | E 60s 27
☑ Bar Americain | W 50s 23
barmarché | NoLita 19
NEW Bar Martignetti | L Italy 18
Battery Gdns. | Financial 18
Beacon | W 50s 22
BG | W 50s 20
Bistro Ten 18 | W 100s 22
Black Duck | Gramercy 20
NEW BLT Market | W 50s –
BLT Prime | Gramercy 24
☑ Blue Hill | G Vill 26
☑ Blue Ribbon | multi. 25
Blue Ribbon Bakery | G Vill 24
Boathouse | E 70s 16
Bouchon Bakery | W 60s 23
Bridge Cafe | Financial 22
Bruckner B&G | Bronx 21
Bull Run | Financial 18
Butter | E Vill 19
CamaJe | G Vill 23
Caviar Russe | E 50s 24
Chestnut | Carroll Gdns 23
Chop't Creative | multi. 20
Cibo | E 40s 20
Clinton St. Baking | LES 24
Cocotte | Park Slope 20
☑ Compass | W 70s 22
Cornelia St. Cafe | G Vill 19
Country | Gramercy 23
☑ Craft | Flatiron 25
Craftbar | Flatiron 22
☑ davidburke/dona. | E 60s 25
David Burke/Bloom. | E 50s 18
Deborah | G Vill 21

NEW Dennis Foy | TriBeCa 24
Devin Tavern | TriBeCa 18
Diner | W'burg 22
District | W 40s 20
Ditch Plains | G Vill 17
D'twn Atlantic | Boerum Hill 19
Dressler | W'burg 24
Duane Park | TriBeCa 24
DuMont | W'burg 23
Eatery | W 50s 19
elmo | Chelsea 15
Essex | LES 20
Etats-Unis | E 80s 25
Farm/Adderley | Ditmas Pk 23
57 | E 50s 22
5 Front | Dumbo 21
5 Points | NoHo 22
NEW Flatbush Farm | Park Slope 19
Food Bar | Chelsea 16
44/X Hell's Kit. | W 40s 21
Fred's at Barneys | E 60s 20
Freemans | LES 21
☑ Garden Cafe | Prospect Hts 27
Gilt | E 50s 25
Giorgio's/Gramercy | Flatiron 22
good | W Vill 20
☑ Gotham B&G | G Vill 27
☑ Gramercy Tavern | Flatiron 27
Greenhouse Café | Bay Ridge 19
☑ Grocery | Carroll Gdns 26
Harrison, The | TriBeCa 24
NEW Hawaiian Tropic | W 40s 16
Hearth | E Vill 25
Henry's End | Bklyn Hts 25
Hope & Anchor | Red Hook 18
HQ | SoHo 19
NEW Hudson R. Café | Harlem –
Ici | Ft Greene 22
NEW Inn LW12 | Meatpacking 19
Isabella's | W 70s 20
Jack the Horse | Bklyn Hts 20
Jane | G Vill 21
Josephina | W 60s 18
Josie's | E 80s 19
Kings' Carriage | E 80s 21
NEW Klee Brass. | Chelsea 21
Knickerbocker | G Vill 20
Lady Mendl's | Gramercy 22
Landmark Tavern | W 40s 18
Lever House | E 50s 22

Little D | **Park Slope**	20
Little Giant | **LES**	22
Little Owl | **W Vill**	24
Magnolia | **Park Slope**	19
NEW Mantra | **E 50s**	–
Mas | **G Vill**	25
Mercer Kitchen | **SoHo**	22
Metrazur | **E 40s**	20
☑ Modern, The | **W 50s**	26
Momofuku Ssäm | **E Vill**	24
Monkey Bar | **E 50s**	–
Morgan | **Murray Hill**	20
Morrell Wine Bar | **W 40s**	19
New Leaf | **Wash. Hts**	20
NEW Noble Food | **NoLita**	–
NoHo Star | **NoHo**	18
Norma's | **W 50s**	25
North Sq. | **G Vill**	22
Oceana | **E 50s**	26
One | **Meatpacking**	18
☑ One if by Land | **G Vill**	23
101 | **multi.**	19
Orchard, The | **LES**	24
☑ Ouest | **W 80s**	25
Paloma | **Greenpt**	19
NEW Park Avenue | **E 60s**	–
Patroon | **E 40s**	21
NEW Perilla | **G Vill**	–
Perry St. | **W Vill**	24
☑ Per Se | **W 60s**	28
Philip Marie | **W Vill**	20
Place, The | **W Vill**	21
NEW p*ong | **G Vill**	21
Pop Burger | **Meatpacking**	19
Prune | **E Vill**	24
Quaint | **Sunnyside**	20
Quality Meats | **W 50s**	24
Queen's Hideaway | **Greenpt**	20
Rachel's American | **W 40s**	17
Red Cat | **Chelsea**	24
Redeye Grill | **W 50s**	20
Regency | **E 60s**	18
Relish | **W'burg**	22
Riingo | **E 40s**	19
☑ River Café | **Dumbo**	26
Riverdale Gdn. | **Bronx**	24
Roebling | **W'burg**	21
Rose Water | **Park Slope**	25
Salt | **multi.**	21
☑ Saul | **Boerum Hill**	27
Savoy | **SoHo**	24
Seven | **Chelsea**	18
NEW Solace | **E 60s**	–
Sorrel | **Prospect Hts**	23
NEW Spitzer's | **LES**	–

NEW STK | **Meatpacking**	20
Stone Park Café | **Park Slope**	24
Sweetwater | **W'burg**	21
☑ Tabla | **Gramercy**	25
Taste | **E 80s**	20
Tasting Rm. | **multi.**	22
☑ Telepan | **W 60s**	25
Thalia | **W 50s**	21
Thor | **LES**	18
☑ Tocqueville | **Union Sq**	26
Tossed | **multi.**	18
Town | **W 50s**	24
Trestle on 10th | **Chelsea**	19
Tribeca Grill | **TriBeCa**	22
12th St. B&G | **Park Slope**	21
212 | **E 60s**	16
☑ Union Sq. Cafe | **Union Sq**	26
☑ Veritas | **Flatiron**	26
Village | **G Vill**	20
Vynl | **multi.**	17
Water's Edge | **LIC**	23
wd-50 | **LES**	23
West Bank Cafe | **W 40s**	20
Whym | **W 50s**	21
York Grill | **E 80s**	23
NEW Zest | **SI**	26
Zoë | **SoHo**	20
NEW Zoë Townhouse | **E 60s**	–

AMERICAN (TRADITIONAL)

Algonquin | **W 40s**	16
Alias | **LES**	23
American Girl | **E 40s**	13
American Grill | **SI**	20
Angus McIndoe | **W 40s**	16
Annie's | **E 70s**	18
Barking Dog | **multi.**	15
NEW Borough Food | **Flatiron**	–
Brooklyn Diner | **multi.**	17
Brown Café | **LES**	25
Bryant Park | **W 40s**	17
Bubba Gump | **W 40s**	14
Bubby's | **multi.**	18
NEW Cafe Cluny | **W Vill**	19
Cafeteria | **Chelsea**	18
Chadwick's | **Bay Ridge**	22
Chat 'n Chew | **Union Sq**	16
Coffee Shop | **Union Sq**	15
Comfort Diner | **multi.**	16
Cookshop | **Chelsea**	23
Corner Bistro | **W Vill**	22
Dirty Bird | **W Vill**	17
Dylan Prime | **TriBeCa**	24
NEW East Village Yacht | **E Vill**	–
E.A.T. | **E 80s**	19

Edward's	**TriBeCa**	16
EJ's Luncheonette	**multi.**	15
Elaine's	**E 80s**	13
Elephant & Castle	**G Vill**	17
ESPN Zone	**W 40s**	12
Fairway Cafe	**multi.**	18
Fraunces Tavern	**Financial**	15
Friend of a Farmer	**Gramercy**	17
Good Enough/Eat	**W 80s**	20
Grand Tier	**W 60s**	19
Hard Rock Cafe	**W 40s**	13
Heartland	**multi.**	14
HK	**Garment**	16
Home	**G Vill**	20
Houston's	**multi.**	20
Hudson Cafeteria	**W 50s**	19
Jackson Hole	**multi.**	17
Joe Allen	**W 40s**	17
Lodge	**W'burg**	16
Mama's Food	**E Vill**	20
Moran's	**Chelsea**	18
Odeon	**TriBeCa**	19
O'Neals'	**W 60s**	17
Penelope	**Murray Hill**	21
Pershing Sq.	**E 40s**	15
Popover Cafe	**W 80s**	18
NEW Public House	**E 40s**	–
Revival	**Harlem**	19
Rock Ctr.	**W 50s**	19
Sarabeth's	**multi.**	20
S'mac	**E Vill**	19
Soda Shop	**TriBeCa**	19
NEW Spotlight Live	**W 40s**	–
Swifty's	**E 70s**	18
☑ Tavern on Green	**W 60s**	15
NEW Ted's Montana	**W 50s**	15
Tupelo Grill	**Garment**	18
12 Chairs	**SoHo**	19
☑ 21 Club	**W 50s**	22
Uno Chicago	**multi.**	14
View, The	**W 40s**	18
Walker's	**TriBeCa**	17
Water Club	**Murray Hill**	20
NEW ☑ Waverly Inn	**W Vill**	18
Westville	**multi.**	23

ARGENTINEAN

Azul Bistro	**LES**	22
Buenos Aires	**E Vill**	21
NEW Caminito	**Harlem**	–
NEW Catch 22	**W'burg**	–
Chimichurri Grill	**W 40s**	21
NEW Estancia	**TriBeCa**	21
NEW Gaucho	**W 50s**	–
Hacienda/Argentina	**E 70s**	21
Industria	**TriBeCa**	20

Novecento	**SoHo**	22
Sosa Borella	**W 50s**	21

ASIAN

☑ Asia de Cuba	**Murray Hill**	23
China Grill	**W 50s**	22
Chino's	**Gramercy**	22
Citrus B&G	**W 70s**	20
East Buffet	**Flushing**	20
Hispaniola	**Wash. Hts**	21

ASIAN FUSION

☑ Buddakan	**Chelsea**	23
☑ Buddha Bar	**Meatpacking**	19
Chow Bar	**W Vill**	21
JJ's Asian Fusion	**Astoria**	25
Nana	**Park Slope**	21
Roy's NY	**Financial**	25
Xing	**W 50s**	21

AUSTRALIAN

Bondi Rd.	**LES**	21
8 Mile Creek	**L Italy**	20
NEW Sheep Sta.	**Park Slope**	19
NEW Wombat	**W'burg**	21

AUSTRIAN

Blaue Gans	**TriBeCa**	20
Café Sabarsky	**E 80s**	22
Cafe Steinhof	**Park Slope**	19
☑ Danube	**TriBeCa**	26
Thomas Beisl	**Ft Greene**	19
Wallsé	**W Vill**	26

BAKERIES

Amy's Bread	**multi.**	23
Blue Ribbon Bakery	**G Vill**	24
Bouchon Bakery	**W 60s**	23
City Bakery	**Flatiron**	21
Clinton St. Baking	**LES**	24
Columbus Bakery	**W 80s**	18
D'twn Atlantic	**Boerum Hill**	19
Ferrara	**L Italy**	22
La Bergamote	**Chelsea**	24
La Flor Bakery	**Woodside**	24
Le Pain Q.	**multi.**	19
Once Upon a Tart	**SoHo**	22
Provence/Boite	**Carroll Gdns**	20

BARBECUE

Blue Smoke	**Gramercy**	22
Brother Jimmy's	**multi.**	16
☑ Daisy May's	**W 40s**	24
Dallas BBQ	**multi.**	15
Dinosaur BBQ	**Harlem**	22
NEW Fette Sau	**W'burg**	19
NEW Georgia's/BBQ	**LES**	–

NEW Hill Country | **Chelsea** -
NEW Johnny Utah | **W 50s** -
Rack & Soul | **W 100s** 20
RUB BBQ | **Chelsea** 20
NEW Smoke Joint | **Ft Greene** 23
Virgil's Real BBQ | **W 40s** 20

BELGIAN

Café de Bruxelles | **W Vill** 21
Le Pain Q. | **multi.** 19
Markt | **Flatiron** 19
Petite Abeille | **multi.** 19
NEW Resto | **Gramercy** -

BRAZILIAN

Cafe Colonial | **NoLita** 20
Casa | **W Vill** 22
Churrascaria | **multi.** 23
Circus | **E 60s** 20
Coffee Shop | **Union Sq** 15
Green Field | **Corona** 19
Malagueta | **Astoria** 26
Porcão | **Gramercy** 21
Rice 'n' Beans | **W 50s** 19
Samba-Lé | **E Vill** 19
SushiSamba | **multi.** 22
Via Brasil | **W 40s** 18
Zebú Grill | **E 90s** 21

BRITISH

ChipShop | **multi.** 18
Spotted Pig | **W Vill** 22
Tea & Sympathy | **W Vill** 19

BURMESE

Mingala Burmese | **multi.** 20

CAJUN

Bayou | **SI** 22
Delta Grill | **W 40s** 19
Great Jones Cafe | **NoHo** 19
Jacques-Imo's | **W 70s** 17
Mara's | **E Vill** 19
NEW NoNO | **Park Slope** 19
107 West | **multi.** 18

CALIFORNIAN

Michael's | **W 50s** 21

CAMBODIAN

NEW Kampuchea | **LES** 20

CARIBBEAN

NEW Cafe & Wine | **W 100s** -
Don Pedro's | **E 90s** 23
Ideya | **SoHo** 20
Ivo & Lulu | **SoHo** 22
Mo-Bay | **Harlem** 21

CAVIAR

Caviar Russe | **E 50s** 24
Petrossian | **W 50s** 24

CHEESE STEAKS

Carl's Steaks | **multi.** 22
99 Mi. to Philly | **E Vill** 18

CHINESE

(* dim sum specialist)
NEW Amazing 66 | **Chinatown** 23
Au Mandarin | **Financial** 20
Big Wong | **Chinatown** 22
Café Evergreen* | **E 60s** 20
Chef Ho's | **E 80s** 22
Chiam | **E 40s** 23
China Chalet | **multi.** 19
China Fun* | **multi.** 16
Chinatown Brass.* | **NoHo** 21
Chin Chin | **E 40s** 22
Congee | **multi.** 21
Dim Sum Go Go* | **Chinatown** 20
Dumpling Man | **E Vill** 19
East Manor* | **Flushing** 19
Empire Szechuan | **multi.** 15
Evergreen* | **Murray Hill** 19
Excellent Dumpling* | **Chinatown** 21
Flor de Mayo | **multi.** 20
Fuleen | **Chinatown** 24
Ginger | **Harlem** 21
Golden Unicorn* | **Chinatown** 20
Goodies | **Chinatown** 20
Grand Sichuan | **multi.** 22
HSF* | **Chinatown** 20
Jing Fong* | **Chinatown** 19
Joe's Shanghai | **multi.** 22
King Yum | **Fresh Meadows** 17
Lili's Noodle | **multi.** 16
Mandarin Court* | **Chinatown** 20
Mee Noodle | **multi.** 18
Mr. Chow | **multi.** 20
☑ Mr. K's | **E 50s** 23
Mr. Tang | **multi.** 19
New Bo-Ky | **Chinatown** 22
New Green Bo | **Chinatown** 22
NoHo Star | **NoHo** 18
Ollie's | **multi.** 16
Oriental Gdn.* | **Chinatown** 24
Our Place | **multi.** 20
NEW Pacificana* | **Sunset Pk** 24
Peking Duck | **multi.** 22
Philippe | **E 60s** 23
Phoenix Gdn. | **E 40s** 24
Pig Heaven | **E 80s** 19
Ping's Sea.* | **multi.** 22
Rickshaw Dumpling | **multi.** 18

Shanghai Cuisine | **Chinatown** 21
Shanghai Pavilion | **E 70s** 21
Shun Lee Cafe* | **W 60s** 21
Shun Lee Palace | **E 50s** 24
Shun Lee West | **W 60s** 23
Spicy & Tasty | **Flushing** 23
Sweet-n-Tart* | **Flushing** 20
Tang Pavilion | **W 50s** 23
Tse Yang | **E 50s** 25
NEW Z Wakiya | **Gramercy** -
Wo Hop | **Chinatown** 21
Wu Liang Ye | **multi.** 21
X.O.* | **Chinatown** 18

COFFEEHOUSES

Cafe Lalo | **W 80s** 19
Edgar's Cafe | **W 80s** 18
Edison | **W 40s** 15
Ferrara | **L Italy** 22
French Roast | **multi.** 14
Le Pain Q. | **multi.** 19
Omonia Cafe | **multi.** 19
Once Upon a Tart | **SoHo** 22

COFFEE SHOPS/DINERS

Brooklyn Diner | **multi.** 17
Burger Heaven | **multi.** 16
Chat 'n Chew | **Union Sq** 16
Clinton St. Baking | **LES** 24
Comfort Diner | **multi.** 16
Diner | **W'burg** 22
Edison | **W 40s** 15
EJ's Luncheonette | **multi.** 15
Empire Diner | **Chelsea** 15
Hope & Anchor | **Red Hook** 18
Junior's | **multi.** 18
La Taza de Oro | **Chelsea** 18
Tom's | **Prospect Hts** 19
Veselka | **E Vill** 18
Viand | **multi.** 16

COLOMBIAN

Tierras | **multi.** 22

CONTINENTAL

Battery Gdns. | **Financial** 18
Café Pierre | **E 60s** 23
Cebu | **Bay Ridge** 21
Z Four Seasons | **E 50s** 25
Gin Lane | **Chelsea** 17
Grand Tier | **W 60s** 19
Jack's Lux. | **E Vill** 24
Lake Club | **SI** 21
Park Place | **Bronx** 20
Petrossian | **W 50s** 24
Russian Samovar | **W 50s** 19
NEW Russian Tea | **W 50s** 19

Sardi's | **W 40s** 16
View, The | **W 40s** 18

CREOLE

Bayou | **SI** 22
Delta Grill | **W 40s** 19
Jacques-Imo's | **W 70s** 17
Mara's | **E Vill** 19
NEW NoNO | **Park Slope** 19

CUBAN

Z Asia de Cuba | **Murray Hill** 23
Cafecito | **E Vill** 21
Cafe Con Leche | **multi.** 18
Café Habana/Outpost | **multi.** 22
Cuba | **G Vill** 21
Cuba Cafe | **Chelsea** 18
Cubana Café | **multi.** 20
Guantanamera | **W 50s** 22
Havana Alma | **W Vill** 21
Havana Central | **multi.** 17
NEW Socialista | **W Vill** -
Son Cubano | **Meatpacking** 21
Victor's Cafe | **W 50s** 21

DELIS

Artie's Deli | **W 80s** 18
Barney Greengrass | **W 80s** 23
Ben's Kosher | **multi.** 17
Z Carnegie Deli | **W 50s** 21
Ess-a-Bagel | **multi.** 23
Katz's Deli | **LES** 23
Leo's Latticini | **Corona** 28
Liebman's | **Bronx** 19
Mill Basin Deli | **Mill Basin** 21
Pastrami Queen | **E 70s** 19
PicNic Market | **W 100s** 20
Sarge's Deli | **Murray Hill** 19
Stage Deli | **W 50s** 20
Zabar's Cafe | **W 80s** 20

DESSERT

Cafe Lalo | **W 80s** 19
Café Sabarsky | **E 80s** 22
ChikaLicious | **E Vill** 24
Chocolate Rm. | **Park Slope** 25
Edgar's Cafe | **W 80s** 18
Ferrara | **L Italy** 22
Junior's | **multi.** 18
NEW Kyotofu | **W 40s** 23
La Bergamote | **Chelsea** 24
Lady Mendl's | **Gramercy** 22
L & B Spumoni | **Bensonhurst** 22
Max Brenner | **multi.** 17
Omonia Cafe | **multi.** 19
Payard Bistro | **E 70s** 24
NEW p*ong | **G Vill** 21

Serendipity 3 | **E 60s** _18_
Soda Shop | **TriBeCa** _19_
Sweet Melissa | **multi.** _21_
NEW Tailor | **SoHo** _-_
Veniero's | **E Vill** _23_

DOMINICAN

Cafe Con Leche | **multi.** _18_
El Malecon | **multi.** _21_
Hispaniola | **Wash. Hts** _21_

EASTERN EUROPEAN

Sammy's Roum. | **LES** _19_

ECLECTIC

NEW Aloe | **E Vill** _-_
NEW BarFry | **G Vill** _-_
Z Bouley, Upstairs | **TriBeCa** _26_
Carol's Cafe | **SI** _26_
NEW Chez Lola | **Clinton Hill** _-_
Colors | **E Vill** _19_
NEW Crave | **E 50s** _-_
East Buffet | **Flushing** _20_
East of 8th | **Chelsea** _16_
NEW Fireside | **E 50s** _21_
5 Ninth | **Meatpacking** _19_
NEW FR.OG | **SoHo** _21_
NEW Gold St. | **Financial** _15_
Z Good Fork | **Red Hook** _26_
Grand Café | **Astoria** _17_
NEW Grayz | **W 50s** _-_
Harry's | **Financial** _22_
Hudson Cafeteria | **W 50s** _19_
Josie's | **multi.** _19_
Little D | **Park Slope** _20_
Native | **Harlem** _19_
Nook | **W 50s** _22_
Public | **NoLita** _23_
Punch | **Flatiron** _19_
NEW Revel | **Meatpacking** _-_
Rice | **multi.** _19_
NEW Saucy | **E 70s** _-_
NEW savorNY | **LES** _-_
Schiller's | **LES** _18_
Stanton Social | **LES** _23_
Trinity Place | **Financial** _18_
Vida | **SI** _20_
wd-50 | **LES** _23_
Whole Foods | **multi.** _19_

ETHIOPIAN

Awash | **multi.** _22_
Ethiopian Rest. | **E 80s** _17_
Ghenet | **NoLita** _22_
Meskerem | **multi.** _20_
NEW Zoma | **Harlem** _23_

EUROPEAN

A.O.C. Bedford | **G Vill** _23_
August | **W Vill** _23_
Bette | **Chelsea** _19_
Z Cru | **G Vill** _26_
Employees Only | **W Vill** _18_
NEW E.U., The | **E Vill** _20_
NEW Klee Brass. | **Chelsea** _21_
Knife + Fork | **E Vill** _23_
NEW Stella Maris | **Seaport** _-_

FILIPINO

Cendrillon | **SoHo** _20_
Kuma Inn | **LES** _24_

FRENCH

Arabelle | **E 60s** _21_
Z Asiate | **W 60s** _24_
NEW Babouche | **multi.** _20_
Barbès | **Murray Hill** _22_
NEW Bistro 33 | **Astoria** _-_
Bouchon Bakery | **W 60s** _23_
Bouillabaisse 126 | **Carroll Gdns** _22_
Z Bouley | **TriBeCa** _28_
Breeze | **W 40s** _20_
Brick Cafe | **Astoria** _20_
NEW Cafe & Wine | **W 100s** _-_
Z Café Boulud | **E 70s** _27_
Z Café des Artistes | **W 60s** _22_
Café du Soleil | **W 100s** _19_
Cafe Gitane | **NoLita** _20_
Café Pierre | **E 60s** _23_
Z Carlyle | **E 70s** _21_
Z Chanterelle | **TriBeCa** _27_
Cocotte | **Park Slope** _20_
Danal | **E Vill** _22_
Z Daniel | **E 60s** _28_
Degustation | **E Vill** _26_
Demarchelier | **E 80s** _17_
Django | **E 40s** _20_
Elephant, The | **E Vill** _21_
Z Eleven Madison | **Gramercy** _26_
Fleur de Sel | **Flatiron** _25_
Frederick's | **multi.** _19_
NEW FR.OG | **SoHo** _21_
NEW Z Gordon Ramsay | **W 50s** _25_
Ici | **Ft Greene** _22_
Indochine | **E Vill** _20_
Ivo & Lulu | **SoHo** _22_
Jack's Lux. | **E Vill** _24_
Z Jean Georges | **W 60s** _28_
Jolie | **Boerum Hill** _20_
Kitchen Club | **NoLita** _22_
La Baraka | **Little Neck** _21_
La Bergamote | **Chelsea** _24_
La Boîte en Bois | **W 60s** _21_

CUISINES

Restaurant	Location	Score
☑ La Grenouille	E 50s	27
☑ L'Atelier/Robuchon	E 50s	27
☑ Le Bernardin	W 50s	28
Le Cirque	E 50s	23
L'Ecole	SoHo	23
Le Colonial	E 50s	20
Le Grainne Cafe	Chelsea	19
Le Pain Q.	multi.	19
Le Perigord	E 50s	24
Le Refuge Inn	Bronx	24
Le Rivage	W 40s	19
Les Enfants	LES	19
Loft	W 80s	17
NEW Maze	W 50s	23
Mercer Kitchen	SoHo	22
Métisse	W 100s	19
☑ Modern, The	W 50s	26
Once Upon a Tart	SoHo	22
Park Terrace	Inwood	22
Pascalou	E 90s	22
☑ Per Se	W 60s	28
Petrossian	W 50s	24
☑ Picholine	W 60s	27
PicNic Market	W 100s	20
René Pujol	W 50s	22
Revival	Harlem	19
NEW Safran	Chelsea	20
Sapa	Flatiron	22
Savann	W 70s	19
718	Astoria	21
Terrace in the Sky	W 100s	22
☑ Tocqueville	Union Sq	26
Triomphe	W 40s	24
26 Seats	E Vill	22
Vong	E 50s	22
Zucco	LES	22

FRENCH (BISTRO)

Restaurant	Location	Score
Alouette	W 90s	20
A.O.C.	W Vill	20
Bandol Bistro	E 70s	19
Belleville	Park Slope	18
Bistro Cassis	W 70s	20
Bistro Citron	W 80s	21
Bistro du Nord	E 90s	18
Bistro Les Amis	SoHo	21
Bistro Le Steak	E 70s	17
Bistro 61	E 60s	20
NEW Cafe Cluny	W Vill	19
Cafe Joul	E 50s	18
Cafe Loup	G Vill	18
Cafe Luluc	Cobble Hill	20
Cafe Luxembourg	W 70s	20
Cafe Un Deux	W 40s	16
CamaJe	G Vill	23
Capsouto Frères	TriBeCa	24
Casimir	E Vill	19
NEW Chat Noir	E 60s	18
Chez Jacqueline	G Vill	18
Chez Josephine	W 40s	20
NEW Chez Lola	Clinton Hill	–
Chez Napoléon	W 50s	20
Chez Oskar	Ft Greene	19
Cornelia St. Cafe	G Vill	19
Cosette	Murray Hill	21
☑ db Bistro Moderne	W 40s	25
Deux Amis	E 50s	19
Félix	SoHo	16
Flea Mkt. Cafe	E Vill	19
Florent	Meatpacking	20
French Roast	multi.	14
Gascogne	Chelsea	22
Gavroche	W Vill	19
Jack Bistro	G Vill	17
Jean Claude	SoHo	22
JoJo	E 60s	24
Jubilee	E 50s	22
Jules	E Vill	19
La Bonne Soupe	W 50s	18
La Goulue	E 60s	20
La Lunchonette	Chelsea	22
La Mangeoire	E 50s	19
La Mediterranée	E 50s	19
La Mirabelle	W 80s	22
Landmarc	multi.	23
La Petite Aub.	Gramercy	20
La Ripaille	W Vill	23
NEW Le Barricou	W'burg	–
Le Bilboquet	E 60s	20
Le Boeuf/Mode	E 80s	21
Le Gamin	multi.	19
Le Gigot	G Vill	24
Le Jardin Bistro	NoLita	18
Le Madeleine	W 40s	20
Le Monde	W 100s	17
L'Entrecote	E 50s	19
NEW Le Petit Bistro	Chelsea	–
NEW Le Petit Marché	Bklyn Hts	22
Le Refuge	E 80s	21
Les Halles	multi.	20
Le Singe Vert	Chelsea	19
Le Tableau	E Vill	24
Le Veau d'Or	E 60s	17
L'Express	Flatiron	17
Loulou	Ft Greene	22
Lucien	E Vill	21
Lucky Strike	SoHo	17
Madison Bistro	Murray Hill	18
Mon Petit Cafe	E 60s	18
Montparnasse	E 50s	19
Moutarde	Park Slope	18

Nice Matin | **W 70s**	20
Odeon | **TriBeCa**	19
Paradou | **Meatpacking**	19
Paris Commune | **W Vill**	18
Pascalou | **E 90s**	22
☑ Pastis | **Meatpacking**	21
Patois | **Carroll Gdns**	21
Payard Bistro | **E 70s**	24
NEW Provence | **SoHo**	21
Provence/Boite | **Carroll Gdns**	20
Quatorze Bis | **E 70s**	21
Quercy | **Cobble Hill**	20
Raoul's | **SoHo**	24
NEW Régate | **LES**	-
Rouge | **Forest Hills**	20
Steak Frites | **Union Sq**	18
Sweetwater | **W'burg**	21
Table d'Hôte | **E 90s**	21
Tartine | **W Vill**	22
Tournesol | **LIC**	24
NEW Tree | **E Vill**	24
Village | **G Vill**	20

FRENCH (BRASSERIE)

Aix Brasserie | **W 80s**	20
☑ Artisanal | **Murray Hill**	23
☑ Balthazar | **SoHo**	23
Brasserie | **E 50s**	20
Brasserie 8½ | **E 50s**	22
Brasserie Julien | **E 80s**	19
Brass. Ruhlmann | **W 50s**	17
Café d'Alsace | **E 80s**	21
☑ Café Gray | **W 60s**	25
Jacques | **multi.**	18
L'Absinthe | **E 60s**	22
Maison | **W 50s**	17
Marseille | **W 40s**	20
NEW Metro Marché | **W 40s**	19
Orsay | **E 70s**	18
Pershing Sq. | **E 40s**	15
Pigalle | **W 40s**	18
Rue 57 | **W 50s**	19

GASTROPUB

NEW Alchemy | **Amer.** | **Park Slope**	18
NEW E.U., The | **Euro.** | **E Vill**	20
NEW Inn LW12 | **Amer.** | **Meatpacking**	19
NEW Nelson Blue | **New Zealand** | **Seaport**	-
NEW Spitzer's | **Amer.** | **LES**	-
Spotted Pig | **British** | **W Vill**	22

GERMAN

Blaue Gans | **TriBeCa**	20
Hallo Berlin | **W 40s**	17

Heidelberg | **E 80s**	17
Killmeyer Bavarian | **SI**	21
Loreley | **LES**	18
Nurnberger Bierhaus | **SI**	21
Rolf's | **Gramercy**	17
Zum Schneider | **E Vill**	18
Zum Stammtisch | **Glendale**	22

GREEK

Agnanti | **multi.**	24
Ammos | **multi.**	22
NEW Anthos | **W 50s**	25
Avra | **E 40s**	24
Cafe Bar | **Astoria**	20
☑ Cávo | **Astoria**	21
Demetris | **Astoria**	21
Eliá | **Bay Ridge**	25
Elias Corner | **Astoria**	22
Ethos | **multi.**	22
Greek Kitchen | **W 50s**	19
NEW Gus' Place | **G Vill**	20
Ithaka | **E 80s**	20
NEW Kefi | **W 70s**	23
Kellari Taverna | **W 40s**	23
Kyma | **W 40s**	18
Meltemi | **E 50s**	18
Mezzo Mezzo | **Astoria**	18
☑ Milos | **W 50s**	26
Molyvos | **W 50s**	22
Omonia Cafe | **multi.**	19
NEW Ovelia | **Astoria**	21
Periyali | **Flatiron**	23
Pylos | **E Vill**	25
S'Agapo | **Astoria**	20
Snack | **SoHo**	24
Snack Taverna | **W Vill**	22
Stamatis | **Astoria**	22
Symposium | **W 100s**	20
Taverna Kyclades | **Astoria**	25
Telly's Taverna | **Astoria**	22
Thalassa | **TriBeCa**	22
Trata Estiatorio | **E 70s**	21
Uncle Nick's | **W 50s**	19

HAMBURGERS

Better Burger | **multi.**	15
Big Nick's Burger | **W 70s**	17
NEW BLT Burger | **G Vill**	19
Blue 9 Burger | **E Vill**	18
NEW brgr | **Chelsea**	18
Burger Heaven | **multi.**	16
burger joint | **W 50s**	24
Corner Bistro | **W Vill**	22
Cozy | **G Vill**	18
☑ db Bistro Moderne | **W 40s**	25
DuMont | **W'burg**	23

NEW Five Guys | multi.	–
goodburger | multi.	18
Hard Rock Cafe | W 40s	13
Island Burgers | W 50s	22
Jackson Hole | multi.	17
J.G. Melon | E 70s	21
NY Burger | Flatiron	18
P.J. Clarke's | multi.	17
Pop Burger | Meatpacking	19
Rare B&G | multi.	21
Shake Shack | Flatiron	23
NEW 67 Burger | Ft Greene	21
NEW Stand | G Vill	19
Zip Burger | E 50s	18

HAWAIIAN

Roy's NY | Financial	25

HEALTH FOOD

(See also Vegetarian)

Energy Kitchen | multi.	18
Ginger | Harlem	21
Josie's | multi.	19
Pump Energy | multi.	19
Whole Foods | multi.	19

HOT DOGS

F & B | multi.	18
Gray's Papaya | multi.	20
Papaya King | multi.	20
Shake Shack | Flatiron	23

ICE CREAM PARLORS

L & B Spumoni | Bensonhurst	22
Serendipity 3 | E 60s	18

INDIAN

Adä | E 50s	23
Amma | E 50s	24
Baluchi's | multi.	18
Banjara | E Vill	23
Bay Leaf | W 50s	19
Bombay Palace | W 50s	18
Bombay Talkie | Chelsea	20
Bukhara Grill | E 40s	20
Cafe Spice | multi.	18
NEW Chennai | E 80s	–
Chennai Gdn. | Gramercy	21
ChipShop | Park Slope	18
Chola | E 50s	23
Curry Leaf | Gramercy	20
Dakshin Indian | E 80s	20
Darbar | E 40s	20
Dawat | E 50s	23
Diwan | E 40s	21
NEW Earthen Oven | W 70s	21
Hampton Chutney | multi.	20
Haveli | E Vill	23

Indus Valley | W 100s	23
Jackson Diner | Jackson Hts	22
Jewel of India | W 40s	20
Kati Roll Co. | multi.	20
Leela Lounge | G Vill	22
Mint | E 50s	19
Mughlai | W 70s	19
Pongal | multi.	21
Salaam Bombay | TriBeCa	20
Sapphire | W 60s	20
Saravanaas | Gramercy	23
NEW Spice Fusion | W 40s	–
Surya | W Vill	24
Swagat Indian | W 70s	19
Tamarind | Flatiron	25
Temple Canteen | Flushing	–
Utsav | W 40s	21
Vatan | Gramercy	23
Yuva | E 50s	24

IRISH

Landmark Tavern | W 40s	18
Neary's | E 50s	15

ISRAELI

Azuri Cafe | W 50s	25
Hummus Place | multi.	23
Miriam | multi.	21

ITALIAN

(N=Northern; S=Southern)

Abboccato | W 50s	22
Acappella | N | TriBeCa	23
NEW Accademia/Vino | E 60s	–
Acqua | S | W 90s	18
Adrienne's Pizza | Financial	23
Agata/Valentina | S | E 70s	18
☑ Al Di La | N | Park Slope	26
Al Forno Pizza | E 70s	19
Alfredo of Rome | S | W 40s	19
Aliseo Osteria | Prospect Hts	23
☑ Alto | N | E 50s	26
Ama | S | SoHo	22
Amarone | W 40s	19
Amorina | Prospect Hts	23
Angelina's | SI	23
Angelo's/Mulberry | S | L Italy	23
Anthony's | S | Park Slope	21
Antica Venezia | W Vill	23
Antonucci | E 80s	20
ápizz | LES	24
Areo | Bay Ridge	25
Arezzo | N | Flatiron	22
Arno | N | Garment	20
Aroma | NoHo	24
Arqua | N | TriBeCa	22
Arté | N | G Vill	19

Arté Café	**W 70s**	18	☑ Carmine's	S	**multi.**	19
Arturo's Pizzeria	**G Vill**	21	Cascina	**W 40s**	18
Aurora	N	**multi.**	26	NEW Catch 22	**W'burg**	–
A Voce	**Gramercy**	25	Celeste	S	**W 80s**	24
☑ Babbo	**G Vill**	27	Cellini	N	**E 50s**	21
Baci & Abbracci	**W'burg**	20	Centolire	N	**E 80s**	20
Baldoria	**W 40s**	22	Centovini	**SoHo**	21
Bamonte's	**W'burg**	23	NEW Centro Vinoteca	**W Vill**	–
Baraonda	**E 70s**	18	'Cesca	S	**W 70s**	23
Barbetta	N	**W 40s**	20	Chianti	**Bay Ridge**	21
Barbuto	**W Vill**	22	Cibo	N	**E 40s**	20
Bardolino	**E 70s**	18	Cipriani Dolci	**E 40s**	18
Barolo	**SoHo**	18	Cipriani D'twn	**SoHo**	20
Bar Pitti	**G Vill**	22	Coco Pazzo	N	**E 70s**	22
NEW Bar Stuzz.	S	**Flatiron**	–	Coppola's	**multi.**	19
Bar Toto	**Park Slope**	19	Cortina	N	**E 70s**	18
Basilica	**W 40s**	19	Crispo	N	**W Vill**	23
NEW Basso56	**W 50s**	23	Cucina di Pesce	**E Vill**	17
Basta Pasta	**Flatiron**	21	Da Andrea	N	**W Vill**	24
☑ Becco	**W 40s**	22	Da Ciro	**Murray Hill**	21
Beccofino	**Bronx**	22	Da Filippo	N	**E 60s**	19
Bella Blu	N	**E 70s**	19	Dani	S	**SoHo**	20
Bella Via	**LIC**	23	Da Nico	**L Italy**	21
Bellavitae	**G Vill**	22	Da Noi	N	**SI**	24
Bello	**W 50s**	20	Da Silvano	N	**G Vill**	20
Beppe	N	**Flatiron**	23	Da Tommaso	N	**W 50s**	20
Bettola	**W 70s**	21	Da Umberto	N	**Chelsea**	25
Bianca	N	**NoHo**	22	DeGrezia	**E 50s**	22
Bice	N	**E 50s**	20	☑ Del Posto	**Chelsea**	25
Biricchino	N	**Chelsea**	20	Destino	**E 50s**	18
Bocca Lupo	**Cobble Hill**	21	NEW Dieci	**E Vill**	23
Bocelli	**SI**	25	Divino	N	**E 80s**	18
Bond 45	**W 40s**	20	Dominick's	**Bronx**	22
Borgo Antico	**G Vill**	19	Don Giovanni	**multi.**	17
Bottega del Vino	**E 50s**	22	Don Peppe	**Ozone Pk**	25
Bottino	N	**Chelsea**	19	Due	N	**E 70s**	22
Bravo Gianni	N	**E 60s**	23	Ecco	**TriBeCa**	21
Bread	**TriBeCa**	19	Elaine's	**E 80s**	13
Bricco	**W 50s**	19	NEW eleven B.	**E Vill**	–
Brick Cafe	**Astoria**	20	Elio's	**E 80s**	23
Brio	**E 60s**	18	Ennio & Michael	**G Vill**	21
Brioso	**SI**	25	Enzo's	**Bronx**	23
Cacio e Pepe	S	**E Vill**	22	Erminia	S	**E 80s**	25
NEW Cacio e Vino	S	**E Vill**	21	Esca	S	**W 40s**	25
Cafe Fiorello	**W 60s**	20	NEW Estancia	**TriBeCa**	21
Caffe Bondi	S	**SI**	22	etc. etc.	**W 40s**	20
Caffe Buon Gusto	**multi.**	18	NEW Fabio Piccolo	**E 40s**	–
Caffe Cielo	N	**W 50s**	19	Falai	**multi.**	25
NEW Caffe Emilia	**E Vill**	–	F & J Pine	**Bronx**	20
Caffe Grazie	**E 80s**	19	☑ Felidia	**E 50s**	25
Caffe Linda	**E 40s**	18	Fiamma Osteria	**SoHo**	25
Caffé/Green	**Bayside**	21	F.illi Ponte	**TriBeCa**	21
Campagnola	**E 70s**	23	Fino	N	**multi.**	20
Canaletto	N	**E 60s**	21	Fiorentino's	S	**Gravesend**	19
Cara Mia	**W 40s**	20	NEW Fiorini	**E 50s**	–

Firenze	N	E 80s	21
Fragole	Carroll Gdns	23
Frank	E Vill	24
Frankies Spuntino	multi.	24
Frank's	Chelsea	19
Franny's	Prospect Hts	23
Fratelli	Bronx	21
Fred's at Barneys	N	E 60s	20
Fresco	N	E 50s	23
Gabriel's	N	W 60s	22
Gargiulo's	S	Coney Is	21
NEW Gemma	E Vill	-
Gennaro	W 90s	25
Giambelli	E 50s	21
Gigino	multi.	20
Gino	E 60s	21
Giorgione	SoHo	23
Giovanni	N	E 80s	22
Girasole	E 80s	20
Gnocco Caffe	N	E Vill	21
Gonzo	G Vill	21
Grace's Tratt.	E 70s	18
Gradisca	G Vill	21
Grifone	N	E 40s	23
Grotta Azzurra	S	L Italy	18
Gusto	G Vill	22
Harry Cipriani	N	E 50s	-
Hearth	N	E Vill	25
I Coppi	N	E Vill	23
Il Bagatto	E Vill	23
Il Bastardo	N	Chelsea	19
NEW Il Brigante	Seaport	21
Il Buco	NoHo	25
Il Cantinori	N	G Vill	22
Il Corallo	SoHo	22
Il Cortile	L Italy	23
Il Fornaio	L Italy	21
Il Gattopardo	S	W 50s	23
Z Il Giglio	N	TriBeCa	26
Il Mattone	TriBeCa	21
Il Menestrello	N	E 50s	22
Z Il Mulino	G Vill	27
Il Nido	N	E 50s	23
Il Palazzo	L Italy	23
Il Postino	E 40s	22
Il Riccio	S	E 70s	21
Z Il Tinello	N	W 50s	26
Il Vagabondo	E 60s	19
'ino	G Vill	24
'inoteca	LES	23
NEW Insieme	W 50s	26
Intermezzo	Chelsea	18
I Tre Merli	N	multi.	18
I Trulli	Gramercy	22
Joe & Pat's	SI	22
John's/12th St.	E Vill	19
Joseph's	N	Financial	21
La Bottega	Chelsea	18
La Cantina Toscana	N	E 60s	24
La Focaccia	W Vill	20
La Giara	Murray Hill	19
La Gioconda	E 50s	20
La Grolla	N	W 70s	20
La Lanterna	G Vill	20
La Locanda Vini	W 40s	21
La Masseria	S	W 40s	22
La Mela	S	L Italy	18
L & B Spumoni	Bensonhurst	22
La Pizza Fresca	Flatiron	22
La Rivista	N	W 40s	18
Lattanzi	S	W 40s	22
Lavagna	E Vill	24
La Vela	N	W 70s	19
La Villa Pizzeria	multi.	21
La Vineria	W 50s	20
Leo's Latticini	Corona	28
Le Zie 2000	N	Chelsea	21
Lil' Frankie Pizza	E Vill	22
Z L'Impero	E 40s	26
Lisca	N	W 90s	20
Locanda Vini	N	Clinton Hill	26
Loft	W 80s	17
Luca	E 80s	20
Lumi	E 70s	19
NEW Lunetta	Boerum Hill	20
Z Lupa	S	G Vill	25
Lusardi's	N	E 70s	24
Macelleria	N	Meatpacking	21
Madison's	Bronx	20
Malatesta	N	W Vill	21
Manducatis	LIC	22
Manetta's	LIC	22
Marco Polo	Carroll Gdns	20
Maremma	N	W Vill	21
Maria Pia	W 50s	19
Marinella	G Vill	23
Mario's	S	Bronx	22
Maruzzella	N	E 70s	22
Maurizio Tratt.	N	G Vill	21
Max	S	multi.	23
Mediterraneo	E 60s	19
Mezzaluna	E 70s	19
Mezzogiorno	N	SoHo	20
Minetta Tavern	N	G Vill	18
Moda	S	W 50s	-
NEW Momento	Astoria	-
NEW Morandi	G Vill	19
Nanni	N	E 40s	24
Naples 45	S	E 40s	17
NEW Natsumi	W 50s	-

Tratt. Pesce | **multi.**	18
Tratt. Romana | **SI**	24
tre dici | **Chelsea**	22
Triangolo | **E 80s**	21
Tuscan Sq. | N | **W 50s**	16
Tuscany Grill | N | **Bay Ridge**	24
Umberto's | **multi.**	18
Uva | **E 70s**	21
Valbella | N | **Meatpacking**	24
V&T | **W 100s**	18
Veniero's | **E Vill**	23
Vento | **Meatpacking**	19
Vespa | **E 80s**	21
Via Emilia | N | **Flatiron**	21
Via Oreto | **E 60s**	19
Via Quadronno | N | **E 70s**	21
ViceVersa | **W 50s**	23
Vico | **E 90s**	21
Villa Berulia | N | **Murray Hill**	23
Villa Mosconi | **G Vill**	20
Vincent's | **L Italy**	21
Vivolo | **E 70s**	20
WaterFalls | **SI**	20
Za Za | N | **E 60s**	20

JAMAICAN

Aki | **G Vill**	25
Maroons | **Chelsea**	22
Negril | **multi.**	20

JAPANESE

(* sushi specialist)

Aburiya Kinnosuke | **E 40s**	24
Aki | **G Vill**	25
Aki Sushi* | **multi.**	19
Aquamarine | **Murray Hill**	21
NEW Asiakan* | **W 90s**	19
Z Asiate | **W 60s**	24
NEW BarFry | **G Vill**	–
NEW Bistro 33 | **Astoria**	–
Blue Ginger | **Chelsea**	22
Z Blue Ribbon Sushi* | **multi.**	25
Bond St.* | **NoHo**	25
Butai | **Gramercy**	22
Chanto | **G Vill**	22
China Fun* | **multi.**	16
Chiyono | **E Vill**	23
Cube 63 | **multi.**	21
Dae Dong | **multi.**	18
Donguri | **E 80s**	27
EN Japanese | **W Vill**	22
NEW 15 East* | **Union Sq**	26
Fushimi* | **SI**	26
Z Gari/Sushi* | **multi.**	26
Geisha | **E 60s**	23
Gyu-Kaku | **multi.**	21

Hakata Grill | **W 40s**	20
Haru* | **multi.**	21
Hasaki* | **E Vill**	23
Hatsuhana* | **E 40s**	24
Ichimura* | **E 50s**	24
Ichiro* | **E 80s**	20
Inagiku* | **E 40s**	23
Iron Sushi* | **multi.**	19
Ise* | **multi.**	22
NEW Izakaya 10 | **Chelsea**	19
Japonais | **Gramercy**	20
Japonica* | **G Vill**	22
Jewel Bako* | **E Vill**	25
Kai | **E 60s**	25
NEW Kaijou* | **Financial**	–
Z Kanoyama* | **E Vill**	27
Katsu-Hama | **E 40s**	20
NEW Ki Sushi | **Boerum Hill**	25
Kitchen Club | **NoLita**	22
Kodama* | **W 40s**	19
Koi* | **W 40s**	23
Korea Palace* | **E 50s**	18
Ko Sushi* | **multi.**	19
Kuruma Zushi* | **E 40s**	28
NEW Kyotofu | **W 40s**	23
Lan* | **E Vill**	25
Le Miu* | **E Vill**	25
Z Masa/Bar Masa* | **W 60s**	27
Z Matsuri* | **Chelsea**	23
Z Megu | **multi.**	24
Menchanko-tei | **multi.**	20
Mishima* | **Murray Hill**	23
Mizu Sushi* | **Flatiron**	22
Momoya* | **Chelsea**	24
Monster Sushi* | **multi.**	18
Z Morimoto | **Chelsea**	24
NEW Natsumi | **W 50s**	–
Nëo Sushi* | **W 80s**	22
Ninja | **TriBeCa**	19
Nippon* | **E 50s**	22
Z Nobu* | **TriBeCa**	27
Z Nobu 57* | **W 50s**	26
Omen | **SoHo**	25
NEW Omido* | **W 50s**	–
Ono* | **Meatpacking**	21
Osaka* | **Cobble Hill**	21
Ota-Ya* | **E 80s**	20
Planet Thailand | **multi.**	19
Z Poke* | **E 80s**	26
Rai Rai Ken | **E Vill**	22
NEW Ramen Setagaya | **E Vill**	–
Riingo | **E 40s**	19
Roppongi* | **W 80s**	19
NEW Rosanjin | **TriBeCa**	25
Rue 57* | **W 50s**	19

Sachiko's* | **LES** — 25
Sakagura | **E 40s** — 24
Sapporo East* | **E Vill** — 21
NEW Sasabune* | **E 70s** — 26
NEW Sense* | **W'burg** — -
Shabu-Shabu 70* | **E 70s** — 20
Shabu-Tatsu | **E Vill** — 20
Soba Nippon | **W 50s** — 22
Soba-ya | **E Vill** — 24
NEW Soto* | **G Vill** — -
NEW Spoon | **E Vill** — -
Z Sugiyama | **W 50s** — 27
Sushi Ann* | **E 50s** — 23
Sushiden* | **multi.** — 25
Sushi Hana* | **multi.** — 21
SushiSamba* | **multi.** — 22
Z Sushi Seki* | **E 60s** — 27
Sushi Sen-nin* | **multi.** — 25
Sushiya* | **W 50s** — 20
Z Sushi Yasuda* | **E 40s** — 28
Sushi Zen* | **W 40s** — 25
NEW Suteishi* | **Seaport** — 25
Takahachi* | **multi.** — 24
Tea Box | **E 50s** — 20
Tenzan* | **multi.** — 23
Todai | **Murray Hill** — 18
Tokyo Pop* | **W 100s** — 20
Z Tomoe Sushi* | **G Vill** — 26
Tomo Sushi* | **W 100s** — 20
Z Yakitori Totto | **W 50s** — 26
Yama* | **multi.** — 24
Yuka* | **E 80s** — 21
Yuki Sushi* | **W 90s** — 21
NEW Yushi* | **multi.** — -
NEW Zenkichi | **W'burg** — 23
Zutto* | **TriBeCa** — 21

JEWISH

Artie's Deli | **W 80s** — 18
Barney Greengrass | **W 80s** — 23
Ben's Kosher | **multi.** — 17
Z Carnegie Deli | **W 50s** — 21
Chickpea | **E Vill** — 19
Edison | **W 40s** — 15
Katz's Deli | **LES** — 23
Lattanzi | **W 40s** — 22
Liebman's | **Bronx** — 19
Mill Basin Deli | **Mill Basin** — 21
Pastrami Queen | **E 70s** — 19
Sammy's Roum. | **LES** — 19
Sarge's Deli | **Murray Hill** — 19
Stage Deli | **W 50s** — 20

KOREAN

(* barbecue specialist)
Bann | **W 50s** — 24
Cho Dang Gol* | **Garment** — 21

Dae Dong* | **multi.** — 18
Do Hwa* | **G Vill** — 21
Dok Suni's | **E Vill** — 21
Gahm Mi Oak | **Garment** — 22
Hangawi | **Murray Hill** — 23
Kang Suh* | **Garment** — 20
Korea Palace* | **E 50s** — 18
Kum Gang San* | **multi.** — 21
Mandoo Bar | **Garment** — 20
Mill Korean | **W 100s** — 19
NEW Moim | **Park Slope** — -
Momofuku Ssäm | **E Vill** — 24
WonJo* | **Garment** — 20
Woo Lae Oak* | **SoHo** — 23

KOSHER

Abigael's | **Garment** — 19
Azuri Cafe | **W 50s** — 25
Ben's Kosher | **multi.** — 17
Caravan/Dreams | **E Vill** — 24
NEW Chennai | **E 80s** — -
Chennai Gdn. | **Gramercy** — 21
Le Marais | **W 40s** — 20
Levana | **W 60s** — 20
Liebman's | **Bronx** — 19
Mill Basin Deli | **Mill Basin** — 21
Pastrami Queen | **E 70s** — 19
Pongal | **multi.** — 21
Prime Grill | **E 40s** — 22
Sacred Chow | **G Vill** — 23
Solo | **E 50s** — 22
Tevere | **E 80s** — 22

LEBANESE

Al Bustan | **E 50s** — 19

MALAYSIAN

Fatty Crab | **W Vill** — 21
Nyonya | **multi.** — 22

MEDITERRANEAN

Aesop's Tables | **SI** — 21
Alta | **G Vill** — 23
NEW Amalia | **W 50s** — 21
Amaranth | **E 60s** — 20
Barbounia | **Flatiron** — 20
Beast | **Prospect Hts** — 20
Bello Sguardo | **W 70s** — 19
Cafe Bar | **Astoria** — 20
Cafe Centro | **E 40s** — 20
Café du Soleil | **W 100s** — 19
Cafe Ronda | **W 70s** — 18
Conviv. Osteria | **Park Slope** — 25
Danal | **E Vill** — 22
Dee's Pizza | **Forest Hills** — 22
Django | **E 40s** — 20
Epices/Traiteur | **W 70s** — 21

Extra Virgin | **W Vill**	21
Fig & Olive | **multi.**	20
5 Points | **NoHo**	22
Frederick's | **multi.**	19
NEW Gus' Place | **G Vill**	20
NEW House | **Gramercy**	22
Il Buco | **NoHo**	25
Isabella's | **W 70s**	20
NEW Island | **Astoria**	18
Jarnac | **W Vill**	22
Levana | **W 60s**	20
Little Owl | **W Vill**	24
Mangia | **multi.**	20
Marseille | **W 40s**	20
Miriam | **multi.**	21
Moda | **W 50s**	-
My Moon | **W'burg**	19
Nice Matin | **W 70s**	20
Nick & Toni's | **W 60s**	18
Olea | **Ft Greene**	20
Olives | **Union Sq**	22
Park, The | **Chelsea**	15
NEW Pera | **E 40s**	22
Z Picholine | **W 60s**	27
Place, The | **W Vill**	21
Red Cat | **Chelsea**	24
Ribot | **E 40s**	19
Salute! | **Murray Hill**	19
Savann | **W 70s**	19
Savoy | **SoHo**	24
NEW Sea Salt | **E Vill**	-
Sezz Medi' | **W 100s**	21
Sharz Cafe | **E 80s**	21
Solo | **E 50s**	22
Superfine | **Dumbo**	18
Taboon | **W 50s**	24
Z Tanoreen | **Bay Ridge**	27
Tempo | **Park Slope**	25
Terrace in the Sky | **W 100s**	22
Trio | **Murray Hill**	21
202 Cafe | **Chelsea**	21

MEXICAN

Alma | **Carroll Gdns**	20
Blockheads Burritos | **multi.**	17
Bonita | **multi.**	19
Café Frida | **W 70s**	19
Café Habana/Outpost | **multi.**	22
Centrico | **TriBeCa**	20
NEW Chiles/Chocolate | **Park Slope**	18
NEW China de Puebla | **Harlem**	-
Chipotle | **multi.**	18
Crema | **Chelsea**	21
Dos Caminos | **multi.**	20
El Centro | **W 50s**	18

El Parador Cafe | **Murray Hill**	20
El Paso | **G Vill**	-
El Paso Taqueria | **multi.**	22
Gabriela's | **W 90s**	17
NEW Guadalupe | **Inwood**	19
Hell's Kitchen | **W 40s**	23
Itzocan | **multi.**	23
La Esquina | **L Italy**	21
La Flor Bakery | **Woodside**	24
La Palapa | **multi.**	20
La Taqueria/Rachel | **Park Slope**	19
NEW Los Dados | **Meatpacking**	-
Mamá Mexico | **multi.**	20
Maya | **E 60s**	23
Maz Mezcal | **E 80s**	20
Mercadito | **multi.**	22
Mexicana Mama | **multi.**	23
Mexican Radio | **NoLita**	18
Mi Cocina | **W Vill**	22
Noche Mexicana | **W 100s**	22
Pampano | **E 40s**	25
Rocking Horse Cafe | **Chelsea**	20
Z Rosa Mexicano | **multi.**	22
Sueños | **Chelsea**	23
NEW Toloache | **W 50s**	-
NEW Vamos! | **Gramercy**	16
Zarela | **E 50s**	21
Zócalo | **multi.**	20
Zona Rosa | **W 50s**	18

MIDDLE EASTERN

Chickpea | **E Vill**	19
Mamlouk | **E Vill**	23
Moustache | **multi.**	21
Taboon | **W 50s**	24
Z Tanoreen | **Bay Ridge**	27
12 Chairs | **SoHo**	19
Zaytoons | **multi.**	22

MOROCCAN

NEW Babouche | **multi.**	20
Barbès | **Murray Hill**	22
Cafe Gitane | **NoLita**	20
Cafe Mogador | **E Vill**	21
Park Terrace | **Inwood**	22
Zerza | **E Vill**	22

NEW ENGLAND

NEW Black Pearl | **Chelsea**	17
NEW Ed's Lobster | **NoLita**	23
Z Pearl Oyster | **G Vill**	26

NEW ZEALAND

NEW Nelson Blue | **Seaport**	-

NOODLE SHOPS

Bao Noodles | **Gramercy**	20
Great NY Noodle | **Chinatown**	22

Kelley/Ping | **multi.**	16
Lili's Noodle | **multi.**	16
Mee Noodle | **multi.**	18
Menchanko-tei | **multi.**	20
Momofuku Noodle | **E Vill**	24
New Bo-Ky | **Chinatown**	22
Pho Bang | **multi.**	21
Rai Rai Ken | **E Vill**	22
NEW Ramen Setagaya | **E Vill**	–
Republic | **Union Sq**	18
Soba Nippon | **W 50s**	22
Soba-ya | **E Vill**	24

NORTH AFRICAN

Nomad | **E Vill**	22

NUEVO LATINO

Beso | **Park Slope**	19
Cabana | **multi.**	21
Calle Ocho | **W 80s**	22
NEW Carniceria | **Cobble Hill**	–
Citrus B&G | **W 70s**	20
Esperanto | **E Vill**	20
Luz | **Ft Greene**	24
Paladar | **LES**	18
Sabor | **E 80s**	19

PACIFIC NORTHWEST

NEW Wild Salmon | **E 40s**	21

PAN-ASIAN

Abigael's | **Garment**	19
Aja | **E 50s**	20
Amber | **E 80s**	22
Aquamarine | **Murray Hill**	21
NEW Asiakan | **W 90s**	19
bluechili | **W 50s**	19
Blue Ginger | **Chelsea**	22
Cendrillon | **SoHo**	20
Chance | **Boerum Hill**	21
Kelley/Ping | **multi.**	16
NEW Mantra | **E 50s**	–
O.G. | **E Vill**	23
Rain | **W 80s**	21
Republic | **Union Sq**	18
Ruby Foo's | **multi.**	19
NEW Spoon | **E Vill**	–
☑ Tao | **E 50s**	23

PAN-LATIN

Boca Chica | **E Vill**	20
Bogota Latin | **Park Slope**	21
NEW Cafe Fuego | **E Vill**	19
NEW Crave | **E 50s**	–
Lucy | **Flatiron**	19
NEW Palo Santo | **Park Slope**	25
NEW Rayuela | **LES**	–

Willie's | **Bronx**	23
Yuca Bar | **E Vill**	21

PERSIAN

Pars Grill | **Chelsea**	21
Persepolis | **E 70s**	19

PERUVIAN

Flor de Mayo | **multi.**	20
Lima's Taste | **W Vill**	21
Mancora | **E Vill**	21
Pio Pio | **multi.**	23

PIZZA

Adrienne's Pizza | **Financial**	23
Al Forno Pizza | **E 70s**	19
Amorina | **Prospect Hts**	23
Angelo's Pizza | **multi.**	20
Anthony's | **Park Slope**	21
ápizz | **LES**	24
Arturo's Pizzeria | **G Vill**	21
Baci & Abbracci | **W'burg**	20
Bella Blu | **E 70s**	19
Bella Via | **LIC**	23
Bettola | **W 70s**	21
NEW Cacio e Vino | **E Vill**	21
Cafe Fiorello | **W 60s**	20
Cascina | **W 40s**	18
Coals | **Bronx**	22
Da Ciro | **Murray Hill**	21
Dee's Pizza | **Forest Hills**	22
Denino's | **SI**	25
☑ Di Fara | **Midwood**	27
Don Giovanni | **multi.**	17
NEW eleven B. | **E Vill**	–
Fornino | **W'burg**	22
Franny's | **Prospect Hts**	23
Gigino | **multi.**	20
Gonzo | **G Vill**	21
☑ Grimaldi's | **Dumbo**	25
NEW Il Brigante | **Seaport**	21
Il Mattone | **TriBeCa**	21
NEW Isabella's Oven | **LES**	–
Joe & Pat's | **SI**	22
Joe's Pizza | **multi.**	23
John's Pizzeria | **multi.**	22
La Bottega | **Chelsea**	18
L & B Spumoni | **Bensonhurst**	22
La Pizza Fresca | **Flatiron**	22
La Villa Pizzeria | **multi.**	21
La Vineria | **W 50s**	20
Lil' Frankie Pizza | **E Vill**	22
Lombardi's | **NoLita**	24
NEW Lucali | **Carroll Gdns**	27
Mediterraneo | **E 60s**	19
Mezzaluna | **E 70s**	19
Naples 45 | **E 40s**	17

Nick's | **multi.** 24
Nino's | **E 40s** 21
Otto | **G Vill** 22
Patsy's Pizzeria | **multi.** 20
Pintaile's Pizza | **multi.** 20
Pizza 33 | **multi.** 21
Posto | **Gramercy** 23
Sac's Place | **Astoria** 21
Savoia | **Carroll Gdns** 21
Sezz Medi' | **W 100s** 21
Tiramisu | **E 80s** 20
Totonno Pizza | **multi.** 22
Two Boots | **multi.** 18
Una Pizza | **E Vill** 23
Uno Chicago | **multi.** 14
V&T | **W 100s** 18
Vezzo | **Murray Hill** 21
Waldy's Pizza | **Chelsea** 21

PORTUGUESE

Alfama | **W Vill** 22
Tintol | **W 40s** 21

PUB FOOD

Elephant & Castle | **G Vill** 17
Heartland | **multi.** 14
J.G. Melon | **E 70s** 21
Landmark Tavern | **W 40s** 18
Neary's | **E 50s** 15
Pete's Tavern | **Gramercy** 14
P.J. Clarke's | **multi.** 17
NEW Public House | **E 40s** –
Walker's | **TriBeCa** 17

PUERTO RICAN

La Taza de Oro | **Chelsea** 18
Sofrito | **E 50s** 22

RUSSIAN

FireBird | **W 40s** 18
Russian Samovar | **W 50s** 19
NEW Russian Tea | **W 50s** 19

SANDWICHES

Amy's Bread | **multi.** 23
Barney Greengrass | **W 80s** 23
Bôi | **E 40s** 19
Bouchon Bakery | **W 60s** 23
Bread | **NoLita** 19
Brennan | **Sheepshead** 19
Chop't Creative | **multi.** 20
Così | **multi.** 16
Dishes | **multi.** 22
DuMont | **W'burg** 23
E.A.T. | **E 80s** 19
Ess-a-Bagel | **multi.** 23
Hale/Hearty | **multi.** 19
Katz's Deli | **LES** 23

Lenny's | **multi.** 19
Liebman's | **Bronx** 19
Nicky's Viet. | **multi.** 21
Panino'teca | **Carroll Gdns** 18
Pastrami Queen | **E 70s** 19
Peanut Butter Co. | **G Vill** 20
Press 195 | **multi.** 20
Roll-n-Roaster | **Sheepshead** 19
Sarge's Deli | **Murray Hill** 19
NEW 67 Burger | **Ft Greene** 21
Stage Deli | **W 50s** 20
Sweet Melissa | **multi.** 21
Tossed | **multi.** 18
'wichcraft | **multi.** 20
Zabar's Cafe | **W 80s** 20

SCANDINAVIAN

AQ Cafe | **Murray Hill** 20
Z Aquavit | **E 50s** 25
Smorgas Chef | **multi.** 19

SEAFOOD

Ammos | **multi.** 22
Z Aquagrill | **SoHo** 26
Artie's | **Bronx** 22
Z Atlantic Grill | **E 70s** 22
Avra | **E 40s** 24
Black Duck | **Gramercy** 20
NEW Black Pearl | **Chelsea** 17
BLT Fish | **Flatiron** 23
Blue Fin | **W 40s** 22
Z Blue Water | **Union Sq** 23
Bond 45 | **W 40s** 20
Brooklyn Fish | **Park Slope** 23
Bubba Gump | **W 40s** 14
Christos | **Astoria** 22
City Crab | **Flatiron** 17
City Hall | **TriBeCa** 21
City Lobster | **W 40s** 18
Ditch Plains | **G Vill** 17
Docks Oyster | **multi.** 19
NEW Ed's Lobster | **NoLita** 23
Elias Corner | **Astoria** 22
Esca | **W 40s** 25
Fish | **G Vill** 20
Francisco's Centro | **Chelsea** 22
fresh | **TriBeCa** 24
Fuleen | **Chinatown** 24
NEW Hudson R. Café | **Harlem** –
Ithaka | **E 80s** 20
Jack's Lux. | **E Vill** 24
Kellari Taverna | **W 40s** 23
Lake Club | **SI** 21
Z Le Bernardin | **W 50s** 28
Lobster Box | **Bronx** 17
London Lennie's | **Rego Pk** 21

Lure Fishbar	SoHo	23
Marina Cafe	SI	18
Mary's Fish Camp	W Vill	25
McCormick/Schmick	W 50s	20
Meltemi	E 50s	18
Mermaid Inn	E Vill	23
☑ Milos	W 50s	26
Neptune Rm.	W 80s	22
Oceana	E 50s	26
Ocean Grill	W 70s	23
Oriental Gdn.	Chinatown	24
Oyster Bar	E 40s	21
Pampano	E 40s	25
☑ Pearl Oyster	G Vill	26
Pearl Room	Bay Ridge	23
Pescatore	E 50s	18
NEW Petite Crev.	Carroll Gdns	24
Ping's Sea.	multi.	22
Portofino's	Bronx	19
Redeye Grill	W 50s	20
Sea Grill	W 40s	24
NEW Sea Salt	E Vill	-
Shaffer City	Flatiron	21
Shelly's Tratt.	W 50s	20
South Fin Grill	SI	20
Stamatis	Astoria	22
Taverna Kyclades	Astoria	25
Telly's Taverna	Astoria	22
Thalassa	TriBeCa	22
Tides	LES	24
Todai	Murray Hill	18
Trata Estiatorio	E 70s	21
Tratt. Pesce	multi.	18
Turquoise	E 80s	22
Umberto's	multi.	18
Water's Edge	LIC	23
NEW Wild Salmon	E 40s	21

SMALL PLATES

(See also Spanish tapas specialist)

Alta	Med.	G Vill	23
NEW Bar Stuzz.	Italian	Flatiron	-
Beast	Med.	Prospect Hts	20
Bellavitae	Italian	G Vill	22
Bello Sguardo	Med.	W 70s	19
Beyoglu	Turkish	E 80s	21
Bocca Lupo	Italian	Cobble Hill	21
Butai	Jap.	Gramercy	22
NEW Centro Vinoteca	Italian	W Vill	-
Chino's	Asian	Gramercy	22
Degustation	French/Spanish	E Vill	26
NEW Dieci	Italian	E Vill	23
EN Japanese	Jap.	W Vill	22
NEW Fireside	Eclectic	E 50s	21

Frankies Spuntino	Italian	multi.	24
NEW Grayz	Amer.	W 50s	-
NEW House	Med.	Gramercy	22
'inoteca	Italian	LES	23
NEW Island	Med.	Astoria	18
NEW Izakaya 10	Jap.	Chelsea	19
Kuma Inn	SE Asian	LES	24
☑ L'Atelier/Robuchon	French	E 50s	27
Little D	Eclectic	Park Slope	20
NEW Maze	French	W 50s	23
Mercadito	Mex.	multi.	22
One	Amer.	Meatpacking	18
Perbacco	Italian	E Vill	24
NEW p*ong	Dessert	G Vill	21
Sakagura	Jap.	E 40s	24
Samba-Lé	Brazilian	E Vill	19
NEW savorNY	Eclectic	LES	-
NEW Spoon	Asian	E Vill	-
Stanton Social	Eclectic	LES	23
NEW Tailor	Amer.	SoHo	-
Tarallucci	Italian	multi.	19
Tasting Rm.	Amer.	multi.	22
Uncle Nick's	Greek	W 50s	19
Vento	Italian	Meatpacking	19
NEW Zenkichi	Jap.	W'burg	23

SOUL FOOD

Amy Ruth's	Harlem	22
Charles' Kitchen	Harlem	24
NEW Cheryl's	Prospect Hts	22
Londel's	Harlem	22
Miss Mamie/Maude	Harlem	21
Mo-Bay	Harlem	21
Pink Tea Cup	W Vill	20
Sylvia's	Harlem	19

SOUP

Cozy	G Vill	18
Hale/Hearty	multi.	19
La Bonne Soupe	W 50s	18

SOUTH AMERICAN

Cafe Ronda	W 70s	18
Don Pedro's	E 90s	23
Empanada Mama	W 50s	20

SOUTHEAST ASIAN

Cafe Asean	G Vill	21
☑ Spice Market	Meatpacking	22

SOUTHERN

Amy Ruth's	Harlem	22
B. Smith's	W 40s	19
Charles' Kitchen	Harlem	24
Duke's	multi.	16
Kitchenette	multi.	19
Londel's	Harlem	22

Maroons | **Chelsea**	22
Miss Mamie/Maude | **Harlem**	21
Pink Tea Cup | **W Vill**	20
Rack & Soul | **W 100s**	20
River Room | **Harlem**	19
NEW Southern Hosp. | **E 70s**	–

SOUTHWESTERN

Agave | **W Vill**	18
Canyon Road | **E 70s**	19
Cilantro | **multi.**	17
Cowgirl | **W Vill**	16
NEW Johnny Utah | **W 50s**	–
Los Dos Molinos | **Gramercy**	21
Z Mesa Grill | **Flatiron**	24
Miracle Grill | **multi.**	18

SPANISH

(* tapas specialist)

Alcala* | **E 40s**	20
Azafran* | **TriBeCa**	21
Bolo | **Flatiron**	24
Boqueria* | **Flatiron**	23
Cafe Español | **G Vill**	20
Casa Mono | **Gramercy**	25
Degustation | **E Vill**	26
El Charro Español | **G Vill**	22
El Cid* | **Chelsea**	21
El Faro* | **W Vill**	23
El Paso | **G Vill**	–
El Pote | **Murray Hill**	21
El Quijote | **Chelsea**	19
Euzkadi* | **E Vill**	21
Flor de Sol* | **TriBeCa**	20
Francisco's Centro | **Chelsea**	22
La Paella* | **E Vill**	20
Las Ramblas* | **G Vill**	23
NEW Mercat* | **NoHo**	–
Oliva* | **LES**	20
NEW Pamplona* | **Gramercy**	–
Pipa* | **Flatiron**	21
Real Madrid | **SI**	21
Sala* | **multi.**	22
Sevilla | **W Vill**	23
Solera* | **E 50s**	22
Sol y Sombra* | **W 80s**	19
Suba | **LES**	21
NEW Tasca* | **W Vill**	20
Tía Pol* | **Chelsea**	24
Xunta* | **E Vill**	19

STEAKHOUSES

AJ Maxwell's | **W 40s**	22
Angelo & Maxie's | **Flatiron**	21
Artie's | **Bronx**	22
Austin's Steak | **Bay Ridge**	21
Ben & Jack's | **E 40s**	23

Ben Benson's | **W 50s**	24
NEW Benjamin Steak | **E 40s**	23
Bistro Le Steak | **E 70s**	17
Blair Perrone | **E 40s**	21
BLT Prime | **Gramercy**	24
BLT Steak | **E 50s**	24
Bobby Van's | **multi.**	22
Bond 45 | **W 40s**	20
Buenos Aires | **E Vill**	21
Bull & Bear | **E 40s**	19
NEW Caminito | **Harlem**	–
Capital Grille | **E 40s**	23
NEW Carniceria | **Cobble Hill**	–
Chimichurri Grill | **W 40s**	21
Christos | **Astoria**	22
Churrascaria | **multi.**	23
City Hall | **TriBeCa**	21
Craftsteak | **Chelsea**	22
Z Del Frisco's | **W 40s**	25
Delmonico's | **Financial**	22
NEW DeStefano's | **W'burg**	–
Dylan Prime | **TriBeCa**	24
Embers | **Bay Ridge**	22
Erawan | **Bayside**	22
Fairway Cafe | **W 70s**	18
Frankie/Johnnie | **multi.**	21
Frank's | **Chelsea**	19
Gallagher's | **W 50s**	20
NEW Gaucho | **W 50s**	–
Green Field | **Corona**	19
Hacienda/Argentina | **E 70s**	21
Harry's | **Financial**	22
Il Bastardo | **Chelsea**	19
Industria | **TriBeCa**	20
Jake's | **Bronx**	24
Keens | **Garment**	24
Knickerbocker | **G Vill**	20
NEW Kobe Club | **W 50s**	20
Le Marais | **W 40s**	20
Les Halles | **multi.**	20
Macelleria | **Meatpacking**	21
Maloney & Porcelli | **E 50s**	22
MarkJoseph | **Financial**	24
Michael Jordan's | **E 40s**	20
Morton's | **E 40s**	24
Nick & Stef's | **Garment**	22
Novecento | **SoHo**	22
Old Homestead | **Meatpacking**	23
Outback | **multi.**	14
Z Palm | **multi.**	24
Patroon | **E 40s**	21
Z Peter Luger | **W'burg**	28
Pietro's | **E 40s**	23
Porcão | **Gramercy**	21
Porter House NY | **W 60s**	22

Post House | **E 60s** — 23
Prime Grill | **E 40s** — 22
Quality Meats | **W 50s** — 24
Rothmann's | **E 50s** — 22
Roth's Westside | **W 90s** — 19
Ruth's Chris | **W 50s** — 23
Shelly's Tratt. | **W 50s** — 20
Shula's | **W 40s** — 20
Smith & Wollensky | **E 40s** — 23
South Fin Grill | **SI** — 20
☑ Sparks | **E 40s** — 25
Steak Frites | **Union Sq** — 18
NEW STK | **Meatpacking** — 20
Strip House | **G Vill** — 25
2 West | **Financial** — 21
Uncle Jack's | **multi.** — 23
Via Brasil | **W 40s** — 18
Willie's | **Bronx** — 23
Wolfgang's | **multi.** — 25
Wollensky's | **E 40s** — 23

TEX-MEX

Burritoville | **multi.** — 16
Mary Ann's | **multi.** — 15
107 West | **multi.** — 18

THAI

Bann Thai | **Forest Hills** — 21
Breeze | **W 40s** — 20
Elephant, The | **E Vill** — 21
Erawan | **Bayside** — 22
Highline | **Meatpacking** — 19
Holy Basil | **E Vill** — 22
NEW Hurapan | **G Vill** — 20
Jaiya Thai | **Gramercy** — 22
Jasmine | **E 80s** — 19
Joya | **Cobble Hill** — 23
Kin Khao | **SoHo** — 22
☑ Kittichai | **SoHo** — 23
Klong | **E Vill** — 19
Kuma Inn | **LES** — 24
Land | **multi.** — 23
Lemongrass Grill | **multi.** — 17
Long Tan | **Park Slope** — 19
NEW Open/Sesame | **LES** — –
Pam Real Thai | **W 40s** — 22
Peep | **SoHo** — 19
Planet Thailand | **multi.** — 19
Pongsri Thai | **multi.** — 20
Prem-on Thai | **G Vill** — 21
Q Thai Bistro | **Forest Hills** — 21
Regional Thai | **multi.** — 18
Room Service | **Chelsea** — 19
Royal Siam | **Chelsea** — 19
Sala Thai | **E 80s** — 21
SEA | **multi.** — 20

Siam Sq. | **Bronx** — 24
Song | **Park Slope** — 24
Spice | **multi.** — 20
☑ Sripraphai | **Woodside** — 26
NEW Sticky Rice | **LES** — 19
Thai Pavilion | **Astoria** — 22
Topaz Thai | **W 50s** — 20
Vong | **E 50s** — 22
Vynl | **multi.** — 17
Wild Ginger | **W Vill** — 19
Wondee Siam | **multi.** — 22

TIBETAN

Tsampa | **E Vill** — 20

TUNISIAN

Epices/Traiteur | **W 70s** — 21

TURKISH

Akdeniz | **W 40s** — 20
NEW A La Turka | **E 70s** — 18
Ali Baba | **Murray Hill** — 23
Bereket | **LES** — 18
Beyoglu | **E 80s** — 21
Dervish Turk. | **W 40s** — 19
Pasha | **W 70s** — 21
NEW Pera | **E 40s** — 22
NEW Peri Ela | **E 90s** — 19
Sahara | **Gravesend** — 20
Sip Sak | **E 40s** — 20
Taksim | **E 50s** — 20
Turkish Cuisine | **W 40s** — 20
Turkish Kitchen | **Gramercy** — 22
Turks & Frogs | **TriBeCa** — 20
Turkuaz | **W 100s** — 19
Uskudar | **E 70s** — 19
Zeytin | **W 80s** — 19

UKRAINIAN

Veselka | **E Vill** — 18

VEGETARIAN

(* vegan)
Angelica Kit.* | **E Vill** — 21
Blossom* | **Chelsea** — 21
Candle* | **E 70s** — 23
Caravan/Dreams* | **E Vill** — 24
NEW Chennai | **E 80s** — –
Chennai Gdn. | **Gramercy** — 21
Counter* | **E Vill** — 22
Gobo* | **multi.** — 22
Hangawi | **Murray Hill** — 23
Hummus Place | **multi.** — 23
Pongal | **multi.** — 21
Pure Food/Wine* | **Gramercy** — 22
Sacred Chow* | **G Vill** — 23
Saravanaas | **Gramercy** — 23
teany* | **LES** — 18

CUISINES

Temple Canteen | **Flushing** | -
Vatan | **Gramercy** | 23
Zen Palate | **multi.** | 19

VENEZUELAN

Caracas | **E Vill** | 26
Flor's Kitchen | **G Vill** | 16

VIETNAMESE

Bao Noodles | **Gramercy** | 20
Bao 111 | **E Vill** | 21
Bôi | **E 40s** | 19
Doyers Viet. | **Chinatown** | 20
Indochine | **E Vill** | 20
Le Colonial | **E 50s** | 20
NEW Mai House | **TriBeCa** | 21

Nam | **TriBeCa** | 22
New Bo-Ky | **Chinatown** | 22
Nha Trang | **Chinatown** | 21
Nicky's Viet. | **multi.** | 21
Omai | **Chelsea** | 23
Pho Bang | **multi.** | 21
Pho Pasteur | **Chinatown** | 21
Pho Viet Huong | **Chinatown** | 23
NEW Safran | **Chelsea** | 20
Saigon Grill | **multi.** | 22
Sapa | **Flatiron** | 22
NEW Silent H | **W'burg** | -
Vermicelli | **E 70s** | 19
VietCafé | **TriBeCa** | 21

subscribe to zagat.com

BROOKLYN

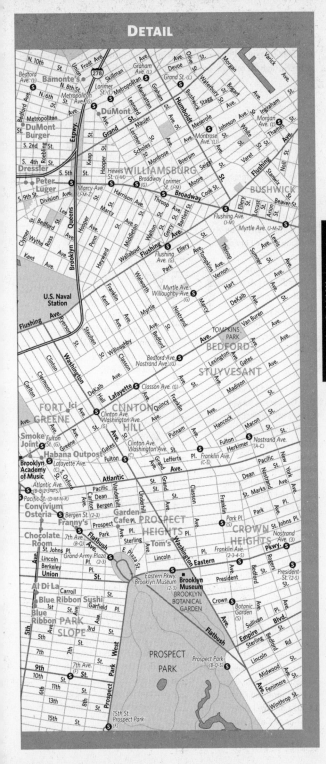

DETAIL

MAPS

Locations

Includes restaurant names, cuisines and Food ratings. ⚡ indicates places with the highest ratings, popularity and importance.

Manhattan

CHELSEA

(24th to 30th Sts., west of 5th; 14th to 24th Sts., west of 6th)

Amy's Bread	*Sandwich*	23
Bette	*Euro.*	19
Better Burger	*Hamburgers*	15
Biricchino	*Italian*	20
⚡ Black Pearl	*Seafood*	17
Blossom	*Vegan/Veg.*	21
Blue Ginger	*Jap./Pan-Asian*	22
Bombay Talkie	*Indian*	20
Bottino	*Italian*	19
⚡ brgr	*Hamburgers*	18
⚡ Buddakan	*Asian Fusion*	23
Cafeteria	*Amer.*	18
Cookshop	*Amer.*	23
Craftsteak	*Steak*	22
Crema	*Mex.*	21
Cuba Cafe	*Cuban*	18
Dallas BBQ	*BBQ*	15
Da Umberto	*Italian*	25
⚡ Del Posto	*Italian*	25
Don Giovanni	*Italian*	17
East of 8th	*Eclectic*	16
El Cid	*Spanish*	21
elmo	*Amer.*	15
El Quijote	*Spanish*	19
Empire Diner	*Diner*	15
Energy Kitchen	*Health*	18
F & B	*Hot Dogs*	18
Food Bar	*Amer.*	16
Francisco's Centro	*Spanish*	22
Frank's	*Italian/Steak*	19
Gascogne	*French*	22
Gin Lane	*Cont.*	17
Grand Sichuan	*Chinese*	22
Hale/Hearty	*Sandwich/Soup*	19
⚡ Hill Country	*BBQ*	-
Il Bastardo	*Italian/Steak*	19
Intermezzo	*Italian*	18
⚡ Izakaya 10	*Jap.*	19
⚡ Klee Brass.	*Amer./Euro.*	21
La Bergamote	*Bakery/French*	24
La Bottega	*Italian/Pizza*	18
La Lunchonette	*French*	22
La Taza de Oro	*Diner*	18
Le Grainne Cafe	*French*	19
⚡ Le Petit Bistro	*French*	-
Le Singe Vert	*French*	19

Le Zie 2000	*Italian*	21
Maroons	*Jamaican*	22
Mary Ann's	*Tex-Mex*	15
⚡ Matsuri	*Jap.*	23
Momoya	*Jap.*	24
Monster Sushi	*Jap.*	18
Moran's	*Amer.*	18
⚡ Morimoto	*Jap.*	24
Negril	*Carib./Jamaican*	20
Omai	*Viet.*	23
Park, The	*Med.*	15
Pars Grill	*Persian*	21
Patsy's Pizzeria	*Pizza*	20
Pepe	*Italian*	21
Pizza 33	*Pizza*	21
Pongsri Thai	*Thai*	20
Red Cat	*Amer./Med.*	24
Regional Thai	*Thai*	18
Rocking Horse Cafe	*Mex.*	20
Room Service	*Thai*	19
Royal Siam	*Thai*	19
RUB BBQ	*BBQ*	20
⚡ Safran	*French/Viet.*	20
Sarabeth's	*Amer.*	20
Sette	*Italian*	18
Seven	*Amer.*	18
Spice	*Thai*	20
Sueños	*Mex.*	23
Tía Pol	*Spanish*	24
tre dici	*Italian*	22
Trestle on 10th	*Amer.*	19
202 Cafe	*Med.*	21
Waldy's Pizza	*Pizza*	21
'wichcraft	*Sandwich*	20

CHINATOWN

(Canal to Pearl Sts., east of B'way)

⚡ Amazing 66	*Chinese*	23
Big Wong	*Chinese*	22
Congee	*Chinese*	21
Dim Sum Go Go	*Chinese*	20
Doyers Viet.	*Viet.*	20
Excellent Dumpling	*Chinese*	21
Fuleen	*Chinese/Seafood*	24
Golden Unicorn	*Chinese*	20
Goodies	*Chinese*	20
Grand Sichuan	*Chinese*	22
Great NY Noodle	*Noodles*	22
HSF	*Chinese*	20
Jing Fong	*Chinese*	19
Joe's Shanghai	*Chinese*	22

Mandarin Court | *Chinese*	20
Mr. Tang | *Chinese*	19
New Bo-Ky | *Noodles*	22
New Green Bo | *Chinese*	22
Nha Trang | *Viet.*	21
Oriental Gdn. | *Chinese/Seafood*	24
Peking Duck | *Chinese*	22
Pho Bang | *Viet.*	21
Pho Pasteur | *Viet.*	21
Pho Viet Huong | *Viet.*	23
Ping's Sea. | *Chinese/Seafood*	22
Pongsri Thai | *Thai*	20
Shanghai Cuisine | *Chinese*	21
Wo Hop | *Chinese*	21
X.O. | *Chinese*	18

EAST 40s

Aburiya Kinnosuke | *Jap.*	24
Alcala | *Spanish*	20
American Girl | *Amer.*	13
Ammos | *Greek*	22
Avra | *Greek*	24
Ben & Jack's | *Steak*	23
NEW Benjamin Steak | *Steak*	23
Blair Perrone | *Steak*	21
Bobby Van's | *Steak*	22
Bôi | *Viet.*	19
Brother Jimmy's | *BBQ*	16
Bukhara Grill | *Indian*	20
Bull & Bear | *Steak*	19
Burger Heaven | *Hamburgers*	16
Burritoville | *Tex-Mex*	16
Cafe Centro | *Med.*	20
Cafe Spice | *Indian*	18
Caffe Linda | *Italian*	18
Capital Grille | *Steak*	23
Chiam | *Chinese*	23
Chin Chin | *Chinese*	22
Chipotle | *Mex.*	18
Cibo | *Amer./Italian*	20
Cipriani Dolci | *Italian*	18
Comfort Diner | *Diner*	16
Darbar | *Indian*	20
Dishes | *Sandwich*	22
Diwan | *Indian*	21
Django | *French/Med.*	20
Docks Oyster | *Seafood*	19
Energy Kitchen | *Health*	18
NEW Fabio Piccolo | *Italian*	–
goodburger | *Hamburgers*	18
Grifone | *Italian*	23
Gyu-Kaku | *Jap.*	21
Hale/Hearty | *Sandwich/Soup*	19
Haru | *Jap.*	21
Hatsuhana | *Jap.*	24
Il Postino | *Italian*	22

Inagiku | *Jap.*	23
Ise | *Jap.*	22
Junior's | *Diner*	18
Katsu-Hama | *Jap.*	20
Kuruma Zushi | *Jap.*	28
☑ L'Impero | *Italian*	26
Mamá Mexico | *Mex.*	20
Mangia | *Med.*	20
Mee Noodle | *Noodles*	18
☑ Megu | *Jap.*	24
Menchanko-tei | *Noodles*	20
Metrazur | *Amer.*	20
Michael Jordan's | *Steak*	21
Morton's | *Steak*	24
Nanni | *Italian*	24
Naples 45 | *Italian*	17
Nino's | *Italian*	21
Osteria Laguna | *Italian*	21
Oyster Bar | *Seafood*	21
☑ Palm | *Steak*	24
Pampano | *Mex./Seafood*	25
Patroon | *Amer./Steak*	21
Pepe | *Italian*	21
NEW Pera | *Med./Turkish*	22
Pershing Sq. | *Amer./French*	15
Phoenix Gdn. | *Chinese*	24
Pietro's | *Italian/Steak*	23
Prime Grill | *Steak*	22
NEW Public House | *Pub*	–
Ribot | *Med.*	19
Riingo | *Amer./Jap.*	19
Sakagura | *Jap.*	24
Sip Sak | *Turkish*	20
Smith & Wollensky | *Steak*	23
Smorgas Chef | *Scan.*	19
☑ Sparks | *Steak*	25
Sushiden | *Jap.*	25
☑ Sushi Yasuda | *Jap.*	28
Two Boots | *Pizza*	18
'wichcraft | *Sandwich*	20
NEW Wild Salmon | *Seafood*	21
Wollensky's | *Steak*	23
Yama | *Jap.*	24
NEW Yushi | *Jap.*	–
Zócalo | *Mex.*	20

EAST 50s

Adä | *Indian*	23
Aja | *Pan-Asian*	20
Al Bustan | *Lebanese*	19
☑ Alto | *Italian*	26
Amma | *Indian*	24
Angelo's Pizza | *Pizza*	20
☑ Aquavit | *Scan.*	25
Baluchi's | *Indian*	18
Bice | *Italian*	20

LOCATIONS

Blockheads Burritos | *Mex.*	17
BLT Steak | *Steak*	24
Bobby Van's | *Steak*	22
Bottega del Vino | *Italian*	22
Brasserie | *French*	20
Burger Heaven | *Hamburgers*	16
Burritoville | *Tex-Mex*	16
Cafe Joul | *French*	18
Caviar Russe | *Amer.*	24
Cellini | *Italian*	21
Chipotle | *Mex.*	18
Chola | *Indian*	23
Chop't Creative | *Amer.*	20
Così | *Sandwich*	16
NEW Crave | *Pan-Latin*	-
David Burke/Bloom. | *Amer.*	18
Dawat | *Indian*	23
DeGrezia | *Italian*	22
Destino | *Italian*	18
Deux Amis | *French*	19
Dishes | *Sandwich*	22
Dos Caminos | *Mex.*	20
Energy Kitchen | *Health*	18
Ess-a-Bagel | *Deli*	23
F & B | *Hot Dogs*	18
☑ Felidia | *Italian*	25
57 | *Amer.*	22
NEW Fiorini | *Italian*	-
NEW Fireside | *Eclectic*	21
☑ Four Seasons | *Cont.*	25
Fresco | *Italian*	23
Giambelli | *Italian*	21
Gilt | *Amer.*	25
goodburger | *Hamburgers*	18
Grand Sichuan | *Chinese*	22
Harry Cipriani | *Italian*	-
Houston's | *Amer.*	20
Ichimura | *Jap.*	24
Il Menestrello | *Italian*	22
Il Nido | *Italian*	23
Jubilee | *French*	22
Korea Palace | *Korean*	18
La Gioconda | *Italian*	20
☑ La Grenouille | *French*	27
La Mangeoire | *French*	19
La Mediterranée | *French*	19
☑ L'Atelier/Robuchon | *French*	27
Le Cirque | *French*	23
Le Colonial | *French/Viet.*	20
Lenny's | *Sandwich*	19
L'Entrecote | *French*	19
Le Perigord | *French*	24
Lever House | *Amer.*	22
Maloney & Porcelli | *Steak*	22
NEW Mantra | *Amer./Pan-Asian*	-

Meltemi | *Greek/Seafood*	18
Mint | *Indian*	19
Monkey Bar | *Amer.*	-
Montparnasse | *French*	19
Mr. Chow | *Chinese*	20
☑ Mr. K's | *Chinese*	23
Neary's | *Pub*	15
Nippon | *Jap.*	22
Oceana | *Amer./Seafood*	26
Our Place | *Chinese*	20
Outback | *Steak*	14
Peking Duck | *Chinese*	22
Pescatore | *Italian/Seafood*	18
P.J. Clarke's | *Pub*	17
Pump Energy | *Health*	19
☑ Rosa Mexicano | *Mex.*	22
Rothmann's | *Steak*	22
San Pietro | *Italian*	24
Serafina | *Italian*	18
Shun Lee Palace | *Chinese*	24
Sofrito | *Puerto Rican*	22
Solera | *Spanish*	22
Solo | *Med.*	22
Sushi Ann | *Jap.*	23
Taksim | *Turkish*	20
☑ Tao | *Pan-Asian*	23
Tea Box | *Jap.*	20
Teodora | *Italian*	22
Tratt. Pesce | *Italian/Seafood*	18
Tse Yang | *Chinese*	25
Vong | *French/Thai*	22
Yuva | *Indian*	24
Zarela | *Mex.*	21
Zip Burger | *Hamburgers*	18

EAST 60s

NEW Accademia/Vino | *Italian*	-
Alice's Tea Cup | *Amer.*	19
Amaranth | *Med.*	20
Arabelle | *Amer./French*	21
☑ Aureole | *Amer.*	27
Bistro 61 | *French*	20
Bravo Gianni | *Italian*	23
Brio | *Italian*	18
Burger Heaven | *Hamburgers*	16
Cabana | *Nuevo Latino*	21
Café Evergreen | *Chinese*	20
Café Pierre | *Cont./French*	23
Canaletto | *Italian*	21
NEW Chat Noir | *French*	18
China Fun | *Chinese*	16
Circus | *Brazilian*	20
Da Filippo | *Italian*	19
☑ Daniel | *French*	28
☑ davidburke/dona. | *Amer.*	25

Fig & Olive	*Med.*	20
Frederick's	*French/Med.*	19
Fred's at Barneys	*Amer./Italian*	20
Geisha	*Jap.*	23
Gino	*Italian*	21
Hale/Hearty	*Sandwich/Soup*	19
Il Vagabondo	*Italian*	19
Jackson Hole	*Amer.*	17
John's Pizzeria	*Pizza*	22
JoJo	*French*	24
Kai	*Jap.*	25
L'Absinthe	*French*	22
La Cantina Toscana	*Italian*	24
La Goulue	*French*	20
Le Bilboquet	*French*	20
Lenny's	*Sandwich*	19
Le Pain Q.	*Bakery/Belgian*	19
Le Veau d'Or	*French*	17
Maya	*Mex.*	23
Mediterraneo	*Italian/Pizza*	19
Mon Petit Cafe	*French*	18
Nello	*Italian*	19
🆕 Park Avenue	*Amer.*	-
Patsy's Pizzeria	*Pizza*	20
Philippe	*Chinese*	23
Pongal	*Indian/Veg.*	21
Portofino Grille	*Italian*	19
Post House	*Steak*	23
Primola	*Italian*	23
Regency	*Amer.*	18
Scalinatella	*Italian*	25
Serafina	*Italian*	18
Serendipity 3	*Dessert*	18
🆕 Solace	*Amer.*	-
Z Sushi Seki	*Jap.*	27
212	*Amer.*	16
Viand	*Coffee Shop*	16
Via Oreto	*Italian*	19
Za Za	*Italian*	20
🆕 Zoë Townhouse	*Amer.*	-

EAST 70s

Afghan Kebab	*Afghan*	19
Agata/Valentina	*Italian*	18
Aki Sushi	*Jap.*	19
🆕 A La Turka	*Turkish*	18
Al Forno Pizza	*Pizza*	19
Annie's	*Amer.*	18
Z Atlantic Grill	*Seafood*	22
Bandol Bistro	*French*	19
Baraonda	*Italian*	18
Bardolino	*Italian*	18
Barking Dog	*Amer.*	15
Bella Blu	*Italian*	19
Bistro Le Steak	*French*	17

Boathouse	*Amer.*	16
Brother Jimmy's	*BBQ*	16
Burritoville	*Tex-Mex*	16
Z Café Boulud	*French*	27
Caffe Buon Gusto	*Italian*	18
Campagnola	*Italian*	23
Candle	*Vegan/Veg.*	23
Canyon Road	*SW*	19
Z Carlyle	*French*	21
Cilantro	*SW*	17
Coco Pazzo	*Italian*	22
Cortina	*Italian*	18
Dallas BBQ	*BBQ*	15
Due	*Italian*	22
EJ's Luncheonette	*Amer.*	15
Z Gari/Sushi	*Jap.*	26
Grace's Tratt.	*Italian*	18
Hacienda/Argentina	*Argent./Steak*	21
Haru	*Jap.*	21
Il Riccio	*Italian*	21
Iron Sushi	*Jap.*	19
J.G. Melon	*Pub*	21
Ko Sushi	*Jap.*	19
Lenny's	*Sandwich*	19
Le Pain Q.	*Bakery/Belgian*	19
Lumi	*Italian*	19
Lusardi's	*Italian*	24
Maruzzella	*Italian*	22
Mezzaluna	*Italian*	19
Mingala Burmese	*Burmese*	20
Nino's	*Italian*	21
Orsay	*French*	18
Parma	*Italian*	22
Pastrami Queen	*Deli*	19
Payard Bistro	*Dessert/French*	24
Per Lei	*Italian*	20
Persepolis	*Persian*	19
Petaluma	*Italian*	18
Quatorze Bis	*French*	21
Regional Thai	*Thai*	18
Sant Ambroeus	*Italian*	22
Sarabeth's	*Amer.*	20
🆕 Sasabune	*Jap.*	26
🆕 Saucy	*Eclectic*	-
Serafina	*Italian*	18
Sette Mezzo	*Italian*	23
Shabu-Shabu 70	*Jap.*	20
Shanghai Pavilion	*Chinese*	21
🆕 Southern Hosp.	*Southern*	-
Spice	*Thai*	20
Sushi Hana	*Jap.*	21
Swifty's	*Amer.*	18
Trata Estiatorio	*Greek/Seafood*	21
Uskudar	*Turkish*	19

LOCATIONS

Uva	*Italian*	21
Vermicelli	*Viet.*	19
Viand	*Coffee Shop*	16
Via Quadronno	*Italian*	21
Vivolo	*Italian*	20
Vynl	*Amer./Thai*	17

EAST 80s

Alice's Tea Cup	*Amer.*	19
Amber	*Pan-Asian*	22
Antonucci	*Italian*	20
Baluchi's	*Indian*	18
Beyoglu	*Turkish*	21
Blockheads Burritos	*Mex.*	17
Brasserie Julien	*French*	19
Burger Heaven	*Hamburgers*	16
Café d'Alsace	*French*	21
Café Sabarsky	*Austrian*	22
Caffe Grazie	*Italian*	19
Centolire	*Italian*	20
Chef Ho's	*Chinese*	22
NEW Chennai	*Indian/Veg.*	-
Cilantro	*SW*	17
Dakshin Indian	*Indian*	20
Demarchelier	*French*	17
Divino	*Italian*	18
Donguri	*Jap.*	27
E.A.T.	*Amer.*	19
Elaine's	*Amer./Italian*	13
Elio's	*Italian*	23
Erminia	*Italian*	25
Etats-Unis	*Amer.*	25
Ethiopian Rest.	*Ethiopian*	17
Firenze	*Italian*	21
Giovanni	*Italian*	22
Girasole	*Italian*	20
Gobo	*Vegan/Veg.*	22
Heidelberg	*German*	17
Ichiro	*Jap.*	20
Ithaka	*Greek/Seafood*	20
Jackson Hole	*Amer.*	17
Jacques	*French*	18
Jasmine	*Thai*	19
Josie's	*Eclectic*	19
Kings' Carriage	*Amer.*	22
Ko Sushi	*Jap.*	19
Land	*Thai*	23
Le Boeuf/Mode	*French*	21
Le Pain Q.	*Bakery/Belgian*	19
Le Refuge	*French*	21
Lili's Noodle	*Noodles*	16
Luca	*Italian*	20
Maz Mezcal	*Mex.*	20
Nicola's	*Italian*	22
One 83	*Italian*	21

Ota-Ya	*Jap.*	20
Our Place	*Chinese*	20
Paola's	*Italian*	23
Papaya King	*Hot Dogs*	20
Pig Heaven	*Chinese*	19
Pintaile's Pizza	*Pizza*	20
Z Poke	*Jap.*	26
Primavera	*Italian*	22
Quattro Gatti	*Italian*	20
Rughetta	*Italian*	22
Sabor	*Nuevo Latino*	19
Sala Thai	*Thai*	21
NEW Sandro's	*Italian*	-
Sharz Cafe	*Med.*	21
Sistina	*Italian*	24
Spigolo	*Italian*	25
Sushi Sen-nin	*Jap.*	25
Taste	*Amer.*	20
Tevere	*Italian*	22
Tiramisu	*Italian*	20
Tony's Di Napoli	*Italian*	18
Totonno Pizza	*Pizza*	22
Tratt. Pesce	*Italian/Seafood*	18
Triangolo	*Italian*	21
Turquoise	*Seafood*	22
Uno Chicago	*Pizza*	14
Vespa	*Italian*	21
Viand	*Coffee Shop*	16
Wondee Siam	*Thai*	22
Wu Liang Ye	*Chinese*	21
York Grill	*Amer.*	23
Yuka	*Jap.*	21
Zócalo	*Mex.*	20

EAST 90s & 100s
(90th to 110th Sts.)

Barking Dog	*Amer.*	15
Bistro du Nord	*French*	18
Brother Jimmy's	*BBQ*	16
Don Pedro's	*Carib./S Amer.*	23
El Paso Taqueria	*Mex.*	22
Itzocan	*Mex.*	23
Jackson Hole	*Amer.*	17
Nick's	*Pizza*	24
Osso Buco	*Italian*	17
Pascalou	*French*	22
NEW Peri Ela	*Turkish*	19
Pinocchio	*Italian*	21
Pintaile's Pizza	*Pizza*	20
Pio Pio	*Peruvian*	23
Sarabeth's	*Amer.*	20
Sfoglia	*Italian*	23
Table d'Hôte	*French*	21
Vico	*Italian*	21
Zebú Grill	*Brazilian*	21

(14th to Houston Sts., east of B'way,
excluding NoHo)

NEW Aloe | *Eclectic*	–
Angelica Kit. | *Vegan/Veg.*	21
Awash | *Ethiopian*	22
Baluchi's | *Indian*	18
Banjara | *Indian*	23
Bao 111 | *Viet.*	21
Blue 9 Burger | *Hamburgers*	18
Boca Chica | *Pan-Latin*	20
Buenos Aires | *Argent.*	21
Burritoville | *Tex-Mex*	16
Butter | *Amer.*	19
Cacio e Pepe | *Italian*	22
NEW Cacio e Vino | *Italian*	21
Cafecito | *Cuban*	21
NEW Cafe Fuego | *Pan-Latin*	19
Cafe Mogador | *Moroccan*	21
NEW Caffe Emilia | *Italian*	–
Caracas | *Venez.*	26
Caravan/Dreams | *Vegan/Veg.*	24
Casimir | *French*	19
Chickpea | *Mideast.*	19
ChikaLicious | *Dessert*	24
Chipotle | *Mex.*	18
Chiyono | *Jap.*	23
Colors | *Eclectic*	19
Counter | *Vegan/Veg.*	22
Cucina di Pesce | *Italian*	17
Dallas BBQ | *BBQ*	15
Danal | *French/Med.*	22
Degustation | *French/Spanish*	26
NEW Dieci | *Italian*	23
Dok Suni's | *Korean*	21
Dumpling Man | *Chinese*	19
NEW East Village Yacht | *Amer.*	–
Elephant, The | *French/Thai*	21
NEW eleven B. | *Italian/Pizza*	–
Esperanto | *Nuevo Latino*	20
NEW E.U., The | *Euro.*	20
Euzkadi | *Spanish*	21
Flea Mkt. Cafe | *French*	19
Frank | *Italian*	24
NEW Gemma | *Italian*	–
Gnocco Caffe | *Italian*	21
Grand Sichuan | *Chinese*	22
Gyu-Kaku | *Jap.*	21
Hasaki | *Jap.*	23
Haveli | *Indian*	23
Hearth | *Amer./Italian*	25
Holy Basil | *Thai*	22
Hummus Place | *Israeli/Veg.*	23
I Coppi | *Italian*	23
Il Bagatto | *Italian*	23
Indochine | *French/Viet.*	20
Itzocan | *Mex.*	23
Jack's Lux. | *Cont./French*	24
Jewel Bako | *Jap.*	25
John's/12th St. | *Italian*	19
Jules | *French*	19
Z Kanoyama | *Jap.*	27
Kelley/Ping | *Pan-Asian*	16
Klong | *Thai*	19
Knife + Fork | *Euro.*	23
Lan | *Jap.*	25
La Paella | *Spanish*	20
La Palapa | *Mex.*	20
Lavagna | *Italian*	24
Le Gamin | *French*	19
Le Miu | *Jap.*	25
Le Tableau | *French*	24
Lil' Frankie Pizza | *Pizza*	22
Lucien | *French*	21
Mama's Food | *Amer.*	20
Mamlouk | *Mideast.*	23
Mancora | *Peruvian*	21
Mara's | *Cajun/Creole*	19
Mary Ann's | *Tex-Mex*	15
Max | *Italian*	23
Max Brenner | *Dessert*	17
Mercadito | *Mex.*	22
Mermaid Inn | *Seafood*	23
Mingala Burmese | *Burmese*	20
Momofuku Noodle | *Noodles*	24
Momofuku Ssäm | *Amer./Korean*	24
Moustache | *Mideast.*	21
Nicky's Viet. | *Sandwich*	21
99 Mi. to Philly | *Cheese Stks.*	18
Nomad | *African*	22
O.G. | *Pan-Asian*	23
Pepe | *Italian*	21
Perbacco | *Italian*	24
Prune | *Amer.*	24
Pylos | *Greek*	25
Rai Rai Ken | *Noodles*	22
NEW Ramen Setagaya | *Noodles*	–
Sal Anthony's | *Italian*	19
Samba-Lé | *Brazilian*	19
Sapporo East | *Jap.*	21
SEA | *Thai*	20
NEW Sea Salt | *Seafood*	–
Shabu-Tatsu | *Jap.*	20
S'mac | *Amer.*	19
Soba-ya | *Jap.*	24
NEW Spoon | *Jap./Pan-Asian*	–
Supper | *Italian*	24
Takahachi | *Jap.*	24
Tarallucci | *Italian*	19
Tasting Rm. | *Amer.*	22

LOCATIONS

NEW Tree | *French*	24
Tsampa | *Tibetan*	20
26 Seats | *French*	22
Two Boots | *Pizza*	18
Una Pizza | *Pizza*	23
Veniero's | *Dessert*	23
Veselka | *Ukrainian*	18
Westville | *Amer.*	23
Xunta | *Spanish*	19
Yuca Bar | *Pan-Latin*	21
Zerza | *Moroccan*	22
Zum Schneider | *German*	18

FINANCIAL DISTRICT

(South of Murray St.)

Adrienne's Pizza | *Pizza*	23
Au Mandarin | *Chinese*	20
Battery Gdns. | *Amer./Cont.*	18
Bobby Van's | *Steak*	22
Bridge Cafe | *Amer.*	22
Bull Run | *Amer.*	18
Burritoville | *Tex-Mex*	16
China Chalet | *Chinese*	19
Chipotle | *Mex.*	18
Così | *Sandwich*	16
Delmonico's | *Steak*	22
Fino | *Italian*	20
Fraunces Tavern | *Amer.*	15
Gigino | *Italian*	20
NEW Gold St. | *Eclectic*	15
Hale/Hearty | *Sandwich/Soup*	19
Harry's | *Eclectic/Steak*	22
Ise | *Jap.*	22
Joseph's | *Italian*	21
NEW Kaijou | *Jap.*	-
Lemongrass Grill | *Thai*	17
Lenny's | *Sandwich*	19
Les Halles | *French*	20
Lili's Noodle | *Noodles*	16
Mangia | *Med.*	20
MarkJoseph | *Steak*	24
P.J. Clarke's | *Pub*	17
Roy's NY | *Hawaii Reg.*	25
Smorgas Chef | *Scan.*	19
Trinity Place | *Eclectic*	18
2 West | *Steak*	21
NEW Yushi | *Jap.*	-
Zen Palate | *Veg.*	19

FLATIRON DISTRICT

(14th to 24th Sts., 6th Ave. to
Park Ave. S., excluding Union Sq.)

Angelo & Maxie's | *Steak*	21
Arezzo | *Italian*	22
Aspen | *Amer.*	20
Barbounia | *Med.*	20
NEW Bar Stuzz. | *Italian*	-

Basta Pasta | *Italian*	21
Beppe | *Italian*	23
BLT Fish | *Seafood*	23
Bolo | *Spanish*	24
Boqueria | *Spanish*	23
NEW Borough Food | *Amer.*	-
Chipotle | *Mex.*	18
City Bakery | *Bakery*	21
City Crab | *Seafood*	17
Comfort Diner | *Diner*	16
Così | *Sandwich*	16
Z Craft | *Amer.*	25
Craftbar | *Amer.*	22
Fleur de Sel | *French*	25
Giorgio's/Gramercy | *Amer.*	22
Z Gramercy Tavern | *Amer.*	27
Haru | *Jap.*	21
La Pizza Fresca | *Italian*	22
Lenny's | *Sandwich*	19
Le Pain Q. | *Bakery/Belgian*	19
L'Express | *French*	17
Lucy | *Pan-Latin*	19
Mangia | *Med.*	20
Markt | *Belgian*	19
Z Mesa Grill | *SW*	24
Mizu Sushi | *Jap.*	22
NY Burger | *Hamburgers*	18
Outback | *Steak*	14
Periyali | *Greek*	23
Petite Abeille | *Belgian*	19
Pipa | *Spanish*	21
Planet Thailand | *Thai*	19
Pump Energy | *Health*	19
Punch | *Eclectic*	19
Rickshaw Dumpling | *Chinese*	18
Z Rosa Mexicano | *Mex.*	22
Sala | *Spanish*	22
Sapa | *French/Viet.*	22
Shaffer City | *Seafood*	21
Shake Shack | *Hamburgers*	23
SushiSamba | *Brazilian/Jap.*	22
Tamarind | *Indian*	25
Tarallucci | *Italian*	19
Tossed | *Amer.*	18
Z Veritas | *Amer.*	26
Via Emilia | *Italian*	21
'wichcraft | *Sandwich*	20

GARMENT DISTRICT

(30th to 40th Sts., west of 5th)

Abigael's | *Pan-Asian*	19
Aki Sushi | *Jap.*	19
Arno | *Italian*	20
Ben's Kosher | *Deli*	17
Brother Jimmy's | *BBQ*	16
Burritoville | *Tex-Mex*	16

Chipotle	*Mex.*	18
Cho Dang Gol	*Korean*	21
Così	*Sandwich*	16
Dae Dong	*Korean*	18
Frankie/Johnnie	*Steak*	21
Gahm Mi Oak	*Korean*	22
Gray's Papaya	*Hot Dogs*	20
Hale/Hearty	*Sandwich/Soup*	19
Heartland	*Pub*	14
HK	*Amer.*	16
Kang Suh	*Korean*	20
Keens	*Steak*	24
Kum Gang San	*Korean*	21
Mandoo Bar	*Korean*	20
Nick & Stef's	*Steak*	22
Osteria Gelsi	*Italian*	24
Pump Energy	*Health*	19
Tratt. Pesce	*Italian/Seafood*	18
Tupelo Grill	*Amer.*	18
Uncle Jack's	*Steak*	23
WonJo	*Korean*	20

GRAMERCY PARK

(24th to 30th Sts., east of 5th;
14th to 24th Sts., east of Park)

Aki Sushi	*Jap.*	19
A Voce	*Italian*	25
Baluchi's	*Indian*	18
Bao Noodles	*Viet.*	20
Black Duck	*Amer./Seafood*	20
BLT Prime	*Steak*	24
Blue Smoke	*BBQ*	22
Butai	*Jap.*	22
Casa Mono	*Spanish*	25
Chennai Gdn.	*Indian/Veg.*	21
Chino's	*Asian*	22
Coppola's	*Italian*	19
Country	*Amer.*	23
Curry Leaf	*Indian*	20
Dos Caminos	*Mex.*	20
Duke's	*Southern*	16
⏢ Eleven Madison	*French*	26
Ess-a-Bagel	*Deli*	23
Friend of a Farmer	*Amer.*	17
NEW House	*Med.*	22
Houston's	*Amer.*	20
I Trulli	*Italian*	22
Jaiya Thai	*Thai*	22
Japonais	*Jap.*	20
Lady Mendl's	*Amer.*	22
La Petite Aub.	*French*	20
Les Halles	*French*	20
Los Dos Molinos	*SW*	21
Novitá	*Italian*	24
NEW Pamplona	*Spanish*	-
Paul & Jimmy's	*Italian*	19

Pete's Tavern	*Pub*	14
Petite Abeille	*Belgian*	19
Pongal	*Indian/Veg.*	21
Pongsri Thai	*Thai*	20
Porcão	*Brazilian/Steak*	21
Posto	*Pizza*	23
Pure Food/Wine	*Vegan/Veg.*	22
NEW Resto	*Belgian*	-
Rice	*Eclectic*	19
Rolf's	*German*	17
Saravanaas	*Indian*	23
⏢ Tabla	*Amer.*	25
Totonno Pizza	*Pizza*	22
Turkish Kitchen	*Turkish*	22
NEW Vamos!	*Mex.*	16
Vatan	*Indian*	23
NEW ⏢ Wakiya	*Chinese*	-
Yama	*Jap.*	24

GREENWICH VILLAGE

(Houston to 14th Sts., west of
B'way, east of 7th Ave. S.)

Aki	*Jap.*	25
Alta	*Med.*	23
Amy's Bread	*Sandwich*	23
⏢ Annisa	*Amer.*	27
A.O.C. Bedford	*Euro.*	23
Arté	*Italian*	19
Arturo's Pizzeria	*Italian*	21
⏢ Babbo	*Italian*	27
Baluchi's	*Indian*	18
NEW BarFry	*Eclectic/Jap.*	-
Bar Pitti	*Italian*	22
Bellavitae	*Italian*	22
NEW BLT Burger	*Hamburgers*	19
⏢ Blue Hill	*Amer.*	26
Blue Ribbon Bakery	*Amer.*	24
Borgo Antico	*Italian*	19
Cafe Asean	*SE Asian*	21
Cafe Español	*Spanish*	20
Cafe Loup	*French*	18
Cafe Spice	*Indian*	18
CamaJe	*Amer./French*	23
Chanto	*Jap.*	22
Chez Jacqueline	*French*	18
Chipotle	*Mex.*	18
Cornelia St. Cafe	*Amer./French*	19
Così	*Sandwich*	16
Cozy	*Hamburgers/Soup*	18
⏢ Cru	*Euro.*	26
Cuba	*Cuban*	21
Cubana Café	*Cuban*	20
Da Silvano	*Italian*	20
Deborah	*Amer.*	21
Ditch Plains	*Seafood*	17
Do Hwa	*Korean*	21

LOCATIONS

El Charro Español	*Spanish*	22	Pizza 33	*Pizza*	21
Elephant & Castle	*Pub*	17	Pó	*Italian*	25
El Paso	*Mex./Spanish*	-	NEW p*ong	*Dessert*	21
Empire Szechuan	*Chinese*	15	Prem-on Thai	*Thai*	21
Ennio & Michael	*Italian*	21	Rare B&G	*Hamburgers*	21
Fish	*Seafood*	20	Rickshaw Dumpling	*Chinese*	18
Flor's Kitchen	*Venez.*	16	Risotteria	*Italian*	21
French Roast	*French*	14	Rocco	*Italian*	20
Gobo	*Vegan/Veg.*	22	Sacred Chow	*Vegan/Veg.*	23
Gonzo	*Italian/Pizza*	21	Saigon Grill	*Viet.*	22
Z Gotham B&G	*Amer.*	27	NEW Soto	*Jap.*	-
Gradisca	*Italian*	21	Spice	*Thai*	20
Gray's Papaya	*Hot Dogs*	20	NEW Stand	*Hamburgers*	19
NEW Gus' Place	*Greek/Med.*	20	Strip House	*Steak*	25
Gusto	*Italian*	22	Z Tomoe Sushi	*Jap.*	26
Home	*Amer.*	20	Tratt. Pesce	*Italian/Seafood*	18
Hummus Place	*Israeli/Veg.*	23	Uno Chicago	*Pizza*	14
NEW Hurapan	*Thai*	20	Village	*Amer./French*	20
Il Cantinori	*Italian*	22	Villa Mosconi	*Italian*	20
Z Il Mulino	*Italian*	27	'wichcraft	*Sandwich*	20
'ino	*Italian*	24	Yama	*Jap.*	24
Jack Bistro	*French*	17		
Jane	*Amer.*	21		

HARLEM/EAST HARLEM

(110th to 157th Sts., excluding Columbia U. area)

Japonica	*Jap.*	22	Amy Ruth's	*Soul*	22
Joe's Pizza	*Pizza*	23	NEW Caminito	*Argent./Steak*	-
John's Pizzeria	*Pizza*	22	Charles' Kitchen	*Southern*	24
Kati Roll Co.	*Indian*	20	NEW China de Puebla	*Mex.*	-
Knickerbocker	*Amer.*	20	Dinosaur BBQ	*BBQ*	22
La Lanterna	*Italian*	20	El Paso Taqueria	*Mex.*	22
La Palapa	*Mex.*	20	Ginger	*Chinese*	21
Las Ramblas	*Spanish*	23	NEW Hudson R. Café	*Amer./Seafood*	-
Leela Lounge	*Indian*	22	Londel's	*Southern*	22
Le Gamin	*French*	19	Miss Mamie/Maude	*Southern*	21
Le Gigot	*French*	24	Mo-Bay	*Carib./Soul*	21
Lemongrass Grill	*Thai*	17	Native	*Eclectic*	19
Lenny's	*Sandwich*	19	Papaya King	*Hot Dogs*	20
Le Pain Q.	*Bakery/Belgian*	19	Patsy's Pizzeria	*Pizza*	20
Z Lupa	*Italian*	25	Z Rao's	*Italian*	22
Marinella	*Italian*	23	Revival	*Amer./French*	19
Mas	*Amer.*	25	River Room	*Southern*	19
Maurizio Tratt.	*Italian*	21	Sylvia's	*Soul*	19
Meskerem	*Ethiopian*	20	NEW Zoma	*Ethiopian*	23
Mexicana Mama	*Mex.*	23		
Minetta Tavern	*Italian*	18		

LITTLE ITALY

(Canal to Kenmare Sts., Bowery to Lafayette St.)

NEW Morandi	*Italian*	19	NEW Almond Flower	*Amer.*	23
Negril	*Carib./Jamaican*	20	Angelo's/Mulberry	*Italian*	23
North Sq.	*Amer.*	22	NEW Bar Martignetti	*Amer.*	18
Z One if by Land	*Amer.*	23	Da Nico	*Italian*	21
Osso Buco	*Italian*	17	8 Mile Creek	*Australian*	20
Otto	*Pizza*	22	Ferrara	*Bakery*	22
Patsy's Pizzeria	*Pizza*	20	Grotta Azzurra	*Italian*	18
Peanut Butter Co.	*Sandwich*	20	Il Cortile	*Italian*	23
Z Pearl Oyster	*Seafood*	26		
NEW Perilla	*Amer.*	-		
Piadina	*Italian*	20		

Il Fornaio | *Italian* 21
Il Palazzo | *Italian* 23
La Esquina | *Mex.* 21
La Mela | *Italian* 18
Nyonya | *Malaysian* 22
Pellegrino's | *Italian* 22
Pho Bang | *Viet.* 21
Positano | *Italian* 21
Sal Anthony's | *Italian* 19
Taormina | *Italian* 24
Umberto's | *Italian/Seafood* 18
Vincent's | *Italian* 21

LOWER EAST SIDE

(Houston to Canal Sts., east of Bowery)

Alias | *Amer.* 23
ápizz | *Italian* 24
Azul Bistro | *Argent./Steak* 22
Bereket | *Turkish* 18
Bondi Rd. | *Australian* 21
Brown Café | *Amer.* 25
Clinton St. Baking | *Amer.* 24
Congee | *Chinese* 21
Cube 63 | *Jap.* 21
Essex | *Amer.* 20
Falai | *Italian* 25
Frankies Spuntino | *Italian* 24
Freemans | *Amer.* 21
NEW Georgia's/BBQ | *BBQ* -
'inoteca | *Italian* 23
NEW Isabella's Oven | *Pizza* -
NEW Kampuchea | *Cambodian* 20
Katz's Deli | *Deli* 23
Kuma Inn | *Filipino/Thai* 24
Les Enfants | *African/French* 19
Little Giant | *Amer.* 22
Loreley | *German* 18
Oliva | *Spanish* 20
NEW Open/Sesame | *Thai* -
Orchard, The | *Amer.* 24
Paladar | *Nuevo Latino* 18
NEW Rayuela | *Pan-Latin* -
NEW Régate | *French* -
Sachiko's | *Jap.* 25
Salt | *Amer.* 21
Sammy's Roum. | *Jewish* 19
NEW savorNY | *Eclectic* -
Schiller's | *Eclectic* 18
NEW Spitzer's | *Amer.* -
Stanton Social | *Eclectic* 23
NEW Sticky Rice | *Thai* 19
Suba | *Spanish* 21
teany | *Vegan/Veg.* 18
Thor | *Amer.* 18
Tides | *Seafood* 24

Two Boots | *Pizza* 18
wd-50 | *Amer./Eclectic* 23
Whole Foods | *Eclectic/Health* 19
Zucco | *French* 22

MEATPACKING DISTRICT

(Gansevoort to 15th Sts., west of 9th Ave.)

Z Buddha Bar | *Asian Fusion* 19
Fig & Olive | *Med.* 20
5 Ninth | *Eclectic* 19
Florent | *French* 20
Highline | *Thai* 19
NEW Inn LW12 | *Amer.* 19
NEW Los Dados | *Mex.* -
Macelleria | *Italian/Steak* 21
Nero | *Italian* 20
Old Homestead | *Steak* 23
One | *Amer.* 18
Ono | *Jap.* 21
Paradou | *French* 19
Z Pastis | *French* 21
Pop Burger | *Amer.* 19
NEW Revel | *Eclectic* -
Son Cubano | *Cuban* 21
Z Spice Market | *SE Asian* 22
NEW STK | *Steak* 20
Valbella | *Italian* 24
Vento | *Italian* 19

MURRAY HILL

(30th to 40th Sts., east of 5th)

Ali Baba | *Turkish* 23
AQ Cafe | *Scan.* 20
Aquamarine | *Pan-Asian* 21
Z Artisanal | *French* 23
Z Asia de Cuba | *Asian/Cuban* 23
Barbès | *French/Moroccan* 22
Barking Dog | *Amer.* 15
Better Burger | *Hamburgers* 15
Blockheads Burritos | *Mex.* 17
Carl's Steaks | *Cheese Stks.* 22
Cosette | *French* 21
Da Ciro | *Italian/Pizza* 21
Duke's | *Southern* 16
El Parador Cafe | *Mex.* 20
El Pote | *Spanish* 21
Ethos | *Greek* 22
Evergreen | *Chinese* 19
Fino | *Italian* 20
Grand Sichuan | *Chinese* 22
Hangawi | *Korean* 23
Iron Sushi | *Jap.* 19
Jackson Hole | *Amer.* 17
Josie's | *Eclectic* 19
La Giara | *Italian* 19

LOCATIONS

Lemongrass Grill | *Thai*	17
Madison Bistro | *French*	18
Mee Noodle | *Noodles*	18
Mishima | *Jap.*	23
Morgan | *Amer.*	20
Notaro | *Italian*	20
Pasticcio | *Italian*	19
Patsy's Pizzeria | *Pizza*	20
Penelope | *Amer.*	21
Pizza 33 | *Pizza*	21
Pump Energy | *Health*	19
Rare B&G | *Hamburgers*	21
Rossini's | *Italian*	23
Salute! | *Italian/Med.*	19
Sarge's Deli | *Deli*	19
Sushi Sen-nin | *Jap.*	25
Todai | *Jap./Seafood*	18
Tratt. Alba | *Italian*	20
Trio | *Med.*	21
Vezzo | *Pizza*	21
Villa Berulia | *Italian*	23
Water Club | *Amer.*	20
'wichcraft | *Sandwich*	20
Wolfgang's | *Steak*	25
Wu Liang Ye | *Chinese*	21

NOHO

(Houston to 4th Sts., Bowery to
B'way)

Aroma | *Italian*	24
Bianca | *Italian*	22
Bond St. | *Jap.*	25
Chinatown Brass. | *Chinese*	21
5 Points | *Amer./Med.*	22
Great Jones Cafe | *Cajun*	19
Il Buco | *Italian/Med.*	25
NEW Mercat | *Spanish*	-
NoHo Star | *Amer.*	18
Rice | *Eclectic*	19
Sala | *Spanish*	22
Serafina | *Italian*	18
Two Boots | *Pizza*	18

NOLITA

(Houston to Kenmare Sts.,
Bowery to Lafayette St.)

barmarché | *Amer.*	19
Bread | *Sandwich*	19
Cafe Colonial | *Brazilian*	20
Cafe Gitane | *French/Moroccan*	20
Café Habana/Outpost | *Cuban/Mex.*	22
NEW Ed's Lobster | *Seafood*	23
Ghenet | *Ethiopian*	22
Jacques | *French*	18
Kitchen Club | *French/Jap.*	22
Le Jardin Bistro | *French*	18

Lombardi's | *Pizza*	24
Mexican Radio | *Mex.*	18
NEW Noble Food | *Amer.*	-
Peasant | *Italian*	24
Public | *Eclectic*	23
Tasting Rm. | *Amer.*	22

SOHO

(Canal to Houston Sts.,
west of Lafayette St.)

Ama | *Italian*	22
Z Aquagrill | *Seafood*	26
Aurora | *Italian*	26
NEW Babouche | *French/Moroccan*	20
Z Balthazar | *French*	23
Baluchi's | *Indian*	18
Barolo | *Italian*	18
Bistro Les Amis | *French*	21
Z Blue Ribbon | *Amer.*	25
Z Blue Ribbon Sushi | *Jap.*	25
Cendrillon | *Asian/Filipino*	20
Centovini | *Italian*	21
Chipotle | *Mex.*	18
Cipriani D'twn | *Italian*	20
Dani | *Italian*	20
Dos Caminos | *Mex.*	20
Falai | *Italian*	25
Félix | *French*	16
Fiamma Osteria | *Italian*	25
NEW FR.OG | *Eclectic/French*	21
Giorgione | *Italian*	23
Hampton Chutney | *Indian*	20
HQ | *Amer.*	19
Ideya | *Carib.*	20
Il Corallo | *Italian*	22
I Tre Merli | *Italian*	18
Ivo & Lulu | *Carib./French*	22
Jean Claude | *French*	22
Kelley/Ping | *Pan-Asian*	16
Kin Khao | *Thai*	22
Z Kittichai | *Thai*	23
L'Ecole | *French*	23
Le Pain Q. | *Bakery/Belgian*	19
Lucky Strike | *French*	17
Lure Fishbar | *Seafood*	23
Mercer Kitchen | *Amer./French*	22
Mezzogiorno | *Italian*	20
Novecento | *Argent./Steak*	22
Omen | *Jap.*	25
Once Upon a Tart | *Coffee*	22
Peep | *Thai*	19
Pepe | *Italian*	21
NEW Provence | *French*	21
Raoul's | *French*	24
Salt | *Amer.*	21

Savoy | *Amer./Med.* 24
Snack | *Greek* 24
NEW Tailor | *Dessert* -
12 Chairs | *Amer./Mideast.* 19
'wichcraft | *Sandwich* 20
Woo Lae Oak | *Korean* 23
Zoë | *Amer.* 20

SOUTH STREET SEAPORT

Cabana | *Nuevo Latino* 21
Heartland | *Pub* 14
NEW Il Brigante | *Italian* 21
NEW Nelson Blue | *New Zealand* -
NEW Stella Maris | *Euro.* -
NEW Suteishi | *Jap.* 25
Uno Chicago | *Pizza* 14

TRIBECA

(Canal to Murray Sts.,
west of B'way)
Acappella | *Italian* 23
Arqua | *Italian* 22
Azafran | *Spanish* 21
Baluchi's | *Indian* 18
Blaue Gans | *Austrian/German* 20
Z Bouley | *French* 28
Z Bouley, Upstairs | *Eclectic* 26
Bread | *Italian* 19
Bubby's | *Amer.* 18
Burritoville | *Tex-Mex* 16
Capsouto Frères | *French* 24
Carl's Steaks | *Cheese Stks.* 22
Centrico | *Mex.* 20
Z Chanterelle | *French* 27
Churrascaria | *Brazilian* 23
City Hall | *Seafood/Steak* 21
Z Danube | *Austrian* 26
NEW Dennis Foy | *Amer.* 24
Devin Tavern | *Amer.* 18
Duane Park | *Amer.* 24
Dylan Prime | *Steak* 24
Ecco | *Italian* 21
Edward's | *Amer.* 16
NEW Estancia | *Argent./Italian* 21
F.illi Ponte | *Italian* 21
Flor de Sol | *Spanish* 20
fresh | *Seafood* 24
Gigino | *Italian* 20
Harrison, The | *Amer.* 24
Z Il Giglio | *Italian* 26
Il Mattone | *Italian/Pizza* 21
Industria | *Argent./Steak* 20
Kitchenette | *Southern* 19
Landmarc | *French* 23

NEW Mai House | *Viet.* 21
Mary Ann's | *Tex-Mex* 15
Max | *Italian* 23
Z Megu | *Jap.* 24
Mr. Chow | *Chinese* 20
Nam | *Viet.* 22
Ninja | *Jap.* 19
Z Nobu | *Jap.* 27
Odeon | *Amer./French* 19
Pepolino | *Italian* 24
Petite Abeille | *Belgian* 19
Roc | *Italian* 21
NEW Rosanjin | *Jap.* 25
Salaam Bombay | *Indian* 20
Z Scalini Fedeli | *Italian* 26
Soda Shop | *Amer./Dessert* 19
Takahachi | *Jap.* 24
Thalassa | *Greek/Seafood* 22
Tribeca Grill | *Amer.* 22
Turks & Frogs | *Turkish* 20
VietCafé | *Viet.* 21
Walker's | *Pub* 17
'wichcraft | *Sandwich* 20
Wolfgang's | *Steak* 25
Zutto | *Jap.* 21

UNION SQUARE

(14th to 17th Sts., 5th Ave.
to Union Sq. E.)
Z Blue Water | *Seafood* 23
Chat 'n Chew | *Amer.* 16
Chop't Creative | *Amer.* 20
Coffee Shop | *Amer./Brazilian* 15
NEW 15 East | *Jap.* 26
Havana Central | *Cuban* 17
Heartland | *Pub* 14
Max Brenner | *Dessert* 17
Olives | *Med.* 22
Republic | *Pan-Asian* 18
Steak Frites | *French* 18
Z Tocqueville | *Amer./French* 26
Z Union Sq. Cafe | *Amer.* 26
Whole Foods | *Eclectic/Health* 19
Zen Palate | *Veg.* 19

WASHINGTON HTS./ INWOOD

(North of W. 157th St.)
Dallas BBQ | *BBQ* 15
El Malecon | *Dominican* 21
Empire Szechuan | *Chinese* 15
NEW Guadalupe | *Mex.* 19
Hispaniola | *Dominican* 21
New Leaf | *Amer.* 20
107 West | *Cajun/Tex-Mex* 18
Park Terrace | *French/Moroccan* 22

LOCATIONS

WEST 40s

AJ Maxwell's	Steak	22
Akdeniz	Turkish	20
Alfredo of Rome	Italian	19
Algonquin	Amer.	16
Amarone	Italian	19
Amy's Bread	Sandwich	23
Angus McIndoe	Amer.	16
Baldoria	Italian	22
Barbetta	Italian	20
Basilica	Italian	19
Ⓩ Becco	Italian	22
Better Burger	Hamburgers	15
Blue Fin	Seafood	22
Bond 45	Italian	20
Breeze	French/Thai	20
Brooklyn Diner	Diner	17
Bryant Park	Amer.	17
B. Smith's	Southern	19
Bubba Gump	Amer./Seafood	14
Burritoville	Tex-Mex	16
Cafe Un Deux	French	16
Cara Mia	Italian	20
Ⓩ Carmine's	Italian	19
Cascina	Italian	18
Chez Josephine	French	20
Chimichurri Grill	Argent./Steak	21
Chipotle	Mex.	18
Churrascaria	Brazilian	23
City Lobster	Seafood	18
Così	Sandwich	16
Ⓩ Daisy May's	BBQ	24
Dallas BBQ	BBQ	15
Ⓩ db Bistro Moderne	French	25
Ⓩ Del Frisco's	Steak	25
Delta Grill	Cajun/Creole	19
Dervish Turk.	Turkish	19
District	Amer.	20
Don Giovanni	Italian	17
Edison	Coffee Shop	15
Energy Kitchen	Health	18
Esca	Italian/Seafood	25
ESPN Zone	Amer.	12
etc. etc.	Italian	20
FireBird	Russian	18
44/X Hell's Kit.	Amer.	21
Frankie/Johnnie	Steak	21
Ⓩ Gari/Sushi	Jap.	26
Hakata Grill	Jap.	20
Hale/Hearty	Sandwich/Soup	19
Hallo Berlin	German	17
Hard Rock Cafe	Amer.	13
Haru	Jap.	21
Havana Central	Cuban	17
NEW Hawaiian Tropic	Amer.	16

Heartland	Pub	14
Hell's Kitchen	Mex.	23
Jewel of India	Indian	20
Joe Allen	Amer.	17
John's Pizzeria	Pizza	22
Junior's	Diner	18
Kati Roll Co.	Indian	20
Kellari Taverna	Greek	23
Kodama	Jap.	19
Koi	Jap.	23
Kyma	Greek	18
NEW Kyotofu	Dessert	23
La Locanda Vini	Italian	21
La Masseria	Italian	22
Landmark Tavern	Amer./Irish	18
La Rivista	Italian	18
Lattanzi	Italian	22
Le Madeleine	French	20
Le Marais	French/Steak	20
Lenny's	Sandwich	19
Le Rivage	French	19
Marseille	French/Med.	20
Meskerem	Ethiopian	20
NEW Metro Marché	French	19
Monster Sushi	Jap.	18
Morrell Wine Bar	Amer.	19
Ollie's	Chinese	16
Orso	Italian	23
Osteria al Doge	Italian	20
Pam Real Thai	Thai	22
Pietrasanta	Italian	19
Pigalle	French	18
Pongsri Thai	Thai	20
Rachel's American	Amer.	17
Ⓩ Rainbow Room/Grill	Italian	19
Re Sette	Italian	23
Ruby Foo's	Pan-Asian	19
Sardi's	Cont.	16
Scarlatto	Italian	21
Sea Grill	Seafood	24
Shula's	Steak	20
NEW Spice Fusion	Indian	–
NEW Spotlight Live	Amer.	–
Sushiden	Jap.	25
Sushi Zen	Jap.	25
Tintol	Portug.	21
Tony's Di Napoli	Italian	18
Tossed	Amer.	18
Tratt. Dopo	Italian	16
Triomphe	French	24
Turkish Cuisine	Turkish	20
Two Boots	Pizza	18
Utsav	Indian	21
Via Brasil	Brazilian/Steak	18
View, The	Cont.	18

Virgil's Real BBQ	*BBQ*	20
West Bank Cafe	*Amer.*	20
'wichcraft	*Sandwich*	20
Wu Liang Ye	*Chinese*	21
Zen Palate	*Veg.*	19

WEST 50s

Abboccato	*Italian*	22
Afghan Kebab	*Afghan*	19
Aki Sushi	*Jap.*	19
NEW Amalia	*Med.*	21
Angelo's Pizza	*Pizza*	20
NEW Anthos	*Greek*	25
Azuri Cafe	*Israeli*	25
Baluchi's	*Indian*	18
Bann	*Korean*	24
Z Bar Americain	*Amer.*	23
NEW Basso56	*Italian*	23
Bay Leaf	*Indian*	19
Beacon	*Amer.*	22
Bello	*Italian*	20
Ben Benson's	*Steak*	24
BG	*Amer.*	20
Blockheads Burritos	*Mex.*	17
NEW BLT Market	*Amer.*	-
bluechili	*Pan-Asian*	19
Bobby Van's	*Steak*	22
Bombay Palace	*Indian*	18
Brasserie 8½	*French*	22
Brass. Ruhlmann	*French*	17
Bricco	*Italian*	19
Brooklyn Diner	*Diner*	17
burger joint	*Hamburgers*	24
Cafe Spice	*Indian*	18
Caffe Cielo	*Italian*	19
Z Carnegie Deli	*Deli*	21
Chez Napoléon	*French*	20
China Grill	*Asian*	22
Così	*Sandwich*	16
Da Tommaso	*Italian*	20
Eatery	*Amer.*	19
El Centro	*Mex.*	18
Empanada Mama	*S Amer.*	20
Gallagher's	*Steak*	20
NEW Gaucho	*Argent./Steak*	-
NEW Z Gordon Ramsay	*French*	25
NEW Grayz	*Eclectic*	-
Greek Kitchen	*Greek*	19
Guantanamera	*Cuban*	22
Hale/Hearty	*Sandwich/Soup*	19
Heartland	*Pub*	14
Hudson Cafeteria	*Amer./Eclectic*	19
Il Gattopardo	*Italian*	23
Z Il Tinello	*Italian*	26
NEW Insieme	*Italian*	26
Ise	*Jap.*	22

Island Burgers	*Hamburgers*	22
Joe's Shanghai	*Chinese*	22
NEW Johnny Utah	*BBQ/SW*	-
NEW Kobe Club	*Steak*	20
La Bonne Soupe	*French*	18
La Vineria	*Italian*	20
Z Le Bernardin	*French/Seafood*	28
Le Pain Q.	*Bakery/Belgian*	19
Lili's Noodle	*Noodles*	16
Maison	*French*	17
Mangia	*Med.*	20
Maria Pia	*Italian*	19
NEW Maze	*French*	23
McCormick/Schmick	*Seafood*	20
Mee Noodle	*Noodles*	18
Menchanko-tei	*Noodles*	20
Michael's	*Calif.*	21
Z Milos	*Greek/Seafood*	26
Moda	*Italian/Med.*	-
Z Modern, The	*Amer./French*	26
Molyvos	*Greek*	22
NEW Natsumi	*Italian/Jap.*	-
Nino's	*Italian*	21
Z Nobu 57	*Jap.*	26
Nocello	*Italian*	21
Nook	*Eclectic*	22
Norma's	*Amer.*	25
NEW Omido	*Jap.*	-
Osteria del Circo	*Italian*	22
Z Palm	*Steak*	24
Patsy's	*Italian*	21
Pepe	*Italian*	21
Petrossian	*Cont./French*	24
Piano Due	*Italian*	25
Pump Energy	*Health*	19
Puttanesca	*Italian*	18
Quality Meats	*Amer./Steak*	24
Redeye Grill	*Amer./Seafood*	20
Remi	*Italian*	22
René Pujol	*French*	22
Rice 'n' Beans	*Brazilian*	19
Roberto Passon	*Italian*	22
Rock Ctr.	*Amer.*	19
Rue 57	*French*	19
Russian Samovar	*Cont.*	19
NEW Russian Tea	*Cont./Russian*	19
Ruth's Chris	*Steak*	23
San Domenico	*Italian*	23
Sarabeth's	*Amer.*	20
Serafina	*Italian*	18
Shelly's Tratt.	*Italian*	20
Soba Nippon	*Jap.*	22
Sosa Borella	*Argent./Italian*	21
Stage Deli	*Deli*	20

LOCATIONS

Sugiyama	*Jap.*	27
Sushiya	*Jap.*	20
Taboon	*Med./Mideast.*	24
Tang Pavilion	*Chinese*	23
NEW Ted's Montana	*Amer.*	15
Thalia	*Amer.*	21
NEW Toloache	*Mex.*	–
Topaz Thai	*Thai*	20
Town	*Amer.*	24
Tratt. Dell'Arte	*Italian*	22
Tuscan Sq.	*Italian*	16
21 Club	*Amer.*	22
Uncle Nick's	*Greek*	19
ViceVersa	*Italian*	23
Victor's Cafe	*Cuban*	21
Vynl	*Amer./Thai*	17
Whym	*Amer.*	21
Wondee Siam	*Thai*	22
Xing	*Asian Fusion*	21
Yakitori Totto	*Jap.*	26
Zona Rosa	*Mex.*	18

WEST 60s

Asiate	*French/Jap.*	24
Bouchon Bakery	*Amer./French*	23
Café des Artistes	*French*	22
Cafe Fiorello	*Italian*	20
Café Gray	*French*	25
Empire Szechuan	*Chinese*	15
Gabriel's	*Italian*	22
Grand Tier	*Amer./Cont.*	19
Jean Georges	*French*	28
Josephina	*Amer.*	18
La Boîte en Bois	*French*	21
Landmarc	*French*	23
Le Pain Q.	*Bakery/Belgian*	19
Levana	*Med.*	20
Masa/Bar Masa	*Jap.*	27
Nick & Toni's	*Med.*	18
Ollie's	*Chinese*	16
O'Neals'	*Amer.*	17
Per Se	*Amer./French*	28
Picholine	*French/Med.*	27
P.J. Clarke's	*Pub*	17
Porter House NY	*Steak*	22
Rosa Mexicano	*Mex.*	22
Sapphire	*Indian*	20
Shun Lee Cafe	*Chinese*	21
Shun Lee West	*Chinese*	23
Tavern on Green	*Amer.*	15
Telepan	*Amer.*	25
Whole Foods	*Eclectic/Health*	19

WEST 70s

Alice's Tea Cup	*Amer.*	19
Arté Café	*Italian*	18

Bello Sguardo	*Med.*	19
Bettola	*Italian*	21
Big Nick's Burger	*Hamburgers*	17
Bistro Cassis	*French*	20
Burritoville	*Tex-Mex*	16
Café Frida	*Mex.*	19
Cafe Luxembourg	*French*	20
Cafe Ronda	*Med./ S Amer.*	18
'Cesca	*Italian*	23
China Fun	*Chinese*	16
Citrus B&G	*Asian/Nuevo Latino*	20
Compass	*Amer.*	22
Coppola's	*Italian*	18
Così	*Sandwich*	16
Dallas BBQ	*BBQ*	15
NEW Earthen Oven	*Indian*	21
Epices/Traiteur	*Med./Tunisian*	21
Fairway Cafe	*Amer.*	18
Gari/Sushi	*Jap.*	26
Gray's Papaya	*Hot Dogs*	20
Hummus Place	*Israeli/Veg.*	23
Isabella's	*Amer./Med.*	20
Jacques-Imo's	*Cajun/Creole*	17
Josie's	*Eclectic*	19
NEW Kefi	*Greek*	23
La Grolla	*Italian*	20
La Vela	*Italian*	19
Lenny's	*Sandwich*	19
Le Pain Q.	*Bakery/Belgian*	19
Mughlai	*Indian*	19
Nice Matin	*French/Med.*	20
Ocean Grill	*Seafood*	23
Pappardella	*Italian*	19
Pasha	*Turkish*	21
Patsy's Pizzeria	*Pizza*	20
Pomodoro Rosso	*Italian*	21
Ruby Foo's	*Pan-Asian*	19
Sambuca	*Italian*	18
San Luigi	*Italian*	16
Savann	*French/Med.*	19
Scaletta	*Italian*	21
Swagat Indian	*Indian*	19
Tenzan	*Jap.*	23
Viand	*Coffee Shop*	16

WEST 80s

Aix Brasserie	*French*	20
Artie's Deli	*Deli*	18
Barney Greengrass	*Deli*	23
Bistro Citron	*French*	21
Brother Jimmy's	*BBQ*	16
Cafe Con Leche	*Cuban/Dominican*	18
Cafe Lalo	*Coffee/Dessert*	19
Calle Ocho	*Nuevo Latino*	22
Celeste	*Italian*	24

Columbus Bakery | *Bakery* 18
Docks Oyster | *Seafood* 19
Edgar's Cafe | *Coffee* 18
EJ's Luncheonette | *Amer.* 15
Flor de Mayo | *Chinese/Peruvian* 20
French Roast | *French* 14
Good Enough/Eat | *Amer.* 20
Hampton Chutney | *Indian* 20
Haru | *Jap.* 21
Jackson Hole | *Amer.* 17
La Mirabelle | *French* 22
Land | *Thai* 23
Lenny's | *Sandwich* 19
Loft | *French/Italian* 17
Nëo Sushi | *Jap.* 22
Neptune Rm. | *Seafood* 22
Ollie's | *Chinese* 16
🅉 Ouest | *Amer.* 25
Popover Cafe | *Amer.* 18
Rain | *Pan-Asian* 21
Roppongi | *Jap.* 19
Sarabeth's | *Amer.* 20
Sol y Sombra | *Spanish* 19
Spiga | *Italian* 21
Sushi Hana | *Jap.* 21
Uno Chicago | *Pizza* 14
Vynl | *Amer./Thai* 17
Zabar's Cafe | *Deli* 20
Zeytin | *Turkish* 19

WEST 90s

Acqua | *Italian* 18
Alouette | *French* 20
NEW Asiakan | *Jap./Pan-Asian* 19
Cafe Con Leche | 18
  Cuban/Dominican
🅉 Carmine's | *Italian* 19
El Malecon | *Dominican* 21
Gabriela's | *Mex.* 17
Gennaro | *Italian* 25
Lemongrass Grill | *Thai* 17
Lisca | *Italian* 20
Mary Ann's | *Tex-Mex* 15
Pio Pio | *Peruvian* 23
Regional | *Italian* 17
Roth's Westside | *Steak* 19
Saigon Grill | *Viet.* 22
Tratt. Pesce | *Italian/Seafood* 18
Yuki Sushi | *Jap.* 21

WEST 100s

(See also Harlem/East Harlem)
Awash | *Ethiopian* 22
Bistro Ten 18 | *Amer.* 20
NEW Cafe & Wine | -
  Carib./French
Café du Soleil | *French/Med.* 19

Empire Szechuan | *Chinese* 15
Flor de Mayo | *Chinese/Peruvian* 20
Havana Central | *Cuban* 17
Indus Valley | *Indian* 23
Kitchenette | *Southern* 19
Le Monde | *French* 17
Mamá Mexico | *Mex.* 20
Max | *Italian* 23
Métisse | *French* 19
Mill Korean | *Korean* 19
Noche Mexicana | *Mex.* 22
Ollie's | *Chinese* 16
107 West | *Cajun/Tex-Mex* 18
PicNic Market | *Deli/French* 20
Pisticci | *Italian* 23
Rack & Soul | *BBQ/Southern* 20
Sezz Medi' | *Med./Pizza* 21
Symposium | *Greek* 20
Terrace in the Sky | *French/Med.* 22
Tokyo Pop | *Jap.* 20
Tomo Sushi | *Jap.* 20
Turkuaz | *Turkish* 19
V&T | *Italian/Pizza* 18

WEST VILLAGE

(Houston to 14th Sts., west of 7th
Ave. S., excluding Meatpacking
District)
Agave | *SW* 18
Alfama | *Portug.* 22
Antica Venezia | *Italian* 23
A.O.C. | *French* 20
August | *Euro.* 23
Barbuto | *Italian* 22
Burritoville | *Tex-Mex* 16
NEW Cafe Cluny | *Amer./French* 19
Café de Bruxelles | *Belgian* 21
Casa | *Brazilian* 22
NEW Centro Vinoteca | *Italian* -
Chow Bar | *Asian Fusion* 21
Corner Bistro | *Hamburgers* 22
Cowgirl | *SW* 16
Crispo | *Italian* 23
Da Andrea | *Italian* 24
Dirty Bird | *Amer.* 17
El Faro | *Spanish* 23
Employees Only | *Euro.* 18
Energy Kitchen | *Health* 18
EN Japanese | *Jap.* 22
Extra Virgin | *Med.* 21
Fatty Crab | *Malaysian* 21
Frederick's | *French/Med.* 19
Gavroche | *French* 19
good | *Amer.* 20
Havana Alma | *Cuban* 21
I Tre Merli | *Italian* 18

Jarnac	*Med.*	22
La Focaccia	*Italian*	20
La Ripaille	*French*	23
Le Gamin	*French*	19
Lima's Taste	*Peruvian*	21
Little Owl	*Amer./Med.*	24
Malatesta	*Italian*	21
Maremma	*Italian*	21
Mary's Fish Camp	*Seafood*	25
Mercadito	*Mex.*	22
Mexicana Mama	*Mex.*	24
Mi Cocina	*Mex.*	22
Miracle Grill	*SW*	18
Monster Sushi	*Jap.*	18
Moustache	*Mideast.*	21
Osteria del Sole	*Italian*	21
Papaya King	*Hot Dogs*	20
Paris Commune	*French*	18
Pepe	*Italian*	21
Perry St.	*Amer.*	24
Petite Abeille	*Belgian*	19
Philip Marie	*Amer.*	20
Piccolo Angolo	*Italian*	25
Pink Tea Cup	*Soul/Southern*	20
Place, The	*Amer./Med.*	21
Sant Ambroeus	*Italian*	22
Sevilla	*Spanish*	23
Smorgas Chef	*Scan.*	19
Snack Taverna	*Greek*	22
NEW Socialista	*Cuban*	-
Spotted Pig	*British*	22
Surya	*Indian*	24
SushiSamba	*Brazilian/Jap.*	22
Tartine	*French*	22
NEW Tasca	*Spanish*	20
Tea & Sympathy	*British*	19
Two Boots	*Pizza*	18
Wallsé	*Austrian*	26
NEW Z Waverly Inn	*Amer.*	18
Westville	*Amer.*	23
Wild Ginger	*Thai*	19

Bronx

Artie's	*Seafood/Steak*	22
Beccofino	*Italian*	22
Bruckner B&G	*Amer.*	21
Coals	*Pizza*	22
Dominick's	*Italian*	22
El Malecon	*Dominican*	21
Enzo's	*Italian*	23
F & J Pine	*Italian*	20
Fratelli	*Italian*	21
Jake's	*Steak*	24
Le Refuge Inn	*French*	24
Liebman's	*Deli*	19

Lobster Box	*Seafood*	17
Madison's	*Italian*	20
Mario's	*Italian*	22
Park Place	*Cont.*	20
Pasquale's Rigoletto	*Italian*	23
Patricia's	*Italian*	22
Pio Pio	*Peruvian*	23
Portofino's	*Italian/Seafood*	19
Riverdale Gdn.	*Amer.*	24
Z Roberto	*Italian*	27
Siam Sq.	*Thai*	24
Tosca Café	*Italian*	21
Umberto's	*Italian/Seafood*	18
Willie's	*Steak*	23

Brooklyn

BAY RIDGE

Agnanti	*Greek*	24
Areo	*Italian*	25
Austin's Steak	*Steak*	21
Cebu	*Cont.*	21
Chadwick's	*Amer.*	22
Chianti	*Italian*	21
Eliá	*Greek*	25
Embers	*Steak*	22
Greenhouse Café	*Amer.*	19
Omonia Cafe	*Greek*	19
101	*Amer./Italian*	19
Pearl Room	*Seafood*	23
Z Tanoreen	*Med./Mideast.*	27
Tuscany Grill	*Italian*	24
Uno Chicago	*Pizza*	14

BENSONHURST

L & B Spumoni	*Dessert/Pizza*	22
Tenzan	*Jap.*	23

BOERUM HILL

(See map on page 298)

Chance	*Pan-Asian*	21
D'twn Atlantic	*Amer.*	19
Jolie	*French*	20
NEW Ki Sushi	*Jap.*	25
NEW Lunetta	*Italian*	20
Nicky's Viet.	*Sandwich*	21
Z Saul	*Amer.*	27

BRIGHTON BEACH

Mr. Tang	*Chinese*	19

BROOKLYN HEIGHTS

(See map on page 298)

Caffe Buon Gusto	*Italian*	18
Chipotle	*Mex.*	18
ChipShop	*British*	18
NEW Five Guys	*Hamburgers*	-
Hale/Hearty	*Sandwich/Soup*	19

Henry's End | *Amer.*	25
Jack the Horse | *Amer.*	20
NEW Le Petit Marché | *French*	22
Noodle Pudding | *Italian*	24
Queen | *Italian*	24

CARROLL GARDENS

(See map on page 298)

Alma | *Mex.*	20
Bouillabaisse 126 | *French*	22
Chestnut | *Amer.*	23
Cubana Café | *Cuban*	20
Fragole | *Italian*	23
Frankies Spuntino | *Italian*	24
☑ Grocery | *Amer.*	26
NEW Lucali | *Pizza*	27
Marco Polo | *Italian*	20
Panino'teca | *Italian*	18
Patois | *French*	21
NEW Petite Crev. | *Seafood*	24
Pó | *Italian*	25
Provence/Boite | *Bakery/French*	20
Savoia | *Pizza*	21
Zaytoons | *Mideast.*	22

CLINTON HILL

(See map on page 298)

NEW Chez Lola | *French*	-
Locanda Vini | *Italian*	26

COBBLE HILL

(See map on page 298)

Bocca Lupo | *Italian*	21
Cafe Luluc | *French*	20
NEW Carniceria | *Steak*	-
Cube 63 | *Jap.*	21
Joya | *Thai*	23
Lemongrass Grill | *Thai*	17
Miriam | *Israeli/Med.*	21
Osaka | *Jap.*	21
Quercy | *French*	20
Sweet Melissa | *Dessert/Sandwich*	21

CONEY ISLAND

Gargiulo's | *Italian*	21
Totonno Pizza | *Pizza*	22

DITMAS PARK

Farm/Adderley | *Amer.*	23

DOWNTOWN

(See map on page 298)

Dallas BBQ | *BBQ*	15
Junior's | *Diner*	18

DUMBO

(See map on page 298)

Bubby's | *Amer.*	18
5 Front | *Amer.*	21

☑ Grimaldi's | *Pizza*	25
Pete's Downtown | *Italian*	18
Rice | *Eclectic*	19
☑ River Café | *Amer.*	26
Superfine | *Med.*	18

DYKER HEIGHTS

Outback | *Steak*	14
Tommaso | *Italian*	23

FORT GREENE

(See map on page 298)

Bonita | *Mex.*	19
Chez Oskar | *French*	19
Café Habana/Outpost | *Cuban/Mex.*	22
Ici | *Amer./French*	22
Loulou | *French*	22
Luz | *Nuevo Latino*	24
Olea | *Med.*	20
Rice | *Eclectic*	19
NEW 67 Burger | *Hamburgers*	21
NEW Smoke Joint | *BBQ*	23
Thomas Beisl | *Austrian*	19
Zaytoons | *Mideast.*	22

GRAVESEND

Fiorentino's | *Italian*	19
Sahara | *Turkish*	20

GREENPOINT

Paloma | *Amer.*	19
Queen's Hideaway | *Amer.*	20

MIDWOOD

☑ Di Fara | *Pizza*	27
Joe's Pizza | *Pizza*	23

MILL BASIN

La Villa Pizzeria | *Italian*	21
Mill Basin Deli | *Deli*	21

PARK SLOPE

(See map on page 298)

NEW Alchemy | *Amer.*	18
☑ Al Di La | *Italian*	26
Anthony's | *Italian*	21
applewood | *Amer.*	25
NEW Babouche | *French/Moroccan*	20
Bar Toto | *Italian*	19
Belleville | *French*	18
Beso | *Nuevo Latino*	19
☑ Blue Ribbon | *Amer.*	25
☑ Blue Ribbon Sushi | *Jap.*	25
Bogota Latin | *Pan-Latin*	21
Brooklyn Fish | *Seafood*	23
Cafe Steinhof | *Austrian*	19
NEW Chiles/Chocolate | *Mex.*	18

ChipShop | *British*	18
Chocolate Rm. | *Dessert*	25
Cocotte | *Amer./French*	20
Conviv. Osteria | *Med.*	25
NEW Flatbush Farm | *Amer.*	19
Joe's Pizza | *Pizza*	23
La Taqueria/Rachel | *Mex.*	19
La Villa Pizzeria | *Italian*	21
Lemongrass Grill | *Thai*	17
Little D | *Amer./Eclectic*	20
Long Tan | *Thai*	19
Magnolia | *Amer.*	19
Miracle Grill | *SW*	18
Miriam | *Israeli/Med.*	21
NEW Moim | *Korean*	-
Moutarde | *French*	18
Nana | *Asian Fusion*	21
NEW NoNO | *Cajun/Creole*	19
NEW Palo Santo | *Pan-Latin*	25
Press 195 | *Sandwich*	20
Rose Water | *Amer.*	25
Scottadito | *Italian*	19
Sette Enoteca | *Italian*	19
NEW Sheep Sta. | *Australian*	19
Song | *Thai*	24
NEW Spirito | *Italian*	-
Stone Park Café | *Amer.*	24
Sweet Melissa | *Dessert/Sandwich*	21
Tempo | *Med.*	25
12th St. B&G | *Amer.*	21
Two Boots | *Pizza*	18

PROSPECT HEIGHTS

(See map on page 298)

Aliseo Osteria | *Italian*	23
Amorina | *Pizza*	23
Beast | *Med.*	20
NEW Cheryl's | *Soul*	22
Franny's | *Pizza*	23
☑ Garden Cafe | *Amer.*	27
Le Gamin | *French*	19
Sorrel | *Amer.*	23
Tom's | *Diner*	19

RED HOOK

(See map on page 298)

Fairway Cafe | *Amer.*	18
☑ Good Fork | *Eclectic*	26
Hope & Anchor | *Diner*	18

SHEEPSHEAD BAY

Brennan | *Sandwich*	19
Roll-n-Roaster | *Sandwich*	19

SUNSET PARK

Nyonya | *Malaysian*	22
NEW Pacificana | *Chinese*	24

WILLIAMSBURG

(See map on page 298)

Aurora | *Italian*	26
Baci & Abbracci | *Italian*	20
Bamonte's | *Italian*	23
Bonita | *Mex.*	19
NEW Catch 22 | *Argent./Italian*	-
NEW DeStefano's | *Steak*	-
Diner | *Diner*	22
Dressler | *Amer.*	24
DuMont | *Amer.*	23
NEW Fette Sau | *BBQ*	19
Fornino | *Pizza*	22
NEW Le Barricou | *French*	-
Lodge | *Amer.*	16
My Moon | *Med.*	19
☑ Peter Luger | *Steak*	28
Planet Thailand | *Jap./Thai*	19
NEW PT | *Italian*	24
Relish | *Amer.*	22
Roebling | *Amer.*	21
SEA | *Thai*	20
NEW Sense | *Jap.*	-
NEW Silent H | *Viet.*	-
Sweetwater | *Amer./French*	21
NEW Wombat | *Australian*	21
NEW Zenkichi | *Jap.*	23

Queens

ASTORIA

Agnanti | *Greek*	24
Ammos | *Greek*	22
NEW Bistro 33 | *French/Jap.*	20
Brick Cafe | *French/Italian*	20
Cafe Bar | *Greek/Med.*	21
☑ Cávo | *Greek*	22
Christos | *Steak*	22
Demetris | *Greek*	21
Elias Corner | *Greek/Seafood*	22
Ethos | *Greek*	22
Grand Café | *Eclectic*	17
NEW Island | *Med.*	18
JJ's Asian Fusion | *Asian Fusion*	25
Malagueta | *Brazilian*	26
Mezzo Mezzo | *Greek*	18
NEW Momento | *Italian*	-
Omonia Cafe | *Greek*	19
NEW Ovelia | *Greek*	21
Piccola Venezia | *Italian*	25
Ponticello | *Italian*	23
Sac's Place | *Pizza*	21
S'Agapo | *Greek*	20
718 | *French*	21
Stamatis | *Greek/Seafood*	22
Taverna Kyclades | *Greek/Seafood*	25

Telly's Taverna | *Greek/Seafood* 22
Thai Pavilion | *Thai* 22
Tierras | *Colombian* 22
☑ Tratt. L'incontro | *Italian* 26
Uno Chicago | *Pizza* 14

BAYSIDE

Ben's Kosher | *Deli* 17
Caffé/Green | *Italian* 21
Dae Dong | *Korean* 18
Erawan | *Thai* 22
Jackson Hole | *Amer.* 17
Outback | *Steak* 14
Press 195 | *Sandwich* 20
Uncle Jack's | *Steak* 23
Uno Chicago | *Pizza* 14

COLLEGE POINT

NEW Five Guys | *Hamburgers* –

CORONA

Green Field | *Brazilian* 19
Leo's Latticini | *Deli/Italian* 28
Park Side | *Italian* 24

ELMHURST

Outback | *Steak* 14
Pho Bang | *Viet.* 21
Ping's Sea. | *Chinese/Seafood* 22

FLUSHING

East Buffet | *Eclectic* 20
East Manor | *Chinese* 19
Joe's Shanghai | *Chinese* 22
Kum Gang San | *Korean* 21
Pho Bang | *Viet.* 21
Spicy & Tasty | *Chinese* 23
Sweet-n-Tart | *Chinese* 20
Temple Canteen | *Indian* –

FOREST HILLS

Baluchi's | *Indian* 18
Bann Thai | *Thai* 21
Cabana | *Nuevo Latino* 21
Dee's Pizza | *Med./Pizza* 22
Nick's | *Pizza* 24
Q Thai Bistro | *Thai* 21
Rouge | *French* 20
Uno Chicago | *Pizza* 14

FRESH MEADOWS

King Yum | *Chinese* 17

GLENDALE

Pasticcio | *Italian* 19
Zum Stammtisch | *German* 22

HOWARD BEACH

La Villa Pizzeria | *Italian* 21

JACKSON HEIGHTS

Afghan Kebab | *Afghan* 19
Jackson Diner | *Indian* 22
Jackson Hole | *Amer.* 17
Pio Pio | *Peruvian* 23
Tierras | *Colombian* 22

LITTLE NECK

La Baraka | *French* 21

LONG ISLAND CITY

Bella Via | *Italian* 23
Manducatis | *Italian* 22
Manetta's | *Italian* 22
Tournesol | *French* 24
Water's Edge | *Amer./Seafood* 23

OZONE PARK

Don Peppe | *Italian* 25

REGO PARK

Grand Sichuan | *Chinese* 22
London Lennie's | *Seafood* 21
Pio Pio | *Peruvian* 23

SUNNYSIDE

Quaint | *Amer.* 20

WOODSIDE

La Flor Bakery | *Bakery* 24
Sapori D'Ischia | *Italian* 25
☑ Sripraphai | *Thai* 26

Staten Island

Aesop's Tables | *Amer./Med.* 21
American Grill | *Amer.* 20
Angelina's | *Italian* 23
Bayou | *Cajun* 22
Bocelli | *Italian* 25
Brioso | *Italian* 25
Caffe Bondi | *Italian* 22
Carol's Cafe | *Eclectic* 26
China Chalet | *Chinese* 19
Da Noi | *Italian* 24
Denino's | *Pizza* 25
Fushimi | *Jap.* 26
Joe & Pat's | *Italian/Pizza* 22
Killmeyer Bavarian | *German* 21
Lake Club | *Cont./Seafood* 21
Marina Cafe | *Seafood* 18
Nurnberger Bierhaus | *German* 21
101 | *Amer./Italian* 19
Real Madrid | *Spanish* 21
South Fin Grill | *Seafood/Steak* 20
Tratt. Romana | *Italian* 24
Vida | *Eclectic* 20
WaterFalls | *Italian* 20
NEW Zest | *Amer.* 26

Special Features

Listings cover the best in each category and include names, locations and Food ratings. Multi-location restaurants' features may vary by branch.
☒ indicates places with the highest ratings, popularity and importance.

BREAKFAST

(See also Hotel Dining)

Annie's	**E 70s**	18
☒ Balthazar	**SoHo**	23
Barney Greengrass	**W 80s**	23
Brasserie	**E 50s**	20
Bubby's	**TriBeCa**	18
Cafe Colonial	**NoLita**	20
Cafe Con Leche	**W 80s**	18
Cafe Luxembourg	**W 70s**	20
Cafe Mogador	**E Vill**	21
Café Sabarsky	**E 80s**	22
☒ Carnegie Deli	**W 50s**	21
City Bakery	**Flatiron**	21
City Hall	**TriBeCa**	21
Clinton St. Baking	**LES**	24
E.A.T.	**E 80s**	19
Edgar's Cafe	**W 80s**	18
EJ's Luncheonette	**multi.**	15
Florent	**Meatpacking**	20
Giorgione	**SoHo**	23
Good Enough/Eat	**W 80s**	20
HK	**Garment**	16
Katz's Deli	**LES**	23
Kitchenette	**multi.**	19
Landmarc	**W 60s**	23
Le Pain Q.	**multi.**	19
Michael's	**W 50s**	21
Naples 45	**E 40s**	17
Nice Matin	**W 70s**	20
NoHo Star	**NoHo**	18
Norma's	**W 50s**	25
☒ Pastis	**Meatpacking**	21
Payard Bistro	**E 70s**	24
Penelope	**Murray Hill**	21
Pershing Sq.	**E 40s**	15
Popover Cafe	**W 80s**	18
Rue 57	**W 50s**	19
Sant Ambroeus	**multi.**	22
Sarabeth's	**multi.**	20
Tartine	**W Vill**	22
Taste	**E 80s**	20
Veselka	**E Vill**	18

BRUNCH

Aix Brasserie	**W 80s**	20
Annie's	**E 70s**	18
A.O.C.	**W Vill**	20
applewood	**Park Slope**	25
☒ Aquagrill	**SoHo**	26

☒ Aquavit	**E 50s**	25
Arté Café	**W 70s**	18
☒ Artisanal	**Murray Hill**	23
☒ Atlantic Grill	**E 70s**	22
☒ Balthazar	**SoHo**	23
Beacon	**W 50s**	22
Beso	**Park Slope**	19
Blue Ribbon Bakery	**G Vill**	24
☒ Blue Water	**Union Sq**	23
Bubby's	**multi.**	18
Cafe Con Leche	**multi.**	18
Café de Bruxelles	**W Vill**	21
☒ Café des Artistes	**W 60s**	22
Cafe Luxembourg	**W 70s**	20
Cafe Mogador	**E Vill**	21
Cafe Ronda	**W 70s**	18
Cafeteria	**Chelsea**	18
Cafe Un Deux	**W 40s**	16
Caffe Cielo	**W 50s**	19
Capsouto Frères	**TriBeCa**	24
☒ Carlyle	**E 70s**	21
☒ Carmine's	**multi.**	19
Cebu	**Bay Ridge**	21
Celeste	**W 80s**	24
Chez Oskar	**Ft Greene**	19
Clinton St. Baking	**LES**	24
Cocotte	**Park Slope**	20
Cornelia St. Cafe	**G Vill**	19
Danal	**E Vill**	22
☒ davidburke/dona.	**E 60s**	25
Delta Grill	**W 40s**	19
Diner	**W'burg**	22
Eatery	**W 50s**	19
Elephant & Castle	**G Vill**	17
☒ Eleven Madison	**Gramercy**	26
elmo	**Chelsea**	15
Essex	**LES**	20
Extra Virgin	**W Vill**	21
Félix	**SoHo**	16
5 Points	**NoHo**	22
Friend of a Farmer	**Gramercy**	17
Gascogne	**Chelsea**	22
good	**W Vill**	20
Good Enough/Eat	**W 80s**	20
Great Jones Cafe	**NoHo**	19
Home	**G Vill**	20
HQ	**SoHo**	19
Isabella's	**W 70s**	20
Jackson Diner	**Jackson Hts**	22

Jane	**G Vill**	21	Beacon	**W 50s**	22
JoJo	**E 60s**	24	Bombay Palace	**W 50s**	18
Le Gigot	**G Vill**	24	Brasserie 8½	**W 50s**	22
Les Halles	**multi.**	20	Bukhara Grill	**E 40s**	20
L'Express	**Flatiron**	17	⚡ Carlyle	**E 70s**	22
⚡ Mesa Grill	**Flatiron**	24	Charles' Kitchen	**Harlem**	24
Miracle Grill	**multi.**	18	Chennai Gdn.	**Gramercy**	21
Miriam	**Park Slope**	21	Chola	**E 50s**	23
Miss Mamie/Maude	**Harlem**	21	Churrascaria	**multi.**	23
Mon Petit Cafe	**E 60s**	18	City Bakery	**Flatiron**	21
Nice Matin	**W 70s**	20	Dakshin Indian	**E 80s**	20
Norma's	**W 50s**	25	Darbar	**E 40s**	20
Ocean Grill	**W 70s**	23	Diwan	**E 40s**	21
Odeon	**TriBeCa**	19	East Buffet	**Flushing**	20
Olea	**Ft Greene**	20	Green Field	**Corona**	19
One	**Meatpacking**	18	Hudson Cafeteria	**W 50s**	19
⚡ Ouest	**W 80s**	25	Jackson Diner	**Jackson Hts**	22
Paris Commune	**W Vill**	18	Jewel of India	**W 40s**	20
⚡ Pastis	**Meatpacking**	21	⚡ Kittichai	**SoHo**	23
Patois	**Carroll Gdns**	21	La Baraka	**Little Neck**	21
Penelope	**Murray Hill**	21	Lake Club	**SI**	21
Petrossian	**W 50s**	24	Mangia	**multi.**	20
Pietrasanta	**W 40s**	19	Porcão	**Gramercy**	21
Pink Tea Cup	**W Vill**	20	⚡ Rainbow Room/Grill	**W 40s**	19
Pipa	**Flatiron**	21	Roy's NY	**Financial**	25
Popover Cafe	**W 80s**	18	Salaam Bombay	**TriBeCa**	20
Prune	**E Vill**	24	Sapphire	**W 60s**	20
Public	**NoLita**	23	South Fin Grill	**SI**	20
Punch	**Flatiron**	19	Surya	**W Vill**	24
⚡ Rainbow Room/Grill	**W 40s**	19	SushiSamba	**W Vill**	22
⚡ River Café	**Dumbo**	26	Todai	**Murray Hill**	18
Riverdale Gdn.	**Bronx**	24	Turkish Kitchen	**Gramercy**	22
Rocking Horse Cafe	**Chelsea**	20	Turkuaz	**W 100s**	19
Rose Water	**Park Slope**	25	2 West	**Financial**	21
Sarabeth's	**multi.**	20	Utsav	**W 40s**	21
Schiller's	**LES**	18	View, The	**W 40s**	18
Sette Enoteca	**Park Slope**	19	Water Club	**Murray Hill**	20
718	**Astoria**	21	Yuva	**E 50s**	24
Spotted Pig	**W Vill**	22			

BYO

Amy Ruth's	**Harlem**	22
Angelica Kit.	**E Vill**	21
NEW Babouche	**Park Slope**	20
Bereket	**LES**	18
NEW Cafe & Wine	**W 100s**	-
NEW Caffe Emilia	**E Vill**	-
Comfort Diner	**E 40s**	16
Cube 63	**LES**	21
⚡ Di Fara	**Midwood**	27
NEW Georgia's/BBQ	**LES**	-
Hummus Place	**G Vill**	23
Ivo & Lulu	**SoHo**	22
NEW Kaijou	**Financial**	-
La Taza de Oro	**Chelsea**	18
NEW Lucali	**Carroll Gdns**	27
Meskerem	**G Vill**	20

Stanton Social	**LES**	23
Stone Park Café	**Park Slope**	24
Sylvia's	**Harlem**	19
Tartine	**W Vill**	22
Taste	**E 80s**	20
Thalia	**W 50s**	21
Tribeca Grill	**TriBeCa**	22
Turkish Kitchen	**Gramercy**	22
Wallsé	**W Vill**	26
Water Club	**Murray Hill**	20
Zoë	**SoHo**	20

BUFFET

(Check availability)

⚡ Aquavit	**E 50s**	25
Arabelle	**E 60s**	21
Bay Leaf	**W 50s**	19

Nook | **W 50s**	22
Peking Duck | **Chinatown**	22
Pho Bang | **multi.**	21
Phoenix Gdn. | **E 40s**	24
☒ Poke | **E 80s**	26
NEW Silent H | **W'burg**	–
NEW Spice Fusion | **W 40s**	–
NEW Sticky Rice | **LES**	19
Sweet Melissa | **multi.**	21
☒ Tanoreen | **Bay Ridge**	27
Tartine | **W Vill**	22
Wondee Siam | **multi.**	22
X.O. | **Chinatown**	18
Zaytoons | **multi.**	22
Zen Palate | **multi.**	19

CELEBRATIONS

☒ Aureole | **E 60s**	27
Beacon | **W 50s**	22
BLT Fish | **Flatiron**	23
BLT Prime | **Gramercy**	24
Bond 45 | **W 40s**	20
☒ Bouley | **TriBeCa**	28
☒ Buddakan | **Chelsea**	23
☒ Café des Artistes | **W 60s**	22
☒ Café Gray | **W 60s**	25
'Cesca | **W 70s**	23
☒ Cru | **G Vill**	26
☒ Daniel | **E 60s**	28
FireBird | **W 40s**	18
☒ Four Seasons | **E 50s**	25
Fresco | **E 50s**	23
Gallagher's | **W 50s**	20
☒ Gotham B&G | **G Vill**	27
Home | **G Vill**	20
☒ La Grenouille | **E 50s**	27
☒ Le Bernardin | **W 50s**	28
Le Cirque | **E 50s**	23
Lobster Box | **Bronx**	17
Mas | **G Vill**	25
☒ Matsuri | **Chelsea**	23
☒ Megu | **TriBeCa**	24
Mercer Kitchen | **SoHo**	22
☒ Modern, The | **W 50s**	26
Molyvos | **W 50s**	22
☒ Nobu 57 | **W 50s**	26
Odeon | **TriBeCa**	19
Olives | **Union Sq**	22
☒ One if by Land | **G Vill**	23
☒ Ouest | **W 80s**	25
☒ Palm | **multi.**	24
☒ Peter Luger | **W'burg**	28
Petrossian | **W 50s**	24
NEW Provence | **SoHo**	21
☒ Rainbow Room/Grill | **W 40s**	19

Raoul's | **SoHo**	24
Redeye Grill | **W 50s**	20
☒ River Café | **Dumbo**	26
River Room | **Harlem**	19
Rock Ctr. | **W 50s**	19
Rolf's | **Gramercy**	17
☒ Rosa Mexicano | **multi.**	22
Ruby Foo's | **multi.**	19
San Domenico | **W 50s**	23
Sea Grill | **W 40s**	24
☒ Tavern on Green | **W 60s**	15
Terrace in the Sky | **W 100s**	22
Tratt. Dell'Arte | **W 50s**	22
View, The | **W 40s**	18
Water Club | **Murray Hill**	20
Water's Edge | **LIC**	23

CELEBRITY CHEFS

Julieta Ballesteros	
Crema | **Chelsea**	21
Dan Barber	
☒ Blue Hill | **G Vill**	26
Lidia Bastianich	
☒ Del Posto | **Chelsea**	25
☒ Felidia | **E 50s**	25
Mario Batali	
☒ Babbo | **G Vill**	27
Casa Mono | **Gramercy**	25
☒ Del Posto | **Chelsea**	25
Esca | **W 40s**	25
☒ Lupa | **G Vill**	25
Otto | **G Vill**	22
April Bloomfield	
Spotted Pig | **W Vill**	22
Saul Bolton	
☒ Saul | **Boerum Hill**	27
David Bouley	
☒ Bouley | **TriBeCa**	28
☒ Bouley, Upstairs | **TriBeCa**	26
☒ Danube | **TriBeCa**	26
Daniel Boulud	
☒ Café Boulud | **E 70s**	27
☒ Daniel | **E 60s**	28
☒ db Bistro Moderne | **W 40s**	25
Anthony Bourdain	
Les Halles | **Gramercy**	20
Antoine Bouterin	
Le Perigord | **E 50s**	24
Jimmy Bradley	
Harrison, The | **TriBeCa**	24
Red Cat | **Chelsea**	24
Terrance Brennan	
☒ Artisanal | **Murray Hill**	23
☒ Picholine | **W 60s**	27

David Burke
- davidburke/dona. | **E 60s** — 25
- David Burke/Bloom. | **E 50s** — 18
- NEW Hawaiian Tropic | **W 40s** — 16

Marco Canora
- Hearth | **E Vill** — 25
- NEW Insieme | **W 50s** — 26

Floyd Cardoz
- Tabla | **Gramercy** — 25

Andrew Carmellini
- A Voce | **Gramercy** — 25

Cesare Casella
- Maremma | **W Vill** — 21

Michael Cetrulo
- Piano Due | **W 50s** — 25
- Scalini Fedeli | **TriBeCa** — 26

Ian Chalermkittichai
- Kittichai | **SoHo** — 23

David Chang
- Momofuku Noodle | **E Vill** — 24
- Momofuku Ssäm | **E Vill** — 24

Rebecca Charles
- Pearl Oyster | **G Vill** — 26

Tom Colicchio
- Craft | **Flatiron** — 25
- Craftbar | **Flatiron** — 22
- Craftsteak | **Chelsea** — 22
- 'wichcraft | **multi.** — 20

Josh DeChellis
- NEW BarFry | **G Vill** — –

Harold Dieterle
- NEW Perilla | **G Vill** — –

Wylie Dufresne
- wd-50 | **LES** — 23

Todd English
- Olives | **Union Sq** — 22

Odette Fada
- San Domenico | **W 50s** — 23

Sandro Fioriti
- NEW Sandro's | **E 80s** — –

Bobby Flay
- Bar Americain | **W 50s** — 23
- Bolo | **Flatiron** — 24
- Mesa Grill | **Flatiron** — 24

Shea Gallante
- Cru | **G Vill** — 26

Alex Garcia
- Calle Ocho | **W 80s** — 22
- NEW Catch 22 | **W'burg** — –
- NEW Gaucho | **W 50s** — –

Kurt Gutenbrunner
- Blaue Gans | **TriBeCa** — 20
- Café Sabarsky | **E 80s** — 22
- Wallsé | **W Vill** — 26

Gabrielle Hamilton
- Prune | **E Vill** — 24

Peter Hoffman
- Savoy | **SoHo** — 24

Daniel Humm
- Eleven Madison | **Gramercy** — 26

Thomas Keller
- Bouchon Bakery | **W 60s** — 23
- Per Se | **W 60s** — 28

Gabriel Kreuther
- Modern, The | **W 50s** — 26

Gray Kunz
- Café Gray | **W 60s** — 25
- NEW Grayz | **W 50s** — –

Anita Lo
- Annisa | **G Vill** — 27
- Rickshaw Dumpling | **Flatiron** — 18

Michael Lomonaco
- Porter House NY | **W 60s** — 22

Pino Luongo
- Centolire | **E 80s** — 20

Waldy Malouf
- Beacon | **W 50s** — 22
- Waldy's Pizza | **Chelsea** — 21

Zarela Martinez
- Zarela | **E 50s** — 21

Sam Mason
- NEW Tailor | **SoHo** — –

Nobu Matsuhisa
- Nobu | **TriBeCa** — 27
- Nobu 57 | **W 50s** — 26

Henry Meer
- City Hall | **TriBeCa** — 21

Marco Moreira
- NEW 15 East | **Union Sq** — 26
- Tocqueville | **Union Sq** — 26

Masaharu Morimoto
- Morimoto | **Chelsea** — 24

Marc Murphy
- Ditch Plains | **G Vill** — 17
- Landmarc | **multi.** — 23

Tadashi Ono
- Matsuri | **Chelsea** — 23

Charlie Palmer
- Aureole | **E 60s** — 27
- Metrazur | **E 40s** — 20

David Pasternack
- Esca | **W 40s** — 25

François Payard
- Payard Bistro | **E 70s** — 24

Zak Pelaccio
- NEW Borough Food | **Flatiron** — –
- Fatty Crab | **W Vill** — 21

SPECIAL FEATURES

Don Pintabona
Dani | **SoHo** 20

Alfred Portale
☑ Gotham B&G | **G Vill** 27

Michael Psilakis
NEW Anthos | **W 50s** 25
NEW Kefi | **W 70s** 23

Gordon Ramsay
NEW ☑ Gordon Ramsay | **W 50s** 25
NEW Maze | **W 50s** 23

Mary Redding
Brooklyn Fish | **Park Slope** 23
Mary's Fish Camp | **W Vill** 25

Cyril Renaud
Fleur de Sel | **Flatiron** 25

Eric Ripert
☑ Le Bernardin | **W 50s** 28

Joël Robuchon
☑ L'Atelier/Robuchon | **E 50s** 27

Michael Romano
☑ Union Sq. Cafe | **Union Sq** 26

Marcus Samuelsson
☑ Aquavit | **E 50s** 25

Aarón Sanchez
Centrico | **TriBeCa** 20
Paladar | **LES** 18

Mark Strausman
Coco Pazzo | **E 70s** 22

Noriyuki Sugie
☑ Asiate | **W 60s** 24

Gari Sugio
☑ Gari/Sushi | **multi.** 26

Nao Sugiyama
☑ Sugiyama | **W 50s** 27

Masayoshi Takayama
☑ Masa/Bar Masa | **W 60s** 27

Bill Telepan
☑ Telepan | **W 60s** 25

Sue Torres
NEW Los Dados | **Meatpacking** -
Sueños | **Chelsea** 23

Laurent Tourondel
NEW BLT Burger | **G Vill** 19
BLT Fish | **Flatiron** 23
NEW BLT Market | **W 50s** -
BLT Prime | **Gramercy** 24
BLT Steak | **E 50s** 24
Brass. Ruhlmann | **W 50s** 17

Alex Ureña
NEW Pamplona | **Gramercy** -

Tom Valenti
☑ Ouest | **W 80s** 25

Jean-Georges Vongerichten
☑ Jean Georges | **W 60s** 28

JoJo | **E 60s** 24
Mercer Kitchen | **SoHo** 22
Perry St. | **W Vill** 24
☑ Spice Market | **Meatpacking** 22
Vong | **E 50s** 22

Yuji Wakiya
NEW ☑ Wakiya | **Gramercy** -

David Waltuck
☑ Chanterelle | **TriBeCa** 27

David Walzog
Strip House | **G Vill** 25

Jonathan Waxman
Barbuto | **W Vill** 22

Michael White
☑ Alto | **E 50s** 26
☑ L'Impero | **E 40s** 26

Jody Williams
NEW Morandi | **G Vill** 19

Roy Yamaguchi
Roy's NY | **Financial** 25

Naomichi Yasuda
☑ Sushi Yasuda | **E 40s** 28

Orhan Yegen
NEW Sea Salt | **E Vill** -
Sip Sak | **E 40s** 20

Patricia Yeo
Monkey Bar | **E 50s** -

Geoffrey Zakarian
Country | **Gramercy** 23
Town | **W 50s** 24

Galen Zamarra
Mas | **G Vill** 25

CHEESE TRAYS

☑ Artisanal | **Murray Hill** 23
☑ Babbo | **G Vill** 27
☑ Café Gray | **W 60s** 25
☑ Chanterelle | **TriBeCa** 27
☑ Craft | **Flatiron** 25
☑ Daniel | **E 60s** 28
☑ Eleven Madison | **Gramercy** 26
NEW ☑ Gordon Ramsay | **W 50s** 25
☑ Gramercy Tavern | **Flatiron** 27
'inoteca | **LES** 23
☑ Jean Georges | **W 60s** 28
☑ La Grenouille | **E 50s** 27
☑ Modern, The | **W 50s** 26
Morrell Wine Bar | **W 40s** 19
Otto | **G Vill** 22
☑ Per Se | **W 60s** 28
☑ Picholine | **W 60s** 27

CHEF'S TABLE

Abigael's | **Garment** 19
☑ Aquavit | **E 50s** 25

Bao 111	E Vill	21
Barbuto	W Vill	22
Brasserie Julien	E 80s	19
Ⓩ Café Gray	W 60s	25
Country	Gramercy	23
Ⓩ Daniel	E 60s	28
NEW Ⓩ Gordon Ramsay	W 50s	25
NEW House	Gramercy	22
Il Buco	NoHo	25
Maloney & Porcelli	E 50s	22
Ⓩ Megu	TriBeCa	24
NEW Mercat	NoHo	–
Olives	Union Sq	22
NEW Palo Santo	Park Slope	25
NEW Park Avenue	E 60s	–
Patroon	E 40s	21
Remi	W 50s	22
NEW Resto	Gramercy	–
Smith & Wollensky	E 40s	23
Turks & Frogs	TriBeCa	20
Valbella	Meatpacking	24
Yuva	E 50s	24
Zoë	SoHo	20

London Lennie's*	Rego Pk	21
Miss Mamie/Maude	Harlem	21
Nick's	multi.	24
Ninja	TriBeCa	19
Peanut Butter Co.	G Vill	20
Pig Heaven	E 80s	19
Rack & Soul*	W 100s	20
Rock Ctr.*	W 50s	19
Rossini's	Murray Hill	23
Sammy's Roum.	LES	19
Sarabeth's	multi.	20
Savoia	Carroll Gdns	21
Shake Shack	Flatiron	23
Soda Shop	TriBeCa	19
NEW Spotlight Live	W 40s	–
Sylvia's*	Harlem	19
Ⓩ Tavern on Green*	W 60s	15
Tony's Di Napoli	multi.	18
Two Boots*	multi.	18
View, The*	W 40s	18
Virgil's Real BBQ*	W 40s	20
Whole Foods	multi.	19
Zum Stammtisch*	Glendale	22

CHILD-FRIENDLY

(See also Theme Restaurants;
* children's menu available)

Alice's Tea Cup*	W 70s	19
American Girl	E 40s	13
Amy Ruth's*	Harlem	22
Annie's	E 70s	18
Antica Venezia	W Vill	23
Artie's Deli*	W 80s	18
Barking Dog*	multi.	15
Beso	Park Slope	19
Blue Smoke*	Gramercy	22
Boathouse*	E 70s	16
Brennan	Sheepshead	19
Bubby's*	multi.	18
Cafe Un Deux	W 40s	16
Ⓩ Carmine's	W 40s	19
Chat 'n Chew*	Union Sq	16
Columbus Bakery	W 80s	18
Comfort Diner*	multi.	16
Cowgirl*	W Vill	16
Dallas BBQ*	multi.	15
Da Nico*	L Italy	21
EJ's Luncheonette*	multi.	15
ESPN Zone*	W 40s	12
Friend of a Farmer*	Gramercy	17
Gargiulo's	Coney Is	21
Good Enough/Eat*	W 80s	20
Hard Rock Cafe*	W 40s	13
Jackson Hole*	multi.	17
Junior's*	multi.	18
L & B Spumoni*	Bensonhurst	22

COMMUTER OASES

Grand Central

Ammos	E 40s	22
Bobby Van's	E 40s	22
Brother Jimmy's	E 40s	16
Burger Heaven	E 40s	16
Cafe Centro	E 40s	20
Cafe Spice	E 40s	18
Capital Grille	E 40s	23
Cipriani Dolci	E 40s	18
Dishes	E 40s	22
Django	E 40s	20
Docks Oyster	E 40s	19
Hale/Hearty	E 40s	19
Hatsuhana	E 40s	24
Junior's	E 40s	18
Menchanko-tei	E 40s	20
Metrazur	E 40s	20
Michael Jordan's	E 40s	20
Morton's	E 40s	24
Nanni	E 40s	24
Oyster Bar	E 40s	21
Patroon	E 40s	21
Pepe	E 40s	21
Pershing Sq.	E 40s	15
NEW Public House	E 40s	–
Ⓩ Sushi Yasuda	E 40s	28
Two Boots	E 40s	18
Zócalo	E 40s	20

Penn Station

| Chipotle | Garment | 18 |
| Gray's Papaya | Garment | 20 |

Nick & Stef's | **Garment**	22
Uncle Jack's | **Garment**	23
Port Authority	
Angus McIndoe | **W 40s**	16
Better Burger | **W 40s**	15
Chez Josephine | **W 40s**	20
Chimichurri Grill | **W 40s**	21
Dallas BBQ | **W 40s**	15
Don Giovanni | **W 40s**	17
Esca | **W 40s**	25
ESPN Zone | **W 40s**	12
etc. etc. | **W 40s**	20
HK | **Garment**	16
John's Pizzeria | **W 40s**	22
Le Madeleine | **W 40s**	20
Marseille | **W 40s**	20
NEW Metro Marché | **W 40s**	19
Rachel's American | **W 40s**	17
Shula's | **W 40s**	20
West Bank Cafe | **W 40s**	20

COOL LOOS

Bette | **Chelsea**	19
Brasserie | **E 50s**	20
Butter | **E Vill**	19
☑ Compass | **W 70s**	22
ESPN Zone | **W 40s**	12
NEW ☑ Gordon Ramsay | **W 50s**	25
NEW Kobe Club | **W 50s**	20
☑ Matsuri | **Chelsea**	23
☑ Megu | **TriBeCa**	24
☑ Modern, The | **W 50s**	26
☑ Morimoto | **Chelsea**	24
Ono | **Meatpacking**	21
Paradou | **Meatpacking**	19
☑ Pastis | **Meatpacking**	21
Peep | **SoHo**	19
P.J. Clarke's | **multi.**	17
Prem-on Thai | **G Vill**	21
Sapa | **Flatiron**	22
Schiller's | **LES**	18
SEA | **W'burg**	20
☑ Tao | **E 50s**	23
Vynl | **multi.**	17
wd-50 | **LES**	23

CRITIC-PROOF

(Gets lots of business despite
so-so food)

Algonquin | **W 40s**	16
Angus McIndoe | **W 40s**	16
Barking Dog | **multi.**	15
Better Burger | **multi.**	15
Boathouse | **E 70s**	16
Brother Jimmy's | **multi.**	16
Bubba Gump | **W 40s**	14

Burger Heaven | **multi.**	16
Burritoville | **multi.**	16
Cafe Un Deux | **W 40s**	16
Chat 'n Chew | **Union Sq**	16
China Fun | **multi.**	16
Coffee Shop | **Union Sq**	15
Comfort Diner | **multi.**	16
Così | **multi.**	16
Cowgirl | **W Vill**	16
Dallas BBQ | **multi.**	15
Duke's | **multi.**	16
East of 8th | **Chelsea**	16
Edison | **W 40s**	15
EJ's Luncheonette | **multi.**	15
Elaine's | **E 80s**	13
elmo | **Chelsea**	15
Empire Diner | **Chelsea**	15
Empire Szechuan | **multi.**	15
ESPN Zone | **W 40s**	12
Fraunces Tavern | **Financial**	15
French Roast | **multi.**	14
Hard Rock Cafe | **W 40s**	13
Heartland | **multi.**	14
Kelley/Ping | **multi.**	16
Lili's Noodle | **multi.**	16
Mary Ann's | **multi.**	15
Ollie's | **multi.**	16
Outback | **multi.**	14
Park, The | **Chelsea**	15
Pershing Sq. | **E 40s**	15
Pete's Tavern | **Gramercy**	14
Sardi's | **W 40s**	16
☑ Tavern on Green | **W 60s**	15
Tratt. Dopo | **W 40s**	16
212 | **E 60s**	16
Uno Chicago | **multi.**	14
Viand | **multi.**	16

DANCING

☑ Cávo | **Astoria**	21
☑ Rainbow Room | **W 40s**	19
River Room | **Harlem**	19
☑ Tavern on Green | **W 60s**	15

ENTERTAINMENT

(Call for days and times of
performances)

Alfama | fado | **W Vill**	22
Algonquin | cabaret | **W 40s**	16
Blue Fin | jazz | **W 40s**	22
Blue Smoke | jazz | **Gramercy**	22
☑ Blue Water | jazz | **Union Sq**	23
Café Pierre | piano/vocals | **E 60s**	23
Chez Josephine | piano | **W 40s**	20
Cornelia St. Cafe | varies | **G Vill**	19
Delta Grill | varies | **W 40s**	19

FireBird | harp/piano | **W 40s** 18
Flor de Sol | flamenco | **TriBeCa** 20
Ideya | jazz | **SoHo** 20
Jules | varies | **E Vill** 19
Knickerbocker | jazz | **G Vill** 20
La Lanterna | jazz | **G Vill** 20
La Lunchonette | accordion/
  vocals | **Chelsea** 22
Londel's | varies | **Harlem** 22
Z Rainbow Room | orchestra |
  W 40s 19
Z River Café | piano | **Dumbo** 26
Son Cubano | Cuban/DJs |
  Meatpacking 21
Sylvia's | varies | **Harlem** 19
Z Tavern on Green | varies | 15
  W 60s
Tommaso | varies | **Dyker Hts** 23
Walker's | jazz | **TriBeCa** 17

FIREPLACES

Adä | **E 50s** 23
Agave | **W Vill** 18
Alta | **G Vill** 23
applewood | **Park Slope** 25
Aspen | **Flatiron** 20
NEW Benjamin Steak | **E 40s** 23
Beppe | **Flatiron** 23
Bistro Ten 18 | **W 100s** 20
Black Duck | **Gramercy** 20
Bruckner B&G | **Bronx** 21
Caffé/Green | **Bayside** 21
NEW Catch 22 | **W'burg** -
Cebu | **Bay Ridge** 21
Cornelia St. Cafe | **G Vill** 19
Cucina di Pesce | **E Vill** 17
Danal | **E Vill** 22
Dee's Pizza | **Forest Hills** 22
Delta Grill | **W 40s** 19
Devin Tavern | **TriBeCa** 18
Employees Only | **W Vill** 18
57 | **E 50s** 22
FireBird | **W 40s** 18
NEW Fireside | **E 50s** 21
Frankie/Johnnie | **Garment** 21
Fraunces Tavern | **Financial** 15
Friend of a Farmer | **Gramercy** 17
Geisha | **E 60s** 23
Giorgione | **SoHo** 23
NEW Grayz | **W 50s** -
Greenhouse Café | **Bay Ridge** 19
Hacienda/Argentina | **E 70s** 21
NEW House | **Gramercy** 22
Ici | **Ft Greene** 22
I Trulli | **Gramercy** 22
Keens | **Garment** 24

Kelley/Ping | **E Vill** 16
Lady Mendl's | **Gramercy** 22
Z La Grenouille | **E 50s** 27
Lake Club | **SI** 21
La Lanterna | **G Vill** 20
Landmark Tavern | **W 40s** 18
La Ripaille | **W Vill** 23
Lattanzi | **W 40s** 22
Le Refuge Inn | **Bronx** 24
Lobster Box | **Bronx** 17
Lumi | **E 70s** 19
Manducatis | **LIC** 22
Manetta's | **LIC** 22
Marco Polo | **Carroll Gdns** 20
Mezzo Mezzo | **Astoria** 18
Moran's | **Chelsea** 18
Notaro | **Murray Hill** 20
Nurnberger Bierhaus | **SI** 21
Z One if by Land | **G Vill** 23
NEW Ovelia | **Astoria** 21
Paola's | **E 80s** 23
Park, The | **Chelsea** 15
Patois | **Carroll Gdns** 21
Pearl Room | **Bay Ridge** 23
Z Per Se | **W 60s** 28
Piccola Venezia | **Astoria** 25
Portofino Grille | **E 60s** 19
Public | **NoLita** 23
Quality Meats | **W 50s** 24
René Pujol | **W 50s** 22
Riverdale Gdn. | **Bronx** 24
Savoy | **SoHo** 24
Serafina | **NoHo** 18
Shaffer City | **Flatiron** 21
NEW Sheep Sta. | **Park Slope** 19
NEW STK | **Meatpacking** 20
Z Telepan | **W 60s** 25
Telly's Taverna | **Astoria** 22
Terrace in the Sky | **W 100s** 22
Tiramisu | **E 80s** 20
Tosca Café | **Bronx** 21
Triomphe | **W 40s** 24
Z 21 Club | **W 50s** 22
Uncle Jack's | **Garment** 23
Vivolo | **E 70s** 20
Water Club | **Murray Hill** 20
Water's Edge | **LIC** 23
NEW Z Waverly Inn | **W Vill** 18
wd-50 | **LES** 23
NEW Zoë Townhouse | **E 60s** -

GRACIOUS HOSTS

Angelina's | *Angelina Malerba* | **SI** 23
Angus McIndoe |
  Angus McIndoe | **W 40s** 16

SPECIAL FEATURES

NEW Anthos | *Donatella Arpaia* | **W 50s** — 25

Barbetta | *Laura Maioglio* | **W 40s** — 20

Z Blue Hill | *Franco Serafin* | **G Vill** — 26

Bricco | *Nino Cituogno* | **W 50s** — 19

Z Chanterelle | *Karen Waltuck* | **TriBeCa** — 27

Chez Josephine | *Jean-Claude Baker* | **W 40s** — 20

Chin Chin | *James Chin* | **E 40s** — 22

Z Danube | *Walter Kranjc* | **TriBeCa** — 26

Z davidburke/dona. | *Donatella Arpaia* | **E 60s** — 25

Degustation | *Grace & Jack Lamb* | **E Vill** — 26

Deux Amis | *Bucky Yahiaoui* | **E 50s** — 19

Due | *Ernesto Cavalli* | **E 70s** — 22

Eliá | *Christina & Pete Lekkas* | **Bay Ridge** — 25

Z Four Seasons | *Julian Niccolini, Alex von Bidder* | **E 50s** — 25

Fresco | *Marion Scotto* | **E 50s** — 23

Z Garden Cafe | *Camille Policastro* | **Prospect Hts** — 27

Z Jean Georges | *P. Vongerichten* | **W 60s** — 28

Jewel Bako | *Grace & Jack Lamb* | **E Vill** — 25

Kitchen Club | *Marja Samsom* | **NoLita** — 22

La Baraka | *Lucette Sonigo* | **Little Neck** — 21

Z La Grenouille | *Charles Masson* | **E 50s** — 27

La Mirabelle | *Annick Le Douaron* | **W 80s** — 22

Le Cirque | *Sirio Maccioni* | **E 50s** — 23

Le Perigord | *Georges Briguet* | **E 50s** — 24

Le Zie 2000 | *Claudio Bonotto* | **Chelsea** — 21

Loulou | *Christine & William Snell* | **Ft Greene** — 22

Luca | *Luca Marcato* | **E 80s** — 20

Neary's | *Jimmy Neary* | **E 50s** — 15

Nino's | *Nino Selimaj* | **E 70s** — 21

Paola's | *Paola Marracino* | **E 80s** — 23

Piccolo Angolo | *R. Migliorini* | **W Vill** — 25

Pig Heaven | *Nancy Lee* | **E 80s** — 19

Primavera | *Nicola Civetta* | **E 80s** — 22

Z Rao's | *Frank Pellegrino* | **Harlem** — 22

San Domenico | *Tony May* | **W 50s** — 23

San Pietro | *Gerardo Bruno* | **E 50s** — 24

Shaffer City | *Jay Shaffer* | **Flatiron** — 21

Sistina | *Giuseppe Bruno* | **E 80s** — 24

Spigolo | *Heather Fratangelo* | **E 80s** — 25

Tamarind | *Avtar & Gary Walia* | **Flatiron** — 25

Tasting Rm. | *Renée Alevras* | **E Vill** — 22

Z Tocqueville | *Jo-Ann Makovitzky* | **Union Sq** — 26

Tommaso | *Thomas Verdillo* | **Dyker Hts** — 23

Z Tratt. L'incontro | *Rocco Sacramone* | **Astoria** — 26

Tratt. Romana | *V. Asoli, A. Lobianco* | **SI** — 24

Turquoise | *Sam Marelli* | **E 80s** — 22

HISTORIC PLACES

(Year opened; * building)

1762 | Fraunces Tavern | **Financial** — 15

1794 | Bridge Cafe* | **Financial** — 22

1853 | Morgan* | **Murray Hill** — 20

1864 | Pete's Tavern | **Gramercy** — 14

1868 | Landmark Tavern* | **W 40s** — 18

1868 | Old Homestead | **Meatpacking** — 23

1875 | Harry's* | **Financial** — 22

1880 | Veniero's* | **E Vill** — 23

1884 | P.J. Clarke's | **E 50s** — 17

1885 | Keens | **Garment** — 24

1887 | Peter Luger | **W'burg** — 28

1888 | Katz's Deli | **LES** — 23

1890 | Walker's* | **TriBeCa** — 17

1892 | Ferrara | **L Italy** — 22

1896 | Rao's | **Harlem** — 22

1900 | Bamonte's | **W'burg** — 23

1902 | Algonquin | **W 40s** — 16

1902 | Angelo's/Mulberry | **L Italy** — 23

1904 | Sal Anthony's* | **E Vill** — 19

1904 | Trinity Place* | **Financial** — 18

1904 | Vincent's | **L Italy** — 21

1907 | Gargiulo's* | **Coney Is** — 21

1908 | Barney Greengrass | **W 80s** — 23

1908 | John's/12th St. | **E Vill** — 19

1910 | Wolfgang's* | **Murray Hill** — 25

1913 | Oyster Bar* | **E 40s** — 21

1917 | Café des Artistes | **W 60s** — 22

1919 | Mario's | **Bronx** — 22

1920 | Leo's Latticini | **Corona** — 28

1920 | Waverly Inn* | **W Vill** — 18

1921 | Sardi's | **W 40s** — 16

1922 | Rocco | **G Vill** — 20

1922 | Tosca Café | **Bronx** — 21

1924	Totonno Pizza	**Coney Is**	22
1925	El Charro Español	**G Vill**	22
1926	Frankie/Johnnie	**W 40s**	21
1926	Palm	**E 40s**	24
1927	Diner*	**W'burg**	22
1927	El Faro	**W Vill**	23
1927	Gallagher's	**W 50s**	20
1929	Empire Diner*	**Chelsea**	15
1929	John's Pizzeria	**G Vill**	22
1929	Russian Tea*	**W 50s**	19
1929	21 Club	**W 50s**	22
1930	Carlyle	**E 70s**	21
1930	El Quijote	**Chelsea**	19
1931	Café Pierre	**E 60s**	23
1932	Pietro's	**E 40s**	23
1933	Patsy's Pizzeria	**Harlem**	20
1934	Papaya King	**E 80s**	20
1934	Rainbow Room/Grill	**W 40s**	19
1936	Monkey Bar*	**E 50s**	–
1936	Tom's	**Prospect Hts**	19
1937	Carnegie Deli	**W 50s**	21
1937	Denino's	**SI**	25
1937	Le Veau d'Or	**E 60s**	17
1937	Minetta Tavern	**G Vill**	18
1937	Stage Deli	**W 50s**	20
1938	Brennan	**Sheepshead**	19
1938	Heidelberg	**E 80s**	17
1938	Wo Hop	**Chinatown**	21
1939	L & B Spumoni	**Bensonhurst**	22
1941	Sevilla	**W Vill**	23
1944	Patsy's	**W 50s**	21
1945	Gino	**E 60s**	21
1945	V&T	**W 100s**	18
1946	Lobster Box	**Bronx**	17
1950	Junior's	**Downtown Bklyn**	18
1952	Lever House*	**E 50s**	22
1953	King Yum	**Fresh Meadows**	17
1953	Liebman's	**Bronx**	19
1954	Pink Tea Cup	**W Vill**	20
1954	Serendipity 3	**E 60s**	18
1954	Veselka	**E Vill**	18
1957	Arturo's Pizzeria	**G Vill**	21
1957	Giambelli	**E 50s**	21
1957	La Taza de Oro	**Chelsea**	18
1957	Moran's	**Chelsea**	18

HOTEL DINING

Affinia Dumont
Barking Dog | **Murray Hill** | 15

Alex Hotel
Riingo | **E 40s** | 19

Algonquin Hotel
Algonquin | **W 40s** | 16

Amsterdam Court Hotel
NEW Natsumi | **W 50s** | –

Blakely Hotel
Abboccato | **W 50s** | 22

Bowery Hotel
NEW Gemma | **E Vill** | –

Bryant Park Hotel
Koi | **W 40s** | 23

Carlton Hotel
Country | **Gramercy** | 23

Carlyle Hotel
Z Carlyle | **E 70s** | 21

Chambers Hotel
Town | **W 50s** | 24

City Club Hotel
Z db Bistro Moderne | **W 40s** | 25

Club Quarters Hotel
Bull Run | **Financial** | 18

Cosmopolitan Hotel
Soda Shop | **TriBeCa** | 19

Dream Hotel
Serafina | **W 50s** | 18

Edison Hotel
Edison | **W 40s** | 15

Elysée Hotel
Monkey Bar | **E 50s** | –

Embassy Suites
Lili's Noodle | **Financial** | 16

Flatotel
Moda | **W 50s** | –

Four Seasons Hotel
57 | **E 50s** | 22
Z L'Atelier/Robuchon | **E 50s** | 27

Gansevoort Hotel
Ono | **Meatpacking** | 21

Gramercy Park Hotel
NEW Z Wakiya | **Gramercy** | –

Helmsley Middletowne
Diwan | **E 40s** | 21

Hilton Garden Inn Times Sq.
Pigalle | **W 40s** | 18

Hotel on Rivington
Thor | **LES** | 18

Hudson Hotel
Hudson Cafeteria | **W 50s** | 19

Inn at Irving Pl.
Lady Mendl's | **Gramercy** | 22

Iroquois Hotel
Triomphe | **W 40s** | 24

Le Parker Meridien
burger joint | **W 50s** | 24
Norma's | **W 50s** | 25

Le Refuge Inn
  Le Refuge Inn | **Bronx** 24

London NYC
  NEW Z Gordon Ramsay | 25
  W 50s
  NEW Maze | **W 50s** 23

Lowell Hotel
  Post House | **E 60s** 23

Mandarin Oriental Hotel
  Z Asiate | **W 60s** 24

Maritime Hotel
  La Bottega | **Chelsea** 18
  Z Matsuri | **Chelsea** 23

Marriott Financial Ctr.
  Roy's NY | **Financial** 25

Marriott Marquis Hotel
  View, The | **W 40s** 18

Mercer Hotel
  Mercer Kitchen | **SoHo** 22

Michelangelo Hotel
  NEW Insieme | **W 50s** 26

Morgans Hotel
  Z Asia de Cuba | **Murray Hill** 23

Muse Hotel
  District | **W 40s** 20

NY Palace Hotel
  Gilt | **E 50s** 25

Omni Berkshire Place Hotel
  NEW Fireside | **E 50s** 21

Park South Hotel
  Black Duck | **Gramercy** 20

Pierre Hotel
  Café Pierre | **E 60s** 23

Plaza Athénée Hotel
  Arabelle | **E 60s** 21

Pod Hotel
  Montparnasse | **E 50s** 19

Regency Hotel
  Regency | **E 60s** 18

Ritz-Carlton
  NEW BLT Market | **W 50s** −

Ritz-Carlton Battery Park
  2 West | **Financial** 21

San Carlos Hotel
  Mint | **E 50s** 19

Shelburne Murray Hill Hotel
  Rare B&G | **Murray Hill** 21

Sherry Netherland
  Harry Cipriani | **E 50s** −

60 Thompson
  Z Kittichai | **SoHo** 23

Surrey Hotel
  Z Café Boulud | **E 70s** 27

Trump Int'l Hotel
  Z Jean Georges | **W 60s** 28

Waldorf-Astoria
  Bull & Bear | **E 40s** 19
  Inagiku | **E 40s** 23

Washington Square Hotel
  North Sq. | **G Vill** 22

Westin NY Times Sq.
  Shula's | **W 40s** 20

W Times Sq.
  Blue Fin | **W 40s** 22

W Union Sq.
  Olives | **Union Sq** 22

JACKET REQUIRED

(* Tie also required)

Café Pierre | **E 60s** 23
Z Carlyle | **E 70s** 21
Z Daniel | **E 60s** 28
Z Four Seasons | **E 50s** 25
NEW Z Gordon Ramsay | 25
W 50s
Z Jean Georges | **W 60s** 28
Z La Grenouille | **E 50s** 27
Z Le Bernardin | **W 50s** 28
Le Cirque | **E 50s** 23
Z Modern, The | **W 50s** 26
Z Per Se | **W 60s** 28
Z Rainbow Room/Grill | **W 40s** 19
Z River Café | **Dumbo** 26
San Domenico | **W 50s** 23
Z 21 Club* | **W 50s** 22

JURY DUTY

(Near Foley Sq.)

Acappella | **TriBeCa** 23
Arqua | **TriBeCa** 22
Big Wong | **Chinatown** 22
Blaue Gans | **TriBeCa** 20
Z Bouley | **TriBeCa** 28
Z Bouley, Upstairs | **TriBeCa** 26
Bread | **TriBeCa** 19
Carl's Steaks | **TriBeCa** 22
Centrico | **TriBeCa** 20
City Hall | **TriBeCa** 21
Dim Sum Go Go | **Chinatown** 20
Doyers Viet. | **Chinatown** 20
Duane Park | **TriBeCa** 24
Ecco | **TriBeCa** 21
Excellent Dumpling | **Chinatown** 21
fresh | **TriBeCa** 24
Fuleen | **Chinatown** 24
Golden Unicorn | **Chinatown** 20
Goodies | **Chinatown** 20
Great NY Noodle | **Chinatown** 22
HSF | **Chinatown** 20
Jing Fong | **Chinatown** 19
Mandarin Court | **Chinatown** 20
Mary Ann's | **TriBeCa** 15

Nam | **TriBeCa**	22
New Bo-Ky | **Chinatown**	22
New Green Bo | **Chinatown**	22
Nha Trang | **Chinatown**	21
Odeon | **TriBeCa**	19
Oriental Gdn. | **Chinatown**	24
Peking Duck | **Chinatown**	22
Petite Abeille | **TriBeCa**	19
Pho Pasteur | **Chinatown**	21
Pho Viet Huong | **Chinatown**	23
Ping's Sea. | **Chinatown**	22
Pongsri Thai | **Chinatown**	20
Shanghai Cuisine | **Chinatown**	21
Soda Shop | **TriBeCa**	19
Takahachi | **TriBeCa**	24
Wo Hop | **Chinatown**	21

LATE DINING

(Besides most diners and delis; weekday closing hour)

Agave | 1 AM | **W Vill**	18
Arturo's Pizzeria | 1 AM | **G Vill**	21
☑ Balthazar | 1 AM | **SoHo**	23
Bao 111 | 2 AM | **E Vill**	21
Baraonda | 1 AM | **E 70s**	18
NEW Bar Martignetti | 2 AM | **L Italy**	18
Bereket | 24 hrs. | **LES**	18
Bette | 1 AM | **Chelsea**	19
Big Nick's Burger | varies | **W 70s**	17
Blue 9 Burger | varies | **E Vill**	18
☑ Blue Ribbon | varies | **multi.**	25
☑ Blue Ribbon Sushi | varies | **SoHo**	25
NEW Borough Food | 2 AM | **Flatiron**	–
Brennan | 1 AM | **Sheepshead**	19
Cafe Lalo | 2 AM | **W 80s**	19
Cafe Mogador | 1 AM | **E Vill**	21
Cafeteria | 24 hrs. | **Chelsea**	18
☑ Carnegie Deli | 3:30 AM | **W 50s**	21
☑ Cávo | 2 AM | **Astoria**	21
Cebu | 3 AM | **Bay Ridge**	21
NEW Centro Vinoteca | 2 AM | **W Vill**	–
Chez Josephine | 1 AM | **W 40s**	20
Chickpea | varies | **E Vill**	19
Coffee Shop | varies | **Union Sq**	15
Congee | varies | **multi.**	21
Corner Bistro | 3:30 AM | **W Vill**	22
Cosi | 1 AM | **G Vill**	16
Cozy | 24 hrs. | **G Vill**	18
Demetris | 1 AM | **Astoria**	21
Ditch Plains | 2 AM | **G Vill**	17
DuMont | 2 AM | **W'burg**	23
Edgar's Cafe | 1 AM | **W 80s**	18

Edward's | 1 AM | **TriBeCa**	16
Elaine's | 2 AM | **E 80s**	13
El Malecon | varies | **Wash. Hts**	21
El Paso Taqueria | 1 AM | **multi.**	22
Empire Diner | 24 hrs. | **Chelsea**	15
Empire Szechuan | varies | **multi.**	15
Employees Only | 3:30 AM | **W Vill**	18
Florent | 24 hrs. | **Meatpacking**	20
Frank | 1 AM | **E Vill**	24
French Roast | 24 hrs. | **multi.**	14
Fuleen | 3 AM | **Chinatown**	24
Gahm Mi Oak | 24 hrs. | **Garment**	22
NEW Gold St. | 24 hrs. | **Financial**	15
Grand Café | 1 AM | **Astoria**	17
Gray's Papaya | 24 hrs. | **multi.**	20
Great NY Noodle | 4 AM | **Chinatown**	22
Grotta Azzurra | 1 AM | **L Italy**	18
NEW Hawaiian Tropic | 1 AM | **W 40s**	16
HK | 1 AM | **Garment**	16
NEW House | 3 AM | **Gramercy**	22
NEW Inn LW12 | 3 AM | **Meatpacking**	19
'ino | 2 AM | **G Vill**	24
'inoteca | 3 AM | **LES**	23
NEW Isabella's Oven | 1 AM | **LES**	–
Jackson Hole | varies | **multi.**	17
J.G. Melon | 2:30 AM | **E 70s**	21
Joe's Pizza | 5 AM | **G Vill**	23
NEW Johnny Utah | 2 AM | **W 50s**	–
Kang Suh | 24 hrs. | **Garment**	20
Kati Roll Co. | varies | **G Vill**	20
Knickerbocker | 1 AM | **G Vill**	20
Kum Gang San | 24 hrs. | **multi.**	21
La Esquina | 2 AM | **L Italy**	21
La Lanterna | 3 AM | **G Vill**	20
La Mela | 2 AM | **L Italy**	18
Lan | 1 AM | **E Vill**	25
Landmarc | 2 AM | **multi.**	23
L'Express | 24 hrs. | **Flatiron**	17
Lil' Frankie Pizza | 2 AM | **E Vill**	22
Lucien | 1 AM | **E Vill**	21
Lucky Strike | varies | **SoHo**	17
Macelleria | 1 AM | **Meatpacking**	21
Maison | 24 hrs. | **W 50s**	17
Mas | 4 AM | **G Vill**	25
Neary's | 1 AM | **E 50s**	15
NEW Nelson Blue | 2 AM | **Seaport**	–
Odeon | 1 AM | **TriBeCa**	19
Ollie's | varies | **W 100s**	16
Omonia Cafe | 4 AM | **multi.**	19

Pastis | varies | **Meatpacking** 21
Ping's Sea. | varies | **Elmhurst** 22
P.J. Clarke's | varies | **multi.** 17
Pop Burger | varies | **Meatpacking** 19
Rai Rai Ken | 2:30 AM | **E Vill** 22
Raoul's | 1 AM | **SoHo** 24
NEW Resto | 1 AM | **Gramercy** –
Roebling | 1 AM | **W'burg** 21
Roll-n-Roaster | 1 AM | 19
  Sheepshead
Sabor | 2 AM | **E 80s** 19
Sahara | 2 AM | **Gravesend** 20
NEW Sandro's | 2 AM | **E 80s** –
Sarge's Deli | 24 hrs. | **Murray Hill** 19
Schiller's | 1 AM | **LES** 18
NEW Southern Hosp. | 2 AM | –
  E 70s
NEW Spitzer's | 4 AM | **LES** –
NEW Spoon | varies | **E Vill** –
Spotted Pig | 2 AM | **W Vill** 22
Stage Deli | 2 AM | **W 50s** 20
Stamatis | varies | **Astoria** 22
Stanton Social | 3 AM | **LES** 23
NEW STK | 1 AM | **Meatpacking** 20
SushiSamba | varies | **multi.** 22
Sushi Seki | 3 AM | **E 60s** 27
NEW Tasca | 2 AM | **W Vill** 20
Tosca Café | 1 AM | **Bronx** 21
Trio | 1 AM | **Murray Hill** 21
Two Boots | varies | **multi.** 18
Umberto's | 4 AM | **L Italy** 18
Uno Chicago | varies | **multi.** 14
Uva | 2 AM | **E 70s** 21
Veselka | varies | **E Vill** 18
Viand | varies | **multi.** 16
Vincent's | 1:30 AM | **L Italy** 21
Walker's | 1 AM | **TriBeCa** 17
West Bank Cafe | 1 AM | **W 40s** 20
Wollensky's | 2 AM | **E 40s** 23
NEW Wombat | 2 AM | **W'burg** 21
WonJo | 24 hrs. | **Garment** 20

MEET FOR A DRINK
(Most top hotels, bars and the
following standouts)
Aix Brasserie | **W 80s** 20
Algonquin | **W 40s** 16
Amaranth | **E 60s** 20
Arno | **Garment** 20
Artisanal | **Murray Hill** 23
Aspen | **Flatiron** 20
Atlantic Grill | **E 70s** 22
Aurora | **W'burg** 26
NEW Babouche | **SoHo** 20
Balthazar | **SoHo** 23
Bandol Bistro | **E 70s** 19

Barbounia | **Flatiron** 20
Beast | **Prospect Hts** 20
Blue Fin | **W 40s** 22
Blue Water | **Union Sq** 23
Boathouse | **E 70s** 16
Bond St. | **NoHo** 25
Boqueria | **Flatiron** 23
Brick Cafe | **Astoria** 20
Bryant Park | **W 40s** 17
Buddakan | **Chelsea** 23
Buddha Bar | **Meatpacking** 19
Bull & Bear | **E 40s** 19
NEW Cafe Fuego | **E Vill** 19
Café Gray | **W 60s** 25
Cafe Luxembourg | **W 70s** 20
Cafe Steinhof | **Park Slope** 19
NEW Centro Vinoteca | **W Vill** –
City Hall | **TriBeCa** 21
Compass | **W 70s** 22
Country | **Gramercy** 23
Daniel | **E 60s** 28
Demarchelier | **E 80s** 17
Devin Tavern | **TriBeCa** 18
Ditch Plains | **G Vill** 17
Django | **E 40s** 20
Dos Caminos | **multi.** 20
Dressler | **W'burg** 24
NEW East Village Yacht | **E Vill** –
Edward's | **TriBeCa** 16
8 Mile Creek | **L Italy** 20
Employees Only | **W Vill** 18
NEW Fette Sau | **W'burg** 19
NEW Flatbush Farm | **Park Slope** 19
Four Seasons | **E 50s** 25
Freemans | **LES** 21
Geisha | **E 60s** 23
NEW Gold St. | **Financial** 15
Gotham B&G | **G Vill** 27
Gramercy Tavern | **Flatiron** 27
NEW Grayz | **W 50s** –
Harry's | **Financial** 22
NEW Hawaiian Tropic | **W 40s** 16
HK | **Garment** 16
NEW House | **Gramercy** 22
Houston's | **multi.** 20
NEW Hudson R. Café | **Harlem** –
Il Bastardo | **Chelsea** 19
'inoteca | **LES** 23
NEW Island | **Astoria** 18
Jean Georges | **W 60s** 28
Keens | **Garment** 24
Kellari Taverna | **W 40s** 23
Koi | **W 40s** 23
Landmarc | **W 60s** 23
Le Cirque | **E 50s** 23

Le Colonial | **E 50s**	20
☑ L'Impero | **E 40s**	26
Lucky Strike | **SoHo**	17
Luz | **Ft Greene**	24
Maloney & Porcelli | **E 50s**	22
Markt | **Flatiron**	19
☑ Masa/Bar Masa | **W 60s**	27
☑ Matsuri | **Chelsea**	23
NEW Maze | **W 50s**	23
NEW Mercat | **NoHo**	–
Michael Jordan's | **E 40s**	20
☑ Modern, The | **W 50s**	26
☑ Morimoto | **Chelsea**	24
NEW Natsumi | **W 50s**	–
NEW Nelson Blue | **Seaport**	–
NEW Noble Food | **NoLita**	–
☑ Nobu 57 | **W 50s**	26
Odeon | **TriBeCa**	19
NEW Omido | **W 50s**	–
One | **Meatpacking**	18
O'Neals' | **W 60s**	17
☑ Ouest | **W 80s**	25
Park, The | **Chelsea**	15
☑ Pastis | **Meatpacking**	21
Patroon | **E 40s**	21
NEW Pera | **E 40s**	22
Piano Due | **W 50s**	25
Porcão | **Gramercy**	21
NEW PT | **W'burg**	24
Quaint | **Sunnyside**	20
NEW Rayuela | **LES**	–
NEW Revel | **Meatpacking**	–
Room Service | **Chelsea**	19
Sala | **NoHo**	22
Samba-Lé | **E Vill**	19
Sapa | **Flatiron**	22
NEW Silent H | **W'burg**	–
☑ Spice Market | **Meatpacking**	22
Stanton Social | **LES**	23
NEW STK | **Meatpacking**	20
Stone Park Café | **Park Slope**	24
☑ Tao | **E 50s**	23
Thor | **LES**	18
Town | **W 50s**	24
212 | **E 60s**	16
NEW Vamos! | **Gramercy**	16
Wollensky's | **E 40s**	23

NATURAL/ORGANIC

(Places specializing in organic, local ingredients)

Angelica Kit. | **E Vill**	21
applewood | **Park Slope**	25
Better Burger | **multi.**	15
Blossom | **Chelsea**	21
NEW BLT Market | **W 50s**	–

☑ Blue Hill | **G Vill**	26
NEW Borough Food | **Flatiron**	–
Brown Café | **LES**	25
Candle | **E 70s**	23
Caravan/Dreams | **E Vill**	24
Chennai Gdn. | **Gramercy**	21
Chestnut | **Carroll Gdns**	23
Cho Dang Gol | **Garment**	21
Chop't Creative | **Union Sq**	20
City Bakery | **Flatiron**	21
Clinton St. Baking | **LES**	24
Cookshop | **Chelsea**	23
Counter | **E Vill**	22
☑ Craft | **Flatiron**	25
Dirty Bird | **W Vill**	17
☑ Eleven Madison | **Gramercy**	26
Employees Only | **W Vill**	18
57 | **E 50s**	22
FireBird | **W 40s**	18
5 Front | **Dumbo**	21
5 Points | **NoHo**	22
NEW Flatbush Farm | **Park Slope**	19
Fornino | **W'burg**	22
☑ Four Seasons | **E 50s**	25
Frankies Spuntino | **multi.**	24
Franny's | **Prospect Hts**	23
fresh | **TriBeCa**	24
Friend of a Farmer | **Gramercy**	17
NEW FR.OG | **SoHo**	21
Gabriel's | **W 60s**	22
Geisha | **E 60s**	23
Ginger | **Harlem**	21
Gobo | **multi.**	22
☑ Grocery | **Carroll Gdns**	26
Home | **G Vill**	20
Ivo & Lulu | **SoHo**	22
Josephina | **W 60s**	18
Josie's | **multi.**	19
L'Ecole | **SoHo**	23
Le Pain Q. | **Flatiron**	19
Mas | **G Vill**	25
New Leaf | **Wash. Hts**	20
Once Upon a Tart | **SoHo**	22
☑ One if by Land | **G Vill**	23
☑ Per Se | **W 60s**	28
PicNic Market | **W 100s**	20
Popover Cafe | **W 80s**	18
Pure Food/Wine | **Gramercy**	22
Rose Water | **Park Slope**	25
Sacred Chow | **G Vill**	23
☑ Saul | **Boerum Hill**	27
Savoy | **SoHo**	24
NEW Silent H | **W'burg**	–
NEW 67 Burger | **Ft Greene**	21
Superfine | **Dumbo**	18

SPECIAL FEATURES

Tasting Rm.	**E Vill**	22
☑ Tocqueville	**Union Sq**	26
Tsampa	**E Vill**	20
Vento	**Meatpacking**	19
Whole Foods	**multi.**	19
Zebú Grill	**E 90s**	21
Zen Palate	**multi.**	19

NOTEWORTHY NEWCOMERS (234)

(* not open at press time, but looks promising)

Accademia/Vino	**E 60s**	-
Adour*	**E 50s**	
Ago*	**TriBeCa**	
A La Turka	**E 70s**	18
Alchemy	**Park Slope**	18
Allen & Delancey*	**LES**	
Almond Flower	**L Italy**	23
Aloe	**E Vill**	-
Amalia	**W 50s**	21
Amazing 66	**Chinatown**	23
Anthos	**W 50s**	25
Asiakan	**W 90s**	19
Babouche	**multi.**	20
Back Forty*	**E Vill**	
Bar Blanc*	**G Vill**	
Bar Boulud*	**W 60s**	
BarFry	**G Vill**	-
Bar Martignetti	**L Italy**	18
Bar Milano*	**Flatiron**	
Bar Tano*	**Park Slope**	
Bar Stuzz.	**Flatiron**	-
Basera*	**W 50s**	
Basso56	**W 50s**	23
Belcourt*	**E Vill**	
Benjamin Steak	**E 40s**	23
Bistro Benoit*	**W 50s**	
Bistro 33	**Astoria**	-
Black Pearl	**Chelsea**	17
Blossom Cafe*	**W 80s**	
BLT Burger	**G Vill**	19
BLT Market	**W 50s**	-
Blue Ribbon Sushi B/G*	**W 50s**	
Bobo*	**W Vill**	
Borough Food	**Flatiron**	-
Brasserie Cognac*	**W 50s**	
brgr	**Chelsea**	18
Broadway East*	**LES**	
Bun*	**SoHo**	
Cacio e Vino	**E Vill**	21
Cafe & Wine	**W 100s**	-
Cafe Cluny	**W Vill**	19
Cafe Fuego	**E Vill**	19
Cafe Tango*	**W 90s**	
Caffe Emilia	**E Vill**	-

Cambodian Cuisine*	**E 90s**	
Caminito	**Harlem**	-
Cantina*	**E Vill**	-
Carniceria	**Cobble Hill**	-
Catch 22	**W'burg**	-
Centro Vinoteca	**W Vill**	-
Chat Noir	**E 60s**	18
Chennai	**E 80s**	-
Cheryl's	**Prospect Hts**	22
Chez Lola	**Clinton Hill**	-
Chiles/Chocolate	**Park Slope**	18
China de Puebla	**Harlem**	-
Co.*	**Chelsea**	
Community Food*	**W 100s**	
Crave	**E 50s**	-
Delicatessen & Mac Bar*	**SoHo**	
Dennis Foy	**TriBeCa**	24
DeStefano's	**W'burg**	-
Dieci	**E Vill**	23
Dovetail*	**W 70s**	
Earthen Oven	**W 70s**	21
East Village Yacht	**E Vill**	-
Ed's Lobster	**NoLita**	23
eighty one*	**W 80s**	
eleven B.	**E Vill**	-
El Quinto Pino*	**Chelsea**	
Estancia	**TriBeCa**	21
E.U., The	**E Vill**	20
Fabio Piccolo	**E 40s**	-
Fette Sau	**W'burg**	19
15 East	**Union Sq**	26
Fiorini	**E 50s**	-
Fireside	**E 50s**	21
Five Guys	**multi.**	-
Flatbush Farm	**Park Slope**	19
FR.OG	**SoHo**	21
Gallo Nero*	**W 40s**	
Gaucho	**W 50s**	-
Gemma	**E Vill**	-
Georgia's/BBQ	**LES**	-
Gold St.	**Financial**	15
☑ Gordon Ramsay	**W 50s**	25
Gottino*	**G Vill**	
Graffiti Bistro*	**E Vill**	
Grange Hall*	**W Vill**	
Grayz	**W 50s**	-
Greenwich Grill*	**TriBeCa**	
Guadalupe	**Inwood**	19
Gus' Place	**G Vill**	20
Hakata Ippudo*	**E Vill**	
Hawaiian Tropic	**W 40s**	16
Hill Country	**Chelsea**	-
House	**Gramercy**	22
Hudson R. Café	**Harlem**	-
Hurapan	**G Vill**	20

Restaurant	Neighborhood	Score
Il Brigante	Seaport	21
Ilili*	Gramercy	
Il Melograno*	W 50s	
Inn LW12	Meatpacking	19
Inside Park/St. Bart's*	E 50s	
Insieme	W 50s	26
Irving Mill*	Gramercy	
Isabella's Oven	LES	-
Island	Astoria	18
Izakaya 10	Chelsea	19
John Dory*	Chelsea	
Johnny Utah	W 50s	-
Kaijou	Financial	-
Kampuchea	LES	20
Kefi	W 70s	23
Ki Sushi	Boerum Hill	25
Klee Brass.	Chelsea	21
Ko*	E Vill	
Kobe Club	W 50s	20
Kopi Tiam*	W 70s	
Kurve*	E Vill	
Kyotofu	W 40s	23
La Bocca di Bacco*	W 50s	
Landmarc	W 60s	23
Le Barricou	W'burg	-
Le Petit Bistro	Chelsea	-
Le Petit Marché	Bklyn Hts	22
Lime Jungle*	W 50s	
Lola*	SoHo	
Los Dados	Meatpacking	-
Lucali	Carroll Gdns	27
Lunetta	Boerum Hill	20
Macho Nacho*	Chelsea	
Madison & Vine*	E 40s	
Mai House	TriBeCa	21
Mantra	E 50s	-
Market Table*	G Vill	
Matilda*	E Vill	
Maze	W 50s	23
Mercat	NoHo	-
Merkato 55*	Meatpacking	
Metro Marché	W 40s	19
Moim	Park Slope	-
Momento	Astoria	-
Morandi	G Vill	19
Natsumi	W 50s	-
Nelson Blue	Seaport	-
Nizza*	W 40s	
Noble Food	NoLita	-
NoNO	Park Slope	19
Nonoosh*	W 60s	
Oak Room*	W 50s	-
Omido	W 50s	
154 South Gate*	W 50s	
Open/Sesame	LES	-
Ovelia	Astoria	21
Pacificana	Sunset Pk	24
Palo Santo	Park Slope	25
Pamplona	Gramercy	-
Park Avenue	E 60s	-
Park Ave. Bistro*	Gramercy	
Pera	E 40s	22
Peri Ela	E 90s	19
Perilla	G Vill	-
Persephone*	E 60s	
Petite Crev.	Carroll Gdns	24
P.J. Clarke's	W 60s	17
p*ong	G Vill	21
Prana*	Gramercy	
Primehouse*	Gramercy	
Provence	SoHo	21
PT	W'burg	24
Public House	E 40s	-
Q*	W Vill	-
Ramen Setagaya	E Vill	-
Rayuela	LES	-
Régate	LES	-
Remedy Diner*	LES	
Resto	Gramercy	-
Revel	Meatpacking	-
Rosanjin	TriBeCa	25
Russian Tea	W 50s	19
Safran	Chelsea	20
Sandro's	E 80s	-
Sasabune	E 70s	26
Saucy	E 70s	-
Savarona*	E 50s	-
savorNY	LES	-
Say*	W Vill	
Sea Salt	E Vill	-
2nd Ave. Deli*	Murray Hill	
Sense	W'burg	-
Sheep Sta.	Park Slope	19
Shorty's B/G*	SoHo	
Silent H	W'burg	-
67 Burger	Ft Greene	21
Smoke Joint	Ft Greene	23
Smith, The*	E Vill	
Smith's*	G Vill	
Socialista	W Vill	-
Solace	E 60s	-
Soto	G Vill	-
Southern Hosp.	E 70s	-
Spice Fusion	W 40s	-
Spirito	Park Slope	-
Spitzer's	LES	-
Spoon	E Vill	-
Spotlight Live	W 40s	-
Stand	G Vill	19
Stella Maris	Seaport	-

Restaurant	
Sticky Rice	LES	19
STK	Meatpacking	20
Suteishi	Seaport	25
Tailor	SoHo	-
Tasca	W Vill	20
T-Bar Steak*	E 70s	
Ted's Montana	W 50s	15
10 Downing*	G Vill	
Toloache	W 50s	
Tree	E Vill	24
Vamos!	Gramercy	16
Vinas*	W'burg	
Visconti*	E 50s	
☑ Wakiya	Gramercy	-
☑ Waverly Inn	W Vill	18
Wild Salmon	E 40s	21
Wildwood*	Flatiron	
Wombat	W'burg	21
Yushi	multi.	-
Zen Burger*	E 40s	
Zenkichi	W'burg	23
Zeppelin*	G Vill	
Zest	SI	26
Zoë Townhouse	E 60s	-
Zoma	Harlem	23

NOTEWORTHY CLOSINGS (88)

Acqua Pazza
Alain Ducasse
Alamo, The
Amici Amore
Anh
Anzu
Aquaterra
Azucar
Barça 18
Basso Est
Blue/Green
Bouillabaisse 126
Bouterin
Brasserie LCB
Bright Food Shop
Café Botanica
Cambalache
Camino Sur
Candela
Chelsea Bistro
Cité
Cité Grill
dévi
dominic
Dona
English is Italian
En Plo
50 Carmine

Fillip's	
Foley's Fish House	
44	
Futura	
Googie's	
Gramercy 24	
Havana Chelsea	
Hedeh	
Honmura An	
Hunan Park	
Ida Mae	
Inside	
In Tent	
Ixta	
Jerry's	
Jezebel	
JivamukTea Cafe	
Jovia	
Kitchen 22	
Lenox Room	
Le Sans Souci	
Little Bistro	
Little Charlie's	
Luxia	
Mangiarini	
Marbella	
March	
Mark's	
Mayrose	
Metsovo	
Meze	
Minnow	
Miss Saigon	
Nice	
Onera	
Pair of 8's	
Pampa	
Paper Moon	
Park East Grill	
Parsonage	
Pinch – Pizza	
Ploes	
Porchetta	
Red Café	
Red Garlic	
Room 4 Dessert	
Sadie Mae's Cafe	
Sascha	
Setacci	
Siam Inn	
Sipan	
66	
Table XII	
Tour	
Tropica	

Ubol's Kitchen
Ureña
Vera Cruz
Vittorio Cucina
Yura & Co.

OUTDOOR DINING

(G=garden; P=patio; S=sidewalk;
T=terrace)

Aesop's Tables | G | **SI**	21
Alma | T | **Carroll Gdns**	20
A.O.C. | G | **W Vill**	20
☑ Aquagrill | T | **SoHo**	26
Barbetta | G | **W 40s**	20
Barolo | G | **SoHo**	18
Bar Pitti | S | **G Vill**	22
Battery Gdns. | G, P, T | **Financial**	18
☑ Blue Hill | G | **G Vill**	26
☑ Blue Water | T | **Union Sq**	23
Boathouse | T | **E 70s**	16
Bottino | G | **Chelsea**	19
Bryant Park | G | **W 40s**	17
Cabana | T | **Seaport**	21
Cacio e Pepe | G, S | **E Vill**	22
Cafe Centro | S | **E 40s**	20
Cafe Fiorello | S | **W 60s**	20
☑ Cávo | G, P | **Astoria**	21
Coffee Shop | S | **Union Sq**	15
Conviv. Osteria | G | **Park Slope**	25
Da Nico | G, S | **L Italy**	21
Da Silvano | S | **G Vill**	20
East of 8th | G | **Chelsea**	16
Employees Only | G | **W Vill**	18
Esca | P | **W 40s**	25
Farm/Adderley | G | **Ditmas Pk**	23
5 Front | G | **Dumbo**	21
Gascogne | G | **Chelsea**	22
Gavroche | G | **W Vill**	19
Gigino | P, S | **multi.**	20
Gnocco Caffe | G | **E Vill**	21
☑ Grocery | G | **Carroll Gdns**	26
Home | G | **G Vill**	20
I Coppi | G | **E Vill**	23
Il Gattopardo | P | **W 50s**	23
Il Palazzo | S | **L Italy**	23
Isabella's | S | **W 70s**	20
I Trulli | G | **Gramercy**	22
Jolie | G | **Boerum Hill**	20
La Bottega | T | **Chelsea**	18
Lake Club | G | **SI**	21
La Lanterna | G | **G Vill**	20
La Mangeoire | S | **E 50s**	19
L & B Spumoni | G | **Bensonhurst**	22
Lattanzi | G, T | **W 40s**	22
Le Jardin Bistro | G | **NoLita**	18
Le Refuge | G | **E 80s**	21

☑ L'Impero | P | **E 40s**	26
Long Tan | G | **Park Slope**	19
Loulou | G | **Ft Greene**	22
Marina Cafe | T | **SI**	18
Markt | S | **Flatiron**	19
New Leaf | P | **Wash. Hts**	20
Ocean Grill | S | **W 70s**	23
One | S | **Meatpacking**	18
Ono | G, S | **Meatpacking**	21
Osaka | G | **Cobble Hill**	21
Pampano | T | **E 40s**	25
Panino'teca | G | **Carroll Gdns**	18
Paradou | G | **Meatpacking**	19
Park, The | G | **Chelsea**	15
☑ Pastis | S | **Meatpacking**	21
Patois | G | **Carroll Gdns**	21
Pete's Tavern | S | **Gramercy**	14
Portofino's | T | **Bronx**	19
Pure Food/Wine | G | **Gramercy**	22
Relish | G | **W'burg**	22
NEW Revel | G | **Meatpacking**	–
Ribot | T | **E 40s**	19
☑ River Café | G | **Dumbo**	26
Riverdale Gdn. | G | **Bronx**	24
Rock Ctr. | T | **W 50s**	19
Sahara | G | **Gravesend**	20
Sea Grill | G | **W 40s**	24
☑ Sripraphai | G | **Woodside**	26
Surya | G | **W Vill**	24
Sweet Melissa | G | **Cobble Hill**	21
Tartine | S | **W Vill**	22
☑ Tavern on Green | G | **W 60s**	15
Terrace in the Sky | T | **W 100s**	22
NEW Tree | G | **E Vill**	24
Vento | S | **Meatpacking**	19
ViceVersa | G | **W 50s**	23
Water Club | P | **Murray Hill**	20
Water's Edge | P | **LIC**	23
Wollensky's | S | **E 40s**	23
Zum Schneider | S | **E Vill**	18

POWER SCENES

☑ Bar Americain | **W 50s**	23
Ben Benson's | **W 50s**	24
BLT Prime | **Gramercy**	24
Bobby Van's | **E 40s**	22
Bull & Bear | **E 40s**	19
☑ Carlyle | **E 70s**	21
China Grill | **W 50s**	22
City Hall | **TriBeCa**	21
Coco Pazzo | **E 70s**	22
☑ Daniel | **E 60s**	28
Delmonico's | **Financial**	22
☑ Del Posto | **Chelsea**	25
Elio's | **E 80s**	23
☑ Four Seasons | **E 50s**	25

SPECIAL FEATURES

Fresco | **E 50s**

Gallagher's | **W 50s** 20

Gilt | **E 50s** 25

Ⓩ Gotham B&G | **G Vill** 27

Harry's | **Financial** 22

Ⓩ Jean Georges | **W 60s** 28

Keens | **Garment** 24

Ⓩ La Grenouille | **E 50s** 27

Ⓩ Le Bernardin | **W 50s** 28

Le Cirque | **E 50s** 23

Lever House | **E 50s** 22

Michael's | **W 50s** 21

Ⓩ Nobu | **TriBeCa** 27

Ⓩ Nobu 57 | **W 50s** 26

Norma's | **W 50s** 25

Patroon | **E 40s** 21

Ⓩ Peter Luger | **W'burg** 28

Rao's | **Harlem** 22

Regency | **E 60s** 18

NEW Russian Tea | **W 50s** 19

Sant Ambroeus | **multi.** 22

Smith & Wollensky | **E 40s** 23

Solo | **E 50s** 22

Ⓩ Sparks | **E 40s** 25

Ⓩ 21 Club | **W 50s** 22

NEWⓏ Wakiya | **Gramercy** -

NEWⓏ Waverly Inn | **W Vill** 18

PRIVATE ROOMS/ PARTIES

(Restaurants charge less at off times; call for capacity)

Arabelle | **E 60s** 21

Barbetta | **W 40s** 20

Battery Gdns. | **Financial** 18

Beacon | **W 50s** 22

Ben & Jack's | **E 40s** 23

BLT Fish | **Flatiron** 23

BLT Prime | **Gramercy** 24

BLT Steak | **E 50s** 24

Ⓩ Blue Hill | **G Vill** 26

Blue Smoke | **Gramercy** 22

Ⓩ Blue Water | **Union Sq** 23

Ⓩ Buddakan | **Chelsea** 23

Ⓩ Café Gray | **W 60s** 25

Capital Grille | **E 40s** 23

Cellini | **E 50s** 21

Centolire | **E 80s** 20

City Hall | **TriBeCa** 21

Ⓩ Compass | **W 70s** 22

Country | **Gramercy** 23

Ⓩ Craft | **Flatiron** 25

Ⓩ Daniel | **E 60s** 28

Ⓩ Danube | **TriBeCa** 26

Ⓩ Del Frisco's | **W 40s** 25

Delmonico's | **Financial** 22

Ⓩ Del Posto | **Chelsea** 25

Ⓩ Eleven Madison | **Gramercy** 26

EN Japanese | **W Vill** 22

ESPN Zone | **W 40s** 12

Ⓩ Felidia | **E 50s** 25

Fiamma Osteria | **SoHo** 25

F.illi Ponte | **TriBeCa** 21

FireBird | **W 40s** 18

Ⓩ Four Seasons | **E 50s** 25

Fresco | **E 50s** 23

Gabriel's | **W 60s** 22

Geisha | **E 60s** 23

Ⓩ Gramercy Tavern | **Flatiron** 27

NEW Grayz | **W 50s** -

Il Buco | **NoHo** 25

Il Cortile | **L Italy** 23

'inoteca | **LES** 23

Ⓩ Jean Georges | **W 60s** 28

Keens | **Garment** 24

Ⓩ La Grenouille | **E 50s** 27

Landmark Tavern | **W 40s** 18

Ⓩ Le Bernardin | **W 50s** 28

Le Cirque | **E 50s** 23

Le Perigord | **E 50s** 24

Lever House | **E 50s** 22

Le Zie 2000 | **Chelsea** 21

Ⓩ L'Impero | **E 40s** 26

Maloney & Porcelli | **E 50s** 22

Ⓩ Matsuri | **Chelsea** 23

Ⓩ Megu | **TriBeCa** 24

Michael's | **W 50s** 21

Mi Cocina | **W Vill** 22

Ⓩ Milos | **W 50s** 26

Ⓩ Modern, The | **W 50s** 26

Moran's | **Chelsea** 18

Mr. Chow | **E 50s** 20

Ⓩ Mr. K's | **E 50s** 23

Ⓩ Nobu | **TriBeCa** 27

Ⓩ Nobu 57 | **W 50s** 26

Oceana | **E 50s** 26

Park, The | **Chelsea** 15

Patroon | **E 40s** 21

Periyali | **Flatiron** 23

Ⓩ Per Se | **W 60s** 28

Ⓩ Picholine | **W 60s** 27

Redeye Grill | **W 50s** 20

Remi | **W 50s** 22

Re Sette | **W 40s** 23

Riingo | **E 40s** 19

Ⓩ River Café | **Dumbo** 26

Rock Ctr. | **W 50s** 19

Sambuca | **W 70s** 18

Shun Lee Palace | **E 50s** 24

Solo | **E 50s** 22

Ⓩ Sparks | **E 40s** 25

☑ Spice Market | **Meatpacking**	22
☑ Tabla | **Gramercy**	25
☑ Tao | **E 50s**	23
☑ Tavern on Green | **W 60s**	15
Terrace in the Sky | **W 100s**	22
Thalassa | **TriBeCa**	22
☑ Tocqueville | **Union Sq**	26
Tribeca Grill | **TriBeCa**	22
☑ 21 Club | **W 50s**	22
212 | **E 60s**	16
Vento | **Meatpacking**	19
Water Club | **Murray Hill**	20

PUBS/MICROBREWERIES

(See Zagat NYC Nightlife)

Angus McIndoe | **W 40s**	16
Chadwick's | **Bay Ridge**	22
ChipShop | **Bklyn Hts**	18
Corner Bistro | **W Vill**	22
8 Mile Creek | **L Italy**	20
NEW E.U., The | **E Vill**	20
Heartland | **multi.**	14
NEW Inn LW12 | **Meatpacking**	19
Jackson Hole | **multi.**	17
J.G. Melon | **E 70s**	21
Joe Allen | **W 40s**	17
Killmeyer Bavarian | **SI**	21
Landmark Tavern | **W 40s**	18
O'Neals' | **W 60s**	17
Pete's Tavern | **Gramercy**	14
P.J. Clarke's | **multi.**	17
NEW Public House | **E 40s**	–
Spotted Pig | **W Vill**	22
Walker's | **TriBeCa**	17
Wollensky's | **E 40s**	23

QUICK BITES

Amorina | **Prospect Hts**	23
Amy's Bread | **multi.**	23
Azuri Cafe | **W 50s**	25
Bereket | **LES**	18
Better Burger | **multi.**	15
NEW BLT Burger | **G Vill**	19
Blue 9 Burger | **E Vill**	18
Brennan | **Sheepshead**	19
Burritoville | **multi.**	16
Caracas | **E Vill**	26
Carl's Steaks | **Murray Hill**	22
China Fun | **multi.**	16
ChipShop | **Park Slope**	18
Chop't Creative | **multi.**	20
City Bakery | **Flatiron**	21
Coals | **Bronx**	22
Columbus Bakery | **W 80s**	18
Così | **multi.**	16
Cozy | **G Vill**	18

☑ Daisy May's | **W 40s**	24
David Burke/Bloom. | **E 50s**	18
Dishes | **E 40s**	22
Dumpling Man | **E Vill**	19
Ess-a-Bagel | **multi.**	23
F & B | **Chelsea**	18
Fresco | **E 50s**	23
goodburger | **E 40s**	18
Good Enough/Eat | **W 80s**	20
Gray's Papaya | **multi.**	20
Hale/Hearty | **multi.**	19
Hampton Chutney | **SoHo**	20
'ino | **G Vill**	24
Island Burgers | **W 50s**	22
Joe's Pizza | **multi.**	23
Kati Roll Co. | **multi.**	20
La Esquina | **L Italy**	21
Leo's Latticini | **Corona**	28
Morgan | **Murray Hill**	20
Nicky's Viet. | **multi.**	21
99 Mi. to Philly | **E Vill**	18
NEW Omido | **W 50s**	–
Once Upon a Tart | **SoHo**	22
Papaya King | **multi.**	20
Pastrami Queen | **E 70s**	19
Peanut Butter Co. | **G Vill**	20
Press 195 | **Park Slope**	20
Pump Energy | **multi.**	19
Rice 'n' Beans | **W 50s**	19
Rickshaw Dumpling | **Flatiron**	18
Risotteria | **G Vill**	21
Shake Shack | **Flatiron**	23
NEW Silent H | **W'burg**	–
NEW Spice Fusion | **W 40s**	–
Tossed | **multi.**	18
Two Boots | **multi.**	18
Westville | **W Vill**	23
Whole Foods | **multi.**	19
'wichcraft | **TriBeCa**	20
Zabar's Cafe | **W 80s**	20
Zip Burger | **E 50s**	18

QUIET CONVERSATION

☑ Alto | **E 50s**	26
Arabelle | **E 60s**	21
Aroma | **NoHo**	24
☑ Asiate | **W 60s**	24
Café Pierre | **E 60s**	23
☑ Chanterelle | **TriBeCa**	27
NEW Dieci | **E Vill**	23
El Paso | **G Vill**	–
Fleur de Sel | **Flatiron**	25
Giovanni | **E 80s**	22
Il Gattopardo | **W 50s**	23
Jarnac | **W Vill**	22
☑ Jean Georges | **W 60s**	28

Kai | **E 60s**	25
Kings' Carriage | **E 80s**	21
Knife + Fork | **E Vill**	23
NEW Kyotofu | **W 40s**	23
Z La Grenouille | **E 50s**	27
NEW Le Barricou | **W'burg**	–
Z Le Bernardin | **W 50s**	28
Lumi | **E 70s**	19
Z Masa/Bar Masa | **W 60s**	27
Z Mr. K's | **E 50s**	23
North Sq. | **G Vill**	22
Z Per Se | **W 60s**	28
NEW Petite Crev. | **Carroll Gdns**	24
Petrossian | **W 50s**	24
Z Picholine | **W 60s**	27
Provence/Boite | **Carroll Gdns**	20
NEW PT | **W'burg**	24
NEW Rosanjin | **TriBeCa**	25
NEW savorNY | **LES**	–
Sfoglia | **E 90s**	23
Sorrel | **Prospect Hts**	23
Terrace in the Sky | **W 100s**	22
Z Tocqueville | **Union Sq**	26
NEW Tree | **E Vill**	24
Tsampa | **E Vill**	20
12 Chairs | **SoHo**	19
NEW Zenkichi | **W'burg**	23

RAW BARS

American Grill | **SI**	20
Angus McIndoe | **W 40s**	16
Z Aquagrill | **SoHo**	26
Z Atlantic Grill | **E 70s**	22
Baldoria | **W 40s**	22
Z Balthazar | **SoHo**	23
Z Bar Americain | **W 50s**	23
Ben & Jack's | **E 40s**	23
NEW Black Pearl | **Chelsea**	17
BLT Fish | **Flatiron**	23
bluechili | **W 50s**	19
Blue Fin | **W 40s**	22
Z Blue Ribbon | **multi.**	25
Blue Smoke | **Gramercy**	22
Z Blue Water | **Union Sq**	23
Bond 45 | **W 40s**	20
Brooklyn Fish | **Park Slope**	23
City Crab | **Flatiron**	17
City Hall | **TriBeCa**	21
City Lobster | **W 40s**	18
Craftsteak | **Chelsea**	22
Ditch Plains | **G Vill**	17
Docks Oyster | **multi.**	19
East Buffet | **Flushing**	20
NEW East Village Yacht | **E Vill**	–
NEW Ed's Lobster | **NoLita**	23
Employees Only | **W Vill**	18

NEW E.U., The | **E Vill**	20
Fish | **G Vill**	20
Gin Lane | **Chelsea**	17
Giorgione | **SoHo**	23
Jack's Lux. | **E Vill**	24
Le Singe Vert | **Chelsea**	19
London Lennie's | **Rego Pk**	21
Lure Fishbar | **SoHo**	23
Markt | **Flatiron**	19
McCormick/Schmick | **W 50s**	20
Mercer Kitchen | **SoHo**	22
Mermaid Inn | **E Vill**	23
Metrazur | **E 40s**	20
NEW Natsumi | **W 50s**	–
Neptune Rm. | **W 80s**	22
Ocean Grill | **W 70s**	23
Olea | **Ft Greene**	20
Oyster Bar | **E 40s**	21
P.J. Clarke's | **E 50s**	17
NEW Provence | **SoHo**	21
San Luigi | **W 70s**	16
Shaffer City | **Flatiron**	21
Shelly's Tratt. | **W 50s**	20
Shula's | **W 40s**	20
South Fin Grill | **SI**	20
NEW Spitzer's | **LES**	–
NEW Stella Maris | **Seaport**	–
Thalia | **W 50s**	21
Tides | **LES**	24
Todai | **Murray Hill**	18
Trata Estiatorio | **E 70s**	21
Umberto's | **multi.**	18
Uncle Jack's | **Garment**	23
Water Club | **Murray Hill**	20
Water's Edge | **LIC**	23
NEW Wild Salmon | **E 40s**	21

ROMANTIC PLACES

Aix Brasserie | **W 80s**	20
Algonquin | **W 40s**	16
Alma | **Carroll Gdns**	20
Alta | **G Vill**	23
Z Asiate | **W 60s**	24
Z Aureole | **E 60s**	27
Z Balthazar | **SoHo**	23
Barbetta | **W 40s**	20
Barolo | **SoHo**	18
Battery Gdns. | **Financial**	18
Z Blue Hill | **G Vill**	26
Blue Ribbon Bakery | **G Vill**	24
Boathouse | **E 70s**	16
Bottino | **Chelsea**	19
Z Bouley | **TriBeCa**	28
Z Café des Artistes | **W 60s**	22
Café Pierre | **E 60s**	23
Caffé/Green | **Bayside**	21

CamaJe | **G Vill**	23
Capsouto Frères | **TriBeCa**	24
Caviar Russe | **E 50s**	24
☒ Chanterelle | **TriBeCa**	27
Chez Josephine | **W 40s**	20
Conviv. Osteria | **Park Slope**	25
Country | **Gramercy**	23
Danal | **E Vill**	22
☒ Daniel | **E 60s**	28
☒ Danube | **TriBeCa**	26
☒ davidburke/dona. | **E 60s**	25
Erminia | **E 80s**	25
FireBird | **W 40s**	18
Firenze | **E 80s**	21
5 Front | **Dumbo**	21
Fleur de Sel | **Flatiron**	25
Flor de Sol | **TriBeCa**	20
☒ Four Seasons | **E 50s**	25
Frankies Spuntino | **LES**	24
☒ Garden Cafe | **Prospect Hts**	27
Gascogne | **Chelsea**	22
Gigino | **Financial**	20
☒ Grocery | **Carroll Gdns**	26
NEW House | **Gramercy**	22
I Coppi | **E Vill**	23
Il Buco | **NoHo**	25
I Trulli | **Gramercy**	22
Jack Bistro | **G Vill**	17
Jack's Lux. | **E Vill**	24
JoJo | **E 60s**	24
Jolie | **Boerum Hill**	20
Kings' Carriage | **E 80s**	21
Kitchen Club | **NoLita**	22
NEW Kyotofu | **W 40s**	23
L'Absinthe | **E 60s**	22
Lady Mendl's | **Gramercy**	22
☒ La Grenouille | **E 50s**	27
La Lanterna | **G Vill**	20
La Mangeoire | **E 50s**	19
La Ripaille | **W Vill**	23
Las Ramblas | **G Vill**	23
Le Gigot | **G Vill**	24
Le Refuge | **E 80s**	21
Le Refuge Inn | **Bronx**	24
☒ L'Impero | **E 40s**	26
Maria Pia | **W 50s**	19
Mas | **G Vill**	25
☒ Mr. K's | **E 50s**	23
Nino's | **E 70s**	21
Oliva | **LES**	20
☒ One if by Land | **G Vill**	23
NEW Ovelia | **Astoria**	21
Pam Real Thai | **W 40s**	22
Paola's | **E 80s**	23
Pasha | **W 70s**	21

Patois | **Carroll Gdns**	21
Periyali | **Flatiron**	23
Petrossian | **W 50s**	24
Philip Marie | **W Vill**	20
Piano Due | **W 50s**	25
Piccola Venezia | **Astoria**	25
Pinocchio | **E 90s**	21
Place, The | **W Vill**	21
Portofino Grille | **E 60s**	19
Primavera | **E 80s**	22
NEW Provence | **SoHo**	21
NEW PT | **W'burg**	24
Quercy | **Cobble Hill**	20
☒ Rainbow Room/Grill | **W 40s**	19
Raoul's | **SoHo**	24
René Pujol | **W 50s**	22
☒ River Café | **Dumbo**	26
Roc | **TriBeCa**	21
Sacred Chow | **G Vill**	23
Savoy | **SoHo**	24
☒ Scalini Fedeli | **TriBeCa**	26
Sistina | **E 80s**	24
☒ Spice Market | **Meatpacking**	22
Suba | **LES**	21
Teodora | **E 50s**	22
Terrace in the Sky | **W 100s**	22
☒ Tocqueville | **Union Sq**	26
Town | **W 50s**	24
Uva | **E 70s**	21
View, The | **W 40s**	18
Wallsé | **W Vill**	26
Water Club | **Murray Hill**	20
Water's Edge | **LIC**	23
NEW Zenkichi | **W'burg**	23

SENIOR APPEAL

Arabelle | **E 60s**	21
Arté | **G Vill**	19
Artie's Deli | **W 80s**	18
☒ Aureole | **E 60s**	27
Baldoria | **W 40s**	22
Bamonte's | **W'burg**	23
Barbetta | **W 40s**	20
Barney Greengrass | **W 80s**	23
Borgo Antico | **G Vill**	19
☒ Café des Artistes | **W 60s**	22
Caffé/Green | **Bayside**	21
Campagnola | **E 70s**	23
Capsouto Frères | **TriBeCa**	24
Chadwick's | **Bay Ridge**	22
Chez Napoléon | **W 50s**	20
Coco Pazzo | **E 70s**	22
Dawat | **E 50s**	23
DeGrezia | **E 50s**	22
☒ Del Posto | **Chelsea**	25
Embers | **Bay Ridge**	22

SPECIAL FEATURES

Felidia | **E 50s**	25
NEW Fiorini | **E 50s**	-
Gallagher's | **W 50s**	20
Giovanni | **E 80s**	22
Grifone | **E 40s**	23
Il Nido | **E 50s**	23
☑ Il Tinello | **W 50s**	26
☑ Jean Georges | **W 60s**	28
La Bonne Soupe | **W 50s**	18
La Goulue | **E 60s**	20
La Mangeoire | **E 50s**	19
La Mediterranée | **E 50s**	19
La Mirabelle | **W 80s**	22
La Petite Aub. | **Gramercy**	20
Lattanzi | **W 40s**	22
Le Boeuf/Mode | **E 80s**	21
Le Marais | **W 40s**	20
Le Perigord | **E 50s**	24
Levana | **W 60s**	20
Lusardi's | **E 70s**	24
MarkJoseph | **Financial**	24
Montparnasse | **E 50s**	19
☑ Mr. K's | **E 50s**	23
Nicola's | **E 80s**	22
Nippon | **E 50s**	22
Pastrami Queen | **E 70s**	19
Paul & Jimmy's | **Gramercy**	19
Piccola Venezia | **Astoria**	25
Pietro's | **E 40s**	23
Ponticello | **Astoria**	23
Primola | **E 60s**	23
Quattro Gatti | **E 80s**	20
☑ Rao's | **Harlem**	22
René Pujol | **W 50s**	22
☑ River Café | **Dumbo**	26
Rossini's | **Murray Hill**	23
Rughetta | **E 80s**	22
NEW Russian Tea | **W 50s**	19
Sal Anthony's | **E Vill**	19
San Pietro | **E 50s**	24
Sardi's | **W 40s**	16
☑ Saul | **Boerum Hill**	27
Scaletta | **W 70s**	21
Shun Lee West | **W 60s**	23
☑ Tavern on Green | **W 60s**	15
12 Chairs | **SoHo**	19

SINGLES SCENES

Angelo & Maxie's | **Flatiron**	21
☑ Asia de Cuba | **Murray Hill**	23
Aspen | **Flatiron**	20
☑ Atlantic Grill | **E 70s**	22
Baraonda | **E 70s**	18
Blue Fin | **W 40s**	22
☑ Blue Ribbon | **multi.**	25
☑ Blue Water | **Union Sq**	23

Boca Chica | **E Vill**	20
Brasserie 8½ | **W 50s**	22
Brother Jimmy's | **multi.**	16
Bryant Park | **W 40s**	17
☑ Buddakan | **Chelsea**	23
☑ Buddha Bar | **Meatpacking**	19
Butter | **E Vill**	19
Cabana | **multi.**	21
Canyon Road | **E 70s**	19
Chinatown Brass. | **NoHo**	21
Citrus B&G | **W 70s**	20
Coffee Shop | **Union Sq**	15
Dos Caminos | **multi.**	20
East of 8th | **Chelsea**	16
NEW East Village Yacht | **E Vill**	-
Elephant, The | **E Vill**	21
elmo | **Chelsea**	15
Employees Only | **W Vill**	18
Essex | **LES**	16
Félix | **SoHo**	16
Flor de Sol | **TriBeCa**	20
Freemans | **LES**	21
NEW Gold St. | **Financial**	15
Heartland | **multi.**	14
Houston's | **multi.**	20
Hudson Cafeteria | **W 50s**	19
Ideya | **SoHo**	20
'inoteca | **LES**	23
Isabella's | **W 70s**	20
NEW Island | **Astoria**	18
Jane | **G Vill**	21
Japonais | **Gramercy**	20
Joya | **Cobble Hill**	23
NEW Kobe Club | **W 50s**	20
Koi | **W 40s**	23
La Esquina | **L Italy**	21
La Goulue | **E 60s**	20
Lure Fishbar | **SoHo**	23
Maloney & Porcelli | **E 50s**	22
Markt | **Flatiron**	19
☑ Mesa Grill | **Flatiron**	24
Monkey Bar | **E 50s**	-
One | **Meatpacking**	18
Otto | **G Vill**	22
Pam Real Thai | **W 40s**	22
☑ Pastis | **Meatpacking**	21
Peep | **SoHo**	19
Pete's Tavern | **Gramercy**	14
Pipa | **Flatiron**	21
Punch | **Flatiron**	19
Ruby Foo's | **multi.**	19
Schiller's | **LES**	18
☑ Spice Market | **Meatpacking**	22
NEW STK | **Meatpacking**	20
Suba | **LES**	21

SushiSamba | **multi.** 22

☑ Tao | **E 50s** 23

Thor | **LES** 18

Tribeca Grill | **TriBeCa** 22

Xunta | **E Vill** 19

Zarela | **E 50s** 21

SLEEPERS

(Good to excellent food, but little known)

Aliseo Osteria | **Prospect Hts** 23

NEW Almond Flower | **L Italy** 23

NEW Amazing 66 | **Chinatown** 23

Amorina | **Prospect Hts** 22

Aroma | **NoHo** 24

Azul Bistro | **LES** 22

Bayou | **SI** 22

Blue Ginger | **Chelsea** 22

Bocelli | **SI** 25

Brioso | **SI** 25

Brown Café | **LES** 25

Butai | **Gramercy** 22

Caffe Bondi | **SI** 22

CamaJe | **G Vill** 23

Chanto | **G Vill** 22

Charles' Kitchen | **Harlem** 24

NEW Cheryl's | **Prospect Hts** 22

Chiyono | **E Vill** 23

Coals | **Bronx** 22

NEW Dieci | **E Vill** 23

Eliá | **Bay Ridge** 25

NEW 15 East | **Union Sq** 26

Ghenet | **NoLita** 22

Giovanni | **E 80s** 22

NEW House | **Gramercy** 22

Ichimura | **E 50s** 22

Ivo & Lulu | **SoHo** 22

JJ's Asian Fusion | **Astoria** 25

NEW Ki Sushi | **Boerum Hill** 25

La Cantina Toscana | **E 60s** 24

La Ripaille | **W Vill** 23

Leela Lounge | **G Vill** 22

Le Miu | **E Vill** 25

Leo's Latticini | **Corona** 28

NEW Le Petit Marché | **Bklyn Hts** 22

Le Refuge Inn | **Bronx** 24

Locanda Vini | **Clinton Hill** 26

Londel's | **Harlem** 22

Loulou | **Ft Greene** 22

NEW Lucali | **Carroll Gdns** 27

Luz | **Ft Greene** 24

Mamlouk | **E Vill** 23

Nippon | **E 50s** 22

Noche Mexicana | **W 100s** 22

Nomad | **E Vill** 22

NEW Pacificana | **Sunset Pk** 24

NEW Palo Santo | **Park Slope** 25

Park Terrace | **Inwood** 22

NEW Petite Crev. | **Carroll Gdns** 24

NEW PT | **W'burg** 24

NEW Rosanjin | **TriBeCa** 25

Sachiko's | **LES** 25

Sacred Chow | **G Vill** 23

Saravanaas | **Gramercy** 23

NEW Sasabune | **E 70s** 26

Siam Sq. | **Bronx** 24

Solo | **E 50s** 25

Sorrel | **Prospect Hts** 23

NEW Suteishi | **Seaport** 25

Tevere | **E 80s** 22

Thai Pavilion | **Astoria** 22

Tides | **LES** 24

NEW Tree | **E Vill** 24

Willie's | **Bronx** 23

Yuva | **E 50s** 24

NEW Zenkichi | **W'burg** 23

Zerza | **E Vill** 22

NEW Zest | **SI** 26

NEW Zoma | **Harlem** 23

Zucco | **LES** 22

SUNDAY BEST BETS

(See also Hotel Dining)

☑ Aquagrill | **SoHo** 26

☑ Aquavit | **E 50s** 25

☑ Artisanal | **Murray Hill** 23

☑ Balthazar | **SoHo** 23

☑ Bar Americain | **W 50s** 23

☑ Blue Hill | **G Vill** 26

☑ Blue Ribbon | **SoHo** 25

☑ Blue Water | **Union Sq** 23

☑ Bouley | **TriBeCa** 28

Café de Bruxelles | **W Vill** 21

☑ Café des Artistes | **W 60s** 22

Chez Oskar | **Ft Greene** 19

Coco Pazzo | **E 70s** 22

☑ davidburke/dona. | **E 60s** 25

Demarchelier | **E 80s** 17

5 Points | **NoHo** 22

☑ Gotham B&G | **G Vill** 27

☑ Gramercy Tavern | **Flatiron** 27

La Mediterranée | **E 50s** 19

Lucky Strike | **SoHo** 17

☑ Lupa | **G Vill** 25

☑ Mesa Grill | **Flatiron** 24

Mi Cocina | **W Vill** 22

Moran's | **Chelsea** 18

Odeon | **TriBeCa** 19

☑ Ouest | **W 80s** 25

Our Place | **E 50s** 20

☑ Peter Luger | **W'burg** 28

Piccolo Angolo | **W Vill**
☑ Picholine | **W 60s** — 27
Prune | **E Vill** — 24
☑ River Café | **Dumbo** — 26
Solo | **E 50s** — 22
Tratt. Dell'Arte | **W 50s** — 22
Tribeca Grill | **TriBeCa** — 22
☑ Union Sq. Cafe | **Union Sq** — 26
Water Club | **Murray Hill** — 20
Zoë | **SoHo** — 20

TASTING MENUS

($ minimum)
☑ Alto | $115 | **E 50s** — 26
Amma | $50 | **E 50s** — 24
☑ Annisa | $68 | **G Vill** — 27
Anthos | $85 | **W 50s** — 25
applewood | $55 | **Park Slope** — 25
☑ Aquavit | $115 | **E 50s** — 25
Asiate | $125 | **W 60s** — 24
Aureole | $95 | **E 60s** — 27
☑ Babbo | $70 | **G Vill** — 27
Blue Hill | $72 | **G Vill** — 27
Café Boulud | $125 | **E 70s** — 27
Café Gray | $135 | **W 60s** — 25
☑ Chanterelle | $125 | **TriBeCa** — 27
Country | $135 | **Gramercy** — 23
☑ Cru | $110 | **G Vill** — 26
☑ Daniel | $155 | **E 60s** — 28
☑ Danube | $90 | **TriBeCa** — 26
☑ davidburke/dona. | $85 | **E 60s** — 25
Dawat | $65 | **E 50s** — 23
☑ Del Posto | $120 | **Chelsea** — 25
Donguri | $85 | **E 80s** — 27
☑ Eleven Madison | $145 | **Gramercy** — 26
Esca | $75 | **W 40s** — 25
Falai | $80 | **LES** — 25
☑ Felidia | $85 | **E 50s** — 25
15 East | $120 | **Union Sq** — 26
Fleur de Sel | $89 | **Flatiron** — 25
☑ Four Seasons | $135 | **E 50s** — 25
fresh | $75 | **TriBeCa** — 24
☑ Gari/Sushi | $70 | **multi.** — 26
Gilt | $105 | **E 50s** — 25
☑ Gordon Ramsay | $120 | **W 50s** — 25
☑ Gramercy Tavern | $110 | **Flatiron** — 27
☑ Grocery | $75 | **Carroll Gdns** — 26
Hearth | $75 | **E Vill** — 25
Insieme | $85 | **W 50s** — 26
Jack's Lux. | $50 | **E Vill** — 24
☑ Jean Georges | $128 | **W 60s** — 28
Jewel Bako | $95 | **E Vill** — 25
JoJo | $65 | **E 60s** — 24

☑ Kittichai | $65 | **SoHo** — 23
Knife + Fork | $45 | **E Vill** — 23
Kuruma Zushi | $250 | **E 40s** — 28
☑ La Grenouille | $130 | **E 50s** — 27
☑ L'Atelier/Robuchon | $190 | **E 50s** — 27
☑ Le Bernardin | $135 | **W 50s** — 28
Le Miu | $55 | **E Vill** — 25
☑ L'Impero | $110 | **E 40s** — 26
Mas | $95 | **G Vill** — 25
☑ Masa | $400 | **W 60s** — 27
Maze | $75 | **W 50s** — 23
☑ Modern, The | $125 | **W 50s** — 26
☑ Morimoto | $120 | **Chelsea** — 24
☑ Nobu | $100 | **TriBeCa** — 27
Oceana | $110 | **E 50s** — 26
Payard Bistro | $72 | **E 70s** — 24
☑ Per Se | $250 | **W 60s** — 28
Piano Due | $85 | **W 50s** — 25
☑ Picholine | $110 | **W 60s** — 27
Pó | $50 | **multi.** — 25
☑ River Café | $115 | **Dumbo** — 26
Rosanjin | $150 | **TriBeCa** — 25
Rose Water | $54 | **Park Slope** — 25
Sasabune | $70 | **E 70s** — 26
☑ Saul | $85 | **Boerum Hill** — 27
☑ Scalini Fedeli | $90 | **TriBeCa** — 26
Spigolo | $70 | **E 80s** — 25
☑ Sugiyama | $86 | **W 50s** — 27
☑ Sushi Seki | $70 | **E 60s** — 27
☑ Tabla | $79 | **Gramercy** — 25
☑ Telepan | $64 | **W 60s** — 25
Tempo | $55 | **Park Slope** — 25
☑ Tocqueville | $90 | **Union Sq** — 26
Town | $95 | **W 50s** — 24
Wallsé | $70 | **W Vill** — 26
Zenkichi | $88 | **W'burg** — 23

TEA SERVICE

Alice's Tea Cup | **multi.** — 19
American Girl | **E 40s** — 13
BG | **W 50s** — 20
Café Pierre | **E 60s** — 23
Danal | **E Vill** — 22
Kings' Carriage | **E 80s** — 21
Lady Mendl's | **Gramercy** — 22
NEW Maze | **W 50s** — 23
Morgan | **Murray Hill** — 20
North Sq. | **G Vill** — 22
Payard Bistro | **E 70s** — 24
Sant Ambroeus | **multi.** — 22
Sarabeth's | **multi.** — 20
Soda Shop | **TriBeCa** — 19
Sweet Melissa | **multi.** — 21
Tea & Sympathy | **W Vill** — 19
Tea Box | **E 50s** — 20

teany | **LES**	18
202 Cafe | **Chelsea**	21

THEME RESTAURANTS

Brooklyn Diner | **multi.**	17
Bubba Gump | **W 40s**	14
Cowgirl | **W Vill**	16
ESPN Zone | **W 40s**	12
Hard Rock Cafe | **W 40s**	13
NEW Hawaiian Tropic | **W 40s**	16
NEW Johnny Utah | **W 50s**	–
Ninja | **TriBeCa**	19
Shula's | **W 40s**	20

TRANSPORTING EXPERIENCES

Z Asiate | **W 60s**	24
Z Balthazar | **SoHo**	23
Boathouse | **E 70s**	16
Z Buddakan | **Chelsea**	23
Z Buddha Bar | **Meatpacking**	19
Z Café des Artistes | **W 60s**	22
Chez Josephine | **W 40s**	20
FireBird | **W 40s**	18
Fraunces Tavern | **Financial**	15
Il Buco | **NoHo**	25
Keens | **Garment**	24
Z La Grenouille | **E 50s**	27
Le Colonial | **E 50s**	20
Z Masa/Bar Masa | **W 60s**	27
Z Matsuri | **Chelsea**	23
Z Megu | **TriBeCa**	24
Ninja | **TriBeCa**	19
Z One if by Land | **G Vill**	23
Z Per Se | **W 60s**	28
Z Rainbow Room/Grill | **W 40s**	19
Z Rao's | **Harlem**	22
Soda Shop | **TriBeCa**	19
Suba | **LES**	21
Z Tao | **E 50s**	23
Z Tavern on Green | **W 60s**	15
Vatan | **Gramercy**	23
Water's Edge | **LIC**	23

VIEWS

Alma | **Carroll Gdns**	20
Antica Venezia | **W Vill**	23
Z Asiate | **W 60s**	24
Battery Gdns. | **Financial**	18
BG | **W 50s**	20
Boathouse | **E 70s**	16
Bouchon Bakery | **W 60s**	23
Bryant Park | **W 40s**	17
Bubby's | **Dumbo**	18
Cabana | **Seaport**	21
Z Café Gray | **W 60s**	25

Caffé/Green | **Bayside**	21
Cipriani Dolci | **E 40s**	18
Fairway Cafe | **Red Hook**	18
F.illi Ponte | **TriBeCa**	21
Gigino | **Financial**	20
Heartland | **Seaport**	14
Hispaniola | **Wash. Hts**	21
NEW Hudson R. Café | **Harlem**	–
NEW Kaijou | **Financial**	–
Lake Club | **SI**	21
Le Refuge Inn | **Bronx**	24
Lobster Box | **Bronx**	17
Marina Cafe | **SI**	18
Metrazur | **E 40s**	20
Michael Jordan's | **E 40s**	20
Z Modern, The | **W 50s**	26
Z Per Se | **W 60s**	28
Pete's Downtown | **Dumbo**	18
P.J. Clarke's | **Financial**	17
Porter House NY | **W 60s**	22
Portofino's | **Bronx**	19
Z Rainbow Room/Grill | **W 40s**	19
Z River Café | **Dumbo**	26
River Room | **Harlem**	19
Rock Ctr. | **W 50s**	19
Sea Grill | **W 40s**	24
South Fin Grill | **SI**	20
NEW Suteishi | **Seaport**	25
Z Tavern on Green | **W 60s**	15
Terrace in the Sky | **W 100s**	22
2 West | **Financial**	21
View, The | **W 40s**	18
Water Club | **Murray Hill**	20
Water's Edge | **LIC**	23

VISITORS ON EXPENSE ACCOUNT

NEW Anthos | **W 50s**	25
Z Bouley | **TriBeCa**	28
Z Carlyle | **E 70s**	21
Z Chanterelle | **TriBeCa**	27
Z Craft | **Flatiron**	25
Craftsteak | **Chelsea**	22
Z Daniel | **E 60s**	28
Z Del Frisco's | **W 40s**	25
Z Del Posto | **Chelsea**	25
Z Four Seasons | **E 50s**	25
Z Gari/Sushi | **W 40s**	26
NEW Z Gordon Ramsay | **W 50s**	25
Harry Cipriani | **E 50s**	–
Harry's | **Financial**	22
Z Il Mulino | **G Vill**	27
Z Jean Georges | **W 60s**	28
NEW Kobe Club | **W 50s**	20
Kuruma Zushi | **E 40s**	28
Le Cirque | **E 50s**	23

☒ Masa/Bar Masa | **W 60s**	27
☒ Megu | **TriBeCa**	24
☒ Milos | **W 50s**	26
☒ Nobu | **TriBeCa**	27
Nobu 57 | **W 50s**	26
☒ One if by Land | **G Vill**	23
☒ Per Se | **W 60s**	28
Petrossian | **W 50s**	24
Roy's NY | **Financial**	25
NEW Russian Tea | **W 50s**	19
NEW ☒ Wakiya | **Gramercy**	–

WATERSIDE

Alma | **Carroll Gdns**	20
Battery Gdns. | **Financial**	18
Boathouse | **E 70s**	16
Cabana | **Seaport**	21
Lake Club | **SI**	21
Marina Cafe | **SI**	18
Pete's Downtown | **Dumbo**	18
Portofino's | **Bronx**	19
☒ River Café | **Dumbo**	26
River Room | **Harlem**	19
South Fin Grill | **SI**	20
Water Club | **Murray Hill**	20
Water's Edge | **LIC**	23

WINNING WINE LISTS

NEW Accademia/Vino | **E 60s**	–
Aix Brasserie | **W 80s**	20
Alfama | **W Vill**	22
☒ Alto | **E 50s**	26
☒ Annisa | **G Vill**	27
☒ Aquavit | **E 50s**	25
Arno | **Garment**	20
☒ Artisanal | **Murray Hill**	23
☒ Asiate | **W 60s**	24
☒ Aureole | **E 60s**	27
A Voce | **Gramercy**	25
☒ Babbo | **G Vill**	27
☒ Balthazar | **SoHo**	23
Barbetta | **W 40s**	20
Barolo | **SoHo**	18
☒ Becco | **W 40s**	22
Ben Benson's | **W 50s**	24
BLT Steak | **E 50s**	24
☒ Blue Hill | **G Vill**	26
☒ Blue Ribbon | **multi.**	25
Bottega del Vino | **E 50s**	22
☒ Bouley | **TriBeCa**	28
☒ Café Boulud | **E 70s**	27
☒ Café Gray | **W 60s**	25
Capital Grille | **E 40s**	23
Casa Mono | **Gramercy**	25
'Cesca | **W 70s**	23
☒ Chanterelle | **TriBeCa**	27

Chiam | **E 40s**	23
City Hall | **TriBeCa**	21
☒ Compass | **W 70s**	22
Conviv. Osteria | **Park Slope**	25
Counter | **E Vill**	22
Country | **Gramercy**	23
☒ Craft | **Flatiron**	25
☒ Cru | **G Vill**	26
☒ Daniel | **E 60s**	28
☒ Danube | **TriBeCa**	26
☒ db Bistro Moderne | **W 40s**	25
☒ Del Frisco's | **W 40s**	25
☒ Del Posto | **Chelsea**	25
☒ Eleven Madison | **Gramercy**	26
Falai | **LES**	25
Fatty Crab | **W Vill**	21
☒ Felidia | **E 50s**	25
Fiamma Osteria | **SoHo**	25
Fleur de Sel | **Flatiron**	25
Gabriel's | **W 60s**	22
Gilt | **E 50s**	25
☒ Gotham B&G | **G Vill**	27
☒ Gramercy Tavern | **Flatiron**	27
Harrison, The | **TriBeCa**	24
Hearth | **E Vill**	25
Il Buco | **NoHo**	25
'ino | **G Vill**	24
'inoteca | **LES**	23
I Trulli | **Gramercy**	22
☒ Jean Georges | **W 60s**	28
Landmarc | **multi.**	23
La Pizza Fresca | **Flatiron**	22
Lavagna | **E Vill**	24
☒ Le Bernardin | **W 50s**	28
Le Cirque | **E 50s**	23
☒ L'Impero | **E 40s**	26
☒ Lupa | **G Vill**	25
Mas | **G Vill**	25
☒ Megu | **TriBeCa**	24
Michael Jordan's | **E 40s**	20
Michael's | **W 50s**	21
☒ Milos | **W 50s**	26
☒ Modern, The | **W 50s**	26
Morrell Wine Bar | **W 40s**	19
Nice Matin | **W 70s**	20
Nick & Stef's | **Garment**	22
Oceana | **E 50s**	26
Orsay | **E 70s**	18
Osteria del Circo | **W 50s**	22
Otto | **G Vill**	22
☒ Ouest | **W 80s**	25
☒ Per Se | **W 60s**	28
☒ Picholine | **W 60s**	27
Post House | **E 60s**	23
NEW PT | **W'burg**	24

subscribe to zagat.com

Raoul's | **SoHo**	24
Ruth's Chris | **W 50s**	23
San Domenico | **W 50s**	23
San Pietro | **E 50s**	24
☑ Scalini Fedeli | **TriBeCa**	26
Sea Grill | **W 40s**	24
Sette Enoteca | **Park Slope**	19
Sharz Cafe | **E 80s**	21
Smith & Wollensky | **E 40s**	23
Solera | **E 50s**	22
☑ Sparks | **E 40s**	25
Strip House | **G Vill**	25
Supper | **E Vill**	24
☑ Tabla | **Gramercy**	25
Tasting Rm. | **multi.**	22
☑ Telepan | **W 60s**	25
☑ Tocqueville | **Union Sq**	26
Tommaso | **Dyker Hts**	23
Town | **W 50s**	24
Tribeca Grill | **TriBeCa**	22
Tse Yang | **E 50s**	25
☑ 21 Club | **W 50s**	22
☑ Union Sq. Cafe | **Union Sq**	26
Uva | **E 70s**	21
☑ Veritas | **Flatiron**	26
Wallsé | **W Vill**	26
West Bank Cafe | **W 40s**	20
Zoë | **SoHo**	20

SPECIAL FEATURES

Wine Vintage Chart

This chart, based on our 0 to 30 scale, is designed to help you select wine. The ratings (by **Howard Stravitz,** a law professor at the University of South Carolina) reflect the vintage quality and the wine's readiness to drink. We exclude the 1991–1993 vintages because they are not that good. A dash indicates the wine is either past its peak or too young to rate. Loire ratings are for dry white wines.

Whites	88	89	90	94	95	96	97	98	99	00	01	02	03	04	05	06
French:																
Alsace	-	25	25	24	23	23	22	25	23	25	27	25	22	24	25	-
Burgundy	-	23	22	-	28	27	24	22	26	25	24	27	23	27	26	24
Loire Valley	-	-	-	-	-	-	-	-	-	24	25	26	23	24	27	24
Champagne	24	26	29	-	26	27	24	23	24	24	22	26	-	-	-	-
Sauternes	29	25	28	-	21	23	25	23	24	24	28	25	26	21	26	23
California:																
Chardonnay	-	-	-	-	-	-	-	-	24	23	26	26	25	27	29	25
Sauvignon Blanc	-	-	-	-	-	-	-	-	-	-	27	28	26	27	26	27
Austrian:																
Grüner Velt./ Riesling	-	-	-	-	25	21	26	26	25	22	23	25	26	25	26	-
German:	25	26	27	24	23	26	25	26	23	21	29	27	24	26	28	-

Reds	88	89	90	94	95	96	97	98	99	00	01	02	03	04	05	06
French:																
Bordeaux	23	25	29	22	26	25	23	25	24	29	26	24	25	24	27	25
Burgundy	-	24	26	-	26	27	25	22	27	22	24	27	25	25	27	25
Rhône	26	28	28	24	26	22	25	27	26	27	26	-	25	24	25	-
Beaujolais	-	-	-	-	-	-	-	-	-	24	-	23	25	22	28	26
California:																
Cab./Merlot	-	-	28	29	27	25	28	23	26	22	27	26	25	24	24	23
Pinot Noir	-	-	-	-	-	-	24	23	24	23	27	28	26	25	24	-
Zinfandel	-	-	-	-	-	-	-	-	-	-	25	23	27	24	23	-
Oregon:																
Pinot Noir	-	-	-	-	-	-	-	-	-	-	-	27	25	26	27	-
Italian:																
Tuscany	-	-	25	22	24	20	29	24	27	24	27	20	25	25	22	24
Piedmont	-	27	27	-	23	26	27	26	25	28	27	20	24	25	26	-
Spanish:																
Rioja	-	-	-	26	26	24	25	22	25	24	27	20	24	25	26	24
Ribera del Duero/Priorat	-	-	-	26	26	27	25	24	25	24	27	20	24	26	26	24
Australian:																
Shiraz/Cab.	-	-	-	24	26	23	26	28	24	24	27	27	25	26	24	-
Chilean:	-	-	-	-	-	-	24	-	25	23	26	24	25	24	26	-

Zagat Products

RESTAURANTS & MAPS

America's Top Restaurants
Atlanta
Boston
Brooklyn (best of)
California Wine Country
Cape Cod & The Islands
Chicago (guide & map)
Connecticut
Downtown NYC
Europe's Top Restaurants
Hamptons (incl. wineries)
Las Vegas (incl. nightlife)
London
London (best of)
Long Island (incl. wineries)
Los Angeles I So. California
(guide & map)
Miami Beach
Miami I So. Florida
Montréal (best of)
New Jersey
New Jersey Shore
New Orleans (best of)
New York City (guide & map)
Palm Beach
Paris
Philadelphia
San Francisco (guide & map)
Seattle
St. Louis
Texas
Tokyo
Toronto (best of)
Vancouver (best of)
Washington, DC I Baltimore
Westchester I Hudson Valley

LIFESTYLE GUIDES

America's Top Golf Courses
Movie Guide
Music Guide
NYC Gour. Shopping/Ent
NYC Shopping

NIGHTLIFE GUIDES

Las Vegas (incl. restaurants)
London
Los Angeles
New Orleans (best of)
New York City
San Francisco

HOTEL & TRAVEL GUIDES

Top U.S. Hotels, Resorts & Spas
U.S. Family Travel
Walt Disney World Insider's Guide
World's Top Hotels, Resorts & Spas

WEB & WIRELESS SERVICES

ZAGAT TO GO^{SM} for handhelds
Subscribe to ZAGAT.com
ZAGAT.mobi

**Available wherever books are sold or at ZAGAT.com. To customize
Zagat guides as gifts or marketing tools, call 800-540-9609.**

ZAGAT®

New York City
Gourmet Shopping
& Entertaining
2008

Please enjoy this complimentary
excerpt spotlighting top-rated food
& entertaining resources

SPECIAL BONUS SECTION

Whether
you love to
cook, entertain
or just "do takeout,"
it's all here in one handy
guide – from bakeries,
caterers and florists to party
sites, wine shops and much more.
The complete 2008 New York City
Gourmet Shopping & Entertaining
guide is available at Barnes & Noble.

Ratings & Symbols

	Zagat Top Spot	Name	Symbols	Category		Zagat Ratings			
						QUALITY	DISPLAY	SERVICE	COST

Area, Address & Contact	☑ Tim & Nina's ◗ *Seafood*			▽ 23	9	13	$15
	W 50s | 4 Columbus Circle (8th Ave.) | 212-977-6000 | www.zagat.com						

Review, surveyor comments in quotes	Fanatical fish fanciers find that the fastest route to "fairly fared fin fare" is a foray to this "grungy grotto" below Columbus Circle, where the catch is "never more than a day old" and "the price is always net"; still, sensitive shoppers say the "surly staffers should be used as fish-bait"; P.S. check out the "daily East River specials" and Tim and Nina's catering service on the A train.

Ratings

Quality, Display and **Service** are rated on a scale of 0 to 30.

0 – 9   poor to fair

10 – 15   fair to good

16 – 19   good to very good

20 – 25   very good to excellent

26 – 30   extraordinary to perfection

▽   low response | less reliable

Cost reflects our surveyors' estimate of the price range, indicated as follows:

I   Inexpensive

M   Moderate

E   Expensive

VE   Very Expensive

Symbols

☑   Zagat Top Spot (highest ratings, popularity and importance)

◗   open until 8:30 PM or later

▣   mail order available via catalog, phone or Web

∅   no credit cards accepted

About This Survey

Here are the results of our 2008 New York City Gourmet Shopping & Entertaining Survey, covering 1,758 establishments in New York City, including 357 party sites. In addition, we've added 75 outstanding online sources. Like all our guides, it's based on the collective opinions of thousands of avid local consumers who have been there before you.

WHO PARTICIPATED: Input from 6,807 avid customers forms the basis for the ratings and reviews in this guide (their comments are shown in quotation marks within the reviews). Of these surveyors, 60% are women, 40% men; the breakdown by age is 12% in their 20s; 28%, 30s; 22%, 40s; 22%, 50s; and 16%, 60s or above. Their collective experience adds up to roughly 655,000 transactions a year. We sincerely thank each of these participants – this book is really "theirs."

HELPFUL LISTS: Whether you're looking for food, flowers, wine or liquor, staff or party locations, or whether you want to save money or splurge, our lists can help you find exactly the right place, including Best Overall, Top Ratings and Best Buys. Included in this Special Bonus Section are highlights from our Top Quality list, broken into categories, from herbs and spices to ice cream to sandwich shops. Our full guide includes 57 handy indexes as well. And, for the first time ever, we've added an Online Sources section to help guide you to the best Web sites for everything from fresh flowers, fish and meat to candy, baked goods and even hard-to-find party accessories. This section also includes Best Overall and Top Quality ratings.

ABOUT ZAGAT: This marks our 29th year reporting on the shared experiences of consumers like you. What started in 1979 as a hobby involving 200 of our friends has come a long way. Today we have over 300,000 surveyors and now cover dining, entertaining, golf, hotels, movies, music, nightlife, resorts, shopping, spas, theater and tourist attractions worldwide.

SHARE YOUR OPINION: We invite you to join any of our upcoming surveys – just register at **zagat.com,** where you can rate and review establishments year-round. Each participant will receive a free copy of the resulting guide when published.

AVAILABILITY: Zagat guides are available in all major bookstores, by subscription at zagat.com and for use on a wide range of mobile devices via **Zagat To Go** or **zagat.mobi.**

New York, NY

Nina and Tim

Nina and Tim Zagat

Top Quality by Category

Ratings are to the left of names. Lists exclude places with low votes. Major Gourmet Markets are listed by the scores they received for the applicable department.

BREAD

29 Grandaisy Bakery
28 Sullivan St. Bakery
Blue Ribbon Market

CAKES

29 Colette's Cakes
28 Dessert Delivery
Payard Pâtisserie

CANDY

29 Kee's Chocolates
La Maison Chocolat
Martine's Chocolates

CHEESE/DAIRY

29 DiPalo Dairy
28 Murray's Cheese
Artisanal

COFFEE

27 D'Amico Foods | *Bklyn*
Jack's Stir Brew
McNulty's Tea

COOKIES

28 Levain Bakery
27 Patisserie Claude
Stork's Pastry | *Qns*

FLOWERS

29 Zezé
28 Belle Fleur
Takashimaya

GIFT BASKETS

29 Sherry-Lehmann
28 Dessert Delivery
Artisanal

HERBS/SPICES

27 Penzeys Spices
Dean & DeLuca
Kalustyan's

ICE CREAM

28 Il Laboratorio
27 Lemon Ice King | *Qns*
L'Arte del Gelato

MEATS/POULTRY

29 Lobel's Meats
Florence Meat
Salumeria Biellese

NUTS/DRIED FRUITS

29 Bazzini, A.L.
27 Sahadi's | *Bklyn*
Kalustyan's

PASTRIES

28 Villabate | *Bklyn*
Artopolis Bakery | *Qns*
Almondine Bakery | *Bklyn*

SANDWICH SHOPS

25 Olive's
Bánh Mì Saigon
24 'wichcraft

SEAFOOD

28 Citarella
Pisacane
Randazzo's | *Bx*

SINGULAR FOCUS

27 Pickle Guys (*pickles*)
Stonehouse (*olive oil*)
25 O&CO. (*olive oil*)

TEA

28 Ito En
27 Two for the Pot | *Bklyn*
Tea Box

WINES/LIQUOR

29 Burgundy Wine
Moore Brothers
Sherry-Lehmann

Z Almondine Bakery ⭑ *Baked Goods* 28 | 23 | 23 | M

Dumbo | 85 Water St. (bet. Dock & Main Sts.) | Brooklyn | 718-797-5027 | www.almondinebakery.com

It's "the real stuff" rave Francophiles of this little shop's "superlative" French bakery staples – notably the "finest" croissants and baguettes and "jewel-like" pastries – considered "the closest thing to Paris" this side of the East River; "master" baker (and Le Bernardin alum) Hervé Poussot is the man behind this operation touted by locals as "one more reason to move to Dumbo."

Z Artisanal 🖃 *Cheese/Dairy* 28 | 25 | 23 | E

Garment Dist | 500 W. 37th St., 2nd fl. (10th Ave.) | 212-239-1200 | www.artisanalcheese.com
Murray Hill | 2 Park Ave. (32nd St.) | 212-532-4033 | www.artisanalbistro.com ●
877-797-1200

"If you're a turophile", "paradise" awaits at Terrence Brennan's Murray Hill bistro, where the "bountiful" retail counter is "the ultimate" "showcase" of "fragrant", "scary-delicious" fromage in a 250-strong "worldwide assortment" that's stocked on-site in carefully calibrated caves; if the "phenomenal selection" "makes your head spin", a "true-believer staff" of "cheese masters" will assist with "queries and discoveries", helping to justify the "lofty prices"; P.S. the Garment District wholesale/mail-order outlet hosts "informative" classes toward cheese degrees.

Z Artopolis Bakery ● *Baked Goods* 28 | 26 | 23 | M

Astoria | Agora Plaza | 23-18 31st St. (23rd Ave.) | Queens | 718-728-8484 | 800-553-2270 | www.artopolis.net

"Transcends" what you'll find in a "neighborhood full of Greek bakeries" rave connoisseurs of this Astoria Hellenic's baked goods touted as some of the "best variety and quality outside of Athens"; its offerings, both traditional and with French leanings, include "outstanding" pastries and cakes, "peasant" breads and some savories ("go for the tiropites and spanakopites"), all arrayed in a "beautiful" space whose marble-and-lacquered pine fittings were imported from Greece.

Bánh Mì Saigon Bakery ⭑ *Deli/Sandwich* 25 | 11 | 16 | I

Chinatown | 138-01 Mott. St. (bet. Grand & Hester Sts.) | 212-941-1541

One of the "best-kept secrets in Chinatown", this Vietnamese hideaway at the back of a Mott Street jewelry store sells what supporters say is the "perfect" *bahn mi* sandwich – roast pork, cilantro, pickled carrots, cucumber and hot peppers loaded up on "crusty" French bread – amounting to a "salty, sweet, spicy, crunchy, delicious" meal for "practically pennies"; seating is limited and "ambiance" nil, but its "filling" "quick fixes" always "satisfy"; N.B. it now offers meatball, chicken and veggie options.

Z Bazzini, A.L., Co. 🖃 *Major Gourmet Mkt.* ▽ 27 | 20 | 21 | E

TriBeCa | 339 Greenwich St. (Jay St.) | 212-334-1280 | www.bazzininuts.com

It's "well known" that this 1880s-vintage TriBeCa fixture "shines" as an "established" source of "delicious nuts" – the "freshest" "A+ quality" with "fantastic" choices from almonds to walnuts – but these days it also "comes up big" as an "excellent gourmet shop" where the "very inviting" draws include "fresh produce" and meats, "tasty" prepared foods, "Italian delicacies" like imported pasta and olive oils, and an "excellent assortment" of dried fruits and candy; yes, it's on the "expensive" side, but it's "def worth it" for anyone driven nutty by the area's "sorely lacking" options.

☑ Belle Fleur *Flowers*   28 | 27 | 25 | VE

Flatiron | 134 Fifth Ave., 4th fl. (bet. 18th & 19th Sts.) | 212-254-8703 | www.bellefleurny.com

"The name says it all" at this Flatiron District florist where "exquisite", "chic blooms" arranged by a "mother-daughter duo" that shares a "gorgeous sense of color" result in "flawless", "artful" ensembles; "exceptional one-on-one service" means "lucky recipients are always thrilled", so even though "price tags are high", it's "the perfect way to say 'I love you – and I'm really rich.'"

☑ Blue Ribbon Market *Baked Goods*   28 | 22 | 23 | E

G Village | 14 Bedford St. (bet. Downing & W. Houston Sts.) | 212-647-0408 | www.blueribbonrestaurants.com

Acclaimed as a "wonderful addition" to the Bromberg brothers' "empire", this "tiny" Greenwich Village storefront allows fans of the famously "fresh, homey" and "delicious" breads baked in the 150-year-old oven of its nearby restaurant sibling, Blue Ribbon Bakery, to "take them home"; it also sells a small selection of spreads, cheeses, smoked fish, oils and condiments to go with the loaves, as well as "superb" 'toasts' (open-faced sandwiches) and soups, all dispensed by a "friendly" low-key crew.

☑ Burgundy Wine Company 🖃 *Wine/Liquor*   29 | 23 | 25 | E

Chelsea | 143 W. 26th St. (bet. 6th & 7th Aves.) | 212-691-9092 | 888-898-8448 | www.burgundywinecompany.com

"Focus" has its rewards, as this "brilliant" Chelsea "pro" demonstrates with its "reliable", "top-notch" selection of Rhônes, Oregonians and, "of course", wines from the namesake French region, all shown off by a staff of "enthusiastic" "experts willing to share their knowledge"; the "prices go with the territory", but it's "simply heaven" for "serious buyers", and "regular folk" "will feel welcome" too; P.S. the tastings every day are simply "amazing."

☑ Citarella 🖃 *Major Gourmet Mkt.*   26 | 23 | 22 | E

E 70s | 1313 Third Ave. (75th St.) | 212-874-0383 ◗
G Village | 424 Sixth Ave. (9th St.) | 212-874-0383 ◗
Harlem | 461 W. 125th St. (bet. Amsterdam & Morningside Aves.) | 212-874-0383
W 70s | 2135 Broadway (75th St.) | 212-874-0383 ◗
866-248-2735 | www.citarella.com

Go "upscale without the attitude" at this famed mini-chain of "one-stop" shops for "the refined gourmet", which "built its reputation" by supplying an "abundant variety" of "impeccable" seafood so "exceptionally fresh" it's practically "still quivering", along with "top-of-the-line meats" from "cheerful" "old-fashioned butchers"; they're also "incredibly helpful" sources of "hearty" prepared foods likened to "edible art", "high-end" deli items, a "super" "array of cheeses", "gorgeous" produce "staples" and "top-drawer" smoked fish and caviar, and though "prices are pretty steep", legions of "happy shoppers" confirm quality is "never an issue."

☑ Colette's Cakes ✍ *Baked Goods*   29 | 28 | 27 | VE

W Village | 681 Washington St. (bet. Charles & W. 10th Sts.) | 212-366-6530 | www.colettescakes.com
By appointment only

West Village wedding and special-occasion cake baker Colette Peters excels at sculptured, "inventive" and "simply exquisite" multilayer creations that are "almost too pretty to eat" – but happily taste "marvelous"; Peters is sweet with the customers as well ("she sat with us for over an hour"), and while naturally "you pay for" such "unbeatable" quality – voted Tops in this Survey – and service, acolytes attest it's "worth every penny."

☑ D'Amico Foods 🖃 *Coffee/Tea*   27 | 19 | 23 | I

Carroll Gardens | 309 Court St. (bet. Degraw & Sackett Sts.) | Brooklyn | 718-875-5403 | 888-814-7979 | www.damicofoods.com

Wake up and "smell the coffee roasting" at this "old-school" Carroll Gardens java merchant, a "real neighborhood" stalwart (since 1948) where an "incredible" selection of beans are toasted daily and scooped straight from the sack to guarantee "the freshest" brews around; it's also an affordable "Italian specialties" grocer and sandwich maker, and locals "love" that "nothing changes" here since it's already "as good as it gets."

☑ Dean & DeLuca 🖃 *Major Gourmet Mkt.*   27 | 26 | 20 | VE

E 80s | 1150 Madison Ave. (85th St.) | 212-717-0800
Financial Dist | Borders Books & Music | 100 Broadway (Pine St.) | 212-577-2153
G Village | 75 University Pl. (bet. 10th & 11th Sts.) | 212-473-1908 ◗
Murray Hill | Borders Books & Music | 576 Second Ave. (32nd St.) | 212-696-1369 ◗
SoHo | 560 Broadway (Prince St.) | 212-226-6800
W 40s | Paramount Hotel | 235 W. 46th St. (bet. B'way & 8th Ave.) | 212-869-6890 ◗
W 40s | 9 Rockefeller Plaza (49th St.) | 212-664-1363 ◗
W 50s | Time Warner Ctr. | 10 Columbus Circle, 2nd fl. (bet. 58th & 60th Sts.) | 212-765-4400 ◗
800-221-7714 | www.deandeluca.com

"The Tiffany's of gourmet groceries", this ever-"fashionable" "fancy food" chain remains "the benchmark" "for the discriminating" with its "exquisite" presentation of "anything your heart desires" in the way of "museum"-grade produce, "exceptional" prepared foods, "scrumptious" baked goods, an "excellent range" of "rare" and "exciting" cheeses, "imaginative" specialty items, "high-quality spices" "you aren't even sure how to spell" and "fantastic kitchenware"; "top-dollar" prices that some deem "prohibitive" "bordering on the outlandish" mean it's "not practical for everyday", but those who go to "shop selectively" or "just to browse" are in for a "true experience"; N.B. the SoHo and Madison Avenue sites stock the full lineup, with the other outlets limited to coffee, prepared foods and baked goods.

☑ Dessert Delivery 🖃 *Baked Goods*   28 | 24 | 26 | E

E 50s | 360 E. 55th St. (bet. 1st & 2nd Aves.) | 212-838-5411 | www.dessertdeliveryny.com

This little shop in East Midtown "can get anyone off their diet" confide cookie connoisseurs citing a clever and "well-edited" selection of sweet treats the likes of "beautiful" cakes that also taste "really delicious", "apple pie that's about the best there is" and what may be "the city's finest black-and-white cookie"; "first-class" owners oversee the "fast, friendly service", assuring that customers get their just desserts; N.B. the Say It With Flour division makes gift baskets.

⊠ DiPalo Dairy   *Cheese/Dairy*   `29` `23` `25` `M`
Little Italy | 200 Grand St. (Mott St.) | 212-226-1033

A "shrine" to "the gospel of cheese", this "family-run" Little Italy "institution" is "legendary" for its "exhaustive" selection of formaggio, voted No. 1 in NYC, featuring "unbeatable" "fresh mozzarella" and ricotta plus a "wide range" of "real Italian" imports from parmigiano to pecorino; also a source of "old-country" "delights" like pasta and olive oil, it's operated "with love" by "chatty" "experts" who "won't rush you" "once your number is up", and though there are often "long lines", that only confirms it's "one of the greats."

⊠ Florence Meat Market ▣ *Meat/Poultry*   `29` `19` `28` `M`
G Village | 5 Jones St. (bet. Bleecker & W. 4th Sts.) | 212-242-6531

Satisfied surveyors consider this "old-time" (circa 1936), sawdust-sprinkled Village butcher among the "best and nicest in the business", known for "exceptional quality", "unparalleled service" ("they trim, season and tie up a roast to perfection") and "some terrific bargains" – especially on "their famous Newport steak" – along with more "pricey cuts" and game too; "if you need to rustle up an amazing dinner, start here"; N.B. call ahead and pre-order – you may be spared a long "wait."

⊠ Grandaisy Bakery ▣ *Baked Goods*   `29` `21` `20` `M`
SoHo | 73 Sullivan St. (bet. Broome & Spring Sts.) | 212-334-9435 | www.grandaisybakery.com

It goes by a new name after a recent ownership split, but otherwise "nothing's changed" at this "small" SoHo Italian bakery (formerly the original branch of Sullivan St. Bakery), whose "to-die-for" artisanal breads are voted "the best in the city"; some say "pane pugliese and filore are the two best loaves", but it's hard to pick favorites among its "unforgettable" offerings, from flatbreads and focaccia-like pizzas to panini and sweets; given such "fresh, wonderful" goods, no one minds much if the service "can be lacking" and the decor's "nothing fancy."

⊠ Il Laboratorio del Gelato ▣⊄ *Ice Cream* `28` `19` `20` `E`
LES | 95 Orchard St. (Broome & Delancy Sts.) | 212-343-9922 | www.laboratoriodelgelato.com

"Fantasies do come true" at this LES "shrine to frozen confections", voted No. 1 for Ice Cream in this Survey, where the "irresistible" gelato is "ambrosia" to devotees; while some find it "ridiculously expensive", virtually all agree the "fantastic, imaginative flavors" "ranging from rich to subtle" are "simply the best" and well "worth the trek Downtown", "the wait on line" and "every penny" spent.

⊠ Ito En ▣ *Coffee/Tea*   `28` `27` `25` `E`
E 60s | 822 Madison Ave. (69th St.) | 212-988-7111 | www.itoen.com

Ranking as the "best tea emporium in NYC", this Upper East Side "sanctuary" "has no peers" in its "superb selection" of "authentic" Japanese, Chinese and Indian leaves "both traditional" and "exotic", packaged and "treated as works of art" in a "so-civilized" "boutique" space that's also stocked with "one-of-a-kind" "accoutrements"; run by one of Japan's "premier producers" and staffed by "sophisticated" sorts who "can make neophytes experts", it's "very expensive" but "worth it" to steep in "tea as spirituality."

Ⓩ Jack's Stir Brew Coffee ▣ *Coffee/Tea*   27 | 23 | 23 | M

G Village | 138 W. 10th St. (bet. Greenwich Ave. & Waverly Pl.) | 212-929-0821 ✦
Seaport | 222 Front St. (bet. Beekman St. & Peck Slip) | 212-227-7631
www.cupajack.com

"Crunchy" types "could live at" this ultra-"cozy" Village coffeehouse, which showcases "awesome" "organic" java of the shade-grown, Fair Trade variety plus "funky teas" and baked goods including chocolate chip cookies so addictive they "should be illegal"; its "quaint" digs and "service with a smile" all but revive the Beat scene, and the new Seaport site may be even more "mellow and welcoming."

Ⓩ Kalustyan's ▣ *Specialty Shop*   27 | 20 | 19 | M

Gramercy | 123 Lexington Ave. (bet. 28th & 29th Sts.) | 212-685-3451 | www.kalustyans.com

A "huge selection of fresh spices" anchors the "mind-boggling" trove of "hard-to-find" "goodies" at this mostly Indian and Mideastern "mecca" in Gramercy, which stocks everything from "excellent" nuts, dried fruits, rice, beans and teas to "wonderful frozen canapés", fresh flatbreads and cookware; it's a favorite of "adventurous chefs" seeking "fair" prices, but its "narrow" aisles also appeal to novices who "eavesdrop on the great recipes people are shopping for", then afterward "sate their hunger" at the moderately priced upstairs cafe.

Ⓩ Kee's Chocolates *Candy/Nuts*   29 | 22 | 24 | E

SoHo | 80 Thompson St. (bet. Broome & Spring Sts.) | 212-334-3284 | www.keeschocolates.com

"OMG!" rave reviewers of the "divine", "creative" chocolates "made by hand on the premises" at this tiny, "hidden-away" SoHo shop – this year voted tops in NYC for Candy – that's owned and run by "master of flavors" Kee Ling Tong, whose "exotic" fillings, many reflecting an Asian influence, are deemed "unforgettable"; "exquisite" product aside, the vibe is "unpretentious" and the staff "a pleasure to talk to", so "treat yourself" – "it's worth every penny", but just "get there early" because they sometimes start "running out" of choices later in the day.

Ⓩ La Maison du Chocolat ▣ *Candy/Nuts*   29 | 28 | 23 | VE

E 70s | 1018 Madison Ave. (bet. 78th & 79th Sts.) | 212-744-7117 | 800-988-5632
W 40s | 30 Rockefeller Plaza, concourse level (bet. 49th & 50th Sts.) | 212-265-9404
www.lamaisonduchocolat.com

Just about "the best this side of Paris – or heaven" – is the word on the "superb" truffles and other "fragrant, intense", "subtly flavored" chocolates imported from France and offered in "jewel"-worthy displays and packaging at this "ultra-high-end" Madison Avenue boutique and its Rock Center offshoot; it's the "Rolls-Royce" of bonbons – with "awe"-inspiring prices to match – though there are a few grumbles about service that, while "knowledgeable and efficient", can be "frosty" at times; P.S. "try the hot chocolate!" (both stores have tea-rooms), and check out the tastings and classes.

L'Arte del Gelato *Ice Cream*   27 | 21 | 24 | M

Chelsea | Chelsea Market | 75 Ninth Ave. (bet. 15th & 16th Sts.) | 212-366-0570 | www.lartedelgelato.com

The gelato hits the "top of the charts" at this Chelsea Market stand where classics such as "heavenly" chocolate share space with "wild" daily changing flavors, and regulars recommend "torta anything" (up-scale ice cream cakes) for parties; the "friendly" service includes "free samples", but cognoscenti caution "if you don't buy once you try, you'll get looks colder than the treats behind the glass."

☑ Lemon Ice King of Corona ●⇗ *Ice Cream*   27 | 15 | 18 | I

Corona | Corona Park | 52-02 108th St. (Corona & 52nd Aves.) | Queens | 718-699-5133 | www.thelemonicekingofcorona.com

"Long live the King" chant the fervent fans of this Corona "treasure", where "nuttin' – I mean nothing – beats" the namesake lemon Italian ice, though there are a "zillion" other flavors to choose from too, all fabulous enough to make it "worth the wait", especially on a "hot summer night"; "may it be there forever."

☑ Levain Bakery ⬛⇗ *Baked Goods*   28 | 18 | 22 | E

W 70s | 167 W. 74th St. (bet. Amsterdam & Columbus Aves.) | 212-874-6080 | 877-453-8246 | www.levainbakery.com

"Cookies will never be the same" after a taste of the "delectable", "softball-size" batter-bombs at this "tiny" Upper West Side bakery, where the "moist and thick" chocolate chip version is "chewy" "decadence defined" – whether to "satiate your sweet tooth" or supply your "last meal"; they also do "off-the-hook" breads, scones and pizzas, and though it's "not the cheapest", most agree it's "worth saving up for", especially since the "nice folks" in charge donate each day's un-sold output to charity.

☑ Lobel's Prime Meats ⬛ *Meat/Poultry*   29 | 25 | 27 | VE

E 80s | 1096 Madison Ave. (bet. 82nd & 83rd Sts.) | 212-737-1373 | www.lobels.com

Voted No. 1 in its category in NYC, this fifth-generation family-run business on the Upper East Side is "the Rolls-Royce of butchers" – "the Cartier", the "Tiffany's" – supplying "absolutely, positively the best meat you will every buy" "anywhere on the planet", "from the hot dogs to the Châteaubriand"; "bloody high" prices are "part of the legend", but the consensus is that the "remarkable variety and quality" make it all worthwhile, so go ahead – "sell the kid, buy a steak"; N.B. prepared foods and online ordering are added bonuses.

☑ Martine's Chocolates ⬛ *Candy/Nuts*   29 | 24 | 22 | VE

E 50s | Bloomingdale's | 1000 Third Ave., 6th fl. (59th St.) | 212-705-2347 ●

E 80s | 400 E. 82nd St. (bet. 1st & York Aves.) | 212-744-6289 www.martineschocolates.com

"Truly freshly made" chocolates – you can "actually see them" being prepared on premises – lure cacao-nnoisseurs to this "sweet asset" on the East Side, whose original Bloomie's location makes the perfect "shoppers' pit stop"; beyond its signature "amazing, rich" filled chocolates, there are novelty offerings "in every shape possible" (think "baseballs and Statue of Libertys") – though naturally such "high quality" comes at a steep price.

McNulty's Tea & Coffee Co. ◐▣ *Coffee/Tea* | 27 | 22 | 23 | M

W Village | 109 Christopher St. (bet. Bleecker & Hudson Sts.) | 212-242-5351 | 800-356-5200 | www.mcnultys.com

"No one can call it trendy", but you "can't do better" for "all things good to brew" than this "old-time" (circa 1895) West Village purveyor of "fine coffees and teas", where the "superb" assortment of "exotic" blends is so wide-ranging it's "hard to pick just one"; count on "courteous" "guidance" from in-house "experts" in a milieu so "atmospheric" that "just a whiff is enough" for a "caffeine fix."

☑ Moore Brothers Wine Co. ◐▣ *Wine/Liquor* | 29 | 27 | 29 | M

Flatiron | 33 E. 20th St. (bet. B'way & Park Ave. S.) | 212-375-1575 | 866-986-6673 | www.moorebrothers.com

"Welcome to NY" – this recent Philadelphia-area import is voted No. 1 for Service in this Survey (and second for Quality in its category), an "elegant", bi-level, 4,000-sq.-ft. "refrigerated" Flatironer whose "limited" but "outstanding" selection of artisanal European wines from "small", independent producers is offered at "reasonable" rates; owners Greg and David Moore "take responsibility" once the bottles "leave the winery" and ensure they're "imported and stored at the right temperature", while in the shop "exceptionally knowledgeable" staffers "go out of their way to inform"; N.B. there are frequent tastings and classes.

☑ Murray's Cheese Shop ▣ *Cheese/Dairy* | 28 | 25 | 25 | E

E 40s | Grand Central Mkt. | Lexington Ave. (43rd St.) | 212-922-1540 ◐
G Village | 254 Bleecker St. (Cornelia St.) | 212-243-3289
888-692-4339 | www.murrayscheese.com

Widely considered "the gold standard of cheese in NY", this Village "wonderland" boasts an "astounding" assortment of "premium" "artisanal and seasonal" fromages "from all over the map", with "congenial" "experts" on staff dispensing advice and taste tests; it also offers an array of "accoutrements" and "tasty" prepared foods, and its "spacious" digs include "caves under the store" plus classrooms offering "a cheese education"; P.S. the small "Grand Central outpost is a godsend" for the 'burbs-bound, albeit with less exotic choices.

O&CO. ▣ *Specialty Shop* | 25 | 25 | 22 | E

E 40s | Grand Central Terminal | main concourse (42nd St. & Vanderbilt Ave.) | 212-973-1472
G Village | 249 Bleecker St. (bet. 6th & 7th Aves.) | 646-230-8373
877-828-6620 | www.oliviersandco.com

"The green lemon olive oil makes your socks roll up and down" – and that's a good thing at this paean to the juice of the pitted fruit in Grand Central Station and Greenwich Village; an "amazing array" of "gorgeously packaged" "regional and infused" olive oil ("and anything made with it" or used to serve it) "tempts" "commuters" to stop in and get "educated" by "knowledgeable salespeople"; the quality is "incomparable", but, alas, so are the markups at this "olive oil lover's version of a wine tasting bar."

	QUALITY	DISPLAY	SERVICE	COST

Z Olive's *Deli/Sandwich* — QUALITY 25 | DISPLAY 19 | SERVICE 18 | COST M

SoHo | 120 Prince St. (bet. Greene & Wooster Sts.) | 212-941-0111 |
www.olivesnyc.com

A perfect quick lunch "stop in SoHo", this tiny storefront is known for
its "addictive", super-"fresh" Med-inflected sandwiches, as well as
"excellent soups", salads, scones and such, offered in appealingly
"substantial portions"; it draws a "trendy crowd" – after all, "the Mac
store is across the street" – despite its lack of seating and sometimes
"slow service"; N.B. you can order online for local deliveries.

Z Patisserie Claude ✝ *Baked Goods* — QUALITY 27 | DISPLAY 19 | SERVICE 19 | COST M

G Village | 187 W. Fourth St. (bet. 6th & 7th Aves.) |
212-255-5911

"If you can survive" Claude's "big-time" "Parisian hauteur" at this
"true French bakery" in the Village, "your palate will be enriched" by
"perfect" croissants that "bring tears to your eyes"; after 25 years, the
"small" but "excellent" selection of "stunning" pastries and cookies
shows that this baker may be "mercurial", but he has "hands of gold."

Z Payard — QUALITY 28 | DISPLAY 28 | SERVICE 21 | COST VE

Pâtisserie & Bistro ◐▤ *Baked Goods*

E 70s | 1032 Lexington Ave. (bet. 73rd & 74th Sts.) | 212-717-5252 |
877-972-9273 | www.payard.com

"Ooh-la-la", this "world-class", "oh-so-French" Upper Eastsider is
"the Louvre" of "edible art", where the *magnifique* pastries, cakes
and chocolates, not to mention ice cream, are "exquisitely" "handcrafted" for "a sugar rush like no other"; all that "froufrou" "indulgence"
is "hard on the wallet" but equally "hard to pass up", so "mortgage the
co-op" and go; P.S. "ladies who lunch" congregate over light bites in
the neighboring cafe or a full menu in the back bistro, while Tastings
by Payard provides catering.

Z Penzeys Spices ◐▤ *Herbs/Spices* — QUALITY 27 | DISPLAY 23 | SERVICE 23 | COST M

E 40s | Grand Central Mkt. | Lexington Ave. (43rd St.) | 212-972-2777 |
800-741-7787 | www.penzeys.com

"Marco Polo would be proud" to see the "wonderful selection" of the
"best, freshest spices and herbs" around at this Grand Central outpost
of a beloved national chain, where the scents can be "intoxicating",
and so can the "unbeatable" prices and quality; "so many spices, so little time to cook" sigh the fans of this "small but substantial" shop
where the "knowledgeable" staff can offer tips on how to use the "unusual" and "fantastic" spice blends and rubs; N.B. there's even greater
variety through its catalog/Web ordering business.

Z Pickle Guys, The ▤ *Specialty Shop* — QUALITY 27 | DISPLAY 18 | SERVICE 23 | COST I

LES | 49 Essex St. (bet. Grand & Hester Sts.) | 212-656-9739 |
www.pickleguys.com

"These guys seem to have eclipsed Gus" marvel longtime brine-lovers
of this descendant of a "Lower East Side icon", where "one of the joys of
living in NYC" is a peck of "pickles like your bubby used to make", served
"straight out of the barrel" with "old-style humor"; from "full sours" and
"snappy half-sours to horseradish-infused" varieties, these "fresh and
flavorful" puppies will "shock a bland palate"; P.S. also "try the pickled
tomatoes and celery" – "and don't forget the kraut"; closed Saturdays.

	QUALITY	DISPLAY	SERVICE	COST

Z Pisacane Midtown *Seafood* — 28 | 19 | 26 | E

E 50s | 940 First Ave. (bet. 51st & 52nd Sts.) | 212-752-7560
A "devoted clientele" has "such faith" in this "reliable", family-run fishmonger on the East Side that many "just ask what is fresh", and the staff "never advises wrong"; a "traditional" kind of place selling both raw and prepared offerings, it "caters to the wealthy", but hey, "these guys know their fish", and sometimes, you really do "get what you pay for."

Z Randazzo's Seafood *Seafood* — 28 | 21 | 24 | M

Bronx | 2327 Arthur Ave. (bet. 183rd & 187th Sts.) | 718-367-4139
Seafood "from all over the world" at "a fraction" of Manhattan prices, "freshness" you "can always count on" and "service with a smile" – "what's not to like?" about this "Arthur Avenue institution" that "continues to be fabulous"; if you're "looking for the unusual", such as baccalà, anchovies and other Italian specialties, "this should be where you're headed"; P.S. "try the clams at the raw bar outside."

Z Sahadi's *Specialty Shop* — 27 | 20 | 22 | I

Brooklyn Heights | 187 Atlantic Ave. (bet. Clinton & Court Sts.) | Brooklyn | 718-624-4550 | www.sahadis.com
"It's worth a trip to the County of Kings" (even on "elbow-to-elbow" weekends) to feast like a sultan on the Mideastern "gold mine" at this "phenomenal" Brooklyn Heights food "bazaar"; the "displays are not high-tech" and you gotta "run to grab a number ticket", but amid the "controlled chaos" you'll find "all sorts of goodies hidden in every corner": "vast selections" of high-quality prepared foods, cheese, chocolates, olives, teas, spices, dried fruits and nuts, rice, grains and beans, coffee, "vinegars and oils" and more – and "all at rock-bottom prices."

Z Salumeria Biellese ⊟ *Meat/Poultry* — 29 | 18 | 24 | M

Chelsea | 376-378 Eighth Ave. (29th St.) | 212-736-7376 | www.salumeriabiellese.com
This second-generation Chelsea salumeria brings out "the Italian in everyone" with its "mind-boggling" array of "super-duper sausages" (some 40 varieties) and "wonderful cured meats", both "housemade" and imported, which it supplies to the public as well as to restaurants the likes of Daniel Boulud's and Thomas Keller's; its "reasonable prices" and appealing "slice-of-the-past" milieu are other reasons to "love" this place; N.B. sells sandwiches and other prepared foods too.

Z Sherry-Lehmann ⊟ *Wine/Liquor* — 29 | 24 | 24 | E

E 60s | 679 Madison Ave. (bet. 61st & 62nd Sts.) | 212-838-7500 | www.sherry-lehmann.com
"Still the standard-bearer", this "classic" East Side "mecca for wine enthusiasts" maintains a "staggering inventory" ("particularly" the "amazing stock of Bordeaux") that's hailed for its "impeccable quality" and "competitive" cost "in all price ranges"; "service second to none" has the "consummate knowledge" to assist everyone from the "upper crust to the regular Joe", though the "awesome" variety – extending to glassware and accessories – is more fully revealed via "catalog or Web"; N.B. plans are in motion to relocate to roomier quarters at 505 Park Avenue in late summer 2007.

GOURMET SHOPPING & ENTERTAINING BONUS SECTION

	QUALITY	DISPLAY	SERVICE	COST

✍ Stonehouse California Olive Oil 🖃 *Specialty Shop* | 27 | 22 | 23 | E |

E Village | 273 E. 10th St. (1st Ave.) | 212-358-8700 | www.stonehouseoliveoil.com

At the tasting bar of this East Village outlet for a California olive grove, "you can sample the oils with bread and make a choice" from among the "delicious" selection, including flavored options like "to-die-for Persian lime" and blood orange–infused; "their bottles are beautiful enough for a collection", but don't leave them on your shelf – "they encourage you to bring them back for refills."

✍ Stork's Pastry Shop *Baked Goods* | 27 | 22 | 21 | M |

Whitestone | 12-42 150th St. (12th Rd.) | Queens | 718-767-9220

Giving Whitestone's sweet tooths a leg to stand on since "back in the day", this "old-school" German bakery and chocolate shop is the "real" thing for "marvelous" cookies, truffles and pastries that provide a "taste of childhood" with "no compromise in quality"; also a nest of "excellent breads" that "bring tears to" traditionalist's eyes, it's a "local" "favorite" that's always "worth the trip over the bridge."

✍ Sullivan Street Bakery *Baked Goods* | 28 | 20 | 22 | M |

W 40s | 533 W. 47th St. (bet. 10th & 11th Aves.) | 212-265-5580 | www.sullivanstreetbakery.com

Though its original location "on Sullivan Street" is now separately owned, groupies of bread "genius" Jim Lahey can still go to the "Hell's Kitchen outpost" of this Italian bakery "mecca" and find the same "distinctive" loaves in all the "crusty, earthy" glory that makes many call them "the best, bar none"; it remains a "standard-bearer" for "classic" pane Pugliese and "slabs" of "Roman-style pizza", and if the "off-the-path location" is "a pain", it's "worth the effort" to acquire the goods that grace "many high-end" eateries and gourmet markets.

✍ Takashimaya Floral Boutique *Flowers* | 28 | 28 | 23 | VE |

E 50s | Takashimaya | 693 Fifth Ave., 6th fl. (bet. 55th & 56th Sts.) | 212-350-0111

"Make a statement" with an "exotic", "exquisite" custom floral arrangement from this "Japanese eden" set within the eponymous Fifth Avenue department store; it's a "lovely place to linger and look" (the "hushed setting" is "almost museumlike") at "amazing", "unusual" blooms of "transporting beauty", but although the "presentation is suitably Zen", the prices are "totally indulgent."

Tea Box, The *Coffee/Tea* | 27 | 24 | 22 | E |

E 50s | Takashimaya | 693 Fifth Ave., lower level (bet. 54th & 55th Sts.) | 212-350-0100 | 800-753-2038

"Hidden" in the basement of Takashimaya, Midtown's "swanky" Japanese department store, is this "wonderful" tea shop proffering some 40 varieties of "high-quality" loose leaves (green, black and herbal), plus "superb accoutrements", presented in "rarefied" displays; the adjacent "Zen-like" tearoom makes a "lovely" "getaway from the Fifth Avenue bustle", but just keep in mind that the "exquisite" afternoon tea here requires more than a little "dough."

☑ Two for the Pot 🍵 Coffee/Tea | 27 | 20 | 25 | M |

Brooklyn Heights | 200 Clinton St. (bet. Atlantic Ave. & Pacific St.) | Brooklyn | 718-855-8173

"You never know what treat you'll find" among the jars, tins and boxes steeply stacked in this old-fashioned Brooklyn Heights emporium, from a "wide range of coffees" and "unusual teas" to herbs and spices, pantry items and equipment; the "genial owner" "loves his store and it shows" in the "knowledgeable", "wonderfully friendly" service and the "well-chosen" stock – he really does "seem to have everything" – just "look around and ask lots of questions."

☑ Villabate | 28 | 24 | 22 | M |
Pasticceria & Bakery ● Baked Goods

Bensonhurst | 7117 18th Ave. (bet. 71st & 72nd Sts.) | Brooklyn | 718-331-8430 | www.villabate.net

Behold "the Italian baker's art" in its "colorful" glory at this "quintessential Brooklyn bakery" in Bensonhurst, where the display cases present a "gorgeous" abundance of the "wonderful pastries and cakes" that "Sicilian dreams" are made of, including "extraordinary cassata", marzipan and rice balls crafted to "perfection" (and "don't forget the cannoli"); "traditional" breads and summertime gelati further confirm it's "the best bet around", so "be prepared for long lines during the holidays."

'wichcraft Deli/Sandwich | 24 | 19 | 18 | E |

Chelsea | 269 Eleventh Ave. (bet. 27th & 28th Sts.) | 212-780-0577
E 40s | 555 Fifth Ave. (bet. 45th & 46th Sts.) | 212-780-0577
Flatiron | 11 E. 20th St. (bet. B'way & 5th Ave.) | 212-780-0577 ●
G Village | 60 E. Eighth St. (Mercer St.) | 212-780-0577
Murray Hill | Equinox | 1 Park Ave. S. (33rd St.) | 212-780-0577 ●
SoHo | Plus One Fitness Clinic | 106 Crosby St. (Prince St.) | 212-780-0577
TriBeCa | 397 Greenwich St. (Beach St.) | 212-780-0577 ●
W 40s | Bryant Park | Sixth Ave. (bet. 40th & 42nd Sts.) | 212-780-0577
866-942-4272 | www.wichcraftnyc.com

"Genius" Tom Colicchio (of Craft and Top Chef fame) casts his spell ever-wider with the proliferating branches of this chain dispensing "ridiculously good" sandwiches along with "delicious soups and salads" and sweets including "unbelievable cupcakes"; its stripped-down digs (most with seating) "feel very of-the-moment" while service is "courteous", but "the sun may set while you wait in line" – and "geez, those prices."

☑ Zezé Flowers | 29 | 28 | 28 | VE |

E 50s | 938 First Ave. (bet. 51st & 52nd Sts.) | 212-753-7767 | www.zezeflowers.com

"Whatever the season, whatever the flowers, you're the winner" at this East 50s "florist to the stars" – rated Best Overall in this Survey – where the "low-key shop" is a dramatic contrast to the "spectacular arrangements" made from "unusual" blooms (including lots of orchids "so exquisite" they would please "Persephone herself"); the staff even "takes the time to talk with you about the recipient to try to capture the perfect mood", and although perfection "will cost you", it's "worth every last penny."

GOURMET SHOPPING & ENTERTAINING BONUS SECTION